JOHN CATT'S
Which School?
2013

88th Edition
Consultant Editor: Tom Wheare MA
Editor: Jonathan Barnes

JOHN
CATT
EDUCATIONAL
LIMITED

Published in 2012 by John Catt Educational Ltd, 12 Deben Mill Business Centre, Old Maltings Approach, Melton, Woodbridge, Suffolk IP12 1BL UK

Tel: 01394 389850   Fax: 01394 386893
Email: enquiries@johncatt.com   Website: www.johncatt.com

Designed and typeset by John Catt Educational Limited
Printed and bound in Great Britain by Cambrian Printers, Aberystwyth.

A CIP catalogue record for this book is available from the British Library.

ISBN: 978 1 908095 57 2
eISBN: 978 1 908095 63 3

Contacts

Consultant Editor
Tom Wheare MA

Editor
Jonathan Barnes
Email: jonathanbarnes@johncatt.com

Advertising & School Profiles
Tel: +44 (0) 1394 389850
Email: sales@johncatt.com

Distribution/Book Sales
Tel: +44 (0) 1394 389863
Email: booksales@johncatt.com

All maps in this guide © MAPS IN MINUTES™ (2012)

Contents

Contents

Directory

Appendices

Examinations and qualifications
Common Entrance, GCSE, GCE, Applied GCE, AEA, Key Skills, Entry Level, IB,
NVQ, BTEC, Diplomas, Projects, Scottish qualifications
and more explained

Awarding organisations and examination dates
Useful dates for those taking exams this year and contact
details for the awarding organisations in the UK

Educational organisations
Useful list of educational organisations, including a brief explanation
of who they are and how to get in contact with them

Helping you make the right choice

Tom Wheare, an independent school Head for 20 years and a former chairman of HMC, introduces the 2013 edition of Which School?

Choosing an independent school for your children is a challenging task. It anticipates a very considerable financial undertaking, particularly problematic in the current economic climate. It is a choice which could, some might say should, determine the course of your children's lives. If choosing the right Head is the most important thing school governors ever do, parents might say the same about choosing a school. To help them, John Catt Educational publishes this annual guide to the independent sector, covering a wide variety of schools and providing an overview from which to select options.

Although there are over 1200 schools in membership of the Independent Schools Council (ISC), you are not going to be interested in all of them, or even most. In fact you might be surprised how quickly you can come up with a manageable list. For instance, if you are not thinking of a boarding school, you can immediately strike out all schools beyond a certain distance. Then again, is it to be single sex or co-ed? Or perhaps you have decided not to go fee-paying from three to 18 but to opt in when you feel the extra input will be most beneficial to your children.

It jars when railways refer to passengers as 'customers' and at first sight it might seem rather odd to think of parents as a school's 'customers'. But that's what you are when you pay for services and you are in a buyer's market. You will find a list of questions on pages 10 and 11 which you may find useful for when you are going round a school. They are good questions, but people selling independent education are well versed in the art of reassuring the anxious and representing their school in an excellent light. What you pick up from the other people you see on a visit and from the physical condition of the plant and premises is every bit as valuable as the Head's accomplished patter. Above all, your own feelings are vital, more important even than those of your child. As a parent, you know perfectly well that the responsibility for decisions rests with you: you get to worry, your child sails through in uninterrupted happiness! And if he or she doesn't, you may blame the school, the other pupils or even your child, but in the end you will blame yourself. So make it a decision you are happy with.

***

In 1825 there were only two universities in England at a time when, north of the border, there were no less than two universities in Aberdeen alone! This changed in the 19th century, but in recent years the number of universities throughout the UK has risen to well over 100. This expansion has inevitably led to an explosion in the number of students going to university, although the introduction of fees may well slow down the growth of the university population. At the same time, various forms of university ranking have become apparent, not just more or less statistically valid league tables, but also less scientific expressions of preference about which are the 'best' universities in this country. Parents and pupils, offered a bewildering variety of choice, also struggle to cope with admissions criteria and procedures. It is often claimed that there are quotas in place to facilitate social engineering but, as Dr Christopher See makes clear in his article, university admissions tutors are simply looking for the best students they can find. Although his article is headed *How to get into Oxbridge*, it offers invaluable advice for all forms of university application.

What to study at university is another big issue. Business is crying out for graduates who are mathematically and scientifically literate and there is work to be done to increase that pool of talent by encouraging more girls to take what are called STEM subjects beyond GCSE. Science, technology and engineering are areas in which this country still has a worldwide reputation, whilst maths is a language that is just as important as Chinese or Spanish on the world market. From the parental point of view, a university degree course which has a high chance of leading to employment is a course we would love to see our children choosing! Don't allow the door to be closed by poor choices at GCSE or in the Sixth Form – that is the message Alex Claydon's energetic Crackergroup is putting across. Giving girls full access to

> Above all, your own feelings are vital, more important even than those of your child. As a parent, you know perfectly well that the responsibility for decisions rests with you: you get to worry, your child sails through in uninterrupted happiness!

education is something the Girls' Day School Trust has been doing for 140 years and an all-girls environment means that no academic discipline is 'out of bounds'. Just like the university admissions tutors, all teachers want to make every educational opportunity available to their students and one of the benefits of the independent sector is the wide variety of schools on offer.

But, they cost! There are scholarships and bursaries, but fees are as much an issue in these schools as they are now at university. Independence is something of a buzzword nowadays as successive governments have promoted the academy concept with its emphasis on free-standing schools. Listed public companies, such as Capita, have also undertaken educational provision and it is reassuring to read Julie Booth's article which makes it clear that even organisations at the cutting edge of capitalism are aware of the needs of parents and the importance of making their educational dreams for their children come true at an affordable price.

But in the end, schools are about people and perhaps the most important single person in a school, after your child, is the Head. Two of the most original and charismatic Heads in the independent sector have contributed articles written with characteristic vigour. Richard Cairns challenges Heads to make an absolutely first-class teaching force their top priority and to use tough love to keep standards high. Ian Walker looks back on 26 years of leading King's Rochester, where he has made the fulfilment of great expectations a reality for his pupils despite, as he makes very clear, the impact of many governmental initiatives. Independence has been crucial to his success.

Education First

International Academy

60 Nations. 3 Campuses. 1 Global Classroom

Andrea, Italy · Tzu Chieh, Taiwan · Manh Tuan, Vietnam · Petro, Ukraine · Renan, Brazil · Ka Wang, Malaysia · Lisa, Germany

Mina, Japan · Zoe, United States · Radolphe, France · Malika, Kazakhstan · Olivia, Denmark · Cherry, China · Paul, South Korea

Hanin, Libya · Melissa, Mexico · Mara, Germany · Roman, Russia · Natalya, Slovakia · Krit, Thailand · Georgina, Germany

Luis, Mexico · Iria, Spain · Sheel, India · Ana Lucia, Columbia · Khanh Quang, Vietnam · Natalie, Norway · Luis and Roxane, Venezuela

Tam, Vietnam · Tom, Netherlands · Titani, Indonesia · Elodie, Canada · Omid, Iran · Mimi, Sweden · Maria, Chile

Study high school with classmates from over 60 countries.

Our world-class faculty empower students to fulfill their greatest potential preparing them
for success in the world byond. Learning along the side of classmates from around the globe,
our students encounter new cultures, perspectives, and beliefs in every classroom exchange.

EF International Academy locations:

Oxford, UK

Tarrytown, NY

Torbay, UK

Academic Programmes offered:

IB Diploma

A-Level

IGCSE

High School Preparation

41% of students

accepted to top 10 UK universities

 facebook.com/efacademy   youtube.com/efprivatehighschools   efacademyblog.wordpress.com/   efacademy.smugmug.com

Learn more at www.ef.com/academy
Schedule a personal consultation +41 41 417 4631

How to use this guide

Which School? has been specifically designed with the reader in mind. There are clearly defined sections providing information for anyone looking at independent education in the UK today.

Are you looking for help and advice? Take a look at our editorial section (pp10-42). Here you will find articles written by experts in their field covering a wide variety of issues you are likely to come across when choosing a school for your child. Each year the editors try to find a differing range of topics to interest and inform you about the uniqueness of independent education.

Perhaps you are looking for a school or college in a certain geographical region? Then you need to look first in the directories, which begin on page D241. Here you will find basic information about all the schools in each region complete with contact details. From this section you will be directed to more detailed information in the guide where this is available. An example of a typical directory entry is given below.

Are you looking for a certain type of school or college in your local area? Then you will need to look in the directories for your local area (see page D242 for a list of all regions). Underneath each school you will find icons that denote the different types of schools or the qualifications that they offer.

Some of you may already be looking for a specific school or college. In which case, if you know the name of the school or college but are unsure of its location, simply go to the index at the back of the guide where you will find all the schools listed alphabetically. Page numbers prefixed with the letter D denote the directory section; those without, the listings.

If, however, you need to find out more information on relevant educational organisations and examinations, then you can look in the appendix where you will find up-to-date information about the examinations and qualifications available. There is also a section giving basic details about the many varied and useful organisations in the education field.

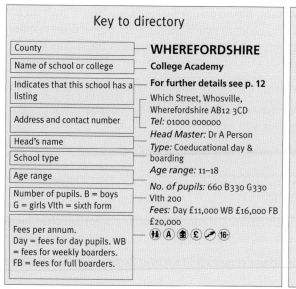

Key to directory

County	**WHEREFORDSHIRE**
Name of school or college	**College Academy**
Indicates that this school has a listing	**For further details see p. 12**
Address and contact number	Which Street, Whosville, Wherefordshire AB12 3CD *Tel:* 01000 000000
Head's name	*Head Master:* Dr A Person
School type	*Type:* Coeducational day & boarding
Age range	*Age range:* 11–18
Number of pupils. B = boys G = girls VIth = sixth form	*No. of pupils:* 660 B330 G330 VIth 200
Fees per annum. Day = fees for day pupils. WB = fees for weekly boarders. FB = fees for full boarders.	*Fees:* Day £11,000 WB £16,000 FB £20,000

Key to directory icons (abridged)

Key to symbols

- Boys' school
- Girls' school
- International school
- Tutorial or sixth form college

Schools offering:

- (A) A levels
- Boarding accommodation
- (£) Bursaries
- Entrance at 16+
- (IB) International Baccalaureate
- Learning support
- Vocational qualifications

The questions you should ask

However much a school may appeal on first sight, you still need sound information to form your judgement

Schools attract pupils by their reputations, so most go to considerable lengths to ensure that parents are presented with an attractive image.

Modern marketing techniques try to promote good points and play down (without totally obscuring) bad ones. But every Head knows that, however good the school prospectus is, it only serves to attract parents through the school gates. Thereafter the decision depends on what they see and hear.

> Research we have carried out over the years suggests that in many cases the most important factor in choosing a school is the impression given by the Head

When you choose a school for your son or daughter, the key factor is that it will suit them. Many children and their parents are instinctively attracted (or otherwise) to a school on first sight. But even if it passes this test, and 'conforms' to what you are looking for in terms of location and academic, pastoral and extracurricular aspects, you will need to satisfy yourself that the school does measure up to what your instincts tell you.

Research we have carried out over the years suggests that in many cases the most important factor in choosing a school is the impression given by the Head. As well as finding out what goes on in a school, parents need to be reassured by the aura of confidence which they expect from a Head. How they discover the former may help them form their opinion of the latter.

So how a Head answers your questions is important. Based on our research, we have drawn up a list of 24 points on which you may need to be satisfied. The order in which they appear below does not necessarily reflect their degree of importance to each parent, but how the Head answers them may help you draw your own conclusions:

- How accessible is the Head, whose personality is seen by most parents as setting the 'tone' of the school?

- Will your child fit in? What is the overall atmosphere?

- To which organisations does the school belong? How has it been accredited?

- What is the ratio of teachers to pupils?

- What are the qualifications of the teaching staff?

- How often does the school communicate with parents through reports, parent/teacher meetings or other visits?

- What is the school's retention rate? Do larger lower classes and smaller upper classes reflect a school's inability to hang on to pupils?

- What are the school's exam results? What are the criteria for presenting them? Are they consistent over the years?

- How does the school cope with pupils' problems?

- What sort of academic and pastoral advice is available?

- What is the school's attitude to discipline?

- Have there been problems with drugs or sex? How have they been dealt with?

- What positive steps are taken to encourage good manners, behaviour and sportsmanship?

- Is progress accelerated for the academically bright?

- How does the school cope with pupils who do not work?

- What is the attitude to religion?

- What is the attitude to physical fitness and games?

- What sports are offered and what are the facilities?

- What are the extracurricular activities? What cultural or other visits are arranged away from the school?

- What steps are taken to encourage specific talent in music, the arts or sport?

- Where do pupils go when they leave – are they channelled to a few selected destinations?

- What is the uniform? What steps are taken to ensure that pupils take pride in their personal appearance?

- What are the timetable and term dates?

- Is it possible to have the names and addresses of parents with children at the school to approach them for an opinion?

How to get into Oxbridge; a tutor's perspective

Dr Christopher See examines what should really motivate applicants for Oxbridge and reveals what selector universities are looking for in their candidates

I'm a personal tutor who doesn't really believe in tuition. What I do believe in is the social mobility granted by universal education and I hate it when people come to me for quick fixes to convince admissions tutors, or how to make something sound more impressive than it actually is. That is a waste of everyone's time.

I also believe in the Oxbridge selection process. Speaking to many admissions tutors in various subjects in research for my latest book, I can safely say they genuinely want the best minds in the country, regardless of any other consideration. They are fuelled by their own passion for their subject, and tell me that they take great care to ensure fairness and meritocracy as far as possible. After these experiences, I'm afraid I'm on their side, not yours.

In fact, I think the only reason that individuals and schools keep approaching me for help is that I'm guilty of really, really liking my own subject. I'm a professional doctor, lecturer and author, and I still actually miss my stop on the Tube because I'm too engrossed in the latest mathematical book I've picked off the shelf. I lecture on topics which no-one writes about but which are deeply interesting to me (and hopefully others) like the Anatomy of Dating or the Physiology of Modern Dance. I get excited about each accident and emergency case that comes through the hospital door because the reward of solving the puzzle is a smile on someone's face.

Dr Christopher See (right) with Medhi Goudarzi who was accepted to read chemical engineering at Robinson College, Cambridge. Picture: Liquid Photo.

I love my discipline both in and out of work and I consider it a great privilege to help young brilliant minds find their own voice and develop their interests, whatever they may be. It is this nurturing which I find so appealing and that is what the term tutoring actually means to me.

So, I refuse to help you get around the system, but I will help you to understand it in full. Here are some suggestions:

1) Convince yourself that you like your subject

Don't convince teachers, parents or peers and don't prepare your opening speech at interview. Sit down and think to yourself what do you like to do and what do you want to study.

If you don't know, that's fine. What you need to do is try something out with a sustained and decent effort and if it doesn't suit you after a proper trial, try something else. Repeat until satisfied.

2) When people tell you that you need to do something to get in, they are wrong

Apart from some technical details such as A level requirements and entrance exams, there is nothing which is an absolute requirement. In fact, it is almost always bad advice.

Don't let people hand you a book and tell you to read it. Go to a bookshop and spend an hour browsing for something which leaps off the shelf at you.

Don't let your school give you an extended project title. Find something you want spend your time on and propose it to your teacher.

Don't ask people 'what should I do?' I get this a lot, as you can imagine. My answer is always, do what you like and tell me why you chose it.

One-size-fits all advice is out there in plentiful supply and admissions tutors are well aware of what it says. Following it is the fastest way to be labelled 'ordinary'.

> The only way you will convince yourself and others that you like a discipline is to actually apply some discipline. That means knowing your subject well, performing well in exams as a result and reading beyond the bounds of what you are given at school. Test yourself by pushing yourself

3) Work hard

The only way you will convince yourself and others that you like a discipline is to actually apply some discipline. That means knowing your subject well, performing well in exams as a result and reading beyond the bounds of what you are given at school. Test yourself by pushing yourself.

4) Get used to liking things just because you like them

You do not ever have to defend or justify your interests. If you like doing any curricular or extracurricular activity, keep doing it. Admissions tutors want to hear what you have been doing, what you have learned from it and how it's been important to you.

In fact, much like in one of my anatomy lectures, when it comes to Oxbridge applications there are many useful things we can learn from the Art of Dating. So, I'm going to impart some dating advice.

Firstly, for the young ladies out there, a word of caution. The guy who you want to go out with is NOT the person who you meet at a party and after five minutes says 'I really like you'. The person you want is the guy who after five rejections is still underneath your balcony at midnight playing a love song he wrote for you on the banjo, whilst your father chases him away with a big stick. This is the guy who shows a real long-term commitment and dedication.

How does this apply to your Oxbridge application? Admissions tutors want to see the efforts you put in on a long-term basis and the hoops you are willing to jump through in order to gain a place. Have you actively chosen to travel to Portsmouth to research the injuries to Admiral Nelson at the battle of Trafalgar, or spent a summer adapting popular Dickens novels to 10-minute Youtube clips for others to enjoy? How do you use your time to show commitment to your subject?

The good news is that the hoops should be enjoyable. The would-be Romeo should enjoy composing his love song for his Juliet-to-be and, in much the same way, you must find ways to make sure that you actually enjoy the pursuit of your chosen discipline. How you express that is up to you.

Ladies and gentlemen, the students who are unsuccessful are those who are forced by internal or external pressures to fit a square peg in a round hole of academia. Even worse are those who are successful in their application but desperately unhappy with three or more years spent in hard toil at a top university. Find what you like, do lots of it and work very hard at it. All other things are just technicalities.

Dr Christopher See graduated from Trinity College, Cambridge, and worked as a junior doctor in accident and emergency before taking up a position lecturing at Manchester University Medical School. He has written extensively on Oxbridge admissions, including How to Get Into Oxbridge, published by Kogan Page.

To order go to www.koganpage.co.uk or email cashsales@tbs-ltd.co.uk. Or visit your favourite online, local or high street bookshop.

Science – it's a girl thing

Maureen Bosch, of the Girls' Day School Trust, explains how to add 50,000 scientists and mathematicians to the UK workforce

What do Wendy Savage, Martha Whitely, Aimee di Marco and Polly Tandy have in common?

Obviously, they're all women, but they are also all women who have worked or still work in different branches of medicine, science or engineering. Martha Whitely was the co-inventor of tear gas used in the trenches in World War One; Dr Wendy Savage is a gynaecologist and an advocate for women's rights in childbirth; and Aimee di Marco is also a doctor, a pioneering surgeon working on the leading edge of robotic surgery.

And Polly Tandy? Polly Tandy is a young drilling engineer in a notoriously male-dominated industry. She used to spend her days on offshore oil rigs and now works with a team designing and drilling wells in incredibly harsh conditions off the Shetland Islands.

The other factor that unites Wendy, Martha, Aimee and Polly is that they all went to girls' schools – more specifically schools belonging to the Girls' Day School Trust (GDST). Why is this noteworthy? Because it vividly demonstrates the level of encouragement that girls in single-sex schools are given to study subjects which are too often seen as 'boys' subjects'.

Studies have shown that women who went to girls' schools are more likely to study subjects commonly stereotyped as 'male', such as maths, physics and chemistry, both at school and at university. This often means they will have careers in more male-dominated industries – and earn more over their lifetime – than women of similar abilities and backgrounds who went to co-ed schools.

More than an education

At the GDST our aim is not just to provide an outstanding education, but to help girls develop into rounded, confident people, happy and resilient, who can meet and overcome the demands life will make of them.

Our 24 schools and two academies are all individual, but this commitment to developing the whole person is part of our shared DNA. Together, we are an extraordinarily effective network, helping girls make the most of their abilities and leading girls' education.

The Belvedere Academy, Liverpool
www.belvedereacademy.net

Birkenhead High School Academy
www.birkenheadhigh.gdst.net

Blackheath High School
www.blackheathhighschool.gdst.net

Brighton & Hove High School
www.bhhs.gdst.net

Bromley High School
www.bromleyhigh.gdst.net

Central Newcastle High School
www.newcastlehigh.gdst.net

Croydon High School
www.croydonhigh.gdst.net

Heathfield School for Girls, Pinner
www.heathfield.gdst.net

Howell's School, Llandaff
www.howells-cardiff.gdst.net

Ipswich High School for Girls
www.ipswichhigh.gdst.net

Kensington Prep School
www.kensingtonprep.gdst.net

Northampton High School
www.northamptonhigh.co.uk

Norwich High School for Girls
www.norwichhigh.gdst.net

Notting Hill & Ealing High School
www.nhehs.gdst.net

Nottingham Girls' High School
www.nottinghamgirlshigh.gdst.net

Oxford High School
www.oxfordhigh.gdst.net

Portsmouth High School
www.portsmouthhigh.co.uk

Putney High School
www.putneyhigh.co.uk

The Royal High School, Bath
www.royalhighbath.gdst.net

Sheffield High School
www.sheffieldhighschool.org.uk

Shrewsbury High School
www.shrewsburyhigh.gdst.net

South Hampstead High School
www.shhs.gdst.net

Streatham & Clapham High School
www.schs.gdst.net

Sutton High School
www.suttonhigh.gdst.net

Sydenham High School
www.sydenhamhighschool.gdst.net

Wimbledon High School
www.wimbledonhigh.gdst.net

Girls' Day
School Trust

Leading girls' education
Independent day schools for girls aged 3-18

Scan this code to download the GDST iPhone app featuring the prospectuses from all our schools

Find us online: twitter.com/GDST
www.facebookcom/TheGDST
www.gdst.net

In GDST schools, figures show that girls are more than twice as likely to study A level physics or chemistry than girls nationally; and that more than 40% of A levels taken each year by GDST pupils are in sciences or maths. This carries forward into university choices where again over 40% of former GDST students do science, medicine or maths as part of their degrees.

Does this matter? Well, yes. There is the matter of the waste of talent and of individual opportunities. How many women are there who, with the right encouragement and support, might have become excellent scientists instead languish in careers for which they aren't best suited, which aren't fulfilling and which mean they're not reaching their full potential? And this is at the time when the nation as a whole is crying out for high-quality scientists, mathematicians and engineers – individuals with STEM (science, technology, engineering and maths) skills.

Employers' organisations like the CBI regularly report concerns from their members that not enough school leavers have the essential maths and science skills that industries will need in the rest of the 21st century. They already report that they have difficulty in recruiting staff with STEM skills and they expect this to be a growing problem in the coming years. There simply aren't enough young people continuing to study STEM subjects post-16 to A level and beyond.

Yet, if the number of girls sitting A levels in physics, chemistry or maths across the country matched the proportion of girls at GDST schools taking these subjects, there would be nearly 9,000 more school-leavers with A level physics, 20,000 with A level chemistry and 21,000 with A level maths in the population every year – figures that could make a real difference.

So how are girls' schools better able to support girls who want to study these subjects than their co-ed peers? Firstly, as in all subjects in single-sex schools, the teaching is tailored to the interests of the pupils and what appeals more to them – for example, lasers might be studied in the context of their use in surgery rather than in heavy industry. Secondly, in a girls' school girls don't have to compete for equipment or for staff attention with boys. Girls will always be the ones doing the experiments themselves, not just recording the results of boys' experimentation.

Thirdly, and perhaps most importantly, there is less stereotyping in a girls' school. Curriculum choices are made in a context in which girls are given every opportunity, without prejudice, to explore and fulfil their potential. When there are only other girls in the classroom, then every subject from art and drama to physics and further maths is naturally a girls' subject, just as when there are only girls in the orchestra, every instrument from the piccolo to the tuba is naturally a girls' instrument.

Teenage girls (and boys for that matter) are often desperate to fit in with their peer group, and can be concerned at the prospect of doing anything that might make them stand out from the crowd, which makes a girl studying a subject which some might view as 'unfeminine' much more of a social risk. The key times for this sort of self-consciousness are the years from age 13 to 16, just when pupils are choosing which subjects they want to take for their GCSEs and A levels.

So when you're considering which school is right for your daughter, do bear in mind the track record of girls' schools in supporting girls and young women to make the right choices for themselves, their aptitudes and abilities, and in giving them the confidence not to be put off by stereotyping or by peer group pressure.

Your daughter may be a budding scientist or a potential artist, a lawyer in the making or a future entrepreneur: she deserves the chance to find out for herself what she's good at and what suits her, and not feel she has to conform to anyone else's expectations.

Maureen Bosch is head of communications at the Girls' Day School Trust

Using the internet to boost engineering and science careers

Alex Claydon, of Crackergroup, outlines a high-tech approach to learning

There has been a lot of media coverage recently concerning the teaching and learning of science, technology, engineering and maths (STEM). Why has this become such a hot topic? Well, there seems to be a growing belief that the education system is neglecting the teaching of STEM subjects and focusing on attempts to broaden the curriculum with the introduction of 'softer' subjects.

However, both government and business leaders believe that the teaching of STEM subjects throughout schools should be prioritised and developed, so that young people are informed about the breadth of STEM career opportunities available to those who have studied STEM subjects, especially maths, in their further and higher education. Research reported by *The Daily Telegraph* found that 49.4% of young people are finding science and maths too boring or hard to study, and 15% think that these subjects are only relevant in jobs relating to medicine. This supports the idea that the teaching of STEM subjects needs highlighting and progressing at a younger age.

According to a study by the Nuffield Foundation, fewer than 20% of students in England, Wales and Northern Ireland take maths to A level which is the lowest proportion in the developed world. In order to match the whopping two million engineers which the Association of Graduate Recruiters (AGR) estimate are needed over the next five to ten years, and to counter the 82,000 trained engineers and scientists which the Sector Skills Council for Science, Engineering and Manufacturing Technologies (Semta), reckons the UK will lose over the next four years through retirement, we must address the unwillingness to take what are perceived to be 'harder' subjects in further and higher education.

This is where the problem lies. How can we get the new generation interested in STEM subjects when the research quoted above tells us many schoolchildren consider these subjects to be too difficult and view them as 'boring'.

To meet the demand for engineers and scientists young people need to be inspired to study a STEM subject and to be made aware of the rewards they could reap if they pursue a career within science, engineering or technology (SET). Not only does a career within SET potentially provide worldwide travel opportunities to exotic and remote locations, but it also offers great starting salaries, excellent career development opportunities and diverse day-to-day tasks. It is these opportunities which young people must be exposed to within lessons, otherwise the nation may witness a decline in talented home-grown engineers and scientists which would have devastating effects to the UK's development and progression as an innovative First World country. According to the AGR, the engineering sector generates nearly £1.15 trillion in turnover – nearly 25% of the turnover for all UK businesses. Engineering is central to our economic recovery and growth and our ability to tackle global challenges such as climate change, health, and food and water security. It is clear that a real emphasis must be put on educating young people to understand and to become aware of the diversity and importance of careers within SET.

Government organisations such as Engineering UK are trying to tackle this problem as best as they can, with the provision of events such as the national Big Bang UK Young Scientists Fair held in March each

year and the Big Bang Near Me events which run throughout the year around the country. These events celebrate and showcase all aspects of STEM subjects in order to increase schoolchildren's knowledge of various industries within SET. However, although these events are on the increase, they are still relatively new, having only started in 2009, and more needs to be done to stress the importance these subjects can have on young people's career options later in life.

The government is also actively trying to promote apprenticeships as an alternative route to university. Although this initiative opens up and creates a new pathway for young people into the SET industries, it does not help to encourage and inspire those pupils who have not been exposed to the diverse career opportunities to which STEM subjects can lead. It is this learning experience which is currently being ignored and which needs to be targeted in order to produce enough engineers and scientists for 2020 and beyond.

My company, Crackergroup, has decided to use its expertise and experience to advance the cause of STEM learning and teaching. Crackergroup publishes gradcracker.com, the careers website for SET university students, so we have extensive knowledge of employers and industry. Building on our experience of launching gradcracker five years ago and developing it into the leading brand that it is today, we are launching our new website, gocracker.com, with one simple aim – to remedy outdated perceptions surrounding the studying of STEM subjects by inspiring and encouraging young people to consider the breadth of careers the SET sector offers.

Schoolchildren will be able to discover careers and advice, find games and access hundreds of links to websites we believe to be informative and supportive of the learning of STEM subjects. In addition, teachers and parents will be able to find resources to help them stimulate young people to explore the inspiring world of SET from both inside and outside the classroom.

Alex Claydon was educated at Gresham's School, Holt,
and studied business management and education at York St John University

Why schools need to make it easier for parents to pay fees

Julie Booth comes up with some ideas for cutting costs and keeping fees down

The ebb and flow of financial and political tides have resulted in a year of mixed fortunes for many families, both in the UK and beyond our shores. But, contrary to what some might have expected, as the British economy entered into double dip recession, figures published by the Independent Schools Council (ISC) in April 2012 revealed that the number of children being educated privately in the UK had risen for the first time since 2008.

According to the ISC's annual census, pupil numbers are up by 0.1% compared to 2011 – and this is despite school fees rising by 4.5%. The figures demonstrate the value parents place on the quality education being delivered in our independent schools. But, with household bills on the rise and many wage packets standing still, should schools be doing more to support parents who have made the often difficult decision to invest in a private education for their child?

Helping parents to balance the books

There is evidence that the challenging economic climate has had a negative impact on many family budgets. Schools north of the border have reportedly handed out more than £35million to help parents who are struggling to pay their child's fees, twice the amount that was being spent just three years ago. Although this may not be the experience of schools in all parts of the country, it does suggest that there is little room for complacency in the independent education marketplace.

One measure being taken by some schools to guard against loss of revenue is to start collecting their fees annually in advance. While this will help protect the school's income, it is likely to put financial pressure on all but the highest earning families and could lead to falling pupil numbers in some areas. This may be particularly apparent in areas where there is a high-performing grammar school or academy within reasonable travelling distance. There are those parents hit hard by the recession who will see these schools as possible alternatives to enrolling their child in a fee-paying school.

As family budgets tighten, independent schools could learn a thing or two from some of the utility companies and other retailers who have introduced different ways of preventing their customers from defaulting on their payments. Some of these measures would be perfectly simple to introduce in a school setting and, more importantly, they could help meet the needs of those families who are increasingly making financial sacrifices in order to keep up to date with their children's school fee payments.

Looking at the options

One alternative is to provide a monthly direct debit facility for settling school fees. This can make payments more manageable for families as they can be set up to coincide with parents' pay day. Direct debit is also a particularly efficient way for those parents who live overseas to pay their children's school fees.

The rapid growth of the digital age has touched almost every area of our lives. We are all becoming increasingly accustomed to receiving information from businesses via text or email to our PCs or mobile devices. Texting payment reminders directly to a mobile phone can give busy parents a gentle nudge when they start to fall behind in their payments and will help them to keep on top of their bills. The ISC figures revealed that the number of non-British pupils attending private schools is up by 5.8% compared to 2011, so it is worth schools considering whether bills and statements for fees could be emailed to parents rather than having them sent out in the post. This is much more convenient for parents as it reduces the risk of paper bills arriving late or getting lost, making it easier for them to keep on track with what they owe.

The way of the future for schools

An added bonus is that implementing some of these initiatives may not require any additional investment from the school, which is something that should delight any bursar.

Most schools now use an electronic management information system to record and store information, such as pupils' addresses and details of their conduct or achievement. Some of these systems allow schools to automate many of the processes associated with producing invoices for fees and communicating with parents. This not only saves time for the school, but also helps them cut down on the cost of printing and posting paper invoices and letters.

Many schools have traditionally resisted taking credit card payments for school fees due to the bank charges incurred. However, it may be a more cost-effective route than employing the services of a credit controller so this could be another option for bursars to consider.

Schools that have gone down a more digital route with the administration of school fees have often been able to manage their finances more efficiently and in some cases have even seen money coming in more quickly than it did when they were relying on the receipt of a cheque at the beginning of term.

As the ISC figures suggest, many families are continuing to invest in a private education for their child. But while the economic forecast remains uncertain, those schools that do all they can to make it easier for parents to pay their fees bills will be helping to ensure that independent schooling remains a priority for many years to come.

***

British fee-paying schools are considered among the best in the world and the Independent School Awards provide a wonderful opportunity for them to celebrate their achievements. The level of commitment in our schools to delivering the highest standards of teaching and learning should be championed and, as an example of Capita's commitment to Independent education, we are delighted to be headline sponsors of the Independent School Awards for 2012 and 2013. Now in their third year, these are the only awards solely dedicated to the independent education sector and they recognise excellence in the strategic and financial management of fee-paying schools delivering British education across the UK and abroad.

Julie Booth is head of independent schools at Capita SIMS.

'Every child has a right to be inspired'

Richard Cairns puts teachers and Headteachers on the spot

Richard Cairns is Head Master of Brighton College

As Headteachers, we all buy in to people and, in our obsession with school structures and systems, it is always good to remind ourselves of what is obvious: that the schools we run are only as good as the people in them. And, specifically, they are only as good as the teachers we employ to enthuse and inspire the children in our care.

Every school leader has, no doubt, been shaped – perhaps forever – by a particular teacher: someone who gave us a love of history or art or physics; someone who made us believe that we could play rugby or netball; someone who persuaded us that we could sing or act or dance. And it is our prime responsibility every day to ask ourselves whether the teachers in our schools are as good as they ought to be.

When the OECD reported on what factor most shapes the educational outcome of young people in any country, they concluded, unsurprisingly, that it wasn't class sizes or facilities or access to the latest IT. Rather, it was the quality of the teachers in our schools.

Those countries like Singapore and Finland that recruit from the top one third of graduates and have robust and meaningful appraisal and professional development do much better than places like the United States where teachers are drawn from the bottom third of graduates and where meaningful appraisal is made impossible by entrenched and powerful trade unions. Here in the UK things are changing. My own sense is that the people joining the teaching profession are of a higher quality than they used to be – better qualified, better trained and more motivated.

But we need more of them. We need to incentivise the brightest and the best to regard our profession as a career of first choice. We could start by offering real incentives to Russell Group graduates with good degrees by waiving their university fees if they go into teaching and stay in teaching for five years. We must not stint on professional development either and we must look for best practice not just in local schools but overseas. From 2013, every one of my heads of department at Brighton College will spend a week in a high performing school overseas, learning new ways to be better.

And let's be clear, we as Headteachers have got a responsibility to deal robustly with poor teachers. Too many of them are shuffled around within our own schools or palmed off on others. That must stop. If we really regard teaching as a life-changing profession, then we must regard bad teaching as life-threatening. We would be shocked if hospitals turned a blind eye to incompetent doctors or nurses, yet we are all aware of incompetent teachers in our educational system. Sometimes, of course, we get an appointment wrong – that is human and forgivable – but what is unforgivable is failing to deal with it.

How you do it is up to each Head. At Brighton College we have pupils playing their part in teacher reviews and appraisals. Every child comments in an online survey on every teacher in their probationary year and their subsequent appraisal years. The vast majority find it immensely rewarding to receive positive, tangible affirmation – perhaps for the first time – of how highly the pupils regard them. But a minority get a wake-up call that leads to a conversation that may lead to a departure.

It is never easy, but it is the right thing to do. No Headteacher should ever tolerate bad teaching, yet up and down the land, that is precisely what is going on. Too many Headteachers are prepared to take their relatively generous salaries yet duck the issue of the bad teacher in the staff room. And who suffers? The children.

My own view is that where Headteachers fail to deal with bad teaching, where Headteachers lack the courage to take on a poor teacher who has been clearly and fairly identified as such, they should themselves be called to account and their own pay should be docked. We can't take on the rewards and privileges of headship if we are not prepared to stand up for the right of every child to be enthused and inspired by outstanding teachers.

Richard Cairns graduated from Oxford University with a First in History and worked as a trainee solicitor in Australia and as a volunteer teacher in a refugee camp in the Gaza Strip before starting his teaching career. In 2006 he became Head Master of Brighton College, named England's Independent School of the Year 2011-12 by The Sunday Times.

Reflections on 26 years as a Head Master

Since 1986 Dr Ian Walker has been one of the most innovative and stimulating Heads in the country, at King's Rochester. Here he recalls some of the highlights of his time...

My greatest pride of all is in the children who have passed through King's over the last 26 years. They are invariably delightful and lovely, confident without being arrogant and I have been happy to stay for such a long time because of them – they give me the most joy and will be what I will miss the most.

Although girls had been admitted to the Sixth Form since 1977, in 1992 King's became co-ed in one fell swoop throughout school. This radically changed the nature of the school and doubled our potential market.

Co-education offers many benefits. I have taught at single sex schools and boys are more oafish without the girls and can be more troublesome. Typically, females have more common sense, stability and intelligence. The maturation of the school came about with the advent of girls and I am really pleased about that and glad that I did it. King's pupils are good company and thoroughly decent people. This is the real joy of the job for me and it is not significantly different to 26 years ago. On the other hand, the school environment was not so conducive to happy relationships then as it is now and I am delighted by the way King's children make friendships for a lifetime. It is glorious to see, especially when they come back to visit.

I teach about four lessons a week, including classics at A level, divinity, GCSE classical Greek, English and history and I've also coached the Colts rugby team. However, the nature of the job has changed over the years, through none of my own making, but forced upon me and my fellow Heads by ever-changing legislation injurious to education. I am not as hands on as I would like to be, since so much of my time is taken up with legislation and this separates me from the children. Trust has been replaced by legislation and a vocation has become a bureaucratised employment.

That is not to say that schools should be exempt from reform. When I arrived at King's, I inherited an antediluvian system of governance, not surprising, perhaps, in a school founded in 604 AD! The school was also, inevitably, Dickensian, at least in terms of its associations with *Great Expectations* and the fact that the administration was located in Satis House. Now we have the King's executive board based on a company model with an open style management reporting to the non-execs who are the governors.

In my time as a Head, education legislation went barmy, starting with the National Curriculum introduced by Kenneth Baker in 1986. He changed O levels and introduced ridiculous coursework and modular exams which resulted in the loss of about a third of each year's teaching. At King's, we have therefore encouraged the advancement of the more rigorous International GCSEs which have no coursework or modules.

1992 saw the introduction of league tables in *The Daily Telegraph* and from that time on 'Mickey Mouse' subjects have appeared in every school's curriculum except King's. I steadfastly refused to accept these courses which are not good for education and do not result in Russell Group university offers. King's was one of very few schools that refused to fall in line. I am delighted that in my final year, 2011-12, King's Rochester is now the best performing, non-selective school in England, ranked at 153 in *The Times* in 2011 with all those above King's being highly selective.

The whole landscape changed with New Labour and its 'dumbing down' of education, pandering to the lowest common denominator rather than stretching children to the highest of their abilities and then, to make it look as if their scheme was working, diluting the hitherto demanding standards that had characterised public examinations.

> We are the most examined country in the world, but education is not about exams but learning and how to live

For example, before 1986 in a religious studies A level Old Testament paper, examinees had the option to answer in Hebrew, or Greek in a New Testament paper! Exams were three hours long and two to five essays had to be completed. Now, they tick boxes. Why? To demonstrate that the policy is working by making exams easier with the result that every year the grades go up. We have lost sight of what education is about: that is to learn, not to pass exams! Fortunately, the coalition are reversing some of these idiocies.

When I was a teacher at Dulwich College, I would give the boys a wodge of papers three inches thick and would say to them 'read that and you will get an A grade – now let's do something interesting like getting a paper published in a learned journal!' Every year, I would receive a letter from the exam board saying that these results were the best in the country, but I didn't teach the syllabus!

We are the most examined country in the world, but education is not about exams but learning and how to live, and it is my biggest regret that in my time in teaching the experience of our pupils has come to this.

With Kenneth Baker's directed hours, professionalism went out the window, but it still exists at King's. In far too many other places you can see the erosion of teaching as a vocation and how it has become just a job. Here, my colleagues have a vocational commitment and a professional pride in seeing the children through these vital formative years. I will miss the teaching most of all and the company of my dedicated and inspiring colleagues. Finally, I have liked being my own boss in a community where no two days are ever the same.

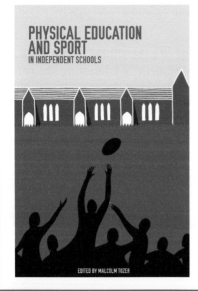

Finding the fees

Chris Procter, joint managing director of SFIA, outlines the planned approach to funding school fees.

Every year the Independent Schools Council (ISC) carries out a survey, which is completed by all 1,221 schools in UK membership, plus two schools from the Republic of Ireland.

This year the census, which was carried out in January 2012, showed that school fees increased by an average of 4.5% – a figure below the education component of the Consumer Price Index (5.1%) and the second lowest rise since 1994.

There are now 508,472 pupils at ISC member schools, up from 506,500 in 2011.

The proportions of day (86.5%) and boarding pupils (13.5%) are broadly in line with last year. The share of girls and boys at ISC schools is very nearly equal, with girls representing 49% of all pupils.

The overall average termly fee is £4,596 (excluding nursery fees). The average boarding fee is £8,780 and the average day fee is £3,903.

The overall cost (including university fees) might seem daunting: the cost of educating one child privately could well be very similar to that of buying a house but, as with house buying, the school fee commitment for the majority of parents can be made possible by spreading it over a long period rather than funding it all from current resources.

It is vital that parents do their financial homework, plan ahead, start to save early and regularly. Grandparents who have access to capital could be beneficial; by contributing to school fees they could help to reduce any inheritance tax liability.

Parents would be well-advised to consult a specialist independent financial adviser (IFA) as early as possible, since a long-term plan for the payment of fees – possibly university as well as school – can prove very attractive from a financial point of view and thus offer greater peace of mind.

Funding fees is neither science nor magic, nor is there any panacea. It is quite simply a question of planning and using whatever resources are available, such as income, capital, or tax reduction opportunities.

The fundamental point to recognise is that you, your circumstances and your wishes, or ambitions for your children, or grandchildren are unique. They might well be similar to those of other people but they will still be uniquely different.

There will, therefore, be no single solution to your problem. Indeed, after a review of all your circumstances, there might not be a problem at all.

So, what are the reasons for seeking advice about educational expenses?

• To reduce the overall cost?

• To get some tax benefit?

• To reduce your cash outflow?

• To invest capital to ensure that future fees are paid?

- To set aside money now for future fees?

- To provide protection for school fees?

- Or just to make sure that as well as educating your children you can still have a life!

Any, some or all of the above – or others not listed – could be on your agenda. The important thing is to develop a strategy.

At this stage, it really does not help to get hung up on which financial product is the most suitable. The composition of a school fee plan will differ for each individual depending on a number of factors. That is why there is no one school fee plan on offer.

The simplest strategy, and in most cases the most expensive option, is to write out a cheque for the whole bill when it arrives and post it back. Like most simple plans that works very well, if you have the money. Even if you do have the money, is that really the best way of doing things? Do you know that to fund £1,000 of school fees as a higher rate taxpayer paying 40% income tax, you currently need to earn £1,667, this rises to £2,000 if you are an additional rate taxpayer where the rate is 50%?

How then do you start to develop your strategy? As with most things in life, if you can define your objective, then you will know what you are aiming at. Your objective in this case will be:

(a) to determine how much money is needed and

(b) when it will be required.

You need to draw up a school fees schedule or what others would term a cash flow forecast.

So: How many children?
Which schools? (or use an average school fee)
When?
Any special needs?
Inflation guesstimate?
Include university costs?

With this basic information, the school fees schedule/cash flow forecast can be calculated and you will have defined what it is you are trying to achieve.

Remember though that senior school fees are typically more than prep school fees – this needs to be factored in. Also be aware that the cost of university is not restricted to the fees alone; there are a lot of maintenance and other costs involved: accommodation, books, food, to name a few.

You now have one side of an equation, the relatively simple side. The other side is you and your resources. This also needs to be defined, but this is a much more difficult exercise. The reason that it is more difficult, of course, is that school fees are not the only drain on your resources. You probably have a mortgage, you want to have holidays, you need to buy food and clothes, you may be concerned that you should be funding a pension.

This is the key area of expertise, since your financial commitments are unique. A specialist in the area of school fees planning knows how to get at these commitments, to record them and help you to distribute your resources according to priority.

The options open to you as parents depend completely upon your adviser's knowledge of these complex personal financial issues. (Did I forget to mention your tax position, capital gains tax allowance, other tax allowances including those of your children and a lower or zero rate tax paying spouse or partner? These could well be used to your advantage.)

A typical school fees plan can incorporate many elements to fund short-, medium- and long-term fees. Each plan is designed according to individual circumstances and usually there is a special emphasis on what parents are looking to achieve, for example, to maximise overall savings and to minimise the outflow of cash.

Additionally it is possible to protect the payment of the fees in the event of unforeseen circumstances that could lead to a significant or total loss of earnings.

Short-term fees

Short-term fees are typically the termly amounts needed within five years: these are usually funded from such things as guaranteed investments, liquid capital, loan plans (if no savings are available) or maturing insurance policies, investments *etc*. Alternatively they can be funded from disposable income.

Medium-term fees

Once the short-term plan expires, the medium-term funding is invoked to fund the education costs for a further five to ten years. Monthly amounts can be invested in a low-risk, regular premium investment ranging from a building society account to a friendly society savings plan to equity ISAs. It is important to understand the pattern of the future fees and to be aware of the timing of withdrawals.

Long-term fees

Longer term funding can incorporate a higher element of risk (as long as this is acceptable to the investor), which will offer higher potential returns. Investing in UK and overseas equities could be considered. Products may be the same as those for medium-term fees, but will have the flexibility to utilise investments that may have an increased 'equity based' content.

Finally, it is important to remember that most investments or financial products either mature with a single payment or provide for regular withdrawals; rarely do they provide timed termly payments. Additionally, the overall risk profile of the portfolio should lean towards the side of caution (for obvious reasons).

There are any number of IFAs in the country but few who specialise in the area of planning to meet school and university fees. SFIA is the largest Independent Financial Adviser which specialises in school fees planning in the UK.

This article has been contributed by SFIA and edited by Chris Procter, Joint Managing Director.

He can be contacted at: SFIA Ltd, 41 London Road, Twyford, Berkshire RG10 9EJ
Tel: 0845 458 3690
Fax: 0118 934 4609
Email: enquiries@sfia.co.uk
Web: www.sfia.co.uk

The British Accreditation Council (BAC) for independent further and higher education

Students are increasingly looking for choice and quality in post-16 education. They can look beyond the traditional options of school and university to find a world of opportunity in independent further and higher education. Offering an enticing and eclectic range of subjects from animal care to gemology, from film, music and fashion to dance and art, independent further and higher education institutions have particular attractions for students from around the world.

There are tutorial colleges, and there are specialist colleges offering A levels that are not widely available elsewhere. There are institutions offering university foundation years, and those providing career or vocationally tailored courses at degree level in subjects such as audio engineering and film production, with strong industry links, and very good graduate employment rates. Vocational courses in a wide range of subjects offer students the opportunity to study for the career of their choice. Classes are often smaller and more focused on the outcomes that students want.

BAC-accredited institutions in the UK now number more than 360, offering everything from website design to yoga to equine dentistry, as well as more standard qualifications in subjects such as business, IT, management and law

The British Accreditation Council (BAC) has now been the principal accrediting body for the independent further and higher education sector for over a quarter of a century. BAC-accredited institutions in the UK now number more than 360, offering everything from website design to yoga to equine dentistry, as well as more standard qualifications in subjects such as business, IT, management and law. As well as our accreditation of institutions offering traditional teaching, BAC has developed a new accreditation scheme for providers offering the more flexible option of blended learning (a combination of online and face-to-face learning), as well as those purely offering distance learning. Some students may also look to study outside UK at one of the institutions holding BAC international accreditation.

One colourful and internationally-renowned example of a BAC-accredited college is the unique and very successful Istituto Marangoni in London, which is a branch of the long-established fashion design school in Milan. Istituto Marangoni offers undergraduate degrees in fashion design, fashion business and fashion styling, validated by Manchester Metropolitan University, along with Masters programmes in womenswear and luxury brand management. By offering a range of courses covering both artistic and business aspects of fashion the school is helping more students to access a very competitive industry. The school itself is ideally situated in the centre of London, allowing students ample opportunity to source garments and accessories for their course projects.

Kings Oxford was the first college to achieve BAC accreditation back in 1985. Kings is a tutorial college that offers GCSEs, A levels and university foundation courses, alongside English language tuition and summer vacation courses. Like many tutorial colleges accredited by BAC, Kings offers tuition that is tailored to the individual and gives them the best chance of achieving their goals, be that university, work or progression to further study. The Advanced Level Foundation and Pre-Masters courses are particularly suitable for international students and can significantly increase a student's chance of gaining a place at a UK university. In addition, tutorial colleges pay particular attention to students' welfare and will usually help with issues such as finding accommodation. Kings Oxford itself has an 'accommodation guarantee' whereby students studying for 24 weeks or more are guaranteed accommodation within walking distance of the college. Once a student arrives at Kings, there are several members of full-time staff assigned solely to student welfare who ensure that students adjust to life away from home as smoothly as possible.

All institutions applying for BAC accreditation undergo a rigorous process of inspections and background checks that scrutinise their premises, the management and staffing of their organisation, their commitment to student welfare, the quality of the actual teaching and academic resources on offer, and how well they manage and monitor the quality of their own provision

It's clear from examples such as these that high-quality study, both of a practical and academic nature, is no longer confined to the familiar world of state schools and universities. Both of the institutions mentioned above provide a tailored and comfortable environment for study without compromising on standards. While the environment may be different from that of a school, it is no less rigorous; both institutions have careful monitoring systems and their students gain very good exam results.

For anyone thinking about post-16 education, it is worth looking at the wealth and diversity of courses and institutions that are available in the independent sector, and the benefits that come from looking beyond state education.

All institutions applying for BAC accreditation undergo a rigorous process of inspections and background checks that scrutinise their premises, the management and staffing of their organisation, their commitment to student welfare, the quality of the actual teaching and academic resources on offer, and how well they manage and monitor the quality of their own provision. We repeat this process every four years and monitor all institutions regularly to check that the standards we require are being maintained. This comprehensive approach to accreditation helps BAC to remain the most respected mark of quality in the private FE and HE sectors.

A directory of BAC-accredited colleges can be found on our website and if you would like to find out more about our work please contact us.

The British Accreditation Council
76 Shoe Lane
London EC4A 3JB
Telephone: 0300 330 1400
Fax: 0300 330 1401
Email: info@the-bac.org
Website: www.the-bac.org

British Accreditation Council
for independent further and higher education

The Independent Schools Council

The Independent Schools Council (ISC) works with its members to promote and preserve the quality, diversity and excellence of UK independent education both at home and abroad

What is the ISC?

ISC brings eight associations together to represent over 1,200 independent schools in the UK. These schools are ranked among the best in the world and educate more than half a million children each year, around 80% of independently educated pupils.

ISC also represents 130 British International schools in more than 50 countries worldwide.

ISC schools

ISC schools provide a world-class education. Even in this time of recession, the number of pupils in ISC schools has risen, demonstrating that parents continue to consider finding fees for independent education a priority.

There are strong reasons for this, including exceptional exam results, extra-curricular opportunity and progression to university.

> ISC schools provide a world-class education. Even in this time of recession, the number of pupils in ISC schools has risen, demonstrating that parents continue to consider finding fees for independent education a priority

6.5% of GCSE entries come from ISC schools, yet the pupils achieve 26% of A* grades. At A level, one third of students who get AAA or better come from ISC schools. ISC schools have a particularly strong track-record in traditional, hard subjects such as modern languages and science. 91% of ISC pupils continue on to higher education.

It is also the commitment to offer a well-rounded education, with excellent provision beyond the classroom particularly in the arts and sport, which attracts so many families year on year.

ISC schools are sympathetic to the financial challenges facing many parents and the amount of fee assistance available has grown to reflect this, with £284million spent on means-tested bursaries in 2012.

ISC associations

There are eight member associations of ISC each with its own distinctive ethos reflected in their entrance criteria and quality assurance:

Girls' Schools Association (GSA) – see page 36
Headmasters' and Headmistresses' Conference (HMC) – see page 37

Independent Association of Prep Schools (IAPS) – see page 39
Independent Schools Association (ISA) – see page 40
The Society of Heads – see page 41

Association of Governing Bodies of Independent Schools (AGBIS)

AGBIS has 751 members which together represent rather more than 751 schools. Not infrequently, two or more schools have the same governing body. AGBIS seeks to support its members by providing advice, support and training in the principles of good governance. The support includes conducting seminars, on-site training, reviews of governance, publications, an e-learning facility and a telephone advisory service. For more information, please visit: www.agbis.org.uk

Independent Schools' Bursars Association (ISBA)

ISBA is a charitable company limited by guarantee whose objects are the advancement of education by the promotion of efficient and effective financial management, administration and ancillary services in independent schools. It is schools, rather than individuals, that are members of the ISBA although their usual point of contact with the association is the bursar. There are currently in excess of 900 schools in membership. For more information, please visit www.theisba.org.uk

Council of British International Schools (COBIS)

COBIS is a global membership association of over 130 quality British International schools in more than 50 countries worldwide. Selecting the right school can be a challenging process, however, parents and families can be reassured that COBIS member schools work within specific guidelines of ethical practice and good governance, which reflect the high standards and ethos of the British style educational system. For more information please visit www.cobis.org.uk

Two further organisations are affiliated to ISC: Boarding Schools Association (BSA) and Scottish Council of Independent Schools (SCIS)

The Independent Schools Council can be contacted at:
St Vincent House
30 Orange Street
London WC2H 7HH

Telephone: 020 7766 7070
Fax: 020 7766 7071
Website: www.isc.co.uk

Choosing a school initially

Educational institutions often belong to organisations that guarantee their standards. Here we give a brief alphabetical guide to what the initials mean

BSA

BSA – The Boarding Schools' Association

Since its foundation in 1966, the Boarding Schools' Association (BSA) has had the twin objectives of the promotion of boarding education and the development of quality boarding through high standards of pastoral care and boarding accommodation. Parents and prospective pupils choosing a boarding school can, therefore, be assured that the 500 schools in membership of the BSA are committed to providing the best possible boarding environment for their pupils.

> Today's quality boarding schools provide each of their pupils with a safe and challenging environment, where communication with home is easy and where the boarding facilities and the pastoral care are of the highest order

A school can only join the BSA if it is in membership of one of the ISC (Independent Schools Council) constituent associations or in membership of SBSA (State Boarding Schools' Association). These two bodies require member schools to be regularly inspected by the Independent Schools' Inspectorate (ISI) or Ofsted. Between April 2007 and August 2011, all boarding inspections, in both independent and state schools, were carried out by Ofsted, whose reports can be found on their website. Boarding inspection of independent schools has been conducted by ISI since September 2012. Ofsted retains responsibility for the inspection of boarding in state schools. Boarding inspections must be conducted every three years. Boarding is judged against the National Minimum Standards for Boarding Schools (revised 2011) with considerable input from the BSA.

Relationship with government

The BSA is in regular communication with the Department for Education (DfE) on all boarding matters. The Children Act (1989) and the Care Standards Act (2001) require boarding schools to conform to national legislation and the promotion of this legislation and the training required to carry it out are matters on which the DfE and the BSA work closely. The key area is in training.

Boarding training

The programme of training for boarding staff whose schools are in membership of the BSA has been supported and sponsored in the past by the DfE. The BSA maintains the high standards expected as a consequence of that support. The Utting Report on the Safeguards for Children Living Away from Home highlighted the importance of the development of 'policy, practice and training for services for children who live away from home'. It focuses on the right of parents to expect that staff looking after children are competent to do so, and points out the responsibility of central government to secure consistent national standards in promoting the welfare of children away from home. The Singleton Review (March 2009) reiterated the importance of rigorous safeguarding of such children.

In addition the BSA organises five conferences and more than 50 seminars a year for governors, heads, deputies, housemasters and housemistresses, and matrons and medical staff where further training takes place in formal sessions and in sharing good practice. The BSA provides the following range of training and information:

- Professional qualifications for both teaching and non-teaching staff in boarding schools. The BSA has been responsible for the development of courses leading to university validated Certificates of Professional Practice in Boarding Education. These certificates, the result of at least two years' study, are awarded by the University of Roehampton.

- A rolling programme of day seminars on current boarding legislation and good practice.

How can the BSA further help parents when they are choosing a boarding school?

Parents are invited to contact the BSA for information on:

- Choosing a boarding school;

- Why boarding might at some stage benefit your child; and

- Details on the 500 member schools of the BSA.

Parents are also invited to contact the BSA for useful publications:

- *Parenting the Boarder* by Libby Purves; and

- *Being a Boarder* by Rose Heiney.

SBSA

The BSA issues information on the 37 state boarding schools in England and Wales and the BSA should be contacted for details of these schools. In these schools parents pay for boarding but not for education, so fees are substantially lower than in an independent boarding school.

In conclusion

Today's quality boarding schools provide each of their pupils with a safe and challenging environment, where communication with home is easy and where the boarding facilities and the pastoral care are of the highest order. The Boarding Schools' Association and its members are committed to this vision for boarding.

National Director: Hilary Moriarty BA(Hons), MA, PGCE
Director of Training: Alex Thomson OBE, BSc(Hons), PGCE, DipEd, FCIPD

Boarding Schools' Association
Grosvenor Gardens House
35-37 Grosvenor Gardens
London SWlW oBS

Tel: 020 7798 1580
Fax: 020 7798 1581
Email: bsa@boarding.org.uk
Website: www.boarding.org.uk

BOARDING SCHOOLS'
ASSOCIATION

GSA

The Girls' Schools Association, to which Heads of leading girls' schools belong

The Girls' Schools Association (GSA) is the professional association of the Heads of almost 180 independent schools for girls in the UK, educating approximately 100,000 pupils. Schools in the Association offer a choice of day, boarding, weekly, and flexi-boarding education, and range in type from large urban schools of 1000 pupils to small rural schools of around 200. Many schools have junior and pre-prep departments, and can offer a complete education from four to 18. A significant proportion of schools also have religious affiliations. The Heads of schools in the Girls' Day School Trust (GDST) are members of the GSA.

GSA schools are widely recognised for their exceptional record of examination achievements. Education is, however, not only about success in exams. Girls' schools offer wider development opportunities, and are special for a number of reasons. They provide an environment in which girls can learn to grow in confidence and ability. In a girls' school, the needs and aspirations of girls are the main focus and the staff are experts in the teaching of girls. Girls hold all the senior positions in the school, and are encouraged by positive role models in the schools' teaching staff and management. Expectations are high. In GSA schools, girls do not just have equal opportunities, they have *every* opportunity. Members of GSA share a commitment to the values and benefits of single-sex schools for girls, and a belief that all girls, regardless of educational setting, deserve the opportunity to realise their potential, to be active and equal, confident and competent leaders, participants and contributors.

The Girls' Schools Association plays a vital role in advising and lobbying educational policy makers on issues relating to girls' schools and the education of girls. As the specialist organisation for the education of girls, the Association is regularly consulted by the Department for Education, the Office for Standards in Education, the Qualifications and Curriculum Authority and other bodies. However, GSA is not only a 'single-issue' organisation, and is a powerful and well-respected voice within the educational establishment. GSA is one of the constituent bodies of the Independent Schools' Council (ISC). The ISC operates, on behalf of GSA, a strict accreditation scheme for schools wishing to join the Association. Once in membership, schools are required to undergo a regular cycle of inspections to ensure that these rigorous standards are being maintained. Schools must also belong to the Association of Governing Bodies of Independent Schools, and Heads must be in membership of the Association of School and College Leaders (ASCL).

A programme of professional development for members ensures that the Heads of all GSA schools are highly trained, and are fully up-to-date with all aspects of their profession. Courses are also regularly held for staff and opportunities are available for subject teachers to meet together on curriculum issues.

The Association's secretariat is accommodated in Leicester in premises shared with the ASCL.

130 Regent Road, Leicester LE1 7PG
Tel: 0116 254 1619   Email: office@gsa.uk.com   Website: www.gsa.uk.com

President 2011: Mrs Louise Robinson, Merchant Taylors' Girls' School.
President Elect: Mrs Hilary French, Central Newcastle High School (GDST)
Vice President 2012 (President 2011): Dr Helen Wright, St Mary's Calne
Executive Director: Ms Sheila Cooper.

HMC

The Headmasters' and Headmistresses' Conference, to which the Heads of leading independent schools belong

Founded in 1869 the HMC exists to enable members to discuss matters of common interest and to influence important developments in education. It looks after the professional interests of members, central to which is their wish to provide the best possible educational opportunities for their pupils.

The Heads of some 253 leading independent schools are members of The Headmasters' and Headmistresses' Conference, whose membership now includes Heads of boys', girls' and coeducational schools. There are up to 16 additional members who are Heads of maintained schools. International membership includes the Heads of around 60 schools throughout the world.

The great variety of these schools is one of the strengths of HMC but all must exhibit high quality in the education provided. While day schools are the largest group, about a third of HMC schools consist mainly of boarders and others have a smaller boarding element including weekly and flexible boarders.

Only those schools that meet with the rigorous membership criteria are admitted and this helps ensure that HMC is synonymous with high quality in education

All schools are noted for their academic excellence and achieve good results, including those with pupils from a broad ability band. Members believe that good education consists of more than academic results and schools provide a wide range of educational co-curricular activities.

Only those schools that meet with the rigorous membership criteria are admitted and this helps ensure that HMC is synonymous with high quality in education. There is a set of membership requirements and a Code of Practice to which members must subscribe. Those who want the intimate atmosphere of a small school will find some with around 350 pupils. Others who want a wide range of facilities and specialisations will find these offered in large day or boarding schools. Some have over 1000 pupils. About 50 schools are for boys only, others are coeducational throughout or only in the sixth form. The first girls-only schools joined HMC in 2006.

Within HMC there are schools with continuous histories as long as any in the world and many others trace their origins to Tudor times, but HMC continues to admit to membership recently-founded schools that have achieved great success. The facilities in all HMC schools will be good but some have magnificent buildings and grounds that are the result of the generosity of benefactors over many years. Some have attractive rural settings, others are sited in the centres of cities.

Pupils come from all sorts of backgrounds. Bursaries and scholarships provided by the schools give about a third of the 200,000 pupils in HMC schools help with their fees. These average about £24,000 per annum for boarding schools and £11,000 for day schools. About 160,000 are day pupils and 40,000 boarders.

Entry into some schools is highly selective but others are well-suited to a wide ability range. Senior boarding schools usually admit pupils after the Common Entrance examination taken when they are 13.

Most day schools select their pupils by 11+ examination. Many HMC schools have junior schools, some with nursery and pre-prep departments. The growing number of boarders from overseas is evidence of the high reputation of the schools worldwide.

The independent sector has always been fortunate in attracting very good teachers. Higher salary scales, excellent conditions of employment, exciting educational opportunities and good pupil/teacher ratios bring rewards commensurate with the demanding expectations. Schools expect teachers to have a good education culminating in a good honours degree and a professional qualification, though some do not insist on the latter especially if relevant experience is offered. Willingness to participate in the whole life of the school is essential.

> The Heads of some 251 leading independent schools are members of The Headmasters' and Headmistresses' Conference, whose membership now includes Heads of boys', girls' and coeducational schools

Parents expect the school to provide not only good teaching that helps their children achieve the best possible examination results, but also the dedicated pastoral care and valuable educational experiences outside the classroom in music, drama, games, outdoor pursuits and community service. Over 90% of pupils go on to higher education, many of them winning places on the most highly-subscribed university courses.

All members attend the Annual Meeting, usually held in a large conference centre in September/October. There are ten divisions covering England, Wales, Scotland and Ireland where members meet once a term on a regional basis.

The chairman and committee, with the advice of the general secretary and membership secretary, make decisions on matters referred by sub-committees (such as academic policy, professional development, universities, junior schools inspection, membership and sports), steering groups (such as finance) and working parties set up to deal with *ad hoc* issues. Close links are maintained with other professional associations in membership of the Independent Schools Council and with the Association of School and College Leaders, which represents Heads of both maintained and independent schools.

Membership Secretary: Ian Power.   Tel: 01858 465260
General Secretary: Dr William Richardson.   Tel: 01858 469059

12 The Point
Rockingham Road
Market Harborough
Leicestershire LE16 7QU
Email: hmc@hmc.org.uk
Website: www.hmc.org.uk

IAPS

The Independent Association of Preparatory Schools (IAPS) is the membership association for the headteachers of leading prep and junior schools in the UK and overseas

With more than 600 members, IAPS' schools represent a multi-billion pound enterprise, educating more than 160,000 children and employing more than 20,000 staff.

Schools are spread throughout cities, towns and the countryside and offer pupils the choice of day, boarding, weekly and flexible boarding, in both single sex and coeducational settings. Sizes vary from 100 to more than 800 per school, with the majority between 150 and 400. Most schools are charitable trusts, some are limited companies and a few are proprietary. There are also junior schools attached to senior schools, choir schools, those with a particular religious affiliation and those that offer specialist provision as well as some schools with an age range extending to age 16 or above.

As the voice of independent prep school education,
IAPS has national influence and actively defends and
promotes the interests of our members

IAPS only accredits those schools that can demonstrate that they provide the highest standards of education and care. Member schools offer an all-round, values-led, broad education, which produces confident, adaptable, motivated children with a lifelong passion for learning. In order to be elected to membership, a Head must be suitably qualified and schools must be accredited through a satisfactory inspection. IAPS offers its members and their staff a comprehensive and up-to-date programme of professional development courses to ensure that high professional standards are maintained.

Pupils are offered a rich and varied school life. The targets of the National Curriculum are regarded as a basic foundation, which is greatly extended by the wider programmes of study offered. Specialist subject teaching begins at an early age and pupils are exposed to a range of cultural and sporting opportunities. Together with more than 30 recreational games, music, art and drama form part of curricular and extracurricular activities. In addition, IAPS organises holiday and term-time sporting competitions for pupils to take part in, including skiing, sailing, judo, swimming, golf, fencing and squash, amongst many others.

IAPS has well-established links with senior independent schools, and experience in methods of transfer and entry to them. As the voice of independent prep school education, it has national influence and actively defends and promotes the interests of its members. It lobbies the government on their behalf and promotes prep school issues on a national and international stage. IAPS works directly with ministers and national policy advisers to ensure that the needs of the prep school sector are met.

IAPS
11 Waterloo Place, Leamington Spa, Warwickshire CV32 5LA
Tel: 01926 887833 Fax: 01926 888014
Email: iaps@iaps.org.uk
Website: www.iaps.org.uk

Excellence in Education
The Independent Association
of Prep Schools

ISA

The Independent Schools Association, with membership across all types of school

The Independent Schools Association (ISA), established in 1879, is one of the oldest of the Headteachers' associations of independent schools that make up the Independent Schools' Council (ISC). It began life as the Association of Principals of Private Schools, which was created to encourage high standards and foster friendliness and cooperation among Heads who had previously worked in isolation. In 1895 it was incorporated as The Private Schools Association and in 1927 the word 'private' was replaced by 'independent'. The recently published history of the association, *Pro Liberis*, demonstrates the strong links ISA has with proprietorial schools, which is still the case today, even though boards of governors now run the majority of schools.

ISA celebrates a wide ranging membership, not confined to any one type of school, but including all: nursery, pre-preparatory, junior and senior, all-through schools, coeducational, single-sex, boarding, day, and performing arts and special schools

Membership is open to any independent school Head or proprietor provided they meet the necessary criteria, which includes the accreditation standards of the Independent Schools Inspectorate (ISI). ISA's executive council is elected by members and supports all developments of the association through its committee structure and the strong regional network of co-ordinators and area committees. Each of ISA's seven areas in turn supports members through regular training events and meetings.

ISA celebrates a wide ranging membership, not confined to any one type of school, but including all: nursery, pre-preparatory, junior and senior, all-through schools, coeducational, single-sex, boarding, day, and performing arts and special schools.

Promoting best practice and fellowship remains at the core of the association, as it did when it began 130 years ago. The 300 members and their schools enjoy high quality national conferences and courses that foster excellence in independent education. ISA's central office also supports members and provides advice, and represents the views of its membership at national and governmental levels. Pupils in ISA schools enjoy a wide variety of competitions, in particular the wealth of sporting, artistic and academic activities at area and national level.

Chief Executive: Neil Roskilly, BA PGCE NPQH FRSA FRGS
ISA, Boys' British School
East Street, Saffron Walden, Essex CB10 1LS
Tel: 01799 523619
Fax: 01799 524892
Email: isa@isaschools.org.uk
Website: www.isaschools.org.uk

INDEPENDENT
SCHOOLS
ASSOCIATION

The Society of Heads

The Society of Heads of Independent Schools represents the interests of the smaller independent secondary schools. The society celebrates its 50th Anniversary in 2011

The Society of Heads represents the interests of the smaller, independent, secondary schools. The Society celebrated its 50th Anniversary in 2011. The Society has as its members over 100 Heads of well-established secondary schools, many with a boarding element, meeting a wide range of educational needs. All member schools provide education up to 18, with sixth forms offering both A and AS levels and/or the International Baccalaureate. Also some offer vocational courses. Many have junior schools attached to their foundation. A number cater for pupils with special educational needs, whilst others offer places to gifted dancers and musicians. All the schools provide education appropriate to their pupils' individual requirements together with the best in pastoral care.

The average size of the schools is about 350, and all aim to provide small classes ensuring favourable pupil:teacher ratios. The majority are coeducational and offer facilities for both boarding and day pupils. Many of the schools are non-denominational, whilst others have specific religious foundations.

The Society believes that independent schools are an important part of Britain's national education system. Given their independence, the schools can either introduce new developments ahead of the maintained sector or offer certain courses specifically appropriate to the pupils in their schools. They are able to respond quickly to the needs of parents and pupils alike.

Schools are admitted to membership of the Society only after a strict inspection procedure carried out by the Independent Schools Inspectorate. Regular inspection visits thereafter ensure that standards are maintained.

The Society is a constituent member of the Independent Schools Council and every full member in the Society has been accredited to it. All the Society's Heads belong to the Association of School and College Leaders (ASCL) or another recognised union for school leaders) and their schools are members of AGBIS.

The Society's policy is: to maintain high standards of education, acting as a guarantee of quality to parents who choose a Society school for their children; to ensure the genuine independence of member schools; to provide an opportunity for Heads to share ideas and common concerns for the benefit of the children in their care; to provide training opportunities for Heads and staff in order to keep them abreast of new educational initiatives; to promote links with higher and further education and the professions, so that pupils leaving the Society's schools are given the best advice and opportunities for their future careers; and to help Heads strengthen relations with their local communities.

The Society of Heads' Office,
12 The Point, Rockingham Road, Market Harborough,
Leicestershire LE16 7QU
Tel: 01858 433760
Fax: 01858 461413
Email: gensec@thesocietyofheads.org.uk
Website: www.thesocietyofheads.org.uk

Listing regions in the UK

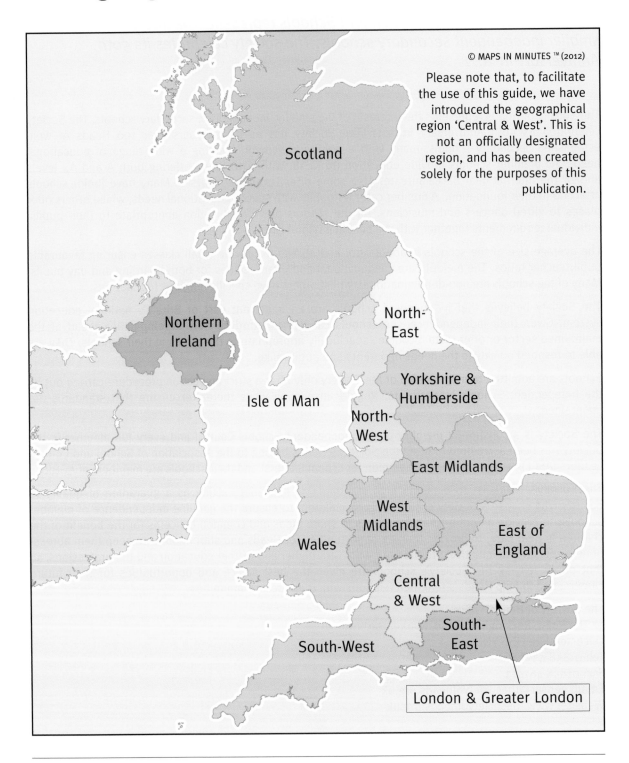

© MAPS IN MINUTES ™ (2012)

Please note that, to facilitate the use of this guide, we have introduced the geographical region 'Central & West'. This is not an officially designated region, and has been created solely for the purposes of this publication.

Scotland

Northern Ireland

North-East

Yorkshire & Humberside

Isle of Man

North-West

East Midlands

West Midlands

Wales

East of England

Central & West

South-East

South-West

London & Greater London

Central & West

Bloxham School

(Founded 1860)

Bloxham, Banbury, Oxfordshire OX15 4PE
Tel: 01295 720222   Email: registrar@bloxhamschool.com
Fax: 01295 721897   Website: www.bloxhamschool.com

Headmaster: Mr Mark E Allbrook MA
Appointed: September 2002
School type: Coeducational Boarding & Day
Boarders from 11 years
Member of: HMC, ASCL, Woodard Corporation
Age range of pupils: 11–18
No. of pupils enrolled as at 1.9.12: 424
Boys: 270 Girls: 154 Sixth Form: 140
Fees per annum as at 1.9.12: Day: £15,750–£22,320
Weekly Boarding: £20,460
Boarding: £28,845
Teacher/pupil ratio: 1:8.5
Religious denomination: Church of England

Bloxham School is, by choice, one of the smaller schools but is happy to be described as 'the small school with a great spirit'. Not that its size should be seen as anything other than a strength boasting, as it does, some quite outstanding facilities which have been considerably enhanced over the past two decades.

Founded in 1860 by local clergyman Rev Philip Egerton the coeducational school now educates about 420 pupils aged between 11 and 18. The school caters for day and boarding pupils but has strong local roots with the majority of pupils coming from within a one-hour travel band of the school. A little over 50% of the pupils board for all or part of the week although this percentage is much higher at the top end of the school as pupils gain valuable independence prior to university.

The school is also seeing an increasing number of pupils migrating from the London area taking advantage of the excellent road and rail links. This is proving particularly popular with families who may be looking to spend the weekends out of London – in the Cotswolds for example. They like Bloxham's flexible, modern approach to boarding as it gives them the access they seek and allows their children to enjoy their schooldays in a rural yet not isolated environment surrounded by wonderful playing fields and other enriching opportunities and facilities.

In Exham House, Bloxham's lower school (Years 7&8) boarding is entirely 'weekly' with the children coming to the house on either a Sunday evening or a Monday morning and going home again on the Friday evening. There is Saturday school in the upper school with lessons until lunchtime followed by a games afternoon. Boarders are free to go home virtually any weekend they choose after their sporting commitment is over. Some opt to stay on at school though to enjoy the organised activities or to simply to relax and socialise with their friends and make the most of the school's wonderful facilities and environment.

Bloxham also has a small number of overseas students (currently around 5%). This figure is kept deliberately low to ensure that those who are coming into the school from abroad will be able to integrate quickly and happily into their new learning and social environment.

The founder handed the school over to the Woodard Corporation in the 1890s and Bloxham is still a proud member of that Corporation of Schools today. The core of each Woodard School is that they all share the founder's vision of a Christian education coupled with a belief in nurturing and enriching each individual. That vision is still strong today encapsulated in the school's new strapline – Discovering the *Spark* in every child.

Bloxham regularly comes high up amongst the North Oxfordshire schools in a league table measuring the 'value added' component of each school. Headmaster Mark Allbrook is particularly pleased with this statistic:

"Bloxham, along with a growing number of independent schools, is not in favour of the old and largely discredited league tables, which simply show where the brightest pupils go to school. The value added tables are a much better guide to parents craving information about the difference a school is capable of making to the individual."

Facilities at the school are outstanding with recent innovations being an outstanding modern library, a sixth form art studio, an extension to the music school that caters for music technology and live recordings and a well-equipped technology centre that will have the addition of a food technology facility from 2012. And on the subject of food Bloxham continues to be known for the excellent food on offer to its pupils. The catering team regularly win awards for the variety and quality of the food on offer and for the healthy lifestyle a good diet helps promote.

The school is also well known for its music, art, technology and sport. In 2012 Bloxham teams became national champions in eventing (equestrian) and with their boys' clay shooting squad!

Bloxham became the first independent school to move away from a printed prospectus in favour of an award winning, online, multimedia experience that can be accessed via the school's website at www.bloxhamschool.com, where further information about the school can be found.

Although the school does hold open mornings each spring and autumn families are strongly advised to make an individual appointment to be shown around the school and to get the feel of this remarkable little Oxfordshire gem.

Bloxham School is a member of the Woodard Corporation, a charity that exists to provide excellent education for children in a Christian environment. Registered charity No. 1076484.

Brockhurst & Marlston House Schools

(Founded 1884)

Hermitage, Thatcham, West Berkshire RG18 9UL
Tel: 01635 200293   Email: info@brockmarl.org.uk
Fax: 01635 200190   Website: www.brockmarl.org.uk

Heads: David Fleming MA(Oxon), MSc & Mrs C E
Riley MA, BEd, CertEd(Southampton)
Appointed: September 2000
School type: Boys' and Girls' Day and Weekly/Flexi
Boarding
Age range of pupils: 3–13
No. of pupils enrolled as at 1.9.12: 275
No. of boarders: 120
Fees per annum as at 1.9.12: Day: £7410–£12,450
Weekly Boarding: £16,530
Boarding: £16,530
Average size of class: 16
Teacher/pupil ratio: 1:7

Brockhurst (Boys) and Marlston House (Girls) are
twin schools sharing the same estate at Marlston,
Hermitage. We offer a unique education with the
best features of small single-sex classes and shared
extracurricular activities at the centre of which is a
magnificent Jacobean style mansion set in stunning
Berkshire countryside.

Specialist and qualified staff promote a family
atmosphere for the 3-13 age range and prepare
children for entry to leading independent schools to
which they regularly gain academic, music, art and
sports scholarships. We have outstanding facilities
with 21 acres of games fields within a 500 acre site,

experiences including the gifted and talented on extended learning programmes, English as a Foreign Language (EFL) taught in very small groups, or individually and support for pupils with learning difficulties thus meeting the specific needs of each child.

We aim:

- to develop successful, independent learners based on sound assessment and prior knowledge
- to identify strengths and barriers to achievement with each child
- to promote self-esteem, a sense of pride and resilience in each child
- to help children to take responsibility for their learning

The two schools offer a broad curriculum, which includes music, art and drama and an exciting range of extracurricular activities. This breadth is reflected in the range of scholarships achieved by our pupils this year.

However, above all, our children leave us as self-confident, well-mannered and enthusiastic individuals equipped to make the most of the opportunities and challenges ahead of them.

Contact Mrs Rachel Harper on 01635 200293 Email: rachel.harper@brockmarl.org.uk
www.brockmarl.org.uk

including a sports hall, indoor 25m swimming pool, tennis courts, art and design studios, ICT suite, new Learning Development Centre (2011) and a superb equestrian school. In addition, we have an 18th century chateau in south-west France where our pupils practise their French. In addition to full boarding and day school, flexi/weekly boarding is a popular choice and we also provide a daily bus service for Hungerford, Ramsbury and district.

At Brockhurst and Marlston House the nursery and pre-prep children have the advantage of a department designed specifically for the age group, adjacent to the main prep school within its own garden and adventure play area. Children join the nursery class following their third birthday and most are introduced to the school day by attending the swimming sessions each Wednesday morning for 'Toddlers and Parents'. These are free sessions for those registered for the nursery class. The curriculum is designed to include the early learning goals, at the Foundation Stage, whilst extending each pupil according to their own pace of learning and individual development as they progress through the school. Much attention is given to social skills and boosting confidence. The pre-prep children use all the facilities of the prep schools and therefore the transition from pre-prep to main school is smooth and automatic.

At the heart of our teaching is the newly-opened (summer 2011) Learning Development Centre, West Berkshire.

Dedicated, trained, experienced staff at the heart of your child's education offer a range of learning

Burford School

(Founded 1571)

Lenthall House, Church Lane, Burford, Oxfordshire OX18 4SA
Tel: 01993 823283   Email: boarding.4040@burford.oxon.sch.uk
Fax: 01993 822041   Website: www.burford.oxon.sch.uk

Headteacher: Mrs K Haig BA, MEd
Head of Boarding: Mr P Johnson BEd
School type: Coeducational Boarding & Day
Member of: SBSA, BSA
Age range of pupils: 11–18
No. of pupils enrolled as at 1.9.12: 1184
Boys: 620 Girls: 564 Sixth Form: 230
No. of boarders: 90
Fees per annum as at 1.9.12:
Boarding: £9600
Average size of class: 25

Curriculum

All National Curriculum subjects are taught – the school provides an option choice of 21 GCSEs and 25 AS and A2 subjects.

Entry requirements

Entry is by interview and reference assessments.

The school is a specialist technology and science college offering excellent ICT facilities within eight computer rooms, additionally it is very well resourced in other curriculum areas.

It offers extensive sporting, cultural and extracurricular opportunities including CCF & ACF.

The flourishing boarding community is housed in the original 1571 site of the school in Burford (Lenthall House), the accommodation is of an excellent standard offering a real home from home for approximately 85 boarders.

Burford is quite simply a very happy and successful school.

Burford is a delightful small Cotswold town that lies between Oxford and Cheltenham (A40) within easy reach of London and all major airports.

The only state boarding school in Oxfordshire.

"Life away from home is more than just boarding." – Year 9 boarder.

"I'm so pleased I persuaded Mum and Dad that boarding was a better option than moving. I have enjoyed it immensely and feel so much more confident about university." – Year 13 boarder.

Boarding: 'An outstanding feature of the school.' – Ofsted inspection.

"Our students enjoy genuine success and have a real sense of purpose." – Head of Boarding.

Chafyn Grove School

(Founded 1876)

Bourne Avenue, Salisbury, Wiltshire SP1 1LR
Tel: 01722 333423   Email: office@chafyngrove.co.uk
Fax: 01722 323114   Website: www.chafyngrove.co.uk

Headmaster: E J Newton BA(Hons) (Cantab), PGCE
Appointed: September 2004
School type: Coeducational Day & Boarding
Boarders from 7 years
Age range of pupils: 3–13
No. of pupils enrolled as at 1.9.12: 323
Boys: 217 Girls: 106
No. of boarders: 54
Fees per annum as at 1.9.12: Day: £7335–£14,550
Boarding: £16,215–£19,755
Average size of class: 16–18
Teacher/pupil ratio: 1:10

Whether it's running to their next class, taking part in a gardening activity, or going out to the local arts centre to play in a jazz concert, Chafyn pupils have a full life! We strive to help all our children reach their full potential whether it is on the sports field, on the stage or in the classroom. A huge variety of extracurricular activities, a committed staff, excellent facilities and small class sizes combine to allow us to aim high in every area of school life. At the same time, a friendly environment, supportive parents and a relaxed atmosphere make for happy days at school. It is this combination that makes Chafyn Grove special.

Our boarding enhances the sense of community and is all about making the most of your time at school, developing independence and making friends for life – our aim is to provide a caring and happy environment in which children thrive and grow. Our boarders benefit from a secure and homely atmosphere and are accommodated in cosy, brightly decorated dormitories, often creatively decorated with their own pictures and posters, their own bedding and of course a teddy or two! There is a full weekly activity programme for boarders, as well as a weekend programme, where both boarding and teaching staff are fully involved with the children.

Small class sizes (maximum 18) and a commitment to high standards allow our pupils to perform impressively in the classroom. In recent years all pupils have reached the school of their choice and 14 scholarships is an average annual haul for our pupils going on to Senior Schools. Pupils go on to many well-known schools including Bryanston, Canford, Dauntsey's, Eton, Godolphin, Marlborough, Sherborne and Winchester. Pupils are also prepared for 11+ to the two Grammar Schools in Salisbury – several Year 6 pupils made the grade last year, although some opted to stay at Chafyn, and who can blame them!

Chesham Preparatory School

(Founded 1938)

Two Dells Lane, Chesham, Buckinghamshire HP5 3QF
Tel: 01494 782619   Email: secretary@cheshamprep.co.uk
Fax: 01494 791645   Website: www.cheshamprep.co.uk

Headmaster: Mr Michael Davies BA, PGCE
Appointed: September 2011
School type: Coeducational Day
Age range of pupils: 3–13
No. of pupils enrolled as at 1.9.12:
Boys: 194 Girls: 156
Fees per annum as at 1.9.12: Day: £8124–£11,931
Average size of class: 18
Teacher/pupil ratio: 1:7

Chesham Preparatory School has a well-justified reputation for being an incredibly friendly school where boys and girls work hard, behave well and achieve wonderful things. The most recent ISI report (2010) is glowing in its praise for a school in which, 'the pupils' achievement is excellent. Children enjoy an outstanding start to their education'.

Founded in 1938, Chesham Prep has developed into a flourishing coeducational school. As a non-selective school which educates pupils from 3 to 13 years of age, it champions the strong belief that boys and girls of prep school age should be educated together. They thrive in the holistic, caring environment and there is a real emphasis on ensuring that every child fulfils his or her potential whatever their varied strengths.

Last September the school was delighted to announce the opening of its nursery – extending the provision offered to children from 3 years old. From that early age, the children are well prepared for a smooth transition into their Reception class and, very importantly, they feel part of the Chesham Prep family.

The school boasts excellent success rates at 11+ and 12+ Grammar school entry, as well as 13+ Common Entrance to senior independent school. All pupils benefit enormously from the wonderful years of personal development at Chesham Prep.

Sports teams are highly skilled and competitive, while there is a fabulous choir and orchestra, as well as a wide range of opportunities for involvement in the creative arts. Children are encouraged to express themselves with joy and passion!

Above all, it is the aim of Chesham Preparatory School to inspire children with a love of learning and a confidence to make the most of their abilities.

EF International Academy Oxford

Pullens Lane, Headington, Oxfordshire OX3 0DT
Tel: +41 41 41 74 525   Email: admissionsia@ef.com
Fax: +44 (0) 1865 759661   Website: www.ef.com/academy

Head of School: Ms Ted McGrath
School type: Coeducational Boarding
Age range of pupils: 15–18
No. of pupils enrolled as at 1.1.12: 160
Fees per annum as at 1.1.12:
Boarding: £22,950

EF International Academy is part of EF Education First, the world leader in international education. With over 45 years of experience, EF has helped more than four million students realise their dream of studying abroad.

The School
Our school is situated in the illustrious city of Oxford, renowned for its scholastic tradition and rich cultural and architectural heritage. EF students join Oxford's vibrant academic community, which attracts leading scholars from around the world. Ten minutes from Oxford's centre, the newly renovated campus has multimedia classrooms, a fully-equipped gym, state-of-the-art science and computer labs, wireless internet access, a library, cafeteria and lounge. The school has a truly international atmosphere, with students from over 60 different countries living and studying alongside each other.

Academics
Education at EF is highly personal and a range of internationally acclaimed programmes are offered to meet the individual needs of each student; including IB Diploma and A level, as well as IGCSE and the High School Preparation Programme. Intensive English language courses are also available. EF has a track record of academic excellence with 45% of students receiving A/A* grades at A level, compared with the national average of 27%.

University Placements
Not only have the majority of our students been accepted into top ranked universities such as Oxford, Cambridge and LSE, they have also been admitted to courses that are deemed to be the best in the country for their subject, such as accounting at the University of Warwick, law at University College London, and chemical engineering at the University of Birmingham.

Pastoral Care
Personal tutors provide one-to-one individualised support and guidance. Each student is assigned a personal tutor whose role is to monitor the student's academic progress, university applications and general welfare. Students are encouraged to nurture their talents and develop new skills and confidence.

Scholarships
Scholarships will be awarded to highly talented and ambitious students who can make a positive contribution to the school community. Two students are awarded Founder's scholarships, which will cover 50% of the total fees. Many other general scholarships are also available for students who demonstrate overall excellence.

Residential Life
Accommodation is offered in on-campus dormitories or with host families, where students can benefit from full immersion into British culture and language; both options provide a safe, supportive and comfortable home away from home.

Rye St Antony

(Founded 1930)

Pullens Lane, Oxford, Oxfordshire OX3 0BY
Tel: 01865 762802   Email: enquiries@ryestantony.co.uk
Fax: 01865 763611   Website: www.ryestantony.co.uk

Headmistress: Miss A M Jones BA, PGCE
Appointed: 1990
School type: Girls' Boarding & Day
Boarders from 5 years
Member of: GSA, BSA
Age range of pupils:
Boys: 3–8
Girls: 3–18
No. of pupils enrolled as at 1.9.12: 400
Boys: 20 Girls: 380 Sixth Form: 70
No. of boarders: 70
Fees per annum as at 1.9.12: Day: £8400–£12,780
Weekly Boarding: £16,800–£19,800
Boarding: £17,790–£20,790
Average size of class: 16-20
Teacher/pupil ratio: 1:8

Rye St Antony is an independent boarding and day school for girls aged 3 to 18 (boys 3 to 8). Set in 13 acres of gardens and woodland a mile from the centre of Oxford, Rye is noted for its happy and purposeful atmosphere, its high academic standards, its wide range of extracurricular activities and its strong sense of community.

Early years education at Rye has consistently been judged by Ofsted as outstanding. A secure, supportive and stimulating environment nurtures enthusiasm, confidence and independence. Throughout the junior years specialist teaching is focused on each pupil as an individual, and the aim is to develop bright and enquiring minds, able to think rationally, creatively and independently, in young people growing steadily in their understanding of themselves and others.

In the senior school stimulating teaching across a broad curriculum encourages curiosity, investigation and discovery. Girls value the opportunity for discussion and research, in school and beyond, and the opportunity to be actively engaged in their learning and confident in learning with others and learning independently.

Results are impressive. At GCSE most girls achieve high grades in ten or more subjects, with over half of these grades being A or A*. Almost all girls completing sixth form achieve university places of their first choice, and last year's AS/A level grades gave an average of AAB for each girl. These same girls also achieved significant successes in music, art, drama and sport, the latter including at international level.

At the heart of each girl's programme is its purpose: to help her complete her school years happy, resilient, wise, keen to embark on the future and keen to make her contribution to the world.

Rye St Antony School is a registered charity (No. 309685) to provide education for girls up to the age of 18 years and boys up to the age of 8 years.

St Margaret's Preparatory School

(Founded 1873)

ST MARGARET'S
PREPARATORY SCHOOL CALNE

Curzon Street, Calne, Wiltshire SN11 0DF
Tel: 01249 857220   Email: office@stmargaretsprep.org.uk
Fax: 01249 857227   Website: www.stmargaretsprep.org.uk

Headmistress: Karen Cordon
School type: Coeducational Day
Age range of pupils: 3–11
No. of pupils enrolled as at 1.9.12: 220
Boys: 95 Girls: 125
Fees per annum as at 1.9.12: Day: £4674–£10,950
Average size of class: 14-18

St Margaret's Preparatory School is an independent co-educational day preparatory school for boys and girls age 3-11, sharing a site with St Mary's School, Calne. The children benefit from excellent facilities including sports pitches, gymnasium, indoor swimming pool, theatre, chapel, and dining hall.

There is a high academic standard throughout the school and the children are thoroughly prepared for Common Entrance and Senior School 11+ examinations. The school has an impressive record of success in gaining major scholarships to leading public schools, both in academic areas and in the arts.

There is a strong sporting tradition and the children compete regularly with other schools. The boys play cricket, rugby and hockey whilst the girls play netball, hockey and rounders. Additionally, athletics, judo, swimming and tennis are sports enjoyed by all.

Music and drama have a high profile. There are two annual major productions in the spring and summer terms and the orchestra and choirs perform at the spring and Christmas concerts.

School hours are between 8.25am and 3.30/4.30pm each day. The school has its own After School Club which is available until 6pm, five days a week. This facility is also open for a number of weeks during the Easter and Summer holidays.

In May 2011 the school was inspected by the Independent Schools Inspectorate (ISI). The inspectors concluded that 'Pupils' achievement is outstanding across a wide range of activities' and also found that 'attainment is judged to be high in relation to age-related expectations'. The report also remarked on how 'the pupils' successes are due, in large measure, to the strong teaching, their positive attitudes, and the excellent relationships'. The overall effectiveness and the quality of provision within the Early Years Foundation Stage were both rated as 'outstanding'.

St Margaret's prides itself on its high standard of pastoral care. Every effort is made to ensure that the children never feel lost or bewildered, and that they quickly find their feet and are given a sense of belonging.

To obtain a prospectus or to arrange a visit, please contact 01249 857220 or visit www.stmargaretsprep.org.uk

St Mary's Calne

(Founded 1873)

Curzon Street, Calne, Wiltshire SN11 0DF
Tel: 01249 857200   Email: office@stmaryscalne.org
Fax: 01249 857207   Website: www.stmaryscalne.org

Headmistress: Dr Helen Wright MA(Oxon),
MA(Leics), EdD(Exeter), PGCE(Oxon), FRSA, MIoD
Appointed: April 2003
School type: Girls' Boarding & Day
Age range of pupils: 11–18
No. of pupils enrolled as at 1.9.12: 335
Sixth Form: 110
No. of boarders: 260
Fees per annum as at 1.9.12: Day: £22,539–£23,001
Boarding: £30,870–£31,500
Teacher/pupil ratio: 1:5

St Mary's Calne is a boarding and day school of
around 335 girls aged 11-18. Approximately 80% of
the girls board and it is a rich boarding life with all
girls taking part in the full curriculum and
extracurricular activities on offer.

St Mary's is committed to providing a broad and
fulfilling education that will challenge and inspire its
pupils, as well as helping them to achieve fantastic
public examination results. In 2011, 36% of all A
level grades were A*s, with over half of the girls
achieving all A*-A grades. At GCSE, 63% of girls
gained eight or more A*-A grades.

The school is small by design and is renowned for

outstanding pastoral care. Every girl is known and
cared for as an individual and has a tutor to support
and guide her through every aspect of school life;
from organisational skills and subject choices through
to university application.

All girls go on to higher education (20% to Oxbridge
in 2011) and the purpose-built Sixth Form Centre, a
tailor-made lecture programme, a women in
corporate culture conference, debating competitions,
careers advice, leadership roles and much more
prepare the girls for university and beyond.

St Mary's sportswomen compete at a national level in
several major sports and the school regularly fields a
successful team for the British Schoolgirls' Ski Races.
All girls work for the Bronze Duke of Edinburgh's
Award with large numbers going on to higher levels.
80% of girls play musical instruments and take part in
a wide variety of ensembles. Drama productions
transfer to the London stage and the Edinburgh
Festival Fringe and the department boasts a unique
relationship with RADA.

Location
Two hours west of London. Escorted travel to and
from London and airports at all holidays and exeats.

Swanbourne House School

(Founded 1920)

Swanbourne, Milton Keynes MK17 0HZ
Tel: 01296 720264   Email: office@swanbourne.org
Fax: 01296 728089   Website: www.swanbourne.org

Joint Heads: Mr S D Goodhart BEd(Hons) & Mrs J S Goodhart BEd
School type: Coeducational Boarding & Day
Boarders from 7
Member of: IAPS, BSA
Age range of pupils: 3–13
No. of pupils enrolled as at 1.9.12:
Boys: 225 Girls: 187
No. of boarders: 70
Fees per annum as at 1.9.12: Day: £7140–£15,255
Boarding: £19,560
Average size of class: 17
Religious denomination: Church of England

Curriculum

Swanbourne House offers a strong academic and scholarship programme by following Common Entrance and also setting our forms for maths, English and French. We have success in preparing children for entry into their chosen public schools.

The school scholarship record is exemplary with 43 scholarships won in the past eight years. Our boarding house was, last year, awarded 'outstanding' in all areas from Ofsted.

Entry requirements

Children may enter the school at any age from 3 years to 11 years. Each child takes a short familiarisation and assessment and then we recommend placement in one of our three, streamed classes. Scholarships are available for highly academic pupils and all-rounders, or for specific talents at 11+. We offer bursaries to forces families. We are keen to meet children who love life and who will thrive through our family care and activity programme.

More information can be gathered from our website: www.swanbourne.org

Swanbourne House School is a registered charity that exists to provide education for children. (No. 310640)

The Grove Independent School

Redland Drive, Loughton, Milton Keynes MK5 8HD
Tel: 01908 690590   Email: office@groveschool.co.uk
Fax: 01908 694043   Website: www.groveschool.co.uk

Principal: Mrs Deborah Berkin
School type: Coeducational Day
Age range of pupils: 3 months–13 years
No. of pupils enrolled as at 1.9.12: 210
Boys: 107 Girls: 103
Fees per annum as at 1.9.12:
Term Time Only: £11,544
(this includes charges for before and after school care)
Fully Inclusive: £12,024
(this includes charges for before and after school care and holiday fun weeks)

The 'Whole Child' approach

"Our interpretation of education is that we are building for life and its values, developing the character as well as the mind of each child entrusted to us." Deborah Berkin – Founder and Principal.

The Grove Nursery was established in 1984, using premises just outside Milton Keynes. The school enrolled its first class of rising fives in 1989.

Since that time the school has grown, with purpose-built classrooms and stimulating amenities. It is ideally located in rural Loughton Valley Park, facing Loughton Equestrian centre. The school is also within ten minutes of the city centre and railway station for ease of access.

From its inception the Grove School has earned an excellent reputation for being a small, friendly place where each child could enjoy much individual attention.

The team of highly qualified and enthusiastic staff has been encouraged to become fully involved in every aspect of the development of both the school and the children entrusted to them.

This ethos has given all pupils the security of knowing everyone, of belonging to a community and of being responsible for others as well as themselves.

The Grove is a member of the Independent Schools Association. We were inspected by the Independent Schools Inspectorate in 2011 and received an excellent report, which can be obtained from our website. 'Their outstanding strength lies in the extent to which curriculum, teaching, and pastoral care work together to support the intellectual, physical, social and emotional development of each child as a whole person.' (ISI 2011)

So, if you are considering the facilities at The Grove Independent School or The Grove Nursery for your child, you will find all of the teaching staff on-hand to answer any questions or concerns. The school's reputation for providing an excellent programme of development in a friendly but productive atmosphere has become widely acknowledged, and is well supported by the school's consistently high results and outstanding inspection reports. Here students can enjoy the benefits of an education tailored to suit their individual needs and stage of development, leaving the school with an excellent start to the rest of their educational and working lives.

Tudor Hall School

(Founded 1850)

Wykham Park, Banbury, Oxfordshire OX16 9UR
Tel: 01295 263434   Email: admissions@tudorhallschool.com
Fax: 01295 253264   Website: www.tudorhallschool.com

Headmistress: Miss W Griffiths BSc
School type: Girls' Boarding & Day
Boarders from 11
Member of: GSA, AGBIS, ASCL
Age range of pupils: 11–18
No. of pupils enrolled as at 1.4.12: 332
Sixth Form: 88
No. of day girls: 86
No. of boarders: 246
Fees per annum as at 1.4.12: Day: £17,175
Boarding: £26,700
Average size of class: 16
Teacher/pupil ratio: 1:8
Religious denomination: Anglican

Curriculum

The curriculum includes English, mathematics, biology, chemistry, physics, information technology, Latin, French, German or Spanish, history, geography, RS, drama, food & nutrition, dance art, music, textiles and DT. In addition, history of art, government & politics, economics, ancient Greek, drama & theatre studies, photography, PE, further mathematics and business studies may be taken up in the sixth form. Italian, Russian and Mandarin are also available. Sports include netball, hockey, lacrosse, tennis, athletics, swimming and rounders. The wide range of extras includes riding, ballet, speech & drama and most musical instruments.

Entry requirements

11+, 13+ Common Entrance, internal exams and interview, and GCSEs and interview for sixth form.

Tudor Hall is a registered charity existing to provide good, quality education for girls aged 11-18 in a lively, stimulating and friendly boarding environment. (No. 1042783.)

Tudor Hall School

Founded 1850

East

Bedford School

(Founded 1552)

De Parys Avenue, Bedford, Bedfordshire MK40 2TU
Tel: +44 (0)1234 362216 Email: admissions@bedfordschool.org.uk
Fax: +44 (0)1234 362283 Website: www.bedfordschool.org.uk

Head Master: Mr J Moule MA
Appointed: 2008
School type: Boys' Boarding & Day
Age range of pupils: 7–18
No. of pupils enrolled as at 1.9.11: 1090
Sixth Form: 278
No. of boarders: 270
Fees per annum as at 1.9.12: Day: £10,518–£16,227
Weekly Boarding: £17,583–£26,157
Full Boarding: £18,444–£27,051
Average size of class: 15-20
Teacher/pupil ratio: 1:10
Religious denomination: Anglican

Bedford School is an independent boarding and day school for boys aged 7 to 18 years, where fundamental traditions combine with innovative educational thinking. In addition to an established reputation for academic excellence, we are renowned for our strengths in music, the arts and sport. Situated on an extensive parkland estate of 40 acres in the heart of Bedford, the school is a lively community of day boys, weekly and full boarders.

Our highly-qualified teaching staff are selected on their ability to communicate and inspire. The result is a vibrant, stimulating environment, were boys can be happy, grow in self-confidence, thrive academically and make the most of the wide range of opportunities on offer. Our broad curriculum offers boys a varied choice of subjects, and our academic success is demonstrated by a long history of impressive examination results at GCSE, A level, and in the International Baccalaureate Diploma. We also offer an impressive range of extracurricular activities with over 80 clubs and societies.

Our music school is one of the largest in the country and has a full programme of concerts and performances throughout the year. Facilities are virtually unrivalled and include a recreation centre with theatre, large sports hall, squash courts, fitness centre and a 25-metre indoor swimming pool; twin Astroturf pitches; an observatory and planetarium and an impressive library.

We offer a generous Access Award & Scholarship Scheme for talented boys, irrespective of background.

We warmly invite you to join us at one of our open mornings or for a private visit to see the school in action, meet the boys and staff, and get a flavour of life at Bedford School. Please contact Vanessa Hicks, Director of Admissions, for further information on 01234 362216 or email admissions@bedfordschool.org.uk.

Bedford School is part of The Harpur Trust.

Company No. 3475202/Charity no. 1066861.

Berkhamsted School

(Founded 1541)

131 High Street, Berkhamsted, Hertfordshire HP4 2DJ
Tel: 01442 358001   Email: admissions@berkhamstedschool.org
Fax: 01442 358040   Website: www.berkhamstedschool.org

BERKHAMSTED
SCHOOL

Principal: Mr Mark Steed MA(Cantab), MA
Appointed: September 2008
School type: Coeducational & single-sex, day &
boarding
Age range of pupils: 3–18
No. of pupils enrolled as at 1.9.12: 1508
Boys: 415 Girls: 316 Sixth Form: 331
Prep: 446
Fees per annum as at 1.9.12: Day: £7770–£17,460
Weekly Boarding: £23,370
Boarding: £27,815
Average size of class: 20

Berkhamsted School offers much to make it worthy of closer consideration: a long-established reputation for excellent educational provision, high-quality facilities and the range of experiences it offers its pupils; an attractive location in a thriving market town with easy access to London; and a range of services that support the lives of busy families.

It is also one of only a small number of schools in the country to offer a 'diamond' structure that combines the best of both single-sex and coeducational teaching. Boys and girls are taught together until the age of 11 (Berkhamsted Pre-Prep and Berkhamsted Prep), separately from 11 – 16 (Berkhamsted Boys and Berkhamsted Girls), before coming back together again in a joint Sixth Form (Berkhamsted Sixth).

Pupils across the School enjoy the benefits of being part of a small, caring community based in an environment appropriate to their specific educational needs, yet with access to the state-of-the-art facilities of a large school; a 550-seat theatre, a six-lane 25m swimming pool and sports centre, spacious, modern dining facilities and one of the best art departments in the country.

Another feature of Berkhamsted is the provision of a range of services that make life easier for parents who are juggling busy schedules; from flexible boarding options that include occasional, weekly or full boarding in high-quality accommodation to a range of coach routes, 'extended day' support, day nursery provision (five months to three years) and wrap-around care 51 weeks of the year.

Academic results are consistently strong with 100% pass rate at A level every year since 2003, and an average of over 85% at A*-B grades in recent years. In 2011, GCSE students achieved a record 69% of grades at A* to A. Thirty six Berkhamsted students have been accepted at Oxford and Cambridge in the past five years and 74% of students achieve places at the top 30 UK universities.

Berkhamsted offers scholarships – academic, art, drama, music and sport – and means-tested bursaries to talented pupils on entry to the school.

Parents are welcome to visit the School at any time: please call 01442 358001 for an appointment and a tour to appreciate what Berkhamsted can offer your child.

Haileybury

(Founded 1862)

Haileybury, Hertford, Hertfordshire SG13 7NU
Tel: +44 (0)1992 706353 Email: registrar@haileybury.com
Fax: +44 (0)1992 470663 Website: www.haileybury.com

The Master: J S Davies MA(Cantab)
Appointed: September 2009
School type: Coeducational Boarding & Day
Age range of pupils: 11–18
No. of pupils enrolled as at 1.9.12: 764
Boys: 458 Girls: 306 Sixth Form: 120
No. of boarders: 483
Fees per annum as at 1.9.12: Day: £13,668–£20,565
Boarding: £17,367–£27,384
Teacher/pupil ratio: 1:7

Make your school days Haileybury days.

All parents want to give their children the best possible start in life and that usually means finding the right school for them. Do they join a new senior school at 11 or at 13? Do they board or not? Thinking ahead means you need to consider whether they would like to opt for A levels or the International Baccalaureate Diploma Programme. Are they passionate about music, drama or art? Do they prefer the sciences or humanities?

Parents should also consider their own needs as well as their children's. If both parents work full-time, perhaps you would like to look at a school that offers a flexible boarding solution, allowing children to be at school uninterrupted during the week but at home for weekends.

If all these options sound impossible to find in a single school on your doorstep, think again! Haileybury, a co-educational, independent boarding school, is only 20 miles north of London in rural Hertfordshire.

Haileybury educates boys and girls aged 11 to 18. As a school, Haileybury has grown, adapted and flourished from its foundation in the 19th century, through the profound changes of the 21st century.

Academic results are most important: we encourage in our pupils a questioning mind and a desire to learn and extend their knowledge and understanding of the world around them. Having offered the International Baccalaureate Diploma Programme most successfully for more than 10 years, we are now widely recognised as one of the leading IB schools in the country and one of the few where pupils can choose between the IB and A levels.

With all this choice on offer, what better incentive is there to come and visit us and see our facilities for yourself? We will be pleased to make an appointment for you to meet The Master, and Housemistresses or Housemasters, and to tour our beautiful site. Please contact Iona Hutchinson, The Registrar, on 01992 706 353 for further information.

Orwell Park School

(Founded 1867)

Nacton, Ipswich, Suffolk IP10 0ER
Tel: 01473 659225   Email: opssecretary@orwellpark.co.uk
Fax: 01473 659822   Website: www.orwellpark.co.uk

Headmaster: Mr Adrian Brown MA(Cantab)
Appointed: September 2011
School type: Coeducational Boarding & Day
Boarders from 7
Member of: IAPS, ISC, BSA
Age range of pupils: 2½–13
No. of pupils enrolled as at 1.9.12: 253
Boys: 150 Girls: 103
No. of boarders: 147
Fees per annum as at 1.9.12:
Pre-Prep (Day): £6045–£9315
Prep (Day): £13,785–£15,285
Prep (Boarding): £17,655–£19,605
Average size of class: 12-14
Teacher/pupil ratio: 1:10
Religious denomination: Interdenominational

Set in more than 100 acres of parkland overlooking the River Orwell in Suffolk, Orwell Park provides a broad and balanced education for boys and girls, boarders and day pupils, between the ages of 3 and 13. A modern, caring and flexible approach to boarding sets Orwell Park apart as a forward-thinking school, which continues to instil traditional values such as commitment, compassion and courtesy in its pupils.

Academically, Orwell Park prides itself on successfully preparing children for entry to senior school at 13+, with more than a third of leavers winning scholarships: for academic excellence or for music, art, sport, design and technology – all to a wide range of senior independent schools. Orwell Park offers academic challenge to all children and learning support for those who need it. In the classroom, a traditional curriculum (including classics) is taught, using the most modern methods. The school employs motivated teachers with a passion for their subject; they will encourage academic self-reliance, helping all children in time to take responsibility for their own learning and personal organisation. The pupil: staff ratio is 10:1.

Extensive grounds provide abundant opportunities for children's games, both formal and informal. Excellent facilities range from assault course to Astroturf, golf course to games pitches, swimming pool to squash courts and sports hall. There is a full fixture list of matches against other schools in which boys and girls of all abilities are selected to play. In addition to sport, an extensive range of activities is also offered.

At Orwell Park, children are encouraged to achieve academic success, to be free to play, explore and learn in one of the most beautiful school settings in England.

St Albans School

(Founded 948)

Abbey Gateway, St Albans, Hertfordshire AL3 4HB
Tel: 01727 855521   Email: hm@st-albans-school.org.uk
Fax: 01727 843447   Website: www.st-albans.herts.sch.uk

Headmaster: Mr A R Grant MA(Cantab), FRSA
Appointed: 1993
School type: Boys' Day
Coeducational Sixth Form
Member of: HMC, AGBIS, ISC
Age range of pupils:
Boys: 11–18
Girls: 16–18
No. of pupils enrolled as at 1.9.12: 820
Boys: 745 Girls: 75 Sixth Form: 300
Fees per annum as at 1.9.12: Day: £14,736
Average size of class: 22
Teacher/pupil ratio: 1:10
Religious denomination: Non-denominational

City Centre and Well Beyond

St Albans has all the advantages of a city centre school and is only a 20 minute train ride from London, but its historic buildings are still surrounded by leafy green trees close to the ancient St Albans Abbey, with which it has shared much of its history.

Pupils benefit from excellent teaching and facilities and are encouraged to work hard. An extensive programme of lectures and seminars complements classroom teaching. The results of this are clear in the latest exam results. In 2011, 94% of A level grades were awarded at A and B, while 55% of GCSE grades were at A*. Students at St Albans are well motivated and active learners, most of whom go on to study at the country's top universities.

There is also a wide range of opportunities outside the classroom and the school has thriving musical, dramatic, sporting and extracurricular traditions. The Woollam Playing Fields are the envy of many schools and 2012 saw the completion of a sports hall and swimming pool on the school site.

The skills gained on home turf are extended by sporting tours, which have travelled as far afield as Canada, New Zealand, Malaysia and Sri Lanka. The school's frequent musical concerts are also augmented by tours, recently to Italy, while the drama studios stage a wide range of dramatic productions.

The Duke of Edinburgh's Award and the CCF teach pupils resilience and teamwork, while the Partnership programme with local primary schools provides students with an opportunity to extend their experience and contribute to the community. The Community Link programme and Charities Committee are active throughout the year. The popularity and success of these schemes shows how highly they are valued.

In all aspects of school life, St Albans School ensures its students maximise their potential and prepares them for a fulfilling life.

St Albans School is a company limited by guarantee. Registered in England No 4400125. It is a registered charity that exists solely to provide education for children. (No. 1092932)

St Edmund's College & Prep School

(Founded 1568)

Old Hall Green, Nr Ware, Hertfordshire SG11 1DS
Tel: 01920 824247 Email: admissions@stedmundscollege.org
Fax: 01920 823011 Website: www.stedmundscollege.org

Head: Paulo Durán BA MA
Appointed: September 2012
School type: Coeducational Day & Boarding
(Boarders from 11 years)
Age range of pupils: 3–18
No. of pupils enrolled as at 1.9.12: 823
Boys: 472 Girls: 351 Sixth Form: 145
No. of boarders: 108
Fees per annum as at 1.9.12: Day: £9465–£14,955
Weekly Boarding: £19,830–£22,575
Boarding: £21,855–£24,990
Average size of class: 20
Teacher/pupil ratio: 1:9

When you arrive at St Edmund's College, England's oldest Catholic school, you cannot help but be impressed by the grandeur of its buildings and delightful location: when you leave, however, what you will remember will be its people.

Time and again visitors say how they are struck by the atmosphere of the college that fosters a special sense of community and self awareness amongst the staff and students who work here.

The school combines excellent facilities and teaching standards with a friendly atmosphere and a strong emphasis on learning and mutual respect. The community spirit of the school encourages students to develop as individuals, to pursue their own interests and achieve their goals, both in academic and extracurricular activities and not to be afraid of a challenge.

Scholarship is at the heart of our mission and our students are encouraged to learn, to explore and to ask the difficult questions. Small class sizes ensure that the academic progress of each student is monitored and at every stage we adjust our teaching to suit the ability and needs of each child.

St Edmund's does not turn out stereotypes. By the time they leave school, the students are confident and caring team players, but most importantly they are secure individuals, comfortable in their own skin and ready to contribute to society.

For the younger pupils, St Edmund's Prep, which is located on the same site, offers a sound preparation for the senior school, providing a healthy balance between academic work and recreational activities with plenty of opportunity for creativity and physical exercise. The prep school also includes Cygnets, which is a nurturing nursery featuring dedicated facilities including its own fun and safe outdoor play area.

For further details about St Edmund's College and St Edmund's Prep, please call the Admissions Office on 01920 824247 or visit www.stedmundscollege.org

The Royal Hospital School

(Crown Charity, founded 1712)

Holbrook, Ipswich, Suffolk IP9 2RX
Tel: +44 (0) 1473 326210   Email: admissions@royalhospitalschool.org
Fax: +44 (0) 1473 326213   Website: www.royalhospitalschool.org

Headmaster: Mr James Lockwood MA
Appointed: September 2012
School type: Coeducational Full Boarding and Day
Member of: HMC, SHMIS, BSA
Age range of pupils: 11–18
No. of pupils enrolled as at 1.9.12: 700
Boys: 410 Girls: 290 Sixth Form: 220
No. of boarders: 290 boys; 220 girls
No. of day pupils: 120 boys; 70 girls
Size of sixth form: 110 boys; 110 girls
No. of boarders: 510
Fees per annum as at 1.9.12: Day: £11,994–£15,672
Weekly Boarding: £19,995–£23,997
Boarding: £19,995–£23,997
Average size of class: 17
Teacher/pupil ratio: 1:8
Religious denomination: Church of England

Founded in 1712 in Greenwich, the Royal Hospital School moved to its present site set in 200 acres of stunning Suffolk countryside overlooking the River Stour, in 1933.

Close pastoral care is at the heart of the school ethos. Every child feels nurtured, supported and encouraged and great emphasis is placed on regular communication between parents, school and pupils. Boarders and day pupils can choose to be members of one of the four girls', five boys' or two coeducational houses and almost all staff live on site, reinforcing the community feel about the school.

Pupils entering the school at 11+ years join a junior house, which aims to help the transition between primary and senior school. The pastoral care and routines are tailored to the needs of younger pupils

The CCF, Duke of Edinburgh's Award Scheme, Community Action Team and huge range of extracurricular activities, provide a wonderful programme of adventure and self improvement. By the time pupils leave the school, they are well equipped to take responsibility, show initiative, think dynamically and to approach life with an open and receptive mind.

Scholarships, discount and bursaries

Scholarships (Academic, Art, Music, Sport and Sailing).

Seafarer discount: 15% off full boarding fee.

Seafarer bursaries: means-tested through parent charity Greenwich Hospital.

Discounts for services families eligible for MOD Continuity of Education Allowance (CEA).

Sibling discounts: 10% off third and subsequent child.

and facilities for day pupils to board on an *ad hoc* basis are popular with busy parents. All pupils, whether moving up from the junior houses or entering the school at 13+, are effectively 'new' when they join the senior houses. In the final year of sixth form pupils move into Nelson House with single studies and facilities that encourage more independent living in preparation for university life and beyond.

The curriculum is broad and balanced, combining the best of academic traditions with the latest technologies and with small class sizes, every pupil receives close individual guidance. Supported by high quality enthusiastic teaching, excellent resources and dedicated tutorial support, pupils are encouraged to aim high, attain their personal best and most importantly to enjoy achieving it.

Music, drama and dance play an important part in school life and this is emphasised by the new £3.6 million music school. The art and design technology departments enjoy an outstanding reputation with pupils' work consistently achieving high grades and being exhibited locally and nationally.

Fitness and wellbeing are promoted through the enjoyment of a wide range of sports, from the traditional games of rugby, hockey, cricket and tennis to more specialist pursuits such as water polo, riding, canoeing, golf, shooting and dry skiing. All pupils joining in Year 7 learn to sail and the very enthusiastic can sail up to four times a week to competition level. As well as a fleet of 40 dinghies, the school's own Cornish Shrimpers are used for coastal cruising at the weekends and holidays.

Tring Park School for the Performing Arts

(Founded 1919)

Tring Park, Tring, Hertfordshire HP23 5LX
Tel: 01442 824255   Email: info@tringpark.com
Fax: 01442 891069   Website: www.tringpark.com

Principal: Mr Stefan Anderson MA, ARCM, ARCT
Appointed: September 2002
School type: Coeducational Boarding & Day
Age range of pupils: 8–19
No. of pupils enrolled as at 1.9.12: 317
Boys: 88 Girls: 229 Sixth Form: 217
No. of boarders: 197
Fees per annum as at 1.9.12: Day: £12,870–£20,100
Boarding: £21,285–£30,030

Tring Park School for the Performing Arts offers a unique opportunity for gifted young people to specialise in Dance, Drama, Musical Theatre or Music, whilst gaining an excellent academic education to GCSE, IGCSE, BTEC and A level. Recent DCSF figures have shown that our 'Value Added' measure has put us in the top 5% of schools in the entire country.

Tring Park is an independent, co-educational boarding and day school, for up to 320 pupils between the ages of 8-19. The school is housed in a former Rothschild mansion and set in beautiful grounds in Tring, Hertfordshire, only 33 miles from central London with easy access via road and rail.

Pupils perform regularly both in Tring Park's purpose-built Markova Theatre as well as in London, throughout the UK and Europe. Performances have included Gershwin's *Crazy for You*, *The Boy Friend* and *Jesus Christ Superstar* at the Shaw Theatre, London. Tring Park annually provides 25 young ballet dancers to perform in the Christmas production of *Nutcracker* with English National Ballet at the London Coliseum.

Recent successes include three alumni all appearing in principal roles in *Mamma Mia*, former students Amy Nuttall and Jessica Brown Findlay both in major roles in ITV's *Downton Abbey*, plus major roles for former students in *Dirty Dancing*, *Rocky Horror Show* and *Legally Blonde*. Lily James played Desdemona in Shakespeare's *Othello* and now stars in the film *Fast Girls*. Tyrone Singleton and Max Westwell are both Soloists at Birmingham Royal Ballet and the school boasts dancers in companies from English National Ballet to New York City Ballet. See www.tringpark.com/alumni for further information.

For information on forthcoming Open Days or to request a prospectus please contact:

Adelia Wood-Smith

adelia.wood-smith@tringpark.com

Tel. 01442 824255

The AES Tring Park School Trust is a registered charity No. 1040330. Tring Park School exists to promote and provide for the advancement of education.

Westbrook Hay Prep School

(Founded 1892)

London Road, Hemel Hempstead, Hertfordshire HP1 2RF
Tel: 01442 256143   Email: admin@westbrookhay.co.uk
Fax: 01442 232076   Website: www.westbrookhay.co.uk

Westbrook Hay
Prep School

Headmaster: Keith D Young BEd(Hons)
Appointed: September 1996
School type: Coeducational Day & occasional Boarding
Age range of pupils: 3–13
No. of pupils enrolled as at 1.9.12: 290
Boys: 190 Girls: 100
Fees per annum as at 1.9.12: Day: £8610–£12,390
Average size of class: Max 18

A thriving independent prep school for boys and girls, from rising three to 13 years old, Westbrook Hay is located between Hemel Hempstead and Berkhamsted, and set in 26 acres of beautiful parkland overlooking the Bourne Valley. Modern, spacious classrooms are coupled with small class sizes to provide an interactive and thoroughly stimulating learning environment.

These small class sizes, together with visionary teaching, fabulous facilities and a broad curriculum enable our children to gain the all-important confidence to succeed. As every parent will know, school is so much more than simply what is taught in lessons. At Westbrook Hay we aim to provide a learning experience that goes far beyond that of the classroom.

Our new and visiting parents are struck by the wonderful atmosphere at Westbrook Hay. The children are clearly confident, happy and secure in their environment, and view the school as an extended family to support them. They display their excellent achievements and forever speak of the next exciting activity they are involved in; be it a competitive sporting event, a music concert, an artistic workshop, an educational trip or visit, one of the school productions or their next favourite lesson.

The greater opportunities provided in technology, art, games, music, dance, drama and a whole range of other extracurricular activities, help to balance the school's high academic expectations and allow the children further opportunities to express themselves and try new things, learning vital skills along the way.

There is a fabulous new purpose-built lower school that offers our youngest children superb space and facilities, giving them the best possible start to their education. Most recently we have opened a state-of-the-art IT suite, with two fully equipped rooms for IT lessons and use across the curriculum.

In the preparation of our children for entry to their chosen senior school, we proudly boast 100% success. Most children go on to local independent schools and are prepared not only for entry but, when appropriate, for scholarship. In the last three years 17 children gained a range of academic, sport, art and music scholarships to their senior schools.

We are delighted with the results and feedback of the most recent inspection report: 'Pupils' achievement is excellent and they are very well educated in accordance with the school's aims for pupils to realise their intellectual, social and physical potential.'

East Midlands

Ashby School

(Founded 1567)

School House, Leicester Road, Ashby-de-la-Zouch, Leicestershire LE65 1DH
Tel: +44 (0) 1530 413759   Email: schoolhouse@ashbyschool.org.uk
Fax: +44 (0) 1530 415241   Website: www.ashbyschool.org.uk

Headteacher: Mr Eddie Green
Appointed: September 2011
School type: Academy International Status School with Specialisms in Technology & Modern Foreign Language, Senior, Sixth Form
Age range of pupils: 11–19
No. of pupils enrolled as at 1.9.12: 1643
Boys: 852 Girls: 791

Established in 1567, this ancient boarding residence forms part of the large and successful Ashby School in the heart of England. This coeducational school has been awarded two specialisms in technology and modern foreign languages with international school status.

Results for A level are consistently high and GCSE results are also very impressive and above the national average.

The boarding residence is home to a family of boys in an attractive Georgian house, set in its own grounds. Ofsted has classified School House as 'outstanding', stating: 'The atmosphere in the house is extremely positive and reflects the care and support provided... Boys present as really caring about each other and their house, which reflects how well they are cared for.'

In addition, School House has recently invested £2.8million to extend its boarding provision, which provides some of the best accommodation in the UK. We are able to offer individual or twin ensuite rooms to our sixth form students. The new building also provides boarders with an additional computer suite, lounges, a sixth form kitchen and a games room.

Sporting and recreational facilities surround the house with sports fields, a large sports hall and floodlit, all-weather courts. There is also an excellent heated indoor swimming pool. A full programme of sport is available and boarders can also take advantage of professional coaching. The school provides a wide variety of recreational clubs including Duke of Edinburgh's Award Scheme, orienteering and residential/cultural exchange programmes. Opportunities are available to boarders throughout the year including visits to places of historical and cultural interest, theme parks, the theatre, shopping trips, bowling, the cinema and ice skating *etc.*

To find out more about this family of boys in the Heart of England please contact Xenia Elias, Director of Boarding, by email or tel: 00 44 (0) 1530 413759.

Laxton Junior School

(Founded 1973)

East Road, Oundle, Peterborough, Northamptonshire PE8 4BX
Tel: 01832 277275   Email: info@laxtonjunior.org.uk
Fax: 01832 277271   Website: www.laxtonjunior.org.uk

Head: Mr Mark Potter BEd(Hons)
Appointed: September 2008
School type: Coeducational Day
Member of: IAPS, NAGC, ISCis, NAHT
Age range of pupils: 4–11
No. of pupils enrolled as at 1.9.12: 244
Boys: 127 Girls: 117
Fees per annum as at 1.9.12: Day: £9270–£10,185
Average size of class: 20 maximum
Religious denomination: Church of England

Curriculum

A broad and balanced curriculum including Key Stage I and II National Curriculum subjects. Emphasis is placed on the importance of each child doing their best at all times, according to their ability.

Entry requirements

Entry requirements are by interview and assessment and then at 7+ by testing the individual child to ensure that they feel academically secure within their peer group.

Examinations offered

Children are prepared for entrance examinations at the age of 11 to a variety of senior schools in the area.

The school was founded in 1973 as a member of Oundle School and moved to a new purpose-built building in 2002, with its own central hall and playing fields.

Inspected in March 2008 we received an 'outstanding' report. For the full report please visit our website.

In addition to the Head, there are 25 fully qualified members of staff full-time plus eight part-time teachers. The school is divided into 14 forms of up to 20 children each.

The school has the use of the Oundle School's swimming pool but has games fields on site; close contact is maintained with the senior school. We also have an Educational Support Unit within the school, whereby all children who may have a specific problem may be assessed.

The aims of the school are to encourage the formation of good work habits and good manners, to lay the foundations for the development of self-discipline, self-confidence and self-motivation, and to offer the children the opportunity of experiencing the satisfaction of achievement.

Laxton Junior School is a registered charity that exists to provide an education of the highest class for boys and girls. (No. 309921)

Northampton High School GDST

(Founded 1878)

Newport Pagnell Road, Hardingstone, Northampton,
Northamptonshire NN4 6UU
Tel: 01604 765765   Email: nhsadmin@nhs.gdst.net
Fax: 01604 709418   Website: www.northamptonhigh.gdst.net

NORTHAMPTON
HIGH SCHOOL

Headmistress: Mrs S Dixon BA
Appointed: September 2007
School type: Girls' Day
Age range of pupils: 3–18
No. of pupils enrolled as at 1.9.12: 680
Sixth Form: 110
Fees per annum as at 1.9.12: Day: £8680–£11,865
Average size of class: 19

From Nursery to Sixth Form, a broad and challenging
curriculum provides exciting lessons, taking learning
to a higher level, and close individual attention
encourages each girl to achieve not only her potential
but more. The Junior and Senior schools are adjacent,
offering a caring environment and continuous
curriculum for pupils from Nursery to Sixth Form.

Beyond the classroom, each girl becomes a fully
rounded individual, with a wide portfolio of skills,
talents and experiences. Creative and performing
arts, sports, a plethora of national and overseas visits
and many more activities play a key part in her
development. The 25-acre sports site has an all-
weather pitch, dance studio and 25m indoor pool.

Underpinning all of this, we treasure a happy,
friendly ambience where kindness, courtesy, service –
and fun! – are important values to us.

Unashamedly a traditional school, we are fortunate
to operate in a very modern setting. With beautiful
facilities, the girls benefit from a superb environment
for learning, leading to rewards throughout their
lives. They leave us as successful, confident young
women who combine integrity with both substance
and style.

In our ISI (Independent Schools Inspectorate)
Inspection we achieved the highest grading of
excellent across all areas. Inspectors' comments
included:

"Girls are confident, articulate and enthusiastic.
They enjoy being at this school."

"An atmosphere of achievement and ambition."

"The younger girls exude enjoyment and warmth and
the seniors are confident and relaxed in an
environment they feel is their own."

"The quality of links with parents, carers and
guardians is excellent."

*Northampton High School is part of the GDST (Girls'
Day School Trust). The GDST is the leading network of
independent girls' schools in the UK. A charity that owns
and runs 24 schools and two academies, it reinvests all its
income in its schools. Registered charity number 306983.*

Stamford Endowed Schools

(Founded 1532)

Brazenose House, St Paul's Street, Stamford, Lincolnshire PE9 2BS
Tel: 01780 750310   Email: ses@ses.lincs.sch.uk
Fax: 01780 750397   Website: www.ses.lincs.sch.uk

Stamford
Endowed
Schools

Principal: Stephen C Roberts
School type: Coeducational Day & Boarding
Age range of pupils: 2–18
No. of pupils enrolled as at 1.9.12: 1690
Sixth Form: 400
No. of boarders: 106
Fees per annum as at 1.9.12: Day: £12,624
7 day boarding: £23,028
5 day boarding: £20,076
3 day boarding: £17,448
Average size of class: 16-19
Teacher/pupil ratio: 1:11.5

Passion, enthusiasm, commitment and care underlie every aspect of life at the Stamford Endowed Schools. Our children are educated in an environment where learning is regarded as a privilege and key to unlocking all of life's possibilities. Our teachers dedicate themselves to inspiring intellectual curiosity in the students in evermore innovative ways, whilst doing their utmost to promote and protect the wellbeing of the children in their care.

As a community our schools work in harmony, blending students of different backgrounds and broadening their horizons with the many opportunities available in and beyond the classroom. As a result, the students are equipped not only with exceptional exam results, but a wide range of experiences that prepare them for whatever path they choose in life.

The Stamford Endowed Schools are made up of the Stamford Junior School and Earlybird Nursery, Stamford High School, Stamford School and the sixth form. Our children begin their journey at the Earlybird Nursery at age two, progressing to Stamford Junior School at age 4 until 11. The children are taught co-educationally.

At age 11, boys begin at Stamford School and girls at Stamford High School. We accept entry into any year although Years 7 and 9 are the most common entry points. Teaching boys and girls separately provides a proven academic advantage during the period from age 11 to GCSEs. Boys and girls are still able to mix in many extracurricular activities.

Girls and boys remain affiliated with their schools and come back into the classroom together in the sixth form, where study requires a more mature character and attention is given to preparing the students for life beyond the schools. Our sixth form is hugely popular and attracts additional students from across the region.

For more information, please visit our website at www.ses.lincs.sch.uk, call 01780 750310 or email ses@ses.lincs.sch.uk. We have dedicated admissions staff who will guide you through the process of joining our schools and answer any questions you might have, from bursary and scholarship information to details of our bus timetable.

Uppingham School

(Founded 1584)

Uppingham, Rutland LE15 9QE
Tel: 01572 822216   Admissions: 01572 820611
Email: admissions@uppingham.co.uk
Fax: 01572 822332   Website: www.uppingham.co.uk

Headmaster: Mr Richard Harman
Appointed: 2006
School type: Coeducational Boarding
Age range of pupils: 13–18
No. of pupils enrolled as at 1.9.12: 790
Boys: 462 Girls: 328 Sixth Form: 380
No. of boarders: 769
Fees per annum as at 1.9.12: Day: £21,300
Boarding: £30,429
Day: £7,100 per term
Boarding: £10,143 per term
Average size of class: 11-18
Teacher/pupil ratio: 1:7

Why Uppingham?
Full Boarding. Full Stop.

Uppingham is one of few that can declare itself a truly full boarding school. Of the School's roll (790), all but a handful are full boarders. The pupils benefit from a singular focus and an economy of scale that enables a remarkable depth and diversity of curricular and extra-curricular opportunity.

Enriching Mix

A strong academic focus underpins the School which is also renowned for music and strength in the performing arts; there is also a strong sporting tradition, now enhanced by the outstanding new sports centre. Pupils pull together, respecting and enjoying each other's achievements and supporting each other enthusiastically in varied activities.

Finding a Voice

Uppingham is unabashedly a "singing school" and Chapel services provide an exhilarating way for pupils and staff to start most days and generate an unmatchable esprit de corps. The Chapel's pulpit is not the sole preserve of the Chaplain and the School regularly enjoys morning assemblies from a diversity of staff, visiting speakers and well-motivated school orators!

Space to Grow

The boarding house environment is where individual identities are fostered and Uppingham's are smaller than many others. Boys' houses are typically 50 strong whilst girls' houses have a maximum of 60, reflecting the 10 or 12 pupils per year group in each. This affords a high degree of pastoral care in each house.

Together at the Table

House dining is another important feature of life at Uppingham. At meal times, house staff have the chance to catch up with their charges each day whilst the pupils themselves benefit from contact with the constantly changing rotation of staff, and guests, who might dine with them at lunch each day, a feature that strengthens the feeling of community, sharing and social engagement.

Supported and Stretched

With all of the academic staff involved as tutors in houses, the needs and demands of boarders are appreciated and understood by them all. There is a common culture and a superb team in each. Confidence is nurtured, academic curiosity encouraged and challenges made, all of which leads to higher expectations and, ultimately, greater achievement.

Greater London
& London

Farringtons School

(Founded 1911)

Perry Street, Chislehurst, Kent BR7 6LR
Tel: 020 8467 0256   Email: fvail@farringtons.kent.sch.uk
Fax: 020 8467 5442   Website: www.farringtons.org.uk

Headmistress: Mrs C E James MA
School type: Coeducational Day & Boarding
Member of: SHMIS, AGBIS, BSA
Age range of pupils: 3–18
No. of pupils enrolled as at 1.9.12: 650
Boys: 221 Girls: 429 Sixth Form: 80
No. of boarders: 60
Fees per annum as at 1.9.12: Day: £9060–£12,120
Weekly Boarding: £21,900
Boarding: £23,280
Average size of class: 15-20
Religious denomination: Methodist

Farringtons is a dynamic and inspirational school with outstanding facilities and resources, and is dedicated to providing your child with the best education possible, within a happy, purposeful and stimulating environment. The school offers a broad and balanced academic, sporting and social curriculum that encourages each pupil to fulfil his or her potential.

Conveniently located close to London, on the border of Kent, in 25 acres of attractive leafy grounds, Farringtons has good local and regional transport links and is also easily accessible from the M25, Eurostar terminals and major airports.

Entry requirements
Junior School: interview with Headmistress and a day spent in school.

Senior School: interview with Headmistress and entrance examination.

Examinations offered
A wide range of traditional and modern GCSE and A level subjects (OCR, Edexcel, AQA-SEG, London, Cambridge and AEB). Music and drama examinations also taken.

Academic & leisure facilities
We offer children a stable, stimulating, enjoyable environment, structured to meet their individual needs and ensure that they are happy, secure and reaching their full potential.

Recent refurbishment and development has provided modern, fully-equipped classrooms and science laboratories, designated learning support and careers centres and impressive technology workshops. Members of the sixth form have their own study centre and IT is widely used throughout the school.

Farringtons School Charitable Trust exists solely to provide a high quality, caring education. Registered charity No. 307916.

Halliford School

(Founded 1921)

Russell Road, Shepperton, Middlesex TW17 9HX
Tel: 01932 223593   Email: registrar@halliford.net
Fax: 01932 229781   Website: www.hallifordschool.co.uk

Head: Mr Philip V Cottam MA(Oxon), FRGS
School type: Independent Day School for Boys
Coeducational Sixth Form
Member of: ISA, SHMIS, AGBIS
Age range of pupils:
Boys: 11–18
Girls: 16–18
No. of pupils enrolled as at 1.9.12:
Boys: 433 Girls: 10
Sixth Form: Boys 90 Girls 10
Fees per annum as at 1.9.12: Day: £12,000
Religious denomination: Non-denominational

Halliford School is an independent day school for boys aged 11-18 with a co-educational sixth form. It aims to prepare its pupils for GCSE, AS, A level and entry to university. Applications are welcome from both boys and girls (for the sixth form only). Entry for boys is normally at 11+ or 13+ but entry can also be considered in other year groups should places be available. Entry for girls is at 16+.

The administrative centre of the school is a fine Georgian House set in six acres beside the River Thames. Passers-by may think the old house is the school, but behind the house are modern buildings housing light and airy classrooms, science laboratories, an information technology centre, art rooms, design & technology workshops, music rooms and four acres of playing fields. There is also a 320-seater theatre incorporating a theatre workshop and a kitchen and dining area. The theatre itself is also equipped as a multimedia lecture theatre.

A new sports hall, sixth form centre and library opened in September 2005, and with the addition of six acres of land providing two additional sports pitches and a cricket square 400 yards from the school gate, are all part of Halliford's provision of

excellent facilities for its pupils. Furthermore, the building of our new music, art and sixth form centre commenced in June 2011, with completion scheduled for autumn 2012.

Halliford School is a small school where, unusually in this day and age, the staff are able to get to know all the pupils personally. The facilities are good, the teaching is excellent and the atmosphere is friendly. Emerging from this secure community the Halliford student goes out into the adult world equipped with self-confidence, a sound education, awareness of the needs of others and often examination results far beyond his or her expectations.

Halliford holds a Saturday Open Morning in October. They hold two days in March and one day in May and two days in November when the school is in session. For entry into the sixth form an Open Evening is held in October. Information on these days and appointments to visit the school at other times can be made by contacting the registrar.

Halliford School, a registered charity, exists to provide high quality education. (No. 312090)

Homefield School

(Founded 1870)

Western Road, Sutton, Surrey SM1 2TE
Tel: 020 8642 0965   Email: administration@homefield.sutton.sch.uk
Fax: 020 8770 1668   Website: www.homefield.sutton.sch.uk

Headteacher: Mr P R Mowbray MA(Cantab)
Appointed: April 1992
School type: Boys' Day
Member of: IAPS, NAHT, ISCis
Age range of pupils: 3–13
No. of pupils enrolled as at 1.9.12: 400
Fees per annum as at 1.9.12: Day: £4290–£9975
Average size of class: 17
Teacher/pupil ratio: 1:9
Religious denomination: Non-denominational

"I don't believe we could have found a better school in the country to bring out the best in both our sons."

Homefield is a preparatory school for 400 boys aged 3 to 13, and 50 staff, housed in an extensive purpose-built complex complemented by a two-acre adjoining playing field. New science labs, art and music suites and an enlarged LRC opened in September 2008.

Homefield School has continued to achieve a 100% pass rate at Common Entrance to 46 senior schools over the last ten years. A record 85 awards for art, music, sport, all-round and academic achievements have been won in the last three years, including a King's Scholarship at Eton.

The school is renowned for its intimacy and family atmosphere, small class sizes, the provision of specialist teaching at the earliest appropriate opportunity, (French, ICT, music and sport from the Foundation stage), its commitment to best practice and its all round academic, musical, dramatic, sporting and artistic achievements. The recent ISI inspection report, now posted on the school's website, states that 'pupils are highly educated and fully prepared for the next stages of their lives. The school's pastoral systems ensure that all pupils are well cared for' and compliments the 'excellent range of extra-curricular activities'.

The school has county or national representatives in table-tennis, squash, athletics, karate, soccer, rugby, cricket and chess.

Awareness of others is encouraged and the pupils are involved in many fundraising charity events, raising on average £6000 every year.

Learning support is available for children with special needs. A wide range of opportunities is planned to extend gifted pupils such as World Class Maths Tests and national competitions in English, French and history.

We offer academic, sporting, art and music scholarships as well as bursaries.

Daily minibuses run to and from Wimbledon and other areas.

Breakfast and after-school clubs are available.

Homefield School is a registered charity (No. 312753). It exists to provide education for boys.

King's House School

(Founded 1946)

68 King's Road, Richmond, Surrey TW10 6ES
Tel: 020 8940 1878   Email: schooloffice@kingshouseschool.org
Fax: 020 8939 2501   Website: www.kingshouseschool.org

Head: Mr Mark Turner BA PGCE NPQH
Appointed: September 2012
School type: Boys' Day
Age range of pupils:
Boys: 3–13
Girls: 3–4
(Nursery only)
No. of pupils enrolled as at 1.9.12: 450
Boys: 430 Girls: 20
Fees per annum as at 1.9.12: Day: £1750–£4250
Average size of class: 15-22
Teacher/pupil ratio: 1:10

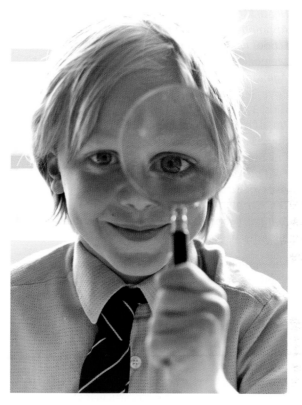

'An excellent all-round, happy prep school that brings out the best in all its boys.' King's House parent, 2012

We believe King's House School is a very special place. With a strong rapport between children, staff and parents the school has a warm family atmosphere where children feel safe, happy and positive about learning and growing up.

We aim to provide the children with an all-round education of the highest quality. From solid academic foundations, we build up their independence, satisfaction in personal achievement and challenge them with new ideas and concepts as well as an understanding of their role in both the local and global community. Their physical and creative development is equally important, pursued through broad curricular and extracurricular activities.

The approach in the classroom is one of praise and encouragement. Throughout the school, the small classes allow for close monitoring and evaluation of each child's progress and well-being.

King's House School is justifiably proud of its 100% pass rate for senior school entry with boys moving on to some of the most academic schools in the country. The emphasis is always on finding the right school for each pupil.

King's House School is an independent day preparatory school for children between the ages of 3 and 13. The Nursery is for girls and boys but from Reception to Year 8, the School is for boys only.

Located in the heart of Richmond, the School enjoys the advantages of close access to London with all the educational opportunities that affords with regular trips to museums, galleries and theatres as well as Richmond Park and Kew Gardens.

Full bursary places are available and there are school bus routes from both Chiswick and Putney.

For more information visit www.kinghouseschool.org or contact our Registrar, Sally Bass, on 020 8940 1878 or bass.s@kingshouseschool.org.

Lyonsdown School Trust

(Founded 1906)

3 Richmond Road, New Barnet, Barnet, Hertfordshire EN5 1SA
Tel: 020 8449 0225   Email: enquiries@lyonsdownschool.co.uk
Fax: 020 8441 4690   Website: www.lyonsdownschool.co.uk

Head: Mrs L Maggs-Wellings BEd
Appointed: September 2005
School type: Independent Coeducational Day
Member of: ISA
Age range of pupils:
Boys: 3–7
Girls: 3–11
No. of pupils enrolled as at 1.9.12: 214
Boys: 31 Girls: 183
(inc pre-school)
Fees per annum as at 1.9.12: Day: £3189–£8103
Average size of class: 18-22
Teacher/pupil ratio: 1:10
Religious denomination: Christian Foundation (but all faiths welcome)

Curriculum

Pupils are nurtured by an experienced and caring staff who help them to maximise their potential. The school has a tradition of high academic standards and achievements within a broad and balanced curriculum.

Music tuition is available for a selection of instruments, as are speech, chess and drama lessons. There is a wide range of extracurricular clubs covering sports and creative activities and we also undertake numerous field trips and educational visits.

Entry requirements

Places in the pre-school are allocated from a waiting list at the age of three. Additional entry into Reception is also non-selective. Early registration is recommended as pressure for places is high. There are occasional places available at other stages, when entry is by assessment and interview.

Lyonsdown School Trust Ltd, a registered charity (No. 312591), aims to keep fees low in order to make independent education available to a wider spectrum of children.

Rokeby School

(Founded 1877)

George Road, Kingston upon Thames, Surrey KT2 7PB
Tel: 020 8942 2247 Email: hmsec@rokeby.org.uk
Fax: 020 8942 5707 Website: www.rokebyschool.co.uk

Head: J R Peck
School type: Boys' Preparatory
Member of: IAPS
Age range of pupils: 4–13
No. of pupils enrolled as at 1.9.12: 370
Fees per annum as at 1.9.12: Day: £9387–£13,659
Religious denomination: Non-denominational and free-thinking

Curriculum

Rokeby has an outstanding record of success in Common Entrance and Scholarships to leading independent schools. Science is taught in two laboratories and the IT facilities are impressive throughout the school. There are two halls and spacious art, design and technology rooms. The music department provides a variety of ensembles, choirs and bands and an excellent variety of instruments are taught in the school. Physical education is in the hands of specialists with football, rugby, cricket, athletics and tennis all catered for at our sports ground in Worcester Park. A full activities programme is available for all boys from chess club to golf. A fabulous new building with six classrooms, performance hall, library and offices is due for completion in Autumn 2012.

Entry requirements

Entry at four to Reception is done by a ballot. There is an entry test for 7+ to the prep school for external candidates. Academic scholarships are offered to entrants at 7+. Occasional places may be available.

The Rokeby Educational Trust Ltd is a registered charity (No. 312653) and aims to help boys achieve their best in all areas of learning. We treat boys as individuals but also train them to work together as a community. We believe that each boy can find their strengths and overcome their weaknesses given the right opportunities, to become smart, skilful and kind.

St Catherine's School

(Founded 1914)

Cross Deep, Twickenham, Middlesex TW1 4QJ
Tel: 020 8891 2898   Email: admissions@stcatherineschool.co.uk
Fax: 020 8744 9629   Website: www.stcatherineschool.co.uk

Headmistress: Sister Paula Thomas BEd(Hons), MA
Appointed: September 2007
School type: Girls' Day
Age range of pupils: 3–18
No. of pupils enrolled as at 1.9.11: 390
Fees per annum as at 1.9.12: Day: £8190–£11,460
Average size of class: 20
Teacher/pupil ratio: 1:11

Focus on the individual.

St Catherine's combines nearly 100 years' experience of Catholic girls' independent education with a modern curriculum that prepares girls for success in the 21st century. We are a Catholic school, in the ecumenical tradition, where every student is a valued member of a happy community. Emphasis is placed on providing a broad education and on responsibility and the importance of respect for others. We are a small school with small class sizes and a strong community spirit and as such are able to focus on the individual and help every girl achieve her personal best. High academic standards are maintained, together with an excellent 'value-added' record.

In the most recent 2011 GCSE exam results the girls achieved 98% 5 A*-C grades, 44% A*/A grades and 79% A*-B grades. An extension for the prep department opened in 2008, including three new classrooms, a library and a practical base. Another new block, which includes a sixth form centre and other new facilities, was opened in September 2010.

The school is regularly in the top ten of the top 50 small schools in the *Sunday Times Parent Power* magazine.

St Helen's College

(Founded 1920)

St HELEN'S COLLEGE

Parkway, Hillingdon, Uxbridge, Middlesex UB10 9JX
Tel: 01895 234371   Email: info@sthelenscollege.com
Fax: 01895 206948   Website: www.sthelenscollege.com

Joint Headteachers: Mr D A Crehan ARCS, BA, BSc, MSc, CPhys & Mrs G R Crehan BA, MA, PGCE
Appointed: 1987
School type: Coeducational Day
Member of: IAPS
Age range of pupils: 3–11
No. of pupils enrolled as at 1.9.12: 351
Boys: 177 Girls: 174
Fees per annum as at 1.9.12: Day: £4725–£7785
Average size of class: 21
Teacher/pupil ratio: varies

'Outstanding' or 'Excellent' in all areas of inspection

St Helen's College is a private school for boys and girls aged 3 to 11. With just over 340 pupils the school has a real family feel. The headteachers (a husband and wife team) have run the school for 25 years. St Helen's College has just received an outstanding inspection report, which judged the school as excellent or outstanding in all areas of inspection (a rare achievement for any school).

'Pupils achieve high standards in both academic work and a wide range of other activities. They are extremely successful in all aspects of their learning and this is reflected in their success in entrance examinations both to maintained grammar and to independent schools' (2011 inspection report).

The staff and Headteachers are keen to nurture the individual qualities of their pupils, recognizing that every child is different and offering encouragement for all-round achievement and academic excellence. The children benefit from highly qualified, specialist teachers in different subject areas, allowing them to study at a high level led by teachers with a real passion for their subject.

A wide range of extracurricular activities provides the children with opportunities to try new skills. Children can try their hand at tag rugby, athletics, sailing, kayaking, climbing, tae kwan do, yoga, film making, debating, art and more. Pupils are offered lessons in a choice of nine musical instruments and there are four choirs. Drama is also one of the school's great strengths with productions held each year at local theatres.

The staff at St Helen's College are justifiably proud of their exceptional inspection report. If you would like to receive a copy please call 01895 234371. Alternatively, the inspection report is available to be viewed on line. Visit www.sthelenscollege.com.

For more information call 01895 234371 or email info@sthelenscollege.com.

St Helen's School

(Founded 1899)

Eastbury Road, Northwood, Middlesex HA6 3AS
Tel: +44 (0)1923 843210   Email: enquiries@sthn.co.uk
Fax: +44 (0)1923 843211   Website: www.sthn.co.uk

Headmistress: Dr Mary Short BA, PhD
Appointed: September 2011
School type: Girls' Day
Member of: GSA, IB
Age range of pupils: 3–18
No. of pupils enrolled as at 1.9.12: 1122
Sixth Form: 155
Fees per annum as at 1.9.12: Day: £9516–£13,830

St Helen's is a highly academic school for able girls. Pupils consistently achieve outstanding public examination results and go on to prestigious universities of their first choice, including Oxford and Cambridge. Since 2004, we have offered the International Baccalaureate Diploma as well as A levels in the sixth form.

The curriculum enables every girl to achieve intellectual and personal fulfilment and to develop her talents fully. Staff are subject specialists and inspire the girls, encouraging them to study independently and develop good study habits through stimulating teaching. Girls study with commitment and particular importance is placed on the prompt completion of homework assignments.

Set in over 20 acres of green space in north-west London, we offer excellent facilities including specialist facilities for science, design and technology, art, drama, music and ICT; a new state-of-the-art sports centre; a digital, multimedia language laboratory; an excellent library housing an extensive collection of books, ICT facilities, newspapers and periodicals; and well-equipped teaching rooms, providing a superb basis for learning. All girls in senior school study two modern languages together with Latin. Sport also features heavily throughout the school with girls competing at county and national level.

St Helen's is a vibrant community with many girls taking advantage of the well organised extracurricular activities, which include concerts, plays, the Combined Cadet Force, run jointly with Merchant Taylors' School, and the Duke of Edinburgh's Award Scheme. Through these activities girls discover interests that complement their academic achievements. High priority is placed on careers education: all girls take part in work experience, with those studying languages in the sixth form having an opportunity to work in Europe.

There is a vertical house system and close relationships with parents by formal contact at least once a term, either by written report or at a Parents Evening. Parents are welcome to contact the school at any time. Social contact is through the thriving Parent Teachers' Association and close links exist with Merchant Taylors' School.

We provide a friendly, secure and disciplined environment, where co-operation and mutual respect are highly valued along with integrity, self-discipline, personal responsibility and respect for others. Girls are encouraged to give of their best, be tolerant and caring, and to make a positive contribution as individuals and team players. Above all, girls are encouraged to chase their dreams, ready to take their place in the adult world.

St Helen's School Northwood is a registered charity (No. 312762), which exists to provide high quality education for girls from the UK and overseas.

St James Senior Boys School

(Founded 1975)

Church Road, Ashford, Surrey TW15 3DZ
Tel: 01784 266930   Email: admissions@stjamesboys.co.uk
Fax: 01784 266938   Website: www.stjamesboys.co.uk

Headmaster: Mr David Boddy
Appointed: 2004
School type: Boys' Day & Weekly Boarding
Age range of pupils: 11–18
No. of pupils enrolled as at 1.9.12: 380
Sixth Form: 65
No. of boarders: 26
Fees per annum as at 1.9.12: Day: £12,660
Weekly Boarding: £5400
Average size of class: 22
Teacher/pupil ratio: 1:9

Over recent years, parents have come to appreciate that in future, their sons will need something different to help them live and enjoy life to the full, to be at peace with themselves and of service to all. They will need to be brilliant through their own talents, but they will also need an inner confidence from learning to be still, to know what they stand for, to be able to communicate, lead, and to be able to use a creative approach to problem solving. They will compete against youngsters from all over the world for the best jobs. Their success will depend on the extent to which they can respond freely in all situations.

St James' response to turning boys into men has been to provide a distinctive education, uniting a philosophic approach to the development of life skills, plus the delivery of academic excellence.

The school has experienced unprecedented demand for this philosophically inspired education and this has led to the need to expand into more spacious premises. This year St James is enjoying its second year at Ashford in Surrey. Boys and staff alike are thriving in the magnificent Victorian/Gothic structure set within 32 acres of grounds.

The school has continued its enlightened selective approach, emphasising character along with academic potential, although the entrance exam has been maintained to ensure that the strong academic curriculum can be met, with or without learning support. Sport and extracurricular activities have also flourished.

Every boy is considered unique, but at the same time he comes to know that every human being shares the same essence. Boys meet this in the space of meditation and quiet time, experienced twice daily, and as a silent pause between lessons.

This contemplative approach to modern education is being sought by discerning parents and there is much interest in the St James model. David Boddy, the Headmaster of St James, has recently been elected to become Chairman of the SHMIS organisation and the school is also a member of The International Boys' School Coalition and the ISA.

Staines Preparatory School Trust

(Founded 1935)

3 Gresham Road, Staines upon Thames, Middlesex TW18 2BT
Tel: 01784 450909   Email: registrar@stainesprep.co.uk
Fax: 01784 464424   Website: www.stainesprep.co.uk

Headmaster: Peter Roberts BSc
Appointed: Nov 1998
School type: Coeducational Day
Age range of pupils: 3–11
No. of pupils enrolled as at 1.9.12: 342
Boys: 195 Girls: 147
Fees per annum as at 1.9.12: Day: £7950–£9150
Average size of class: 17
Teacher/pupil ratio: 1:13

Whether you visit one of the classrooms, the sports pitch or playground at Staines Prep, you're sure to witness contented children joining in with an enthusiasm you'll only find in a school where enjoyment is an important part of the learning experience.

Founded in 1935, Staines Prep is the area's longest established co-educational school for children aged 2½ – 11. The school has a unique ethos, where each pupil is encouraged to achieve their full potential within a secure, happy environment.

SPS focuses on far more than academic achievements encouraging personal research and fostering a lifelong love of learning. The children's wider involvements in music, drama, art and sporting activities bring to life the true spirit of the school, helping to discover and nurture life skills that help each pupil to draw the utmost enjoyment from their time there.

As Headmaster Peter Roberts said recently: "It remains vitally important to focus on the whole child and provide wide-ranging opportunities that help develop their confidence and general well-being. At Staines Prep we provide all of this in a nurturing environment that enables the pupils to flourish."

Staines Prep, as part of its commitment to striving for excellence, has commissioned a £3m project to build new state-of-the-art teaching and performance facilities. The development, which started in April 2012 is set for completion by the end of the year. The project will provide a new full-size bespoke multi-function hall, contemporary changing room and toilet facilities, two large fully-equipped classrooms, which will be used as the School's new art, design & technology and science suites, plus six additional standard classrooms.

Visit us at www.stainesprep.co.uk, or contact the registrar on 01784 450909 or via registrar@stainesprep.co.uk. For assistance with fee planning and other fee information please contact the bursar. Means-tested bursaries available subject to assessment.

The Royal Masonic School for Girls

(Founded 1788)

Rickmansworth Park, Rickmansworth, Hertfordshire WD3 4HF
Tel: 01923 773168   Email: enquiries@royalmasonic.herts.sch.uk
Fax: 01923 896729   Website: www.royalmasonic.herts.sch.uk

Headmistress: Mrs Diana Rose MA(Cantab)
School type: Girls' Day & Boarding
(including weekly and flexi boarding) Boarders
from 7 and mixed Pre-school
Age range of pupils: 4–18
Pre-school 2–4
No. of pupils enrolled as at 1.9.12: 917
Boys: 26 Girls: 891 Sixth Form: 175
Pre-school: 83
No. of boarders: 150
Fees per annum as at 1.9.12: Day: £8490–£14,550
Weekly Boarding: £14,850–£23,535
Boarding: £15,105–£24,120
Pre-school fees: Upon application
Average size of class: 20
Teacher/pupil ratio: 1:12
Religious denomination: Non-denominational

At the Royal Masonic School for Girls we enable each girl to fulfil her potential and to find an area in which she can excel. We appreciate that girls have many and varied talents, and we seek to cultivate and foster those talents. RMS girls are socially skilled, courteous and friendly, and they thrive in a school that promotes tolerance and mutual respect.

We offer an exceptionally wide-ranging curriculum in a supportive and friendly environment, where the highest standards prevail. Girls receive individual attention and are given the confidence to succeed. The most notable feature, however, is the distinctive ethos of RMS – we are committed to fostering the achievement of all without undue pressure. Girls are encouraged to focus on stretching themselves in as many fields as possible, not only academically, but also on the sports field and in art, design technology, music and drama. Extracurricular activities abound for girls of all ages, including the Duke of Edinburgh's Award Scheme and Young Enterprise.

The range of 27 subjects in the sixth form enables all pupils to succeed. Our A level pass rate last year was 100% with 86% at grade A or B. 92% of girls gained places at their university of first choice.

Boarding pupils are cared for in well-appointed and spacious houses, with experienced, caring residential staff. We attach a great deal of significance to the quality of our pastoral care for each girl.

The school occupies a stunning site of 315 acres, which creates a serenity rarely found in today's schools, yet we are only 30 minutes from central London by train. Heathrow and Gatwick airports are both serviced by the M25 motorway, which is less than a mile from the school.

Generous open scholarships are available and a discount to HM forces personnel. We also offer a number of means-tested bursaries.

The Royal Masonic School Charitable Trust exists for the advancement of education. Charity No. 276784.

Cameron House

(Founded 1980)

4 The Vale, Chelsea, London SW3 6AH
Tel: 020 7352 4040   Email: info@cameronhouseschool.org
Fax: 020 7352 2349   Website: www.cameronhouseschool.org

Headmistress: Mrs Lucie Moore BEd(Hons)
Principal: Miss Josie Cameron Ashcroft BSc(Hons), DipEd
School type: Coeducational Day
Member of: IAPS, ISC, BDA
Age range of pupils: 4–11
No. of pupils enrolled as at 1.9.12: 116
Boys: 53 Girls: 63
Fees per annum as at 1.9.11: Day: £15,285
Religious denomination: Church of England, all denominations welcome
Scholarships: Academic scholarships are available.

The curriculum

'The school fully meets its aim of maintaining high academic standards and helping each pupil to do their best.' (ISI Inspection 2010). Our academic curriculum prepares all our children for Common Entrance exams. The children study a comprehensive range of subjects using techniques that encourage them to explore, work co-operatively and be creative.

Setup and atmosphere

Cameron House has a nurturing environment that gives children a strong sense of belonging and purpose. With the guidance of the highly qualified staff, children of all abilities achieve excellent standards.

Games and the arts

Essential to life at Cameron House is sport, as well as music, drama and specialist art lessons. These are all integral to the curriculum.

Pastoral care

We encourage all our children to consider and care for others. 'Exemplary pastoral care is a strong feature of the school and staff are united in their approach to the promotion of pupils' well-being and development.' (ISI Inspection 2010).

Outstanding characteristics

Cameron House is a vibrant school well-known for maintaining high academic standards while encouraging individual creativity. Children leave Cameron House as independent thinkers, brimming with intellectual curiosity. Children move on to St Paul's, Godolphin & Latymer, Wycombe Abbey, Benenden, Alleyn's, Westminster Under, Colet Court, City of London, Francis Holland and many more.

'The headteacher is highly skilled at moulding the staff into a unified team who work with a shared goal of a positive and caring approach towards each individual pupil, that has produced the outstanding response in the attitudes of pupils towards learning and to school' (ISI Report, 2010).

City of London School
A rounded education in the Square Mile
(Founded 1442)

Queen Victoria Street, London EC4V 3AL
Tel: 020 7489 0291   Email: admissions@clsb.org.uk
Fax: 020 7329 6887   Website: www.clsb.org.uk

CITY of **LONDON**
SCHOOL

Headmaster: Mr D Levin MA
Appointed: 1999
School type: Boys' Day
Age range of pupils: 10–18
No. of pupils enrolled as at 1.9.12: 920
Sixth Form: 250
Fees per annum as at 1.9.12: Day: £13,401

"There is no such thing as a typical City boy. What characterises the education offered is a true preparation for life."

City of London is a truly unique independent school not least because of its unrivalled location on the banks of the Thames, between St. Paul's Cathedral and the Tate Modern. We are at the heart of the capital and our pupils benefit enormously from all that is on offer on our doorstep.

We are a modern and forward-looking institution drawing on clever boys from all social, economic and ethnic backgrounds and in so doing truly reflect the diversity of the capital in the 21st century. Boys travel to City from all over London and come from a huge number of both state primary and independent preparatory schools and, once here, receive an academic yet liberal education.

Our examination results are excellent, but, more importantly, boys leave us with a sense of identity and an independence of thought and action that are rare among leavers from private schools; it is significant that the vast majority of boys go on to their first choice of university.

Facilities are outstanding (the school moved downstream to its new buildings in 1986) and are continually updated.

Access to the school is not restricted by money, and we are generously endowed with academic, music and sport scholarships (for academic merit) and also academic and livery bursaries for families who may not be able to afford the full fees. In addition, the bursary campaign has raised significant funding for several full-fee places to be awarded each year to those who could not otherwise afford even a proportion of the fees. In this way, the school seeks to maintain the socio-economic mix that has always been its tradition and strength.

For a prospectus and to book onto one of our numerous parental visits, please contact:

Mrs J Brown, the Admissions Secretary,

Tel: 020 7489 0291

Or email: admissions@clsb.org.uk

Or write to: City of London School, Queen Victoria Street, London EC4V 3AL

Devonshire House Preparatory School

(Founded 1989)

2 Arkwright Road, Hampstead, London NW3 6AE
Tel: 020 7435 1916   Email: enquiries@devonshirehouseprepschool.co.uk
Fax: 020 7431 4787   Website: www.devonshirehouseschool.co.uk

Headmistress: Mrs S Piper BA(Hons)
School type: Preparatory, Pre-preparatory &
Nursery Day School
(The Oak Tree Nursery)
Member of: IAPS, ISC
Age range of pupils:
Boys: 2½–13
Girls: 2½–11
No. of pupils enrolled as at 1.5.12: 600
Boys: 324 Girls: 276
Fees per annum as at 1.9.12: Day: £7650–£14,550
Religious denomination: Non-denominational

Curriculum

Early literacy and numeracy are very important and the traditional academic subjects form the core curriculum. The combined sciences form an increasingly important part of the timetable as the children grow older and the use of computers is introduced from an early age. Expression in all forms of communication is encouraged with classes having lessons in art, music, drama and French. Physical exercise and games are also part of the curriculum. Much encouragement is given to pupils to help to widen their horizons and broaden their interests. The school fosters a sense of responsibility amongst the pupils, and individuality and personal attention for each pupil are considered most important.

Entry requirements

The Junior School: For children entering the junior school from the ages of three to five, places are offered on the basis of an assessment made at interview. From the age of six, places are subject to a written test taken at the school. At eight, children normally transfer directly into the upper school. Parents and their children are welcome to visit for interview and to see around the school.

The school has its own nursery, The Oak Tree Nursery, which takes children from 2½ years of age.

The Upper School: Entry to the upper school is principally from the junior school. For pupils seeking to join the school from elsewhere, places are normally subject to a written entrance test.

Academic & leisure facilities

The school is situated in fine premises in the heart of Hampstead with their own walled grounds. The aim is to achieve high academic standards whilst developing enthusiasm and initiative throughout a wide range of interests. It is considered essential to encourage pupils to develop their own individual personalities and a good sense of personal responsibility.

Durston House

(Founded 1886)

12-14 Castlebar Road, Ealing, London W5 2DR
Tel: 020 8991 6532   Email: info@durstonhouse.org
Fax: 020 8991 6547   Website: www.durstonhouse.org

Headmaster: Mr Ian Kendrick MA, BEd(Hons)
Appointed: January 2005
School type: Boys' Day
Age range of pupils: 4–13
No. of pupils enrolled as at 1.9.12: 415
Fees per annum as at 1.9.12: Day: £9810–£12,570
Average size of class: 16
Teacher/pupil ratio: 1:10

Durston House opened its doors for the first time in January in 1886, since when it has been in continuous operation as a major West London day preparatory school for boys aged 4-13. Our aim is to provide an education that allows learning to be an adventure, and where academic excellence is balanced with a wider curriculum, including performing arts and team sports.

The size of Durston – we have 400 pupils – does not preclude our aim of developing a family environment, with a framework of values and expectations that create the best atmosphere for each pupil to grow in all respects. At a pastoral level, we never lose sight of each child as an individual, ensuring that every pupil achieves his potential. Our House system, with its smaller vertical group meetings, ensures that old and young interact with each other in a positive and caring manner.

London day schools, such as St Paul's and Merchant Taylors', attract the majority of our boys; but each year several pupils depart for leading boarding schools. In 2012, 22% of our leavers will join their senior schools with scholarships.

Such achievement is only a fraction of the story, however; personal development and well-being are high on the agenda of any forward thinking school. Education is not actually fraught with complexities. At Durston we seeking the answers to fundamental questions: *What is worth knowing? What is worth doing?* The desire to learn, to try new things, to develop skills to a high level, individually, is not difficult to pursue and the encouragement of such aspirations remains paramount in our philosophy.

We hope all of our pupils will remember their time at Durston as happy. We hope all of them will carry with them values of respect, consideration and responsibility that make them worthy players in life's arena.

Dwight School London
Formerly North London International School

(Founded 1885)

6 Friern Barnet Lane, London N11 3LX
Tel: +44 (0)20 8920 0600   Email: admissions@nlis.org
Fax: +44 (0)20 8211 4605   Website: www.dwightlondon.org

DWIGHT SCHOOL LONDON
Igniting the spark of genius in every child
PERSONALISED LEARNING · COMMUNITY · GLOBAL VISION

Head: Mr David Rose MA(Ed), BA, CertEd, FRSA
School type: Coeducational Day
Member of: ISA, ECIS, IAPS, LISA, IB, ISCis
Age range of pupils: 2–18
No. of pupils enrolled as at 1.9.12: 356
Kindergarten (ages 2-4): 18 boys 16 girls
Lower School (ages 4-6): 15 boys 17 girls
Lower School (ages 6-11): 73 boys 33 girls
Upper School (ages 11-16): 95 boys 43 girls
Upper School (ages 16-19): 21 boys 25 girls
Fees per annum as at 1.9.12: Day: £3390–£16,290
Boarding: £10,000
Average size of class: Max 20
Religious denomination: Non-denominational

Curriculum

Dwight School London aims to provide a secure, well-ordered and happy environment with the learning process at its core, offering the finest possible education for all pupils in order for them to reach their full potential. Serving a cosmopolitan and diverse North London community, great importance is attached to respect, understanding and empathy with everyone's cultures, religions and backgrounds.

Students follow the International Baccalaureate (IB) curriculum, starting at aged three with the Primary Years Programme, moving on to the Middle Years Programme at age 11 and the IB Diploma Programme at age 16. The programmes are designed to encourage the development of learning skills and to meet a child's academic, social, physical, emotional and cultural needs. Through enquiry-based learning and various disciplines, subject interrelatedness is accentuated, preparing students for the pre-university Diploma Programme.

The school recognises that students can have a variety of different learning styles. The Quest Programme is designed for students who need help developing strategies to assist them to study effectively. Through one-to-one tuition from specialist staff, students can reach their full potential, further enhanced by the school's teacher-student ratio.

Entry requirements

Students are accepted for entry at any time throughout the school year.

Kindergarten and Lower School (ages 2-11). Students are invited to attend for half a day and may be asked to complete a basic assessment.

Upper School (ages 11-16). Students attend an interview with the Head of the school, are invited to visit the school for a day and may be required to complete a basic assessment.

Entry to the upper school is automatic for students in the lower school.

Upper School (ages 16-19). Diploma Programme applicants are invited for interview with the programme coordinator. Students would be expected to have five or six GCSE passes, with B, A or A* grades for subjects to be studied at Higher Level.

Examinations offered
PYP Project Exhibition, IBMYP and IB Diploma.

Facilities
The school has dedicated IT, music, art and design technology facilities for all students. The commitment to the use of ICT in all subject areas is highlighted by IT and graphics suites, individual student home drives and email accounts, student dedicated laptops and wireless network.

Students' physical development is considered as important as academic development and the school's sports fields provide excellent facilities for football, cricket, athletics, hockey, tennis and softball. The school's hall, playgrounds and local amenities are also utilised to offer further activities such as basketball, badminton, squash, swimming, table tennis, ice-skating and skiing. Matches and tournaments between local schools are regular fixtures.

The school is able to provide a bus service for students living in the local area in addition to the excellent bus, tube and train routes from the rest of London and the surrounding area.

GEMS Hampshire School

(Founded 1928) ISC Accredited

15 Manresa Road, Chelsea, London SW3 6NB
Tel: 020 7352 7077   Email: info@ghs.gemsedu.co.uk
Fax: 020 7351 3960   Website: www.ths.westminster.sch.uk

Principal: Mr Stephen J Chynoweth
School type: Coeducational Day
Age range of pupils: 3–13
No. of pupils enrolled as at 1.9.12:
Early Years: 51
Pre-Preparatory: 96
Preparatory: 89
Fees per annum as at 1.9.12: Day: £10,305–£14,460
Average size of class: 15
Teacher/pupil ratio: 1:6.4

About the school

Founded in 1928 and located in the Royal Borough of Kensington and Chelsea, GEMS Hampshire School provides the top-class education you would expect from a traditional British Preparatory school, combined with a caring approach and family feel. An independent, inter-denominational day school, we cater for boys and girls between the ages of 3 and 13.

Curriculum

Through personal attention from our dedicated staff and a stimulating curriculum, we ensure that learning is fun and that every child feels confident and valued. We place an emphasis on achievement and celebration of success in all areas of our school community, working in partnership with parents to encourage children to be active learners, independent thinkers and caring individuals. Children are encouraged to study the history and development of their environment by regular visits to museums, art galleries and exhibitions.

Academic & leisure facilities

Our excellent facilities include a galleried library, gymnasium, science laboratory, art and design studio, fully equipped stage, garden and state-of-the-art ICT suite. Interactive whiteboards in every teaching space in the main school, along with computers in every classroom, allow ICT to be accessed in all aspects of learning. We also provide, within our fees, access to the Maths Whizz online system of individualised home tutoring for every child.

Francis Holland School, Regent's Park, NW1

(Founded 1878)

Clarence Gate, Ivor Place, Regent's Park, London NW1 6XR
Tel: 020 7723 0176   Email: registrar@fhs-nw1.org.uk
Fax: 020 7706 1522   Website: www.francisholland.org.uk

Head: Mrs Vivienne Durham MA(Oxon)
School type: Independent Girls' Day
Member of: GSA, ISC
Age range of pupils: 11–18
No. of pupils enrolled as at 1.9.12: 450
Sixth Form: 120
Fees per annum as at 1.9.12: Day: £15,000
Average size of class: 18 (GCSE) and 8 (Sixth Form)
Religious denomination: Church of England

Curriculum

Girls on arrival are placed in one of three parallel forms and taught a broad curriculum. In the second year they start a second language – Italian, German or Spanish. Girls usually take nine or ten subjects for GCSE, 11 in some cases. All girls take at least four AS levels and three A2s. They proceed to university, art or music college. The curriculum is kept under constant review, and there is regular consultation with parents about each girl's programme of study. Many sixth formers successfully complete the Extended Project, a qualification designed to challenge the most able students beyond A level.

Entry requirements

Entry at 11 is by means of written tests in English and mathematics, together with an interview. A few girls are accepted into the sixth form each year and into other years as vacancies occur.

Examinations offered

GCSE subjects offered: art, classical civilisation, English, English literature, French, German, geography, Greek, history, Italian, Latin, mathematics, music, PE, religious studies, Spanish, physics, chemistry and biology. Additional subjects at A level include history of art, economics, politics, psychology and theatre studies.

Academic & leisure facilities

The school has its own swimming pool and gymnasium and uses Regent's Park for tennis, hockey, rounders and netball. The Gloucester Wing, opened by HRH The Duke of Gloucester in May 2009, provides additional classrooms and seminar rooms, a fourth art studio and a performance area for music, drama and theatre studies. There are two school orchestras, several choirs and a jazz band.

Music, drama, art and sport play an important part in the school. Individual instrumental lessons and lessons in speech and drama are popular.

The school seeks to foster a happy atmosphere in which pupils will thrive academically and enjoy a wide range of extracurricular clubs, activities and excursions.

Scholarships and bursaries

Academic, music and art scholarships available at Year 7 and sixth form. Entry bursaries up to 100% of fees.

Francis Holland School Charitable Trust exists to provide high quality education for girls and religious instruction in accordance with the principles of the Church of England. Registered charity No. 312745.

Francis Holland School, Sloane Square, SW1

(Founded 1881)

39 Graham Terrace, London SW1W 8JF
Tel: 020 7730 2971   Email: registrar@fhs-sw1.org.uk
Fax: 020 7823 4066   Website: www.francisholland.org.uk

Head: Mrs Lucy Elphinstone MA(Cantab)
Appointed: September 2012
School type: Independent Girls' Day
Member of: GSA, GBA, ISC
Age range of pupils: 4–18
No. of pupils enrolled as at 1.9.12: 470
Sixth Form: 70
Fees per annum as at 1.9.12: Day: £13,350–£15,300
Average size of class: 12 (GCSE) and 6 (Sixth Form)
Religious denomination: Church of England

Academic and pastoral

Girls throughout the school follow a strong academic curriculum including a compulsory modern language, Latin, separate sciences and drama. At GCSE three subjects are added to a core of six or seven subjects and in the sixth form four ASs leading to three or four A levels is the norm. On leaving school all girls proceed to higher education, sometimes following a gap-year. Destinations include art or music colleges, Oxford, Cambridge and other traditional UK universities as well as newer universities in the UK or abroad. Consistently high A level results: in 2011 85% of all A level grades achieved were A*/A/B. The recent ISI inspection report noted: 'the pupils' attitudes to learning are excellent.' Girls are known as individuals and encouraged and supported in a happy and purposeful environment.

Entry requirements

Entry at 4+ is by means of a school-based assessment and at 11+ there are written tests in English and mathematics, and a further half-day school assessment including an interview. A few girls are accepted into the sixth form each year and into other years as vacancies occur.

Examinations offered

GCSE subjects offered: art, classical civilisation, English, English literature, French, German, geography, Greek, history, drama, Latin, mathematics, music, PE, religious studies, Spanish, physics, chemistry and biology. Additional subjects at A level include history of art, economics and psychology.

Extracurricular

The extensive extracurricular programme, comprising music, drama, art and sport, has been further strengthened by Carmel Hall, the new performing arts centre. The ISI report noted: 'Outstanding achievements are seen in many extracurricular pursuits.' Charitable activities are strongly encouraged and girls undertake ambitious projects that not only raise thousands of pounds, but also develop leadership and team working skills. Duke of Edinburgh's Award Scheme is also popular. Ballet, drama and instrumental lessons are popular and all girls have numerous opportunities to go on day and residential trips at home and abroad.

Scholarships and bursaries

Academic scholarships and music scholarships are available at Year 7 and sixth form. Entry bursaries up to 100% of fees.

Francis Holland School Charitable Trust exists to provide high quality education for girls and religious instruction in accordance with the principles of the Church of England. Registered charity No. 312745.

Hawkesdown House School Kensington

(Founded 2001)

27 Edge Street, Kensington, London W8 7PN
Tel: 020 7727 9090   Email: admin@hawkesdown.co.uk
Fax: 020 7727 9988   Website: www.hawkesdown.co.uk

HAWKESDOWN HOUSE SCHOOL

Head: Mrs C Bourne MA(Cantab)
Appointed: January 2010
School type: Boys' Independent Pre-Prep Day
Age range of pupils: 3–8
No. of pupils enrolled as at 1.9.12: 140
Fees per annum as at 1.9.12: Day: £12,825–£14,685
Average size of class: 15-18
Teacher/pupil ratio: 1:8
Religious denomination: Non-denominational;
Christian ethos

Hawkesdown House in an independent school for boys from the ages of three to eight. The school was the first free standing pre-preparatory school to be elected to IAPS (Independent Association of Preparatory Schools) and it has continued to remain in IAPS under the leadership of a new Head, Mrs Claire Bourne. Early literacy and numeracy are of prime importance and the traditional academic subjects form the core curriculum. A balanced

education helps all aspects of learning and a wide range of interests is encouraged. The school finds and fosters individual talents in each pupil. Boys are prepared for entry at eight to the main London and other preparatory schools. The Head places the greatest importance on matching boys happily and successfully to potential schools and spends time with parents ensuring that the transition is smooth and free of stress.

Sound and thorough early education is important for success, and also for self-confidence. The thoughtful and thorough teaching and care at Hawkesdown House ensures high academic standards and promotes initiative, kindness and courtesy. Hawkesdown is a school with fun and laughter, where boys develop their own personalities together with a sense of personal responsibility.

The school provides an excellent traditional education, with the benefits of modern technology, in a safe, happy and caring atmosphere. Many of the boys coming to the school live within walking distance and the school is an important part of the Kensington community.

There are clear expectations and the boys are encouraged by positive motivation and by the recognition and praise of their achievements, progress and effort. Individual attention and pastoral care for each of the boys is of great importance.

Hawkesdown House has a fine building in Edge Street, off Kensington Church Street.

Parents who would like further information, or to visit the school and meet the Head, should contact the School Office for a prospectus or an appointment.

Highgate School

(Founded 1565)

North Road, Highgate, London N6 4AY
Tel: 020 8340 1524   Email: office@highgateschool.org.uk
Fax: 020 8340 7674   Website: www.highgateschool.org.uk

Head Master: Mr A S Pettitt MA
Appointed: September 2006
School type: Coeducational Day
Member of: HMC, ISC
Age range of pupils: 3–18
No. of pupils enrolled as at 1.9.12: 1492
Boys: 827 Girls: 665 Sixth Form: 305
Fees per annum as at 1.9.12: Day: £14,565–£16,815
Average size of class: 8-22
Teacher/pupil ratio: 1:8
Religious denomination: Church of England

Curriculum
GCSE, AS and A2 levels. 18 GCSE subjects offered, 24 at AS and A2 level.

Vocational
Work experience available.

Computing facilities
Extensive Pentium PC network, computer-aided design and desktop publishing.

Languages
French, German, Mandarin, Russian, Spanish, Latin and ancient Greek at GCSE and A level.

Entry requirements
Total age range 3 to 18. Senior department 11-18. Main entry at 7, 11, 13 and 16. Interview and own exam used at 7, 11 and 13. Sixth form entry by interview (A grades preferred in AS level subjects). Scholarships and bursaries available.

Sir Roger Cholmeley's School at Highgate is a registered charity that exists to provide excellent education. (Registered No. 312765)

HOUSE SCHOOLS GROUP

Bassett House School	**Orchard House School**	**Prospect House School**
Kensington	Chiswick	Putney/Wandsworth

Bassett House School
60 Bassett Road, London W10 6JP
Tel 020 8969 0313, info@bassetths.org.uk
www.bassetths.org.uk

Orchard House School
16 Newton Grove, Bedford Park, London W4 1LB
Tel 020 8742 8544, info@orchardhs.org.uk
www.orchardhs.org.uk

Prospect House School
75 Putney Hill, London SW15 3NT
Tel 020 8780 0456, info@prospecths.org.uk
www.prospecths.org.uk

Bassett House in Kensington, **Orchard House** in Chiswick and **Prospect House** in Putney are prep schools for children aged three and above. All are member schools of the prestigious IAPS association for prep schools and each participates in the Early Years Grant scheme, which reduces fees charged for children aged under five years old. All three schools are coeducational to age 11 when the children sit competitive entrance exams for their senior schools (although some children occasionally sit entrance exams to other schools at age seven or eight).

The schools are non-selective for younger children, yet the academic expectations are high and the achievement distinguished. We believe this is for two principal reasons. First, we provide at each of our schools a nurturing, positive and happy yet structured environment. We know that happiness and success go hand in hand and we celebrate success at every level and in every sphere of school life, be it in academic work, sport, music or the arts. Secondly we have a low pupil-to-teacher ratio and an abundance of resources. Together these bring out the best in each and every child.

Examination results both at age eight and for senior schools have consistently been excellent: the schools are proud of their hard-won and long-lasting reputations.

Parents usually register their children early to secure places in each school's nursery or reception classes but vacancies in other year groups arise from time to time. If you wish to consider one of these schools for your child, we strongly encourage you to visit us. Please call the school secretary of the relevant school, who will be happy to arrange for you to visit the school and see it in action. In addition, there are occasional open days which give an even greater opportunity to speak to our strongest supporters, namely the children!

Leiths School of Food & Wine

(Founded 1975)

16-20 Wendell Road, Shepherd's Bush, London W12 9RT
Tel: 020 8749 6400   Email: info@leiths.com
Website: www.leiths.com

Managing Director: Camilla Schneideman
School type: Coeducational Day
Age range of pupils: 17–99
No. of pupils enrolled as at 1.9.12: 96
Fees per annum as at 1.9.12:
Essential Certificate: £3,035
Two Term Diploma: £15,250
Three Term Diploma: £19,850
Average size of class: 16
Teacher/pupil ratio: 1:8

Leiths School of Food and Wine is a leading London cookery school for professional and amateur cooks. Established by Prue Leith and Caroline Waldegrave in 1975, Leiths' culinary qualifications are highly regarded in the food industry, with graduates going on to work in Michelin-starred kitchens, star in cooking shows and work for top food magazines. If you have a keen interest in cooking and want to learn an essential skill that will serve you for life, Leiths runs a four-week Essential Certificate each year, as well as a ten-week course in September. Both courses are exam based certificate courses that include a food hygiene certificate as well as offering budgeting, healthy eating and menu planning advice and are designed to build your cookery skills and confidence. Leiths List, our agency for cooks, can help place you in a suitable job once qualified. Leiths also run one week cookery classes throughout the year that are ideal for university survival, teaching you to cook delicious simple food on any budget. Whether you are an aspiring professional or enthusiastic amateur, you will leave Leiths armed with the essential skills and confidence necessary to be a culinary success.

Contact Leiths for a prospectus now on +44 (0) 20 8749 6400 or view all our courses at www.leiths.com alternatively for any other questions please email us info@leiths.com

LYNDHURST HOUSE SCHOOL

IAPS Preparatory School for boys 4 to 13.
Main entry at 4 plus and 7 plus,
other places subject to availability

*A small, friendly, non-denominational school in a quiet
Hampstead side street. Lyndhurst provides first-rate all
round education and a happy environment in which to grow.*

Open Mornings

Come to one of our open
mornings held once a term
9.30 to 11.00am.

The next ones are:
Wednesday 17th October 2012
Wednesday 13th February 2013
Wednesday 22nd May 2013

Call 020 7435 4936

for further details or
visit our website
www.lyndhursthouse.co.uk
Lyndhurst House School
24 Lyndhurst Gardens
London NW3 5NW
pmg@lyndhursthouse.co.uk

Parkgate House School

(Founded 1987)

80 Clapham Common North Side, London SW4 9SD
Tel: 020 7350 2461   Email: admissions@parkgate-school.co.uk
Fax: 020 7738 1633   Website: www.parkgate-school.co.uk

Principal: Miss C M Shanley
School type: Coeducational Day
Age range of pupils: 2–11 years
No. of pupils enrolled as at 7.1.12: 243
Fees per annum as at 7.1.12: Day: £4200–£11,550
Religious denomination: Non-denominational

Parkgate House School is an independent school educating over 200 children aged from 2 to 11 years. Residing in a historic Georgian Grade II listed building overlooking Clapham Common, the school is supported by an impressive staff of over 40 teaching professionals. Children receive focused attention in one of three specialised areas: the Montessori Nursery for 2 to 4 year olds; the Pre-Preparatory Department for those aged 4 to 7 and the Preparatory Department for the 7 to 11 age range. At any age, children enjoy an expansive, high quality curriculum, which is further enhanced by an established after school programme including choir, IT, drama, French, sport and horse riding. A recent Ofsted report praised Parkgate House: 'The quality of the curriculum provided by Parkgate House School is outstanding for pupils of all ages.

Pupils thrive as they move through the school.'

Parkgate House School believes that happy, confident children will realise their full potential. The school has high academic expectations of its pupils and is extremely proud of its impressive record of academic success over the years. Pupils are fully prepared for entry into leading senior schools in the London area and beyond. The school has an established record of excellent 11+ examination results where first choice senior school places are achieved, and where art, music and academic scholarships are annually awarded from top London day schools and country boarding schools.

Parkgate House School celebrates success at every level and in every sphere of school life, be it academic, sport, music or the arts. Parents' assemblies provide the school with an excellent opportunity for this, as do annual music recitals, art exhibitions, award ceremonies and drama productions.

For all these reasons you will find Parkgate House a very special and unique school, providing your child with the very best education has to offer.

SINCLAIR HOUSE SCHOOL

*Montessori Nursery and Preparatory
School for Boys and Girls from 2-11 years*

- Small School
- Small Classes
- Academic Excellence
- Catholic Ethos
- French CNED Curriculum
- Extra Curricular Activities

159 Munster Road, Fulham, London SW6 6DA
Tel: 020 7736 9182
www.sinclairhouseschool.co.uk
Email: info@sinclairhouseschool.co.uk
Principal: Mrs Carlotta TM O'Sullivan

St Augustine's Priory

(Founded 1634)

Hillcrest Road, Ealing, London W5 2JL
Tel: 020 8997 2022   Email: registrar@staugustinespriory.org.uk
Fax: 020 8810 6501   Website: www.saintaugustinespriory.org.uk

Headteacher: Mrs Sarah Raffray MA
Appointed: September 2012
School type: Girls' Independent Day School
(Boys accepted in the Nursery)
Age range of pupils: 3–18
No. of pupils enrolled as at 1.9.12: 494
Fees per annum as at 1.9.12: Day: £8250–£11,760
Average size of class: 29 (maximum in class 24)24
Teacher/pupil ratio: 1:12.2
Religious denomination: Catholic, all faiths welcome

'A school out of the ordinary'

Founded in 1634 St Augustine's Priory is both one of the oldest established girls' schools in the country, and also a truly vibrant, dynamic and modern community.

A rare luxury for a London School, St Augustine's is set in 13 acres of beautiful grounds. High on a hill, our windows afford impressive views across London, and both literally and figuratively keep us outward-looking.

St Augustine's offers an exciting range of activities which complement study and add colour and fulfilment to lives. Academic achievement is one part of our success, but we are committed to developing every individual's all-round potential.

Our purpose built Nursery is open to both girls and boys. The Early Years Department believe that the child is at the centre of the learning process. Their interests and experiences are valued and acknowledged as a starting point for learning.

Our Prep and Junior Departments offer girls a stimulating, varied and challenging curriculum, and teachers invest considerable time in knowing their pupils well and discovering the unique talents of each individual.

We offer a wide range of GCSE courses, and girls can study almost any combination of the 23 subjects available at A level. Sixth form tutors work closely with them to assist with university and course selection, Oxbridge applications, and prepare them to be successful in whatever they choose to do.

We are proud of our record of academic success across the whole curriculum and are committed to high standards. The GCSE pass rate with 5 grades A* to C and the A Level pass rate are both currently 100%. Our experience is that if the bar is set high, our girls rise to the challenge. We teach girls that there are no limitations, save those which we impose upon ourselves.

St Mary's School Hampstead

(Founded 1926)

47 Fitzjohn's Avenue, Hampstead, London NW3 6PG
Tel: 020 7435 1868   Email: enquiries@stmh.co.uk
Fax: 020 7794 7922   Website: www.stmh.co.uk

ST MARY'S SCHOOL HAMPSTEAD

Head: Miss Angela Rawlinson BA, MA(1st Class Honours), DipTchng, NPQH
Appointed: April 2004
School type: Coeducational Day
Member of: IAPS, ISC, AGBIS, CISC, ISBA
Age range of pupils:
Boys: 2 years 9 months–7 years
Girls: 2 years 9 months–11 years
No. of pupils enrolled as at 1.5.12: 300
Boys: 17 Girls: 283
Fees per annum as at 1.9.12: Day: £6312–£11,700
Average size of class: 18
Teacher/pupil ratio: 1:9.5
Religious denomination: Roman Catholic

We have a thriving nursery. The boys are prepared for transference to popular London boys preparatory schools. The girls are prepared for the Common Entrance and the entrance examinations for the London senior schools at the age of 11 years.

Pupils enjoy a broad curriculum and also benefit from a wider range of activities that are seen as essential to the rounded development of a healthy child. Importance is attached to physical education, drama and the arts. Extra curriculum classes include Mandarin, Italian, Spanish, ballet, violin, recorder, flute and piano. School trips abroad are arranged for older children.

The school seeks to provide an opportunity for all children to receive the highest standard of Catholic education. Bursaries are available to provide assistance towards fees and other costs (100%+). Contact the Bursar for further information and an application pack: charlotte.hall@stmh.co.uk.

This Roman Catholic school is a registered charity (No. 1006411) that exists to provide a high standard of preparatory education for girls and boys, and is managed by a majority of lay trustees and governors.

St Paul's Cathedral School

(Founded 12th Century or earlier)

2 New Change, London EC4M 9AD
Tel: 020 7248 5156   Email: admissions@spcs.london.sch.uk
Fax: 020 7329 6568   Website: www.spcslondon.com

Headmaster: Mr Neil Chippington MA, FRCO
Appointed: September 2009
School type: Coeducational Pre-Prep, Day Prep &
Boarding Choir School
Boarders from 7
Member of: IAPS, CSA
Age range of pupils: 4–13
No. of pupils enrolled as at 1.4.12: 250
Boys: 163 Girls: 87
No. of boarders: 33
Fees per annum as at 1.4.12: Day: £11,550–£12,435
Boarding: £7194
Average size of class: 15-20
Teacher/pupil ratio: 1:10
Religious denomination: Church of England,
admits pupils of all faiths

Curriculum

A broad curriculum prepares all pupils for 11+ and
13+ examinations including scholarship and Common
Entrance examinations. There is a strong musical
tradition and choristers' Cathedral choral training is
outstanding. A wide variety of games is offered.

Entry requirements

Entry at 4+ and 7+ years: Pre-prep and day pupils
interview and short test; Choristers voice trials and
tests in October, February and May for boys between
6½-8½ years. Further information from the school.

*St Paul's Cathedral School is a registered charity (No.
312718), which exists to provide education for the
choristers of St Paul's Cathedral and for children living in
the local area.*

The Lloyd Williamson School

(Founded 2000)

12 Telford Road, London W10 5SH
Tel: 020 8962 0345   Email: admin@lws.org.uk
Fax: 020 8962 0345   Website: www.lws.org.uk

Co-Principals: Lucy Meyer & Aaron Williams
Appointed: April 2000 & Sept 2006
School type: Coeducational Day
Age range of pupils: 6 months–14 years
Fees per annum as at 1.9.12: Day: £10,440
Average size of class: 12-16
Teacher/pupil ratio: 1:12

Over the past 12 years, the Lloyd Williamson School has built an excellent reputation for being a school with high academic standards, personalised learning for individual children and a friendly, happy environment in which to learn. We foster initiative and a love for learning. 'Outstanding' (Ofsted).

We are pleased to offer parents important extras:

- Breakfast and after-school club at NO extra cost (the school and nurseries are open 7.30am – 6.00pm).

- Holiday clubs (we are open 50 weeks of the year).

- Small classes (maximum of 16).

- Competitive fees.

- Home-cooked meals freshly prepared every day by our in-house chefs.

We boast an outstanding playground with excellent facilities, a homely atmosphere with school pets, and dedicated teachers who support the children to be focused, positive and enthusiastic.

'Throughout the school, relationships between staff and children are excellent, which gives the pupils security and confidence to succeed.' (Ofsted)

In the words of our children:

"I'm really happy here – the teachers really listen and if I get stuck they help!"

"I really like the sports; we have a great football team!"

"There is always someone who listens to me."

"I like the way the big children look after the little children."

And the parents:

"You always know a Lloyd Williamson child – they're so polite!"

"I think the school is, beyond doubt, the best I could wish for."

"The best-kept secret in London!"

To visit the school or nurseries, please contact the school administrator, Emma Cole on: 020 8962 0345.

The Villa Pre-Preparatory School & Nursery

54 Lyndhurst Grove, Peckham, London SE15 5AH
Tel: 020 7703 6216   Email: enquiries@thevillaschoolandnursery.com
Website: www.thevillaschoolandnursery.com

Head Teacher: Lisa Mason-Jones MA, BA(Hons), Dip TTC
Appointed: September 2012
Proprietor: Dr Ivan Stoyanov
Nursery Manager: Amy Wan BSc
School type: Nursery & Pre-prep day school
Age range of pupils: 2–7
No. of pupils enrolled as at 1.9.12: 210
Fees per annum as at 1.9.12:
Nursery: £5,054–£15,106
Pre-prep: £8,820
Average size of class: 18

Situation

The Villa is a nursery and pre-preparatory school based in a handsome family house, set within a lovely walled garden filled with trees and shrubs. The Villa was designed as a Victorian family home and the building still reflects the essence of family rather than institution. Our dedicated team is passionate about the importance of excellent teaching as a foundation for high self-esteem and success. From when they start at the age of 2, children at The Villa flourish in the happy, caring environment we have created, and move on confidently to their new schools when they are 7.

Entry requirements

Nursery: children are admitted on a first-come-first-served basis.

School: children in our nursery are given priority. Those transferring from other nurseries are subject to an informal assessment and interview.

Curriculum

We believe that the individual nature of a child should be respected and that school life should be a positive, happy and stimulating experience. We know that it is important to encourage good manners, self-confidence and consideration for others and that fair and firm discipline is the basis for security within a child.

Classes are small and the children benefit from the high teacher-pupil ratio, which means that we have the freedom to extend the curriculum and study topics in greater depth. Children are very well prepared for the junior school that they move on to at the end of Year 2.

We appreciate that good communication between parent and teacher is vital to the success of everything we achieve and is a fundamental part of your child's school life. We hold regular parents' evenings and detailed reports are given annually.

The White House Preparatory School & Woodentops Kindergarten

(Founded 1985)

24 Thornton Road, London SW12 0LF
Tel: 020 8674 9514   Email: schooloffice@WhiteHouseSchool.com
Website: www.whitehouseschool.com

Head: Ms Mary McCahery
Appointed: 1999
School type: Coeducational Day
Age range of pupils: 2–11
No. of pupils enrolled as at 1.9.12:
Boys: 65 Girls: 65
Fees per annum as at 1.9.12: Day: £9800–£10,500
Average size of class: 16
Teacher/pupil ratio: 1:8

The White House Preparatory School and Woodentops Kindergarten is a coeducational school for pupils aged from 2½ to 11. The school is situated in Clapham, South London, and was established in 1985. The White House School is situated in a beautiful Grade II listed Victorian villa built in 1850 and designed by Thomas Cubitt. It provides a warm, friendly and inviting place for children to discover, learn and grow in confidence. A safe and stimulating environment, combined with high expectations of the children from our well qualified and dedicated staff, result in a positive learning journey for all the children. The White House stimulates and challenges pupils well beyond the boundaries of the National Curriculum. At their last inspection in 2011, Ofsted stated that "The White House Preparatory School and Woodentops Kindergarten provide an outstanding quality of education".

All classes have their own class teacher and they are also taught by specialist subject teachers in well-equipped classrooms. The class teacher is responsible for each child's academic and pastoral welfare. With an average class size of 16, each pupil is able to receive individual help and attention. The school also offers a variety of after school clubs, including a teatime homework club to 6pm.

Parents receive written reports twice a year and individual in depth meetings with form staff are arranged termly. There are two open mornings and an open evening for parents to view their children's work. In addition there are musical evenings, art exhibitions, sports, drama and charity events, which parents are encouraged to attend.

In 2011 the school expanded to include a day nursery for children between 6 months and 5 years. In addition to this recent expansion the school has heavily invested in new facilities over the last 12 months and is soon to unveil a new computer suite, music room, art, design and technology workshop as well as a small theatre which will support the already well-established drama department. Sport is also renowned at The White House with a dedicated head of girls' and head of boys' sports.

Should you require any further information please do not hesitate to call us on 020 8674 9514, or visit our website at www.whitehouseschool.com

Westminster School

(Founded 1560)

17 Dean's Yard, Westminster, London SW1P 3PF
Tel: 020 7963 1003   Email: registrar@westminster.org.uk
Fax: 020 7963 1002   Website: www.westminster.org.uk

Headmaster: Dr Stephen Spurr
Appointed: September 2005
School type: Boys' Boarding & Day
Girls Boarding & Day in Sixth Form
Member of: HMC
Age range of pupils:
Boys: 13–18
Girls: 16–18
No. of pupils enrolled as at 1.9.12: 750
Boys: 615 Girls: 135
No. of boarders: 185
Fees per annum as at 1.9.12: Day: £21,078–£23,538
Boarding: £31,350
Average size of class: 20

Situated next to Westminster Abbey and the Houses of Parliament, Westminster is the only ancient school in London that still occupies its original site. Academically it is one of the most successful schools in the country. In 2011, 55% of A level passes were A* (or Pre-U equivalent) and 98% of grades were A*/A/B. 90 leavers went to Oxford or Cambridge in 2010. The school also has strong traditions in music, drama and sport. Girls were first admitted as full members of the school in 1973. Westminster still operates as a boarding school with many members of staff living on site. For day pupils this means that they are members of a community that does not close down when the ordinary school day finishes – many will remain at school until well into the evening and can join the boarders for supper. Most Westminster boarders live in or close to London and return home at weekends but boarders from overseas are also welcome.

Westminster is an academic school in the 'liberal tradition'. It is an exciting place where individual and collective excellence are expected and promoted. Central to Westminster's ethos is the rapport between teachers and their pupils whether in the classroom or in tutorials. This inspires passion for the subject, conveys knowledge and develops skills of rational, independent thought.

For 13+ entry boys should ideally be registered by the time they enter Year 6 (age 10 or 11). During Year 6 they will be invited to Westminster for tests and interview. Boys who are offered conditional places must still qualify for entry at 13 by taking either Common Entrance or Westminster's scholarship examinations.

Entry at 16+ is by competitive examination. Candidates should register at the start of Year 11 (aged 15).

Boys may enter Westminster Under School at 7+, 8+ or 11+. For information please email: under.school@westminster.org.uk

or telephone: 020 7821 5788.

Westminster School is a registered charity (No. 312728) and a public boarding school for young persons.

Westminster Tutors

(Founded 1934)

86 Old Brompton Road, South Kensington, London SW7 3LQ
Tel: 020 7584 1288   Email: info@westminstertutors.co.uk
Fax: 020 7584 2637   Website: www.westminstertutors.co.uk

Principal: Virginia Maguire BA, MLitt
School type: Coeducational Day
Age range of pupils: 14–mature
No. of pupils enrolled as at 1.9.12:
Boys: 25 Girls: 25 Sixth Form: 40
Fees per annum as at 1.9.12: Day: £6300–£20,400
Average size of class: 2
Teacher/pupil ratio: 1:1

Established in 1934, Westminster Tutors has been providing top-flight tuition for over 75 years. We are a small coeducational college with a friendly, informal atmosphere and excellent examination results in a wide range of subjects. The small size of the teaching groups allows a great deal of attention to be paid to the individual needs of students, helping them to achieve their full potential. Each student has a personal tutor who monitors academic progress and general wellbeing, and all students receive personal higher education and career guidance from the Principal. We keep in close contact with parents and send regular reports on each student's progress and achievements. Students have access at all times to computing facilities, including the use of the internet, and are encouraged to develop their IT skills wherever possible. Both traditional and modern methods of research and study are encouraged.

Westminster Tutors specialises in A level courses taken over one or two years or, for intensive re-take courses, as little as three months. We also offer revision courses and private tuition throughout the year. Students do not always require five GCSE passes to be accepted onto our A level courses; nonetheless, 70% of the grades achieved by recent A level students have been A* to B grade. Nearly all our students go on to higher education, and we have been preparing students for Oxford and Cambridge entrance for over 75 years with outstanding success. We also provide specialist tuition for all university admissions tests.

All our tutors have excellent degrees from top universities, and many are graduates from Oxford and Cambridge. Our links with these, and many other universities, ensure that our students are best placed to make strong applications to higher education.

Westminster Tutors is in attractive premises on Old Brompton Road, close to South Kensington underground station and Hyde Park.

North-East

Durham School

(Founded 1414)

Durham DH1 4SZ
Tel: 0191 386 4783   Email: d.woodlands@durhamschool.co.uk
Fax: 0191 383 1025   Website: www.durhamschool.co.uk

Headmaster: Mr Martin George
Appointed: April 2009
School type: Coeducational Day & Boarding
Age range of pupils: 3–18
No. of pupils enrolled as at 1.9.12: 590
Boys: 416 Girls: 174 Sixth Form: 143
No. of boarders: 119 (senior school)
Fees per annum as at 1.9.12: Day: £6225–£15,225
Weekly Boarding: £17,175–£20,985
Boarding: £19,497–£23,097
Overseas Boarders (Years 7-13): £20,400–£24,285
(The overseas boarding fee includes Saturday
School where the English language standard is
below: that level normally required for that point
of entry)
Average size of class: 15-20
Teacher/pupil ratio: 1:10
Religious denomination: Church of England

Motto: *Floriat Dunelmia* (Let Durham Flourish)

Confidence for Life
One of the oldest schools in Britain, Durham School
is an independent day and boarding school offering a
complete education for boys and girls from the age of
3-18. It consists of Bow, our own day preparatory
school from 3-11, and the senior school, which offers
both boarding and day education from 11-18.
Founded in 1414, we moved to our present site in
1844, a site that today provides our pupils with the

opportunity for a first class, modern education in a
uniquely beautiful and rural setting in the heart of
this historic and rapidly developing university city.

*"At Durham School we see children from the ages of
three to 18 thriving on all fronts; academic, social,
physical, personal and moral. For this to be possible we
need to have first rate staff and facilities, underpinned by
pervasive values of compassion, endeavour, aspiration
and respect. For nearly 600 years Durham School has
helped generations to take their place in the world
equipped with the knowledge, skills, confidence and
principles to succeed. This remains our aim. We provide
a developing blend of tradition and progress, of family
values and a modern outlook, of balanced educational
aims, of high standards and high expectations, of care and
compassion.*

*"Above all Durham School is a family and from your
very first contact it is our intention to make you feel part
of our community. Our pupils are happy pupils, that is
why they succeed. We want our parents to be happy
parents and to be part of the pupils' success. So please
come and see us to discover why a Durham School
education really is Confidence For Life."*

Mr Martin George
Headmaster

*Durham School is a registered charity (No. 1023407),
which exists to advance the education of children and
young people.*

North-West

Abbey Gate College

(Founded 1977)

Saighton Grange, Saighton, Chester, Cheshire CH3 6EN
Tel: 01244 332077   Email: admin@abbeygatecollege.co.uk
Fax: 01244 335510   Website: www.abbeygatecollege.co.uk

Head: Mrs Lynne M Horner
Appointed: September 2006
School type: Coeducational Day
Member of: SHMIS, AGBIS, ISA
Age range of pupils: 4–18
No. of pupils enrolled as at 15.5.12: 513
Sixth Form: 75
Fees per annum as at 1.9.12: Day: £7116–£10,404
Average size of class: Average 20
Teacher/pupil ratio: 1:15

Abbey Gate College is a well-established, coeducational school for pupils aged 4 to 18 on the outskirts of Chester. The college emphasises the importance of building self-esteem and a love of learning in a friendly and caring environment. The extracurricular programme provides opportunities for pupils to experience challenge and the pursuit of excellence. The music department is renowned for the quality of its choral singing, with strong links to Chester Cathedral. Drama, sport and the Duke of Edinburgh's Award Scheme are thriving and outdoor adventures and leadership courses help children to build confidence and teamwork.

Recent investment in facilities has been considerable at both senior and junior sites; including a new art suite, design and technology workshop, science laboratory, sixth form centre, learning support base and atrium at Aldford. Similarly there have been

positive developments in teaching and learning with increased ICT provision and individualised monitoring of each pupil's progress. These improvements, along with the dedication of the staff, have had a positive impact on academic performance, as shown by the strong results at GCSE and A level.

The idyllic village location of the junior department at Aldford boasts extensive playing fields, purpose-built shaded area and an ecology park. The juniors and infants have use of the extensive facilities at the senior school.

We value each and every child, whatever their age or ability; the potential in every pupil is nurtured and encouraged. Education is far greater than simply achieving super examination results; at Abbey Gate College the journey itself is of equal importance, providing a stimulating experience, widening opportunities and providing an education for life.

The students' enthusiasm and varying talents are guided and encouraged; when they go out into the community we are confident that they are sensible and mature young people.

Abbey Gate College is a successful and happy school, committed to maintaining traditional standards and high educational ideals and in the most recent inspection report (March 2010) ISI inspectors commended the high standards of teaching, learning and especially behaviour in the college:

'The college fully meets its aim to encourage students to achieve their personal ambitions in an atmosphere that is caring but challenging. The students' personal qualities are outstanding and fully supported within the college by the positive family type ambience. The community awareness is outstanding; relationships between staff and students themselves are outstanding and conducive to excellent behaviour.'

Abbey Gate College is a registered charity (No. 273586) to promote and provide for the advancement of education.

Bridgewater School
'Outstanding' inspection and excellent A level and GCSE results

(Founded 1950)

Drywood Hall, Worsley Road, Worsley, Manchester, Greater Manchester M28 2WQ
Tel: 0161 794 1463   Email: admin@bwslive.co.uk
Fax: 0161 794 3519   Website: www.bridgewater-school.co.uk

Head Teacher: Mrs J A T Nairn CertEd(Distinction)
School type: Coeducational Day
Age range of pupils: 3–18
No. of pupils enrolled as at 1.9.12: 467
Boys: 237 Girls: 230
Fees per annum as at 1.9.12: Day: £6750–£9000

Bridgewater School is a coeducational, independent day school for pupils aged between 3 and 18 years. Established as a boys' school in 1950 and having moved to its present, delightful, semi-rural setting soon afterwards, the school has since grown considerably – admitting girls and developing a sixth form. We draw pupils from the immediate locality, but also from a much wider area, well served as we are by the motorway network and by other major road links.

Bridgewater is by design not a large school. This enables us to provide small classes and high levels of attention to the needs of individual pupils. We seek to maximise education attainment all through a child's development, not least in the years of external examinations at GCSE and A level.

In addition to its academic goals, Bridgewater seeks to retain the intimate atmosphere it has had since its inception. We greatly value our capacity to offer provision across the full age range, from the nursery years to university entrance, for families wanting this continuity of individual attention for their children.

At the same time, however, pupils must look outward to the wider community and to the society in which they will live as adults. We see it as an integral part of Bridgewater's role to foster high standards of behaviour and self-discipline, as well as to develop an awareness of personal and social responsibility. Vital, too, are the many activities which take place outside the classroom – sport, music, drama clubs and societies, language exchange visits and outdoor activity breaks to name but a sample of the range available.

Entrusting your child's education to a school is a very big decision. We are mindful of our responsibility to justify a parent's decision to send their child to us, and of the need for that child's education to be a partnership between school and home. We aim, by the end of this partnership, to produce rounded, articulate young people who are well prepared for the challenges of adult and business life.

The school governors, staff and pupils share a sense of excitement about Bridgewater's future. The school has developed rapidly in recent years, with splendid new buildings and facilities and a considerable increase in pupil numbers. We have a commitment to continual development and improvement. If you have not yet visited us then may we recommend that you do so soon. We would be delighted to meet you and to show you how much Bridgewater School has to offer you and your child.

Sedbergh School

(Founded 1525)

Sedbergh, Cumbria LA10 5HG
Tel: 015396 20535
Fax: 015396 21301
Email: admissions@sedberghschool.org
Website: www.sedberghschool.org

SEDBERGH
SCHOOL

Headmaster: Mr A Fleck MA
Appointed: 2010
School type: Coeducational Boarding & Day
Member of: HMC, BSA, IAPS, AGBIS, ASCL, ISC
Age range of pupils: 4–18
No. of pupils enrolled as at 1.9.12: 550
Boys: 387 Girls: 163 Sixth Form: 209
No. of boarders: 470
Fees per annum as at 1.9.12:
Day: £6,774–£20,790
Weekly: £16,062–£17,940 (7-13 only)
Boarding: £16,695–£28,215
Average size of class: 16
Teacher/pupil ratio: 1:9
Religious denomination: Church of England

Sedbergh has faced up to the demands of the 21st century without losing its traditional values and ethos, and today has an excellent reputation for its ability to provide a dynamic and challenging educational environment. Virtually all of the boys and girls at the senior school are seven-day-a-week boarders in a House system providing pastoral care of the highest standard from a resident Housemaster/mistress, tutor and matron. Through living, eating and studying in one of the ten houses (seven boys, three girls), pupils develop a lifelong sense of pride and belonging.

Academic success is taken for granted with nearly 100% pass rates at A level and IGCSE, and the School has close links with several Oxbridge colleges. Most of the pupils leave to go on to the universities of their choice or to gap-year activities. Scholarships and awards are available (academic, music, art, design technology, sport, drama and all rounder). These are offered by examination in Lent term each year and Michaelmas term for sixth form entry. Means-tested bursaries are available for promising individuals who might not otherwise be able to consider the school.

Sedbergh retains its reputation as a formidable force on the sports field but, away from there, enormous opportunities exist for pupils interested in music and drama, art, design technology and the CCF. A school-wide programme of outdoor pursuits ensures everyone has the chance to enjoy the environment that is unique to the school.

Entry requirements are by Common Entrance examination or scholarship/award at 13+, and at 16+ subject to a minimum of five GCSE passes and interview.

Located only ten minutes from the M6 (junction 37) and just over one hour from Manchester Airport, the life-enhancing education offered at Sedbergh is readily accessible from other parts of the UK as well as further afield.

Sedbergh has its own coeducational junior school from ages 4 to 13. SJS offers day, flexi, weekly and full boarding.

Parents can visit Sedbergh School at any time by arrangement. There are formal open days each term at the junior school. Visit the website or telephone for further information.

Sedbergh School is a registered charity, which exists to provide high quality education for boys and girls. (No. 1080672)

Stonyhurst College

(Founded 1593)

Stonyhurst, Clitheroe, Lancashire BB7 9PZ
Tel: 01254 826345   Email: admissions@stonyhurst.ac.uk
Fax: 01254 827131   Website: www.stonyhurst.ac.uk

Headmaster: A Johnson BA
Appointed: 2006
School type: Coeducational Boarding & Day
Age range of pupils: 13–18
No. of pupils enrolled as at 1.9.12: 470
Sixth Form: 221
No. of boarders: 289
Fees per annum as at 1.9.12: Day: £6681–£15,915
Weekly Boarding: £17,289–£23,703
Boarding: £20,406–£28,443
Average size of class: 10-22
Teacher/pupil ratio: 1:8

Stonyhurst takes pupils from 3-18, starting from our pre-prep Hodder House, moving on to our prep school St Mary's Hall and completing their education at Stonyhurst College. We foster and celebrate the talents of each child, helping them to do their best in the extensive range of activities that we provide. Our achievements are confirmed by outstanding inspection reports in all areas of academic, pastoral and extracurricular education and these can be read on our website. Our academic results far outstrip the national average each year and we pride ourselves on the value we can add to child's educational achievements, helping them to improve on expectations time and time again. Children of all levels achieve more at Stonyhurst than they would have done had they not come to us. Pupils at the end of their time at Stonyhurst go on to top universities across the UK.

Rooted in our Jesuit ethos, Stonyhurst pupils develop lifelong values to become 'men and women for others', so that they can respond to where there is need and serve generously. This means that young people here take part in fundraising for several of our designated charities. Our older pupils are also involved in a programme that takes them out into the community as volunteers.

While at school young people can also take part in the many and varied activities on offer in our extracurricular programme, these include scuba diving, orienteering, dance, car maintenance, essay writing and golf on our own nine hole golf course. The all-round education offered at Stonyhurst is available to all pupils whether they board or are day pupils.

More details are available at www.stonyhurst.ac.uk or from the Admissions Office on 01254 827073/93, admissions@stonyhurst.ac.uk.

The Ryleys School

(Founded 1877)

Ryleys Lane, Alderley Edge, Cheshire SK9 7UY
Tel: 01625 583241   Email: ryleysoffice@btconnect.com
Fax: 01625 581900   Website: www.theryleys.com

Headmaster: Paul Berry BSc(Hons), PGCE, NPQH
Appointed: September 2012
School type: Coeducational Day
Age range of pupils: 3–13
No. of pupils enrolled as at 1.9.12: 261
Boys: 186 Girls: 75
Fees per annum as at 1.9.12: Day: £8400–£9750
Average size of class: 17
Teacher/pupil ratio: 1:13

The Ryleys has developed a reputation as one of the best independent preparatory schools in Cheshire, with places at the school being much sought after. And with nine out of ten new registrations coming as a result of recommendations, what better endorsement of a school's credentials could you wish for?

Starting at age 3, the extremely popular nursery gently prepares its pupils for the start of their educational journey, and provides the boys and girls with the advantage of familiarity with the school when they come to take the next step on to formal education.

As the children move through the school, the small class sizes and subject specialist teaching ensures that each and every child receives the individual attention, motivation and encouragement necessary to fulfil their potential.

The Ryleys provides so much more than just an academic education; it provides unrivalled opportunities to discover and nurture talents outside of the classroom, including music, sport, art and drama.

By the time they leave The Ryleys, pupils are equipped with the skills, character and confidence to see them achieve their future goals. All leavers go on to achieve places at highly regarded day and boarding schools of their choice, with many winning prestigious music, sports or academic scholarships.

You don't just choose your child's school. You choose their future.

Tower College

(Founded 1948)

Mill Lane, Rainhill, Prescot, Merseyside L35 6NE
Tel: 0151 426 4333   Email: missoxley@towercollege.com
Fax: 0151 426 3338   Website: www.towercollege.com

Principal: Miss R J Oxley NNEB, RSH
Appointed: 1993
School type: Coeducational Day
Age range of pupils: 3–16
No. of pupils enrolled as at 1.9.12: 486
Boys: 234 Girls: 252
Fees per annum as at 1.9.12: Day: £5013–£5895
Average size of class: 20
Teacher/pupil ratio: 1:17

Tower College is a family run, coeducational day school which provides an academic course and the highest level of care for 490 boys and girls of three to sixteen. The emphasis is on high standards of education and care, in a Christian environment. Pupils of all faiths, or none, are welcomed and all attend the Bible-based religious studies lessons and morning assemblies. All parents welcome the school's values of tolerance, caring and respect.

The school enjoy the benefits of their membership of the Independent Schools Association, which gives opportunities for competition between schools in sport, music, drama, essay writing and art. The school is very proud of its excellent record of success in all areas!

The Independent Schools Inspectorate visit every three years to inspect all aspects of school life – from exam results to health and safety, and everything in between. Inspection reports can be found at www.towercollege.com and www.isi.net

Coaches bring pupils from Ormskirk, Rainford, St Helens, Culcheth, Warrington, Runcorn, Widnes, the Wirral, Liverpool, Huyton, Knowsley and Prescot. There is a Breakfast Club for those who need to arrive early, and a 'Twilight Zone' after-school facility where pupils can work, rest or play after having refreshments, for parents' convenience.

The pupils enjoy extracurricular activities such as dance, salsasize, science clubs, theatre trips, debating and drama societies, music and sports as well as the Duke of Edinburgh Scheme which provides a variety of outdoor pursuits and voluntary activities. The

'House' system gives opportunity for competition in all areas of school which encourages the pupils to strive to be the best and to nurture their talents.

Throughout the school the pupils are nurtured and encouraged by a team of dedicated, well-motivated staff. There is a great rapport between all departments from nursery to fifth form and all of the Staff are delighted when, every year, excellent GCSE results are received. Last year the pupils passed an average of 10.9 subjects per pupil and 50% of all examinations taken were passed at A* or A. We look forward to more successes this year. Although it is very rewarding to be ranked so highly in terms of examination success, Tower College is more proud of the character and confidence of the caring young adults who have gained so much from a Tower College education.

On 2nd April 2012, the school opened Tower Tots, an Early Years Provision for 25 children aged three months to three years. It is already thriving, and the babies and toddlers are enjoying their first experiences of nursery life. The babies are a delight and even the oldest senior pupils enjoy seeing them on their walks around the school gardens!

Tower Tots, EY437686 Tel: 0151 289 2674, www.towertots.com

South-East

Burgess Hill School for Girls

(Founded 1906)

Keymer Road, Burgess Hill, West Sussex RH15 0EG
Tel: 01444 241050   Email: registrar@burgesshill-school.com
Fax: 01444 870314   Website: www.burgesshill-school.com

Headmistress: Mrs Ann Aughwane BSc, CertEd, NPQH
Appointed: 2006
School type: Girls' Day & Boarding
Boarders from 11 years
Member of: GSA, AGBIS
Age range of pupils:
Boys: 2½–4
Girls: 2½–18
No. of pupils enrolled as at 1.9.12: 640
Sixth Form: 65
No. of boarders: 56
Fees per annum as at 1.9.12: Day: £6750–£14,250
Boarding: £25,200
Average size of class: Max 20
Teacher/pupil ratio: 1:17
Religious denomination: Inter-denominational

Burgess Hill School for Girls is an independent day and boarding school for girls aged between 2½ and 18 years. Boarding is offered from the age of 11 years. Boys are accepted in the Nursery.

Burgess Hill School is small enough that children are known as individuals yet large enough to offer breadth, choice and opportunity. The School has high expectations of all its pupils and upholds the best of traditions. Girls are able to strive for excellence wherever their talents lie and the mix of ages, working together on the same site, gives the School a special character. The aim of the School is to provide each girl with the opportunity to realise her potential in every way and the focus is firmly on girls and the way they learn.

The School stands in 14 acres of beautiful grounds close to the centre of Burgess Hill town. The School is a five minute walk from Burgess Hill railway station, which is on the mainline from London to Brighton. Coaches and minibuses also collect girls from outlying areas of East and West Sussex.

Students are encouraged to pursue an active and healthy life with a good balance between work and enrichment. Extracurricular activities cater for all ages and abilities in sports, music, arts and specialist subjects including sailing, golf, horse riding and chess. There are opportunities to go on educational and residential trips and the Duke of Edinburgh Awards are popular. Girls also benefit from the School's links with the local community and they take part in local festivals, competitive events and workshops with other schools. In the Senior School, careers conferences are held with national companies and inspirational speakers to encourage the girls to plan for their futures. In the Sixth Form students take Life Skills lessons and have a networking dinner to build their interpersonal skills and establish key contacts for work experience or careers advice.

Burgess Hill School has three well presented and homely boarding houses. They are ideal for those who live too far away to travel on a daily basis and for international students who are looking for an excellent English education. The boarding community is a caring and supportive extended family unit where experienced housemistresses and

staff know and understand the girls. Extensive refurbishment of the boarding houses took place in 2011. The rooms and common rooms are spacious, light and pleasantly furnished.

The curriculum offers a wide choice of subjects at GCSE and A level. The majority of students take nine GCSEs and go on to study A level qualifications before progressing on to university. The vast majority of the girls go on to universities across the UK, including Exeter, London, Oxford, Cambridge, Cardiff and St Andrews.

Last summer (2011) the school celebrated another successful year of GCSE results. All students passed and over 97% achieved grades A* to C. All students achieved at least five A* to C grades including mathematics and English. The School also celebrated an excellent set of A level results with 84.2% of all A level results being awarded A* to B grades. Almost two thirds of the year group gained A* to B in all their subjects and a third of the girls gained at least one A*.

Each individual at Burgess Hill School is encouraged to develop her skills to become confident and independent young women. Burgess Hill School consistently 'adds value' to students' academic results by focusing on each individual student, keeping class sizes small, understanding how girls learn and investing in good resources and high quality teaching. In 2011 Burgess Hill School was ranked 5th out of 632 independent and maintained schools in the UK for 'value added' performance by the Centre for Educational Monitoring at University of Durham.

Burgess Hill School for Girls' fees are competitive. Entry to the Junior and Senior School is by the school's own examination. Entry to the infants is by informal activity sessions. Scholarships are awarded each year for academic and/or musical excellence for Years 3, 4, 7, 9 and Lower Sixth. Creative scholarships (including Drama, Sport and Art) are also awarded into Year 9 and Lower Sixth. Parents and students may visit the school by making an appointment with the Head of Admissions or attending the school's Open Days which are held in September, November, March and May.

For more information about Burgess Hill School for Girls and for a copy of the school prospectus, please contact the Head of Admissions by telephone on 01444 241050 or by email at registrar@burgesshill-school.com.

Bradfield College

(Founded 1850)

Bradfield, Reading RG7 6AU
Tel: 0118 964 4500   Email: admissions@bradfieldcollege.org.uk
Fax: 0118 964 4513   Website: www.bradfieldcollege.org.uk

Headmaster: Mr Simon Henderson
Appointed: September 2011
School type: Coeducational Boarding
Age range of pupils: 13–18
No. of pupils enrolled as at 1.4.12: 734
Boys: 483 Girls: 251 Sixth Form: 299
No. of boarders: 619
Fees per annum as at 1.9.12: Day: £24,708
Boarding: £30,885
Average size of class: Max 20
Teacher/pupil ratio: 1:9

A leading coeducational, independent boarding school, Bradfield College provides an outstanding all-round education so as to prepare young people for success in a fast-changing world. The College cares about the individual and prides itself in the warmth of a community in which pupils feel happy and valued. It fosters an environment of high expectations in which all pupils are encouraged to believe in themselves, to be inquisitive, to be resilient and to show ambition within and beyond the classroom. Its all-inclusive ethos embraces the extended 'Bradfield family', which includes pupils past and present and extensive links with the wider community.

The modern College combines values and attributes essential to 21st century life with those of its founder, Thomas Stevens, who established St Andrew's College in 1850. Alongside an excellent academic education, offering both A levels and IB at Sixth Form, all partake of the 'Bradfield experience', which permits each individual to find his or her special niche. The classroom atmosphere engenders a love of learning for its own sake; the participatory culture ensures that expert and enthusiast alike thrive within the broad spectrum of co-curricular activities.

Pastoral care is paramount; boys and girls move on to senior houses after Faulkner's, a coeducational house in which all spend their first year at the College. Each house has a dedicated team of staff and every pupil benefits from the care of a housemaster or housemistress, a personal tutor and a matron.

The superb facilities at Bradfield include modern teaching and learning environments within the beautiful brick-and-flint original buildings. There is a music school, sports complex with indoor swimming pool, a tennis centre and two floodlit all-weather pitches. Alongside these a new state-of-the-art science centre opened its doors to pupils and the local community in September 2010. Set in its own mediaeval village in 250 acres of beautiful Berkshire countryside the College enjoys exceptional playing fields, golf course and stunning views across the Pang valley. All this is within 40 minutes of Heathrow and an hour from central London.

Admission to the College is at both 13+ and into the large and vibrant Sixth Form. Scholarships, exhibitions and awards are available at both levels of entry.

Bradfield College, registered charity No. 309089, is a college for the careful education of boys and girls.

Churcher's College

(Founded 1722)

Petersfield, Hampshire GU31 4AS
Tel: 01730 263033   Email: enquiries@churcherscollege.com
Fax: 01730 231437   Website: www.churcherscollege.com

Headmaster: Mr Simon Williams MA, BSc
Appointed: September 2004
School type: Coeducational Day
Member of: HMC, SHMIS, AGBIS, ISBA
Age range of pupils: 4–18
No. of pupils enrolled as at 1.9.12: 1055
Boys: 606 Girls: 449 Sixth Form: 216
Fees per annum as at 1.9.12: Day: £7350–£11,550
Average size of class: 24
Teacher/pupil ratio: 1:12
Religious denomination: Non-denominational

Churcher's College is a leading HMC independent, coeducational day school that, within the foundation of a junior and senior school, nurtures the educational development of children from 4 to 18. The school seeks to give the widest range of experiences but also the opportunity to be the best. No education can hope to provide the answer to all the questions a person might face during their lifetime but, by developing the full academic, creative and sporting talents within the context of social awareness, the pupils at Churcher's are fully prepared for all they will face in the dynamic and challenging world we live in.

Excellent examination results are clearly important; the achievement of these forms a core element of a child's time at Churcher's College. Averaging around 76% A and B grades at A level puts Churcher's very much in the top echelons in the country.

What makes this school so exceptional is that the pupils achieve outstanding academic results whilst maintaining a very full involvement in a whole host of activities outside the classroom, including music, drama, sport, adventurous activities and expeditions to far flung places.

The classroom opportunities are matched by an extraordinary range outside: 140 students were involved in the Duke of Edinburgh's Award Scheme this year, 30 at gold level; 200 in a thriving, three section voluntary Combined Cadet Force;

expeditions to Machu Picchu, Mount Kilimanjaro, Nepal and Tibet, Vietnam and Cambodia, the Moroccan deserts and mountains of Turkey; unbeaten rugby and netball teams at a range of levels; pupils with starring roles in major West End musical productions; racing car successes at Goodwood; celebrated musicians, exhibited artists and many more exciting avenues to success.

There is a well-known saying that 'nothing succeeds like success'. This is something Churcher's likes to embrace. The breadth of involvement ensures that there is always one niche in which a pupil can really flourish, feeling the satisfaction and rewards of success and, as a consequence, the self-motivation to develop their skills in all areas.

This expands to a very active involvement in the community. The pupils generally raise over £25,000 per annum for a range of local, national and international charities.

All good schools will promise to maximise the potential of their pupils. Churcher's achieves that aim in a happy, well-disciplined and extremely caring community on a beautiful, spacious site overlooking the South Downs.

Churcher's College is a registered charity that exists to provide education for children. (No. 307320)

Eagle House School

(Founded 1820)

SUBLIMIORA PETAMUS

Sandhurst, Bracknell Forest GU47 8PH
Tel: 01344 772134   Email: info@eaglehouseschool.com
Fax: 01344 779039   Website: www.eaglehouseschool.com

Headmaster: Mr A P N Barnard BA(Hons), PGCE
Appointed: September 2006
School type: Coeducational Day & Boarding
Boarders from 7 years
Member of: IAPS
Age range of pupils: 3–13
No. of pupils enrolled as at 1.9.12: 360
Boys: 220 Girls: 140
No. of boarders: 65
Fees per annum as at 1.9.12: Day: £9300–£14,850
Boarding: £19,950
Average size of class: 16
Teacher/pupil ratio: 1:8

Eagle House is more than just a school, it is a way of life for all our pupils. In the classroom, on the sports field, in the music or drama halls, on part of our extensive activities programme or just having fun in the wonderful grounds that make up Eagle House, our boys and girls are living life to the full. We believe in a broad education for all our pupils and, as such, offer a huge range of opportunities for all.

Eagle House offers day and boarding for boys and girls aged 3 to 13. The school, located between Sandhurst and Crowthorne, is within easy reach of the M3 and M4 and is served by good rail services as well as being close to Heathrow and Gatwick airports. The school operates morning bus services from surrounding areas. The school has a proud history of producing successful pupils and dates back to 1820. Tradition is important and we are proud of our history but we also realise the need to be at the forefront of modern day education.

The high quality of our teaching and resources mean that all our children achieve to a high standard. A consistent record of academic success as well as frequent achievement in music, drama, art and sports show that we are helping to bring the best out of our boys and girls.

The Eagle House experience begins at aged 3 with our nursery, The Nest, and right from the start we believe in excellence. In a recent Ofsted nursery report our quality of teaching and care in The Nest and reception was given the highest praise. Into the pre-prep with reception and Years 1 and 2, and the learning experience and opportunities continue to help our children to give of their best. The prep school, starting with Year 3 and moving up to Year 8, encourages our boys and girls to grow mentally and physically and helps them to reach their potential in all they do. Our unique Golden Eagle Programme enables every child to develop life skills and take part in a superb range of activities.

The children who leave us in Year 8 are testament to the fact that Eagle House delivers. The school exists to provide a happy, well-balanced education for children and parents; children and staff believe passionately in achieving this goal.

Eagle House caters for all. In the 21st century our school is the right choice for success, happiness and opportunity. With excellent facilities and the flexibility to help with modern day living by offering late stay facilities and flexible boarding, can you afford not to take a look?

Eagle House is a registered charity (No. 309093) for the furtherance of education.

Eastbourne College

(Founded 1867)

Old Wish Road, Eastbourne, East Sussex BN21 4JX
Tel: 01323 452323   Email: admissions@eastbourne-college.co.uk
Fax: 01323 452354   Website: www.eastbourne-college.co.uk

Headmaster: Mr S P Davies MA
Appointed: 2005
School type: Co-educational Boarding & Day
Age range of pupils: 13–18
No. of pupils enrolled as at 1.9.11: 621
Boys: 355 Girls: 266 Sixth Form: 273
No. of boarders: 302
Fees per annum as at 1.9.11: Day: £17,985
Boarding: £27,315
Teacher/pupil ratio: 1:9

Eastbourne College is one of only two independent senior schools in the south-east delivering the full boarding experience, seven days a week. For example, every Sunday of term (other than exeat weekends) over 300 boarders enjoy brunch before participating in the wide range of activities on offer at weekends. The vast majority of boarders come from within 90 minutes of the College and the proportion from abroad is notably low.

In the report following the school's 2008 ISI inspection, the value of the extended day and full week for both boarders and day pupils alike was recognised and the college's distinctive co-curricular programme was identified as one of the outstanding features of the school: 'The school succeeds in providing a coherent and excellent co-educational boarding experience for boys and girls, boarders and day pupils. Eastbourne College is a happy and inspiring community that successfully emphasises the key values for which it stands.'

'By giving its pupils a coherent, full and challenging boarding education, Eastbourne College amply fulfils its principal aim. Its day pupils, as much as its boarders, make the most of all that the school offers.'

During 2010, the charities of Eastbourne College and St Andrew's School amalgamated under a single charity, guaranteeing the long-term future of top quality independent education for children aged two to 18 in Eastbourne and beyond. The two schools continue to operate independently with each benefiting from shared expertise and resources.

The Birley Centre, which was completed in September 2011, is one such resource. This initial phase of the College's exciting development programme has provided a first rate facility with an auditorium, exhibition space and a state-of-the-art home for the teaching, performance and recording of music. Completing the cultural quarter of Eastbourne, the Birley Centre is a valuable asset for the town itself.

Gordon's School

(Founded 1885)

West End, Woking, Surrey GU24 9PT
Tel: 01276 858084   Email: registrar@gordons.surrey.sch.uk
Fax: 01276 855335   Website: www.gordons.surrey.sch.uk

Head Teacher: Andrew Moss MEd
School type: Coeducational Boarding & Day
Boarders from 11
Age range of pupils: 11–18
No. of pupils enrolled as at 24.4.12:
Boys: 379 Girls: 348 Sixth Form: 160
Fees per annum as at 5.9.12:
Boarding: £13,083–£14,181
Average size of class: 18

Gordon's is a non-selective state boarding school catering for both boarders and day pupils and is regularly in the top 20 non-selective schools in Britain. As a state school, parents pay for boarding only.

Following a two day inspection of boarding, Ofsted inspectors have described Gordon's as 'outstanding' in all areas. Almost uniquely for any school, Ofsted made no recommendations for action.

Quotes from Ofsted inspections:

'Gordon's is an outstanding school in every respect.'

'The quality of care provided by the school for the pupils is exceptional.'

'Teaching and learning are outstanding.'

'The quality of the extracurricular programme goes beyond excellence.'

'Gordon's provides an outstanding level of care for the pupils who board there.'

'Pupils emerge from the school as articulate, pleasant, well-rounded and confident youngsters.'

At Gordon's, great importance is placed on the quality of teaching in the classroom because we strongly believe that schools are first and foremost centres for learning. Coupled with this is a very firm commitment to traditional values: we insist on high standards, good discipline and the values that parents and society respect.

In 2011, 89.7% of students gained five or more pass grades A* to C at GCSE, (88.8% including English and maths). In value added terms Gordon's attained 1014.8 points, which is significantly above the national average. At GCE A level, 88% of the grades were A* to C, the key grades required to get into the most highly regarded universities.

Such results are, of course, very pleasing. However schools should never be judged on examination results alone. At Gordon's we believe that the only way to gain an accurate picture of a school is to see it in action during a typical working day, to visit lessons and to talk with staff and pupils.

If you would like to visit Gordon's, please contact us on 01276 858084, and ask for our admissions registrar, Mrs Tozer, who will arrange a tour of the school for you and your child.

Gordon's School is a registered charity (No. 312092) to educate or contribute to the education of boys and girls, having particular regard to those with a specific boarding or educational need.

Great Walstead School

(Founded 1925)

East Mascalls Lane, Lindfield, Haywards Heath, West Sussex RH16 2QL
Tel: 01444 483528   Email: admin@greatwalstead.co.uk
Fax: 01444 482122   Website: www.greatwalstead.co.uk

Headmaster: Mr C Baty NPQH, BEd(Waikato NZ)
Appointed: November 2010
School type: Boys' and Girls' Day and Weekly/Flexi
Boarding
Age range of pupils: 2½–13
No. of pupils enrolled as at 1.9.12: 400
Boys: 235 Girls: 165
No. of boarders: 62
Fees per annum as at 1.9.12: Day: £6780–£13,200
Weekly boarding: supplement of £2,655 pa
Average size of class: 16-20
Teacher/pupil ratio: 1:9 + assistants

Where the possibilities and the grounds are endless

Great Walstead School is a coeducational prep
school, taking children from 2½ to 13 years. Set in a
wonderful location in the heart of the Sussex
countryside, Great Walstead provides a full, rich and
varied education.

With over 270 acres, the surrounding grounds play a
big part in the learning and development of the
children at the school. Pupils use the outdoor
facilities daily to explore, learn and take part in
educational activities.

Here at Great Walstead our teachers are leaders in
their field. They combine excellence in education
with teaching pupils fundamental lessons in life, such
as kindness and good manners, and help to prepare
them for the outside world.

Great Walstead's five core values are Christian faith,
dedication, success, the environment and
communication, all of which our children adopt in
everything they do. But above all else we take
academic subjects very seriously.

This year, Great Walstead has once again seen great
success with over half of the school's Year 8s leaving
with a scholarship or an award to the senior school of
their choice.

As Colin Baty, Headmaster, comments: "Here at
Great Walstead we are very proud of the results our
pupils achieve each year with all children gaining
entry to the school of their choice and a high
percentage of scholarships and awards to a number of
senior schools both locally and further afield. These
exceptional results demonstrate that we individually
prepare our pupils to the highest levels."

Alongside the academic work the children enjoy
fabulous opportunities in sports and visual and
performing arts. From singing at the O2 to a cricket
tour in South Africa, Great Walstead offers a varied
and inspirational school life for all its pupils whatever
their interests and abilities.

**For more information or to come and see what
makes Great Walstead such a special place visit
www.greatwalstead.co.uk; we would love to show
you around anytime.**

Hoe Bridge School

(Founded 1987)

Hoe Place, Old Woking Road, Woking, Surrey GU22 8JE
Tel: 01483 760018 & 01483 772194
Email: enquiriesprep@hoebridgeschool.co.uk
Fax: 01483 757560   Website: www.hoebridgeschool.co.uk

HOE BRIDGE SCHOOL
Celebrating 25 Years of Success

Head: Mr N Arkell BSc
Appointed: September 2009
School type: Coeducational Day
Member of: IAPS
Age range of pupils: 2½–14
No. of pupils enrolled as at 1.1.12:
Boys: 339 Girls: 130
Fees per annum as at 1.1.12: Day: £1800–£12,840
Average size of class: 19
Teacher/pupil ratio: 1:10
Religious denomination: Non denominational

Hoe Bridge School, on the outskirts of Woking, stands in its own grounds of twenty acres, which afford admirable facilities for games and outdoor pursuits.

The curriculum at Hoe Bridge is broad and balanced, and offers not only all of the National Curriculum subjects, but also additional programmes of study in classical subjects such Latin, therefore covering all the requirements for Common Entrance. Small class sizes ensure that each pupil is able to receive individual attention from their teacher, and that they are given the opportunity to perform to the best of their ability.

A longer school day for children aged 7 and above allows for a wide range of afternoon activities, sport and games sessions, which encourage physical activity and teamwork. Obviously, with such a long day, fresh wholesome meals are important and are prepared by a professional chef to meet the nutritional requirements of growing children.

Facilities at the school are first class, with outstanding music, art and design departments complemented by state-of-the-art technology. The entire school is wired for internet access, with computers introduced to the children at nursery level. The pastoral side of education is not neglected, however, as spiritual awareness and self-knowledge are fostered at all levels through the curriculum, but particularly in religious studies, the expressive arts and the regular school assemblies.

Recent refurbishment of the Sports Hall Block has provided the school with up-to-date facilities, including three large modern laboratories, an extended boys changing room and additional classrooms.

Entry requirements
Entry to the kindergarten, nursery and pre-prep is by interview. Entry to the prep school is by assessment and interview.

Hoe Bridge School is a charitable trust aiming to provide a high quality, well-rounded education for boys and girls aged 2½-14 years. (Charity No. 295808)

Hurstpierpoint College

(Founded 1849)

Hassocks, West Sussex BN6 9JS
Tel: 01273 833636
Fax: 01273 835257   Website: www.hppc.co.uk

Headmaster: Mr T J Manly BA, MSc
School type: Coeducational Boarding & Day
Age range of pupils: 4–18
No. of pupils enrolled as at 1.9.12: 1030
Fees per annum as at 1.9.12: Day: £19,785
Weekly Boarding: £24,945
Boarding: £27,885–£29,430
Boarding is only available in the Senior School:
Flexiboarding: £23,385

Hurstpierpoint College offers outstanding day and boarding education for boys and girls aged 4 to 18 years. Set in Sussex countryside just north of the Downs, its 140-acre campus provides superb academic, sporting and cultural facilities.

The core belief at Hurst is that education is all about pupils' achievement of personal bests – academic, extracurricular and in their relationships with others.

Every child has access to all the opportunities at Hurst, whether sporting, creative, activity or community related. For example, every child has the chance to be in a sports team, join a choir or musical ensemble, tackle the Duke of Edinburgh Silver award and participate in one or more of over 20 different theatrical productions a year.

Alongside this commitment to inclusion and real engagement, Hurst seeks to achieve true excellence. In 2011/12, a large academic cohort headed off to Oxford and other first rate universities, athletes competed regionally and nationally, the outstanding Cadet Force numbered over 250, a Young Enterprise team swept the prizes locally and 20 Duke of Edinburgh Gold Award winners are to collect their awards at Buckingham Palace.

"A school which is going from strength to strength under the strong leadership of its dynamic headmaster. It is now the first choice for many parents who would traditionally have sent their children further afield. Fantastic value added, where each child is tracked and challenged to reach their full potential in all areas of their lives, and where they are encouraged to push themselves beyond their comfort zone." *The Good Schools Guide's report on Hurstpierpoint College, June 2012*

To find out what Hurstpierpoint College can offer your child, we invite you to arrange a personal family visit or to attend one of our open mornings.

Kent College Pembury

(Founded 1886)

Old Church Road, Pembury, Tunbridge Wells, Kent TN2 4AX
Tel: 01892 822006   Email: admissions@kentcollege.kent.sch.uk
Fax: 01892 820221   Website: www.kent-college.co.uk

Kent
College

Headmistress: Mrs Sally-Anne Huang MA(Oxon), MSc, PGCE
Head of Prep: Mrs Ann Lawson BEd Hons
School type: Girls' Day & Boarding
Boarders from 10
Age range of pupils: 3–18
Prep School 3–11
No. of pupils enrolled as at 1.9.12: 600
Sixth Form: 102
No. of boarders: 90
Fees per annum as at 1.9.12: Day: £7584–£18,156
Boarding: £20,646–£26,850
Day: £7047–£10,611
Boarding: £12,788
Flexi-boarding: £35 per night
Average size of class: 16
Teacher/pupil ratio: 1:9

Set in 75 acres of parkland, Kent College is an idyllic oasis, providing a safe, natural environment where girls enjoy living and learning. The thriving school is a happy, caring home for boarders who can join at age ten. The Christian ethos gives a clear moral framework; pupils are well mannered, tolerant and respectful of one another. It is a busy, vibrant school where we enjoy doing things as a whole community, be it a barbecue lunch, arts festival or theatre trip to London's West End.

A broad and balanced approach

Academic standards are high, with excellent GCSE and A level results, and pupils gain places at top universities to do a variety of courses, from medicine to engineering. The curriculum and approach is broad and balanced. Success is achieved by nurturing the girls' confidence and inspiring a love of learning. The school has a reputation for excellence in performing arts and sport.

Exciting opportunities

An impressive and diverse range of 140 activities enables students to discover new talents and nurture existing ones. Exciting exchanges to Australia, Europe and America, and international sport, music and drama tours are an important part of school life. Along with the school's thriving Gymnastics Academy which competes to a very high standard at national competitions, and Swimming Academy, the school is set to launch an exciting new Theatre Academy from September 2012 which will deliver workshops in drama, dance & singing.

Facilities and location

Modern, architect-designed facilities include homely boarding houses, a state-of-the-art theatre, large sports hall, music school, dance studio, on-site outdoor 'adventure course', science laboratories and an indoor swimming pool. Sixth formers benefit from their own study centre. An iconic library and art centre will be opened in 2013. The school is only three miles from the town of Royal Tunbridge Wells, 15 minutes from the M25 and 40 minutes from London by train.

Scholarships and admissions

Main intakes for boarders are at age 10, 11, 13 and 16. Academic, music, drama, sport and art scholarships and bursaries are available.

Royal Grammar School, Guildford

(Founded 1509)

High Street, Guildford, Surrey GU1 3BB
Tel: 01483 880600   Email: admissions@rgs-guildford.co.uk
Fax: 01483 880602   Website: www.rgs-guildford.co.uk

Headmaster: Dr J M Cox BSc, PhD
Appointed: 2007
School type: Boys' Day
Age range of pupils:
Boys: 11–18
No. of pupils enrolled as at 1.9.12: 900
Fees per annum as at 1.9.12: Day: £14,070–£14,325
Average size of class: 10-25
Teacher/pupil ratio: 1:10

Located in the centre of the historic town of Guildford, the RGS is an independent day school for boys from age 11 to 18. The school dates its foundation from 1509 and, as a flagship for boys' education, has a national reputation for academic excellence but also prides itself on its traditional values of decency and respect, supported by very strong pastoral care. RGS boys have the opportunity to experience the widest range of enriching activities providing them with a broad and balanced education. They enjoy learning at the RGS in an environment that allows them fully to realise their natural potential.

Academic excellence is at the heart of the school's philosophy. The RGS is consistently one of the top five boys' schools in the country at both A level and GCSE: in 2011, 82% of all grades at A level were achieved at grades A*/A with 41% of grades at the A*; 94.6% of all GCSE results were passed at A*/A. The school is extremely proud of its Oxbridge record; in the last six years 200 offers have been achieved including 34 offers in the recent round of admissions for 2012 entry.

Sport, music, drama and art, as integral parts of each boy's development, are thriving in the school. Every boy is encouraged to participate fully in the wider life of the school; a number of boys have recently achieved national and international recognition. Opportunities abound for adventurous training through the outdoor pursuits programme.

Respect, tolerance and understanding of others are a feature of the school; the outstanding pastoral care enables the boys to thrive in an environment in which they feel safe, valued and able to express themselves. A strong sense of community is nurtured and the boys are involved actively in a range of innovative educational projects in conjunction with national and international partners.

Further details, including information about bursaries, are available from:

admissions@rgs-guildford.co.uk

Royal Alexandra and Albert School
under the patronage of Her Majesty the Queen
(Founded 1758)

Gatton Park, Reigate, Surrey RH2 0TD
Tel: 01737 649 000   Email: admissions@gatton-park.org.uk
Fax: 01737 649 002   Website: www.raa-school.co.uk

Headmaster: P Spencer Ellis BA, MPhil, NPQH
Appointed: 2001
School type: State Maintained, Preparatory, Senior, Sixth Form
Age range of pupils: 7–18
No. of pupils enrolled as at 1.4.12: 1000
Boys: 510 Girls: 490 Sixth Form: 200
No. of boarders: 450
Teacher/pupil ratio: 1:11-8
Religious denomination: Church of England

The Royal Alexandra and Albert School has experienced extraordinary success over the last few years. Excellent results combined with affordable fees (around £4000/term for full boarding) have made us the first choice for many parents who are looking for a top quality, well-rounded education. This is a true boarding school with Saturday morning lessons, longer holidays and a vast range of sporting and other activities in the afternoons, evenings and at weekends. Set in 260 acres of parkland, yet close to London, we are convenient for families who live in the UK and overseas.

Curriculum
The National Curriculum is followed in the primary school and for Key Stage 3 (Years 7-9). Pupils then take a wide range of GCSE and vocational courses in Key Stage 4. Our Sixth Form offers the widest possible range of courses and subjects.

Sixth Form
The strong ethos of the secondary school is carried through to the Sixth Form. Many of our Sixth Formers choose to board and there are 42 brand new study bedrooms with en suite shower rooms providing university standard accommodation.

The new purpose-built Sixth Form Centre has a spacious common room, café, study and resource rooms together with a fully equipped computer suite.

Advice on academic work, pastoral matters and careers is provided by a tutor, who remains the student's tutor for the full two years of the Sixth Form.

Sixth Form students are very much part of the whole school and are expected to mentor younger pupils, help run clubs and activities and lead school projects.

Boarding ethos
With up to 450 boarding pupils, we are one of the largest boarding schools in the country. All children, including those who are not full boarders, enjoy an extended day at the school, which includes all meals, activities and support in the boarding houses. We have maintained the atmosphere and traditions of a boarding school, but have kept pace with the changing needs and expectations of young people and their parents.

Staffing levels in our nine boarding houses are high, with an average of six staff in each house.

Study bedrooms for two, three or four pupils provide a comfortable, modern home-from-home atmosphere for our older pupils.

We are the only state boarding school to offer boarding to junior pupils and we have up to 60 boarders aged 7-11.

Our purpose-built health centre staffed by qualified nurses provides round the clock high quality medical care for pupils.

The school community

For over 250 years this school has been transforming the lives of young people and we are proud of our heritage. The world has moved on since 1758 but we still aim to nurture and develop the children who come to this school so that they enter the adult world fully prepared to meet any challenge.

We are a church school and are committed to fostering Christian principles within a caring community, where people of all faiths and beliefs are made welcome. Whilst we encourage pupils to strive to do their best we also expect them to be tolerant and sensitive to the needs of others.

Entry requirements

Entry is by confidential reference from the current school and interview, to assess suitability for boarding. No EAL provision is available. Only UK/EU passport holders and those with a right of residence in the UK are eligible for places.

Examinations offered

Key Stage 2 and 3 tests; GCSEs; GCE A levels and vocational qualifications in the Sixth Form.

Academic & leisure facilities

Purpose-built teaching facilities include state-of-the-art ICT systems providing internet and intranet access for all staff and pupils. Sports facilities are exceptional and include our own riding school with indoor and outdoor sand school, indoor swimming pool, dance studio and flood-lit all weather pitches. Scouts, cadets and Duke of Edinburgh's Award Scheme are popular; music and dance are outstanding.

Religious activities

The school has its own chapel and a full-time Anglican Chaplain.

Scholarships

Means-tested bursaries are available to children whose home circumstances make a boarding education desirable.

The Royal Alexandra & Albert School Foundation, a registered charity (No. 311945) provides boarding, pastoral care and bursary support for pupils at the Royal Alexandra & Albert School.

Seaford College

(Founded 1884)

Lavington Park, Petworth, West Sussex GU28 0NB
Tel: 01798 867392   Email: admissions@seaford.org
Fax: 01798 867606   Website: www.seaford.org

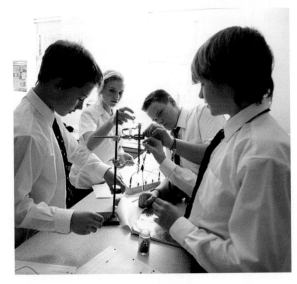

Headmaster: T J Mullins MBA, BA
School type: Coeducational Boarding & Day
Member of: SHMIS, HMC, BSA, IAPS
Age range of pupils: 7–18
No. of pupils enrolled as at 1.9.12: 621
Boys: 436 Girls: 185 Sixth Form: 143
No. of boarders: 137
Fees per annum as at 1.9.12: Day: £8100–£16,890
Weekly Boarding: £17,400–£22,500
Boarding: £16,440–£26,700
Average size of class: 15-20
Teacher/pupil ratio: 1:9
Religious denomination: Church of England

Seaford College is a coeducational independent day and boarding school for pupils aged 7 to 18, situated amid 400 acres of picturesque, rolling parkland in West Sussex. The college, with its excellent amenities and outstanding panoramic views, offers an inspirational environment that nurtures academic excellence, sporting success and creative talent.

Seaford College aims to provide a distinctive and inclusive educational experience in which individual pupils are known, have the opportunity to discover themselves and are valued for their contribution to school life.

The college uses its resources to provide and enhance educational, cultural, spiritual and social opportunities within the local community so that students leave school as confident, articulate and well-rounded individuals.

The college has an excellent record for academic achievement, sport, art and music. Past pupils have obtained music scholarships to some of the country's leading music schools, including the Royal College of Music and Oxford and Cambridge universities, and art scholarships to Central St Martin's College of Art and Design and other leading UK art colleges.

Seaford College offers outstanding sports facilities, including an all-weather water-based Astroturf hockey pitch, golf course and driving range. Students regularly play at county level, with the opportunity to explore action and adventure with the CCF in a lively programme of outdoor pursuits.

Pupils in the recently-opened Preparatory school at Seaford College share the superb facilities with the senior school and enjoy a seamless education from 7 to 18.

The prep school prides itself on its friendly atmosphere and all pupils are encouraged to develop their skills of tolerance and an understanding of others. Weekly chapel services, conducted by the school Chaplain, encourage the strong Christian ethos of the school and pupils participate in weekday assemblies.

The school has a proud record in supporting local charities through its many fundraising activities. Strong emphasis is placed on a disciplined framework where good manners and a smart appearance are expected and where staff and parents work closely together for the common good of the children.

Boarding is offered to students from the age of 10 and around 40% of pupils at Seaford College elect to board, in order to take full advantage of the social, sporting and extracurricular activities on offer. The college offers not only full boarding, but also weekly and flexible boarding in order to meet the needs of pupils and their parents.

Traditional buildings blend beautifully with the recent 21st century improvements: a new boys' boarding house, accommodating 90 students in individual and twin bedrooms, opened in summer 2011, and work is shortly due to commence on a new indoor swimming pool and sports centre.

Other recent developments include an exciting new music suite, which consists of individual teaching and practice rooms, a computer and keyboard room, with large flexible teaching and performance space, a sound-proofed band practice room and outdoor concert arena.

A state-of-the-art maths and science block offers the latest technologies and facilities, while the college has long been recognised as a centre of excellence for art and design. A specialist art library and large exhibition gallery are incorporated into the purpose-built arts faculty, which offers options in fine art, photography and ceramics, as well as design and technology.

All the usual academic subjects are taught, with 24 subjects available to students at GCSE and 28 at A level. The college also offers preparation for the Cambridge Pre-U.

Overseas students are expected to study English as a foreign language and study for the International Language Testing System, which is a requirement for UK university entrance.

Seaford sees its sixth form very much as a transitional stage between school and university or the workplace and treats its students as young adults. They have their own social centre – The Hollington Centre –

which has facilities for individual study, a coffee bar with internet cafe, a lounge area and several classrooms where subjects such as economics, business studies, media studies and politics are taught.

Sixth form boarders have individual study bedrooms, as well as their own common room and dining room. Students are divided into small tutor groups but most commonly meet on a 1-1 basis with their tutors to discuss aspects of their work and progress.

Most of Seaford's sixth formers go on to university or higher education – all are equipped with self-confidence and entrepreneurial skills, as well as a passion for life and a willingness to succeed.

Entry to the college is by test and Trial Day and, although intake is non-selective, expectations are high. If your child is talented and enthusiastic, the college offers a range of scholarships at 11+, 13+ and sixth form, including academic studies, music, art and sport.

The college has its own dedicated learning support unit, catering for pupils with dyslexia, dyscalculia and dyspraxia.

Whatever their chosen path, Seaford College seeks to prepare young people for adult life so that they have the personal skills, confidence and enthusiasm to make it a success.

Seaford College is a registered charity that exists to enhance children's educational opportunities. The Johnson Trust. Registered charity no. 277439.

St Andrew's School

St.Andrew's

SCHOOL · WOKING

(Founded 1937)

Church Hill House, Horsell, Woking, Surrey GU21 4QW
Tel: 01483 760943   Email: admin@st-andrews.woking.sch.uk
Fax: 01483 740314   Website: www.st-andrews.woking.sch.uk

Headmaster: Mr A Perks
Appointed: 2008
School type: Coeducational Day Preparatory
Age range of pupils: 3–13
No. of pupils enrolled as at 1.9.12: 300
Boys: 217 Girls: 83
Fees per annum as at 1.9.12: Day: £3222–£12,930
Average size of class: 16-18
Teacher/pupil ratio: 1:10

St Andrew's School was founded in 1937 and is a respected and thriving coeducational prep school, set in 11 acres of grounds approximately half a mile from Woking town centre. The school seeks to create a nurturing and happy environment of trust and support in which all pupils are encouraged and enabled to develop their skills, talents, interests and potential to the full – intellectually, physically and spiritually.

At St Andrew's children feel secure and confident and are highly motivated to perform to the best of their ability in all aspects of school life. They are competitive without losing sight of their responsibility to share and they are justifiably proud of their school and their own personal achievements. Children are prepared for entrance and scholarship exams to a wide range of independent senior schools and there are specialist teaching facilities for all subjects including science, ICT, music and art.

The curriculum is broad and the school places great emphasis on music, sport and the arts.

St Andrew's is very proud of its excellent on-site facilities including an all weather sports surface, sports pitches, tennis courts, cricket nets and a newly refurbished swimming pool. We are very fortunate to enjoy the benefits of carefully designed school grounds that meet the needs of the children's physical and social development. Main school games are football, hockey, cricket, netball and rounders.

Other activities include rugby, cross-country running, swimming, tennis and athletics.

Children can be supervised at school from 8am and, through our extensive after-school activities programme for Year 3 and above, until 6/6.30 pm most evenings during the week. An after-school club is available from 4pm to 6pm (chargeable) for Pre-Prep and Year 3 children.

Children are assessed for entry into Year 2 and above. The school has a number of scholarships and bursaries available at 7+ and 11+.

The Oratory School

(Founded 19th Century)

Woodcote, Reading RG8 OPJ
Tel: 01491 683500   Email: enquiries@oratory.co.uk
Fax: 01491 680020   Website: www.oratory.co.uk

Head Master: Mr C I Dytor MC, KHS, MA(Cantab), MA(Oxon)
Appointed: August 2000
School type: Boys' Boarding & Day
Boarders from 11 years
Age range of pupils: 11–18
No. of pupils enrolled as at 1.9.12: 420
Sixth Form: 120
No. of boarders: 220
Fees per annum as at 1.9.12: Day: £14,835–£20,565
Boarding: £19,920–£28,395
Teacher/pupil ratio: 1:8

The Oratory School is the UK's only All Boys' Independent Catholic Senior Boarding and Day School with 420 boys aged from 11-18yrs with Catholic and non-Catholic families. Set in acres of beautiful Chiltern countryside in South Oxfordshire, the School is within easy reach of Heathrow and other major airports and the M4.

Founded in 1859 by Blessed John Henry Newman, a brilliant original man, who combined two traditions: Academic excellence with Christian pastoral care for the individual boy. He believed in an education system based on sound moral principles, a scientific and methodical approach to academic study and a personal concern for the welfare of every pupil. Newman's personal motto became the School's: 'Cor ad Cor Loquitur' ('Heart speaking to Heart'), and this continues to flow through the life of the School. Oratory boys are known for their spirit and 'can-do' attitude to life.

The Head Master believes that this focus on body, mind and spirit, so vital for success and happiness, is at the heart of Catholic education and of the School today.

The School ensures there is a close monitoring of work, with an academic timetable designed to provide the widest choice possible. Boys are encouraged to achieve the highest standards in every area of school life and the development of leadership skills play an important part in this grounding. The School has excellent sporting facilities. Along with rugby and football pitches, cricket squares and tennis courts, there is also a golf course, Real Tennis court, indoor shooting range and a boathouse on the River Thames. The award-winning Art & Design department offers Foundation Course status and the arts in general flourish assisted by the Hopkins Society, which takes boys on visits to literary festivals, concerts, plays, the opera and ballet.

The Oratory is now entering into its second 10-year development phase with a new 'cutting edge' performing arts centre to be ready for September 2012 and a massive new sports centre complex planned to be developed over the next two years, with new swimming pool and café facilities.

Clive Dytor, the Head Master, is determined to keep The Oratory at the forefront of boys' education.

Vinehall School

(Founded 1938)

Robertsbridge, East Sussex TN32 5JL
Tel: 01580 880413   Email: registrar@vinehallschool.com
Fax: 01580 882119   Website: www.vinehallschool.com

Vinehall School

Headmaster: Richard Follett
Appointed: January 2011
School type: Coeducational Day & Boarding
Member of: IAPS, BSA, ISBA, ISC
Age range of pupils: 2–13
No. of pupils enrolled as at 1.9.12: 270
Boys: 146 Girls: 124
No. of boarders: 35
Fees per annum as at 1.9.12: Day: £1035–£15,180
Boarding: £19,440–£26,400
Average size of class: 18
Teacher/pupil ratio: 1:10

Vinehall School is a traditional Prep School with a 21st century approach, combining a noticeably friendly and happy atmosphere with impressive achievements in academics, music, art, sport and drama. Set within 47 acres of beautiful countryside on the East Sussex/Kent border, Vinehall offers an extensive range of excellent modern facilities which enhance both the curricular and extra-curricular opportunities for the pupils. These include:

- An attractive, modern and spacious Pre Prep School within the grounds
- A magnificent Millennium Building, comprising classrooms, a dedicated IT suite, numerous additional computers and a Library
- A science block
- A dedicated music building
- An art, design and technology centre
- An excellent purpose-built theatre with seating for 250
- A sports hall with adjoining indoor swimming pool
- An all weather Astroturf pitch
- An adventure playground, extensive playing fields and a nine hole golf course

The curriculum is based on the National Curriculum but extends far beyond, for example, the innovative 'Learning Journey' curriculum (which begins in Year 3), stimulates enquiring young minds. In Years 7 and 8, Vinehall prepares its pupils for Common Entrance, local grammar school entrance and scholarship entrance to a variety of independent senior schools at 13+ including Battle Abbey, Benenden, Brighton College, Charterhouse, Cranbrook, Eastbourne College, Eton, King's Canterbury, Millfield, Sevenoaks, St Bedes, St Leonards-Mayfield, Tonbridge, Winchester and Worth.

We are selective but not academically 'elitist'. Our intake is broad and one of our strengths is working with each individual child to encourage them to make the most of every opportunity, to develop self confidence and self belief and to help them achieve the very best of which they are capable.

Games and the arts are an integral part of the Vinehall timetable. Pupils participate in all major team sports and everyone has a chance to represent the School. Creative arts are also strong, with flourishing art, music and drama departments, all of which exhibit/perform regularly both inside and outside School. Carpentry and wood-turning are also offered.

Boarding is at the very heart of the School and Vinehall has a well established boarding community, the majority being from Sussex, Kent and London. Junior Boarding is offered in Years 3-6 (four nights per week) with children moving on to full boarding in Years 7 and 8. There are regular exeat weekends and a full and varied programme of weekend activities. Pastoral care is excellent. Our February 2012 ISI Inspection report said: 'Pupils' personal development, including their spiritual, moral, social and cultural development is excellent. Thanks to the excellent relationships and the warm, caring atmosphere, pupils thrive and develop faith in their abilities. Pupils are exceptionally well looked after and arrangements for safeguarding are exemplary'.

Vinehall School is an educational charity No. 307014.

West Hill Park Preparatory School

(Founded 1910)

Titchfield, Fareham, Hampshire PO14 4BS
Tel: 01329 842356   Email: admissions@westhillpark.com
Fax: 01329 842911   Website: www.westhillpark.com

Headmaster: A P Ramsay BEd(Hons), MSc
Appointed: September 2009
School type: Coeducational Boarding & Day
Age range of pupils: 2–13
No. of pupils enrolled as at 1.9.12: 288
Boys: 180 Girls: 108
No. of boarders: 35
Fees per annum as at 1.9.12: Day: £8985–£14,985
Boarding: £13,785–£19,785
Average size of class: 10 -18
Teacher/pupil ratio: 1:14

At West Hill Park School, your child will be welcomed into a happy, supportive community in which everyone is valued and where we encourage everyone to show respect and care for one another.

Excellent academic performance is central to the school's ethos. However, we are careful not to measure children by academic achievement alone and place real value on the breadth of experience they gain. Effort, enthusiasm and conduct are highly esteemed and the resulting growth in confidence is the key to unlocking other accomplishments.

Up to Year 5, our classes are currently taught in mixed ability groups with differentiation to at least three levels. From Year 6, pupils are streamed and set for Maths, English and Science. In this way, each child's individual strengths and weaknesses are catered for both academically and socially.

Art, Design and Technology, ICT, Music, Dance and Drama all stimulate creativity and imagination.

Boarding (judged by Ofsted to be 'outstanding') has to be appealing to children and here, boarding is very much based on feeling happy and safe, and having a lot of fun. There is a firm but fair routine; time set aside for study, music practice and quiet relaxation as well as regular fun nights and special weekend activities. We offer full, weekly, flexible or a one night boarding experience to suit your family.

Extensive games and athletics fields, an astro hockey surface, heated indoor swimming pool, netball and tennis courts all provide the necessary facilities to allow us to compete at a high level with independent schools locally, and also at County and National levels.

Breadth and diversity are crucial to the philosophy of West Hill Park. We encourage children to take every opportunity life brings and to appreciate the world around them. The comprehensive activities programme epitomises the school's attitude that 'children are capable of anything, if only we let them try'.

As children progress through the school, they are encouraged to take more responsibility for their learning, and their contribution to school life. They grow to understand their importance in the community, both through instruction and example. This provides them with a strong platform from which they can confidently move into their senior school as independent, self-reliant individuals.

www.winchestercollege.org

Winchester College (boarding school for boys age 13 – 18, 690 pupils)
One of the most distinguished schools in the World
Admissions: Tel +44 (0)1962 621247

Winchester College is a registered charity – No. 1139000

South-West

EF International Academy Torbay

EF House, Castle Road, Torquay, Torbay TQ1 3BG
Tel: +41 41 41 74 525   Email: admissionsia@ef.com
Fax: +44 1803 202 943   Website: www.ef.com/academy

Head of School: David Davies
School type: Coeducational Boarding
Accommodation in home-stays
Age range of pupils: 14–18
No. of pupils enrolled as at 1.1.12: 150
Fees per annum as at 1.1.12:
Boarding: £19,950

EF International Academy is part of EF Education First, the world leader in international education. With over 45 years of experience, EF has helped more than four million students realise their dream of studying abroad.

The School
The EF International Academy campus is situated in the heart of Torbay, a popular tourist destination on England's scenic south-west coast. London, Oxford and Stonehenge are a train-ride away. The school is housed in a fully modernised historic building, which provides a safe, comfortable learning environment, complete with state-of-the-art science and language labs, wireless internet, library facilities, a dining area and lounge.

Academics
Education at EF is highly personal and a range of internationally renowned programmes are offered to meet the individual needs of each student; including IB Diploma and A level, as well as IGCSE and the High School Preparation programme. Intensive English language courses are also available. EF has a track record of academic excellence with 45% of students receiving A/A* grades at A level, compared with the national average of 27%.

University Placements
The EF International Academy class of 2011 is on course for another year of success. Our students have been accepted on to courses that are deemed to be the best in the country for their subject, such as medicine at the University of Leicester and mathematics at the University of Oxford. 36% of our students have been admitted into one of the top ten UK universities for their chosen subject.

Pastoral Care
Personal tutors provide one-to-one individualised support and guidance. Each student is assigned a personal tutor whose role is to monitor the student's academic progress, university applications and general welfare. Students are encouraged to nurture their talents and develop new skills and confidence.

Scholarships
Scholarships will be awarded to highly talented and ambitious students who can make a positive contribution to the school community. Two students are awarded Founder's scholarships, which will cover 50% of total fees. Many other general scholarships are also available for students who demonstrate overall excellence.

Residential Life
Students stay with host families and benefit from full immersion into British culture and language. Host families are rigorously vetted and many have years of experience in offering a safe, supportive home away from home to EF Torbay students.

Kingsley School

(Founded 2009)

Northdown Road, Bideford, Devon EX39 3LY
Tel: 01237 426200   Email: admissions@kingsleyschoolbideford.co.uk
Fax: 01237 425981   Website: www.kingsleyschoolbideford.co.uk

KINGSLEY SCHOOL
BIDEFORD

Headmaster: Mr Andy Waters BEd, MA
Appointed: September 2006
School type: Coeducational Boarding & Day
Boarders from age 8
Age range of pupils: 3 months–18 years
No. of pupils enrolled as at 1.1.12: 400
Sixth Form: 80
No. of boarders: 70
Fees per annum as at 1.9.11: Day: £5010–£11,640
Boarding: £14,430–£22,200
Average size of class: 12
Teacher/pupil ratio: 1:9

Kingsley School Bideford, a single campus co-educational boarding and day school for pupils aged 3 to 18, is committed to discovering, nurturing and celebrating the talents and achievements of each and every one of its pupils. Set in 25 acres of playing fields, gardens and woods, the school is a stone's throw from North Devon's stunning surf beaches and within easy reach of Exmoor and Dartmoor national parks.

Kingsley students consistently achieve excellent results in public examinations. GCSE results are 50% higher than the UK national average and more than 90% of Kingsley sixth formers go on to the university of their choice. The academic curriculum is broad and includes sports and creative subjects such as music, drama and art.

Matching the breadth of the academic subjects is the exceptional range of sports and other activities available to every student of every ability level. Many of the outdoor activities take advantage of the school's wonderful location – surfing and rowing are extremely popular, while Dartmoor provides the dramatic setting for the annual Ten Tors Challenge. Kingsley's gymnastics squad consistently wins major competitions. The Judo Academy has a unique partnership with the University of Bath, enabling Kingsley's elite players to benefit from the renowned Team Bath training resources. Kingsley's drama and music departments stage a series of outstanding performances throughout the year in our purpose-designed theatre, while the Duke of Edinburgh Awards programme is always popular.

Kingsley boarders enjoy excellent accommodation, good food, a secure, happy environment and a well-planned programme of social activities. Free transport is provided to and from Heathrow Airport. Everything is supervised by our enthusiastic and committed team of houseparents and resident staff, all of whom are dedicated to providing an 'extended family' atmosphere.

Milton Abbey School

(Founded 1954)

Blandford Forum, Dorset DT11 0BZ
Tel: 01258 880484   Email: admissions@miltonabbey.co.uk
Fax: 01258 881194   Website: www.miltonabbey.co.uk

MILTON
ABBEY

Headmaster: G E Doodes MA
Appointed: 2010
School type: Coeducational Boarding & Day
Age range of pupils: 13–18
No. of pupils enrolled as at 1.9.12: 228
Boys: 201 Girls: 27 Sixth Form: 106
No. of boarders: 221
Fees per annum as at 1.9.12: Day: £21,300
Boarding: £28,350
Average size of class: 12

Milton Abbey is a small co-educational boarding and day school committed to the individual, and delivers an education that is meant to challenge, stretch and develop young men and women into leaders and assured adults who possess confidence without arrogance. At Milton Abbey's heart is a philosophy of developing each and every girl and boy into fully rounded people academically, culturally, spiritually, and within a caring, supportive environment.

Milton Abbey is inclusive and ambitious for every pupil. Success, in whatever form, is celebrated. No one is overlooked. The small size allows for a level of care that is unsurpassed in bigger schools. However, our size does not diminish from our expectations of pupils – we want them to have big achievements, big ambitions and big hearts.

Throughout their time at Milton Abbey, our main responsibility to pupils is to find a spark that will light a passion. This may be in the classroom, as academic excellence is promoted thoroughly throughout the school. It could be on the games field, or in the theatre or concert hall, where we endeavour to engender a sense of pride in teamwork and individual performance. It could be on the school farm, the pheasant pens, the school shoot or in the ferret shed, as environmental awareness and a passion for the outdoors is a key feature of our life here.

Recent investment has seen the building of two new boarding houses and the renovation and opening of a new girl's 13-18 house in September 2012.

We warmly welcome you to visit us. For further details please contact The Admissions Office on 01258 882182 / admissions@miltonabbey.co.uk or visit our website www.miltonabbey.co.uk.

West Midlands

Abbots Bromley School

(Founded 1875)

High Street, Abbots Bromley, Rugeley, Staffordshire WS15 3BW
Tel: 01283 840232   Email: enquiries@abbotsbromley.net
Fax: 01283 840988   Website: www.abbotsbromley.net

Abbots Bromley School

Headmistress: Mrs J Dowling MA(Cantab), PGCE, NPQH
School type: Co-educational Pre-prep & Prep Girls Senior Boarding and Day
Age range of pupils:
Boys: 3–11
Girls: 3–18
No. of pupils enrolled as at 1.9.12: 251
Boys: 4 Girls: 247 Sixth Form: 54
No. of boarders: 59
Fees per annum as at 1.9.12: Day: £4386–£14,910
Weekly Boarding: £16,545–£20,925
Boarding: £20,295–£24,975

At Abbots Bromley School, there is so much on offer to suit a wide variety of individuals. Our friendly boarding community caters for weekly, flexi or occasional boarders. The safe haven of Abbots Bromley allows our pupils to grow up in beautiful natural surroundings, but at the same time we are never too far from locations where the students may benefit from cultural and intellectual experiences.

In Roch House Preparatory School, we educate boys and girls from Kindergarten to Year 6. This coeducational school sits within the main site with its own dedicated facilities. There is a happy friendly atmosphere in Roch House. The small class sizes, broad and stimulating curriculum, lively extracurricular programme and experienced staff all contribute to making Roch House a place for children to thrive and succeed.

In the Senior School, we offer a girls-only programme from the age of 11. Alongside our academic programme, our students are able to take a variety of qualifications to a high level in areas such as riding, dance and musical theatre without jeopardising any future plans they may have too early in their careers. We are lucky to have our own equestrian centre on site, fabulous dance facilities and a newly-refurbished theatre, where pupils can display their talents.

We offer excellent sporting facilities for budding sports women in a variety of disciplines including swimming and the opportunities for musicians are enhanced with an annual overseas tour to share their music with different communities.

Academic, art, dance, music, riding and sport scholarships are available as well as bursaries.

For students wishing to join us from overseas three airports lie within close proximity: East Midlands, Birmingham and Manchester.

We enjoy showing visitors all that we have to offer and invite you to come and see for yourself the wealth of opportunities available to your child.

Malvern St James

(Founded 1893)

Avenue Road, Great Malvern, Worcestershire WR14 3BA
Tel: 01684 584624   Email: registrar@malvernstjames.co.uk
Fax: 01684 566204   Website: www.malvernstjames.co.uk

Head Teacher: Mrs Patricia Woodhouse
BMus(Hons)
Appointed: September 2010
School type: Girls' Boarding & Day
Age range of pupils: 4–18
No. of pupils enrolled as at 1.9.12: 400
Fees per annum as at 1.9.12: Day: £7095–£15,645
Weekly Boarding: £15,240–£27,030
Boarding: £16,935–£29,955
Average size of class: 12-16
Teacher/pupil ratio: 1:7

"...an environment in which pupils can grow in self-esteem, self-confidence and respect." ISI 2011.

Malvern St James Girls' School is a leading boarding and day school that presents an imaginative vision of education for girls from the age of 4 through to 18, taught within a positive, purposeful atmosphere. 'MSJ' fosters creativity and bold-thinking; we challenge and encourage every girl to extend her personal horizons and realise her full potential. The school is home to a warm and welcoming community with a buoyant atmosphere of shared celebration, extolling personal success in every field of endeavour.

Curriculum and facilities

Small classes, led by dedicated and dynamic teachers, provide a first class education tailored to the individual. Our teaching facilities include a state-of-the-art science centre, multimedia language centre and new sports centre with fitness suite, all of which provide the best in 21st century teaching facilities. We offer a busy and varied weekend programme of activities to suit all interests, including watersports, rock climbing, abseiling, music, drama and expeditions leading to the Duke of Edinburgh's Award.

Scholarships

Academic, music, art, riding and sport scholarships are available for middle school entry; academic, music, art, riding, drama and sport scholarships for sixth form entry.

A scholarship is worth up to a maximum of 20% of annual fees and an exhibition is worth up to a maximum of 10% of the current fees. In both cases, means-tested top up bursaries can be awarded.

Entrance examinations

Prep and Pre-prep: informal assessment.

Middle School: cognitive ability tests (CAT 3) and a comprehension examination or the Common Entrance examination.

Sixth Form: subject entrance paper and general essay.

Location

Situated at the foot of the beautiful Malvern Hills in the heart of Worcestershire. InterCity trains run from Great Malvern, the M5 and M50 are nearby and London, Birmingham and Manchester airports are within easy reach.

Malvern St James is a registered charity (No. 527513) that exists to support excellent education for girls.

Packwood Haugh School

(Founded 1892)

Ruyton XI Towns, Shrewsbury, Shropshire SY4 1HX
Tel: 01939 260217   Email: enquiries@packwood-haugh.co.uk
Fax: 01939 262077   Website: www.packwood-haugh.co.uk

Headmaster: Clive Smith-Langridge BA (Hons), PGCE
Appointed: September 2012
School type: Coeducational Day & Boarding
Boarders from 7 years
Age range of pupils: 4–13
No. of pupils enrolled as at 1.9.12: 240
Boys: 160 Girls: 80
No. of boarders: 128
Fees per annum as at 1.9.12: Day: £6669–£14,919
Boarding: £18,645
Average size of class: 13.5
Teacher/pupil ratio: 1:7

Packwood Haugh has a national reputation for achievement and for providing an education tailored to the needs of pupils, in an environment where each child is happy. Happy to strive for excellence in the classroom and on the games field, happy to contribute selflessly to the community, and happy to enjoy everything that the school offers.

The school is well-equipped with an outstanding theatre which is used daily for assemblies as well as for full scale productions, superb sports fields and well-equipped classrooms; a new sports hall complex was completed in 2007 which includes extensive facilities for art and craft design and technology teaching. Each form has time in the computer suite, and children use the school's network and the internet.

Quality teaching inspires children of all abilities to aim high and the infectious Packwood 'work ethic' ensures that potential is fulfilled. Packwood Haugh pupils regularly secure places at senior schools including Downe House, Eton, Gordonstoun, Harrow, Malvern, Oundle, Radley, Rugby, Shrewsbury, Uppingham, Winchester and Wycombe Abbey and a 100% pass rate at Common Entrance is usual. The school has a strong record of sporting achievement.

Pastoral care from staff, and from the older children to the younger, creates a friendly, and positive 'home from home' in which to live, learn and grow... There are 50 clubs on offer with a wide choice of activities from archery to xylophones.

Most pupils board, with girls and boys living in separate houses. Boarding facilities are continually improved and children often choose to board to enjoy the fun. The school offers a full boarding routine in term time with fixed exeats and half term and escorted travel to and from London.

Quote: "No one could ever suffer from boredom in this boarding school; this is very much acknowledged by the pupils who appreciate all the opportunities available to them." (ISI inspection report)

Packwood Haugh is a Registered Charity (No. 528411) and exists to educate children and serve the community.

Rugby School

(Founded 1567)

Rugby, Warwickshire CV22 5EH
Tel: 01788 556274   Email: admissions@rugbyschool.net
Fax: 01788 556277   Website: www.rugbyschool.net

Rugby School

Headmaster: P S J Derham
Appointed: September 2001
School type: Coeducational Boarding & Day
Age range of pupils: 11–18
No. of pupils enrolled as at 1.9.12: 792
Boys: 442 Girls: 350 Sixth Form: 344
No. of boarders: 647
Fees per annum as at 1.9.12: Day: £15,165
Weekly Boarding: £17,700
Boarding: £27,225
Average size of class: 15
Teacher/pupil ratio: 1:8.2

In truth, most schools can say most of the following. But only one school can say it all.

We're an all round coeducational school, where pupils are actively encouraged to develop their own individual skills and talents. Every child has something special inside them; it's our job to find out what that is.

We're a school which values outstanding academic performance – but never at the expense of achieving excellence in other fields. In our experience, a hothouse isn't necessarily a place where many pupils will blossom.

We're a school located in the Midlands, and we're often noted for our remarkably unsnobby atmosphere. But amongst pupils and teachers alike, you'll detect a fierce pride about being here.

We're a school with a strong sense of service to the community. We're blessed with some marvellously well-equipped facilities, and we think it's only fair we afford wider access to them whenever we can.

We also think it's fair to give children a chance to come here who couldn't otherwise afford to do so. Our aim is to have 1 in 10 of our pupils granted full Arnold Foundation bursaries by the year 2020.

We're a true 7-day a week school with a strong boarding ethos. The place doesn't empty at weekends for the simple reason that there's so much going on here.

We're a school that loves to innovate and try out new things. Just because 'it's never been done before' doesn't mean we shouldn't give it a go now.

Without being over-pious about it, we're a Christian foundation, where tolerance and understanding are taught with just the same skill and dedication as English and maths.

We're a school with a strong House structure, and a long tradition of in-house dining. This means there's an unusual emphasis on individual pastoral care, so being here really is the next best thing to being back home.

After five years of receiving one of the best school educations in the world, all of our pupils finally leave Rugby.

But Rugby never, ever leaves them.

Yorkshire & Humberside

Fulneck School

(Founded 1753)

Fulneck, Pudsey, Leeds, West Yorkshire LS28 8DS
Tel: 0113 2570235   Email: enquiries@fulneckschool.co.uk; admissions@fulneckschool.co.uk
Fax: 0113 2557316   Website: www.fulneckschool.co.uk

Principal: Mrs Deborah Newman
Appointed: 2012
School type: Coeducational Day & Boarding
Age range of pupils: 3–18
No. of pupils enrolled as at 1.9.12: 440
Sixth Form: 67
No. of boarders: 89
Fees per annum as at 1.9.12: Day: £6210–£11,010
Weekly Boarding: £15,390–£18,585
Boarding: £16,725–£20,700
Average size of class: Av 15
Teacher/pupil ratio: 1:8

Fulneck School is an outstanding day and boarding school, located in Leeds. We educate boys and girls between the ages of 3 and 18; boarders are accepted from the age of 9.

Fulneck School provides an all-round education of exceptional quality (Best Sixth Form in Leeds, 2010 and 2011) and 'an excellent learning experience for all its pupils' (ISI Inspection Report Dec 2010) who thrive in the stimulating and challenging yet caring environment. The school has a strong system of pastoral care in which pupils feel valued whilst at the same time 'achieving outstanding personal development' (ISI 2010).

Fulneck's exceptional teaching and learning environment was confirmed recently by three outstanding inspection reports. In addition to the The Independent School Inspectorate (ISI), Ofsted also awarded Fulneck an 'outstanding' mark for the boarding provision and the Council for the Registration of Schools Teaching Dyslexic Pupils (CReSTeD) inspection re-confirmed the prestigious DU status, the highest grade awarded for a mainstream school. Furthermore, Fulneck School received the highest accolade of Ofsted Outstanding Provider.

The inspection report praised Fulneck's tailored teaching and highlighted that the 'outcomes for children are outstanding. Children reach exceptional levels of achievement in all areas of learning' (ISI 2010).

Entry requirements
Entry by assessment at all ages commensurate with expected National Curriculum levels. Consideration is given to pupils with special needs/dyslexia.

Academic & leisure facilities
Fulneck offers modern facilities within historic Grade I listed buildings. There are well equipped ICT suites, modern junior and senior libraries, a professional theatre, art studio, gymnasia, science laboratories, separate sixth form centre, designated common rooms, sports fields, tennis and netball courts, adjacent golf course and nearby full length swimming pool, fitness club and horsing riding school and livery.

Fulneck provides early and late care in addition to an exciting Holiday Club for junior pupils.

Children with learning difference can access the outstanding CReSTeD DU category Learning Support Unit. Fulneck also has a dedicated specialist English as Additional Language unit for students from overseas.

Fulneck School provides an outstanding education experience for boys and girls between the ages of 3 and 18. Registered charity no. 251211.

Wharfedale Montessori School

(Founded 1990)

Bolton Abbey, Skipton, North Yorkshire BD23 6AN
Tel: 01756 710452   Email: secretary@wharfedalemontessori.co.uk
Fax: 01756 710452   Website: www.wharfedalemontessori.co.uk

Headmistress/Principal: Mrs J Lord
Appointed: 1990
School type: Coeducational Day
Age range of pupils: 2–12
No. of pupils enrolled as at 1.9.12:
Boys: 17 Girls: 24
Fees per annum as at 1.9.12: Day: £6225
Teacher/pupil ratio: 1:8

Pre-school and primary education following the Montessori approach, where the child always comes first.

Wharfedale Montessori School offers places for children from 2½ to 12 years of age. The School is situated in one of the most beautiful parts of Wharfedale, in a setting adjacent to Strid Wood SSSI on the beautiful Bolton Abbey Estate.

The School has two main sections, the Pre-school at Strid Cottage and the Primary school housed in a Scandinavian-style custom-built log cabin. Pupils who enter at around three years old normally spend the first three years of their school life in the Pre-school, or Children's House, and transfer to the Primary school around the age of six. The time of transfer depends not only on academic progress but also on a child's personal, social and emotional development.

Here at Wharfedale Montessori School, we provide an excellent academic education for our children, but in addition to this, our setting is totally dedicated to meeting the needs of the individual and celebrating the abilities and achievements of all the children in our care.

Increasingly in mainstream education for pre-school and primary age children, we are seeing a shift in emphasis towards recognising the needs of the child as an individual. This is the approach in Montessori settings, carried out by means of constant observation, monitoring and recording of progress.

This process of ongoing observation replaces the need for testing. When children are not constantly being measured and judged one against the other, all can blossom and enjoy their learning, while achieving results to be proud of.

In Wharfedale Montessori School, this approach teaches children how to be independent learners, giving them the ability to be creative thinkers, to be confident in their own self-image, and to show initiative and enthusiasm for their work.

We are proud of our consistently good inspection reports. Our most recent Ofsted inspection gave us 'outstanding' in many different areas of learning, teaching, behaviour and development. We were the first Montessori setting in Yorkshire to receive Montessori Education Accreditation Board accreditation, and we are certificated as a 'Highly Effective Setting' by North Yorkshire County Council.

If you are trying to decide which school is right for your child, come and take a look at how the increasingly highly respected Montessori approach to education is implemented at Wharfedale Montessori School.

Woodhouse Grove School

(Founded 1812)

Apperley Bridge, Bradford, West Yorkshire BD10 0NR
Tel: 0113 250 2477   Email: gilks.tv@woodhousegrove.co.uk
Fax: 0113 250 5290   Website: www.woodhousegrove.co.uk

Headmaster: David C Humphreys BA
Appointed: 1996
School type: Coeducational Day & Boarding
Member of: HMC
Age range of pupils: 11–18
No. of pupils enrolled as at 1.9.12: 718
Boys: 437 Girls: 281 Sixth Form: 176
No. of boarders: 103
Fees per annum as at 1.9.12: Day: £10,650–£10,920
Weekly Boarding: £20,550–£20,850
Boarding: £22,080–£22,200
Average size of class: 20
Teacher/pupil ratio: 1:10

Situated on a 70 acre campus with extensive grounds yet conveniently located close to major air, railway and motorway networks, the Grove provides a first class all round education for boys and girls, day and boarders alike. Our Junior School, Bronte House, lays excellent foundations from 3-11; however we welcome 50% of the Grove's pupils from other schools at 11, 13 and 16.

Our outstanding facilities, excellent academic results, wide range of extracurricular activities and a

beautiful setting ensure that we can provide your child with the best opportunities and the preparation for a life beyond the classroom. Our boarders enjoy modern, well equipped boarding houses, a secure and caring environment, a 'home from home' atmosphere, and an ever changing list of activities which contribute to the fun and enjoyment of being a boarder at the Grove.

The school's Christian foundation and forward thinking combine with excellent facilities that include an impressive 25m competition swimming pool, state-of-the-art sports and performing arts centre and a purpose-built music and drama facility.

We are a school with traditional values but ambitions for the future, an unpretentious school that seeks to nurture all. Visitors to Woodhouse Grove often comment on our warm and friendly atmosphere – come and see! Meet the pupils and talk to the Headmaster. You will find a friendly welcome and a school with a proud past and an exciting future.

Woodhouse Grove School is a registered charity (No. 529205), which exists to provide education for children.

Scotland

Kilgraston School
NURSERY • PREP • SENIOR • SIXTH FORM

(Founded 1931)

Bridge of Earn, Perth, Perth & Kinross PH2 9BQ
Tel: 01738 812257   Email: headoffice@kilgraston.com
Fax: 01738 813410   Website: www.kilgraston.com

Winner
The
**Independent School
Awards 2011**

*Independent School
of the Year 2011*

Principal: Mr Frank Thompson MA, MPhil, PGCE
Appointed: September 2012
School type: Girls' Day & Boarding
Age range of pupils:
Boys: 2½–9
Girls: 2½–18
No. of pupils enrolled as at 1.9.12: 321
Boys: 4 Girls: 317 Sixth Form: 91
No. of boarders: 132
Fees per annum as at 1.9.12: Day: £8265–£14,490
Boarding: £19,620–£24,705
Average size of class: Av 15
Teacher/pupil ratio: 1:9

Kilgraston is a girls boarding and day school set in 54 acres of pristine Scottish parkland in Bridge of Earn, just south of Perth. It has recently won the prestigious prize of 'Independent School of the Year' at the Independent School Awards.

The school was nominated for the Outstanding Strategic Initiative Award in recognition of the changes the school has made to achieve a 55% growth over the last five years. It also received the Outstanding Financial/Commercial Initiative prize for the ongoing multi-million pound investment in facilities and the introduction of new sports academies developed to nurture young sporting talent. The judges also took into account the recent excellent HMIe inspection and the most successful examination results to date with an exceptional 57% A grades (95% A-C) for Higher and an outstanding 54% A grades (92% A-C) at Advanced Higher. The culmination of these led to the nomination for Independent School of the Year and eventual success.

Kilgraston has pushed its academic capabilities over the last decade and often has the highest grades in Scotland being in the top three for Advanced Highers in the past four years. Kilgraston's academic record is helped due to the small class sizes; the sixth form often has less than 10 pupils per class and the lower ages with around 15.

With an equestrian centre with 60m x 40m floodlit arena (only school in Scotland with this facility on site), a new international-sized all-weather hockey pitch, 8 all-weather tennis courts, sports hall with climbing wall and fitness suite and a new 25m indoor swimming pool there is enough to keep the girls occupied!

Means-tested scholarships and bursaries are available on top of a 10% discount for armed forces families. Please visit our website or contact Mrs Linda-Anne Drane, Principal's PA, for more information or to arrange a visit.

Merchiston Castle School

(Founded 1833)

294 Colinton Road, Edinburgh EH13 0PU
Tel: 0131 312 2200   Email: admissions@merchiston.co.uk
Fax: 0131 441 6060   Website: www.merchiston.co.uk

MERCHISTON
EDINBURGH | Boys first

Headmaster: Mr A R Hunter BA
Appointed: September 1998
School type: Boys' Boarding & Day
Age range of pupils: 8–18
No. of pupils enrolled as at 1.9.12: 470
Sixth Form: 157
No. of boarders: 330
Fees per annum as at 1.9.12: Day: £12,120–£19,545
Boarding: £17,070–£26,655
Teacher/pupil ratio: 1:9

Merchiston is set in 100 acres of beautiful parkland, four miles from the centre of Edinburgh and just 20 minutes from Edinburgh's international airport, which has over 100 direct routes. Only an hour's flight from London, Edinburgh's rich culture offers stimulation and excitement to the boys, whether they are visiting an art gallery or attending an international rugby fixture.

With an ethos based on traditional values, Merchiston encourages self-reliance and independence, as well as respect and tolerance for others. The School's goal is to help every boy reach his full potential and leave Merchiston ready for the world. Merchiston has strong and effective approaches to develop each boy's personal achievement and boasts an impressive record of helping boys excel far beyond their expected results at GCSE and A level. Merchiston was named the Top Scottish School for A levels in 2011 (Daily Telegraph and The Herald) and has an unrivalled reputation for providing a first rate all-round education. Merchiston was rated 'Excellent' for the Quality of Care and Support and Quality of Environment by The Care Inspectorate in 2010.

"My time at Merchiston allowed me to develop into a young man who was ready to head into further education and on into the real world. The combination of first class pastoral care, a style and standard of teaching which allowed a smooth transition into university, with a co-curricular programme second to none and the friendships built up along the way made my time at Merchiston some of the best of my life so far."
Merchistonian

There is a long and successful tradition of sport at Merchiston, with equal emphasis on recreation and excellence. Within fantastic facilities, there are over 20 sports on offer which cater for all interests and levels of ability. As one of the leading innovators of sports education in the UK, the School established Scotland's first tennis academy in 2007 and more recently its own golf academy. The School is currently represented at national and international level in many sports including athletics, cricket and rugby.

"The school provided excellent opportunities and activities for me to participate in, which catered for my interests, as well as giving me the best teaching and tuition, which led to my gaining a place at Cambridge."
Merchistonian

"Our main objective is to motivate pupils to try their hardest and to strive to achieve the highest levels possible in all areas, whilst living as part of a community. Whilst we are concentrating on the academic platform of each boy, alongside the importance of co-curricular activities, we also try to focus on developing boys who are all-rounders with a sense of values."

Andrew Hunter, Headmaster

Queen Victoria School

(Founded 1908)

Dunblane, Perth & Kinross FK15 0JY
Tel: 0131 310 2927   Email: admissions@qvs.org.uk
Fax: 0131 310 2926   Website: www.qvs.org.uk

Head: Mrs W Bellars MA(Hons), PGCE, DipEd, MA(Ed Man)
Appointed: January 2007
School type: Coeducational Boarding
Age range of pupils: 11–18
No. of pupils enrolled as at 21.8.12: 270
Boys: 141 Girls: 129 Sixth Form: 28
No. of boarders: 270
Fees per annum as at 21.8.12:
Boarding: £1179
Religious denomination: Inter-denominational

Queen Victoria School (QVS) is a non-academically selective, fully boarding, coeducational school for the children of Armed Forces personnel who are Scottish or who have served in Scotland.

A small parental contribution (currently around £1179 a year) is levied, but there are no fees. Tuition, boarding, uniform, books and most other costs are met by the Ministry of Defence. In cases of need, the parental contribution can sometimes be paid by one of the Services' Benevolent Funds or similar.

Entry to QVS is decided on the basis of need. Our reason for existing is to provide continuity and stability of education for children who would otherwise be moved around the country, and perhaps the world, several times in the course of their school careers, as a result of their serving parent's postings. We are also tasked by the Ministry of Defence with providing for those families who could not otherwise afford boarding education.

Children can come to QVS from Primary 7, around the age of ten-and-a-half, and this is our main point of entry: this is where most places are available. Children who come into Primary 7 have a year of adjusting to boarding school life before moving into the senior school. The P7 year also allows a year-group who will be at different stages in their academic development when they arrive (as a result of being educated in different schools and different education systems) to achieve some shared level of attainment and content covered, before moving into the senior school. Some QVS students have been to as many as 11 different primary schools before coming to us!

Because all QVS entrants are the children of serving personnel, there is a very special kind of support provided by them for one another. Nowadays, when many parents are on unaccompanied tours, it is particularly reassuring to our children and to their families to know that they are not unusual here. Everyone knows what it is like to be part of a Service family. Several staff have Service experience too, and all are committed to the unique requirement of looking after Services children in a fully boarding environment.

Academic
We offer a range of subject choices and consistently achieve pass rates well above the Scottish national averages.

Sport
These are a very important part of QVS life. Rugby, hockey and football are the main team sports, with very high standards being achieved by both teams and individuals.

Ceremonial
The pipes, drums and dancers of Queen Victoria School have earned an international reputation. Piping,

drumming or dancing lessons are compulsory for every younger pupil, and many maintain their interest and commitment through to Secondary 6 and beyond.

Extracurricular activities

A wide range of hobbies is on offer. Pupils are encouraged to take up at least one each season, and some do several each week.

QVS has a lively Combined Cadet Force (CCF) and all S2 pupils are given an induction year in which they spend time with each of the three Service sections – Navy, Army and Air Force.

The Duke of Edinburgh's Award Scheme operates at all three levels – bronze, silver and gold – at QVS.

Application to join QVS

In February/March each year the admissions board will interview eligible candidates for places in August of that year. The closing date for applications is January 15th in the same year. This is a deadline that we have to adhere to firmly, because of the need to obtain reports on the candidates before the admissions board sits. Applications can be made at any time before January 15th, with most being made in the autumn of the preceding year. An open morning is held for prospective applicants and their families in September of each year, but visits to the school can be made at any time by contacting the admissions secretary. We do not however recommend that visits are made during QVS holidays.

There are more places available in P7 each year than in any other year, although it is possible for older

© Simon Williams

children to apply. Each year a small number of places is offered in older year-groups, according to the availability of bed space.

Although the school prospectus and DVD can give you a hint of what we offer, there is no substitute for visiting the school and talking with current pupils and staff. Our pupils are the best ambassadors for the school, and current and past parents can also be very helpful in telling prospective QVS parents what the experience is like. If you are a serving parent, it is very possible that someone on your unit will have experience of QVS, so do ask around!

If you would like to visit the school or find out more, please contact the admissions secretary on +44 (0) 131 310 2927 or military 94745 2927.

Strathallan School

(Founded 1913)

Forgandenny, Perth, Perth & Kinross PH2 9EG
Tel: 01738 812546
Fax: 01738 812549
Email: admissions@strathallan.co.uk
Website: www.strathallan.co.uk

STRATHALLAN
Opportunities *for all* to excel

Headmaster: Mr B K Thompson MA(Oxon)
Appointed: 2000
School type: Coeducational Boarding & Day
Age range of pupils: 9–18
No. of pupils enrolled as at 1.9.12: 567
Boys: 318 Girls: 249 Sixth Form: 200
No. of boarders: 368
Fees per annum as at 1.9.12: Day: £4044–£6163
Boarding: £6479–£9083
Average size of class: 11
Teacher/pupil ratio: 1:7

Holding an international reputation within its own portfolio of achievements, Strathallan School in Perthshire needs little introduction to those seeking a high-quality boarding and day establishment for their sons and daughters aged nine to 18.

Reputation is one thing, the means by which it is earned is, perhaps, less well appreciated. Looking at academic performance first, there are two key aspects for success:

• A nurturing environment.

• Support from teachers who are passionate about their subjects as well as being high quality practitioners.

Each pupil receives support from an academic tutor and there is also a full-time careers advisor to help with opportunities beyond School.

Central to this is accomplishment:

• 82% of this year's A level entries were graded A*/B.

Strathallan achieves this, it contends, by tailoring work to individual needs. 'We prepare pupils for entry to top universities.'

Certainly the location offers pupils every advantage:

• Set in glorious countryside on a site of 153 acres.

• Offering a safe and secure environment for children to grow and develop.

• It is still within easy reach of the City of Perth and Scotland's International Airports, Edinburgh 40mins & Glasgow (1hour). This makes the commute to London Heathrow less than two hours and considerably more accessible for those living around the world.

The serious business of excellence in academic outcome is but one aspect of independent education. Strathallan prides itself on being friendly and welcoming with a strong sense of community, the aim being to support and to motivate each individual to realise potential in all areas. "We celebrate what pupils achieve and strive to create an ethos which demonstrates that with hard work and expert tuition, they can achieve."

• There is wireless broadband throughout the school.

• Senior Houses feature individual study bedrooms for privacy, and common room and leisure facilities for socialising and relaxation.

• The Junior House is designed to cater for children who wish to enter the School at ages nine to 13 and is situated within its own campus, as well as enjoying the facilities of the main School.

"We are convinced that we made the right decision in placing our son at Strathallan. The School has been instrumental in his achieving his highest academic potential and ultimately gaining a place at Cambridge, quite apart from having a wonderful time which I know he will look back on with great fondness for the rest of his life." a former parent.

Wales

Rydal Penrhos School

(Founded 1880)

Pwllycrochan Avenue, Colwyn Bay, Conwy LL29 7BT
Tel: +44 (0)1492 530155 Email: info@rydal-penrhos.com
Fax: +44 (0)1492 531872 Website: www.rydalpenrhos.com

RYDAL PENRHOS SCHOOL

Headmaster: Mr P A Lee-Browne MA
Appointed: April 2008
School type: Coeducational Day & Boarding
plus flexi and weekly boarding
Member of: HMC, IAPS, SHMIS, ARS, IB
Affiliations: BSA
Age range of pupils: 2½–18
No. of pupils enrolled as at 1.6.12: 617
Boys: 355 Girls: 262
No. of boarders: 148
Fees per annum as at 1.6.12: Day: £5970–£14,055
Weekly Boarding: £20,460–£25,245
Boarding: £22,740–£28,020
Teacher/pupil ratio: 1:8

Location

Rydal Penrhos School is in a wonderful safe and unique location, nestled on the North Wales coast in Colwyn Bay, but also on the doorstep of the Snowdonia National Park. It is also within easy reach of Manchester and Liverpool airports, with London less than three hours away, via an express rail link.

Ethos

Rydal Penrhos School plays a huge part in our pupils' journey from youth into adulthood. As well as providing scholarship and intellectual fulfilment, we also tend to an individual's spiritual and personal wellbeing, all within a powerful framework of Christian values provided by the school's Methodist foundation. Achievement is the primary goal, but in a spirit of community, tolerance and respect, to ensure that every pupil leaving Rydal has a set of qualities, values and skills to last a lifetime.

School life: inside the classroom and out

Small class sizes, coupled with an individual tutor system, mean we can tailor the learning process to our pupils' individual intellectual needs and capabilities. We set great store by self-development through independent reflection and learning. We have a culture that embraces drama, music and the visual arts and the facilities to support them.

Rydal Penrhos School has the on-campus facilities to offer sports such as rugby (2010 saw the opening of a new rugby academy in partnership with the WRU), hockey, cricket, netball and swimming, as well as squash, tennis, basketball and even Eton Fives. However, it also runs a vast array of other outdoor activities that exploit Snowdonia and the Irish Sea: for example, sailing (the school is a Royal Yacht Association training centre), kayaking, golf, climbing, gorge scrambling, orienteering, mountain biking and skiing.

Curriculum

The school has offered the IB diploma since 2003, and has produced excellent results from the outset. We provide the full range of subjects at GCSE and a wide choice for IB (or A level) in the sixth form as well as a pre-sixth/pre IB course.

Boarding

There are five well-established boarding houses, each looked after by experienced house parents and matrons who lead a team of tutors drawn from academic staff. The Health Centre and the central care team provide further support. There is a full and well-supported out of hours and weekend activity programme for boarders and day pupils to ensure good integration of all pupils and a real sense of belonging.

St John's College

College Green, Cardiff CF3 5YX

Tel: 029 2077 8936   Email: admin@stjohnscollegecardiff.co.uk

Fax: 029 2077 6182   Website: www.stjohnscollegecardiff.com

Headmaster: Dr D J Neville MA(Cantab), BSc, MusD, FRSA, AWACM, PGCE
School type: Coeducational Day
Member of: SHMIS, WISC, ASCL, CSA, CISC
Age range of pupils: 3–18
No. of pupils enrolled as at 1.9.12: 480
Boys: 260   Girls: 220
Fees per annum as at 1.9.12: Day: £6390–£12,072
Religious denomination: Roman Catholic welcoming other faiths

Outstanding recent inspection report referred to the school's exceptional ethos and results, which lead Wales and are amongst the best in the UK.

Curriculum

GCSE results at grades A*, A, B and C have been consistently outstanding. The school has been consistently at the top of Government tables in Wales especially in A level performance at grades A*, A and B.

The school has an outstanding record of admission to major British universities in all subject areas.

There is an early start during primary school years in the European languages French, Welsh and Spanish, with early experience of experimental science in laboratory circumstances taught by science specialists.

As a choir school, our Cathedral choirs and orchestras achieve exceptional standards of performance and in 2011 performed in Notre Dame Cathedral, Paris. There is an outstanding programme of competitive sport and drama, accessible to all.

The school is situated in a beautiful Grade II listed building in landscaped grounds with excellent access to the M4 and the A48M and with private sports grounds in close proximity.

Means tested public benefit bursaries are available.

Entry requirements

Children are assessed for admission during a one-day visit to the school, and by interview with parents.

St John's College is a registered charitable trust that exists to provide education for boys and girls. (Charity No. 701294)

St John's-on-the-Hill

(Founded 1923)

Tutshill, Chepstow, Monmouthshire NP16 7LE
Tel: 01291 622045   Email: registrar@stjohnsonthehill.co.uk
Fax: 01291 623932   Website: www.stjohnsonthehill.co.uk

Headmaster: Mr N Folland BSc
Appointed: 2011
School type: Coeducational Day & Boarding
Boarders from 7 years; Pre-Prep & Day Nursery
Age range of pupils: 3 months–13 years
No. of pupils enrolled as at 1.9.12: 302
Fees per annum as at 1.9.12: Day: £6675–£11,025
Weekly Boarding: £15,525
Boarding: £15,525
Average size of class: 16
Teacher/pupil ratio: 1:10

St John's-on-the-Hill is situated in extensive, attractive grounds on the border of Monmouthshire and Gloucestershire, overlooking Chepstow Castle and the beautiful Wye Valley. Served by an excellent motorway system, just three miles from the old Severn Bridge, St John's provides a consistently high standard of care and education.

Discovering and developing individual talent
The family atmosphere ensures that even the youngest child feels a sense of belonging. A high standard of teaching and small class sizes, combined with first-class facilities, ensure boys and girls can develop both their academic ability and character to the full. Emphasis is on mutual respect, integrity and the need to discover and develop individual talents, whether they are creative, intellectual or athletic.

Celebrating achievement
Children are encouraged to develop skills and achieve success across the curriculum. Sport, art, design technology, music and performing arts are therefore an important part of school life. Children are encouraged to be creative from an early age and to take part in regular drama productions, either front or backstage. Traditional and modern choral music is a particular strength within the school.

Scholarships and bursaries
Scholarships and awards are made for academic, music, sporting and dramatic ability. HM Forces bursaries are also available.

Boarding at St John's
Children can board from the age of seven on a full, weekly, or 'flexi' basis. The boarding house is family-run and has a friendly, homely atmosphere with spacious accommodation.

Creating the future
On leaving St John's, children enter a wide range of senior schools of their choice and with more than 100 senior school scholarships awarded to St John's children in the last five years, the school is justifiably proud of its scholarship record and senior school links.

St John's-on-the-Hill and Brightlands School Trust Limited is a registered charity (No. 312953) founded for the education of children.

Boarding Schools

Bloxham School

(Founded 1860)

Bloxham, Banbury, Oxfordshire OX15 4PE
Tel: 01295 720222   Email: registrar@bloxhamschool.com
Fax: 01295 721897   Website: www.bloxhamschool.com

Headmaster: Mr Mark E Allbrook MA
Appointed: September 2002
School type: Coeducational Boarding & Day
Boarders from 11 years
Member of: HMC, ASCL, Woodard Corporation
Age range of pupils: 11–18
No. of pupils enrolled as at 1.9.12: 424
Boys: 270 Girls: 154 Sixth Form: 140
Fees per annum as at 1.9.12: Day: £15,750–£22,320
Weekly Boarding: £20,460
Boarding: £28,845
Teacher/pupil ratio: 1:8.5
Religious denomination: Church of England

Bloxham School is, by choice, one of the smaller schools but is happy to be described as 'the small school with a great spirit'. Not that its size should be seen as anything other than a strength boasting, as it does, some quite outstanding facilities which have been considerably enhanced over the past two decades.

Founded in 1860 by local clergyman Rev Philip Egerton the coeducational school now educates about 420 pupils aged between 11 and 18. The school caters for day and boarding pupils but has strong local roots with the majority of pupils coming from within a one-hour travel band of the school. A little over 50% of the pupils board for all or part of the week although this percentage is much higher at the top end of the school as pupils gain valuable independence prior to university.

The school is also seeing an increasing number of pupils migrating from the London area taking advantage of the excellent road and rail links. This is proving particularly popular with families who may be looking to spend the weekends out of London – in the Cotswolds for example. They like Bloxham's flexible, modern approach to boarding as it gives them the access they seek and allows their children to enjoy their schooldays in a rural yet not isolated environment surrounded by wonderful playing fields and other enriching opportunities and facilities.

In Exham House, Bloxham's lower school (Years 7&8) boarding is entirely 'weekly' with the children coming to the house on either a Sunday evening or a Monday morning and going home again on the Friday evening. There is Saturday school in the upper school with lessons until lunchtime followed by a games afternoon. Boarders are free to go home virtually any weekend they choose after their sporting commitment is over. Some opt to stay on at school though to enjoy the organised activities or to simply to relax and socialise with their friends and make the most of the school's wonderful facilities and environment.

Bloxham also has a small number of overseas students (currently around 5%). This figure is kept deliberately low to ensure that those who are coming into the school from abroad will be able to integrate quickly and happily into their new learning and social environment.

The founder handed the school over to the Woodard Corporation in the 1890s and Bloxham is still a proud member of that Corporation of Schools today. The core of each Woodard School is that they all share the founder's vision of a Christian education coupled with a belief in nurturing and enriching each individual. That vision is still strong today encapsulated in the school's new strapline – Discovering the *Spark* in every child.

Bloxham regularly comes high up amongst the North Oxfordshire schools in a league table measuring the 'value added' component of each school. Headmaster Mark Allbrook is particularly pleased with this statistic:

"Bloxham, along with a growing number of independent schools, is not in favour of the old and largely discredited league tables, which simply show where the brightest pupils go to school. The value added tables are a much better guide to parents craving information about the difference a school is capable of making to the individual."

Facilities at the school are outstanding with recent innovations being an outstanding modern library, a sixth form art studio, an extension to the music school that caters for music technology and live recordings and a well-equipped technology centre that will have the addition of a food technology facility from 2012. And on the subject of food Bloxham continues to be known for the excellent food on offer to its pupils. The catering team regularly win awards for the variety and quality of the food on offer and for the healthy lifestyle a good diet helps promote.

The school is also well known for its music, art, technology and sport. In 2012 Bloxham teams became national champions in eventing (equestrian) and with their boys' clay shooting squad!

Bloxham became the first independent school to move away from a printed prospectus in favour of an award winning, online, multimedia experience that can be accessed via the school's website at www.bloxhamschool.com, where further information about the school can be found.

Although the school does hold open mornings each spring and autumn families are strongly advised to make an individual appointment to be shown around the school and to get the feel of this remarkable little Oxfordshire gem.

Bloxham School is a member of the Woodard Corporation, a charity that exists to provide excellent education for children in a Christian environment. Registered charity No. 1076484.

Brockhurst & Marlston House Schools

(Founded 1884)

Hermitage, Thatcham, West Berkshire RG18 9UL
Tel: 01635 200293
Fax: 01635 200190

Email: info@brockmarl.org.uk
Website: www.brockmarl.org.uk

Heads: David Fleming MA(Oxon), MSc & Mrs C E Riley MA, BEd, CertEd(Southampton)
Appointed: September 2000
School type: Boys' and Girls' Day and Weekly/Flexi Boarding
Age range of pupils: 3–13
No. of pupils enrolled as at 1.9.12: 275
No. of boarders: 120
Fees per annum as at 1.9.12: Day: £7410–£12,450
Weekly Boarding: £16,530
Boarding: £16,530
Average size of class: 16
Teacher/pupil ratio: 1:7

Brockhurst (Boys) and Marlston House (Girls) are twin schools sharing the same estate at Marlston, Hermitage. We offer a unique education with the best features of small single-sex classes and shared extracurricular activities at the centre of which is a magnificent Jacobean style mansion set in stunning Berkshire countryside.

Specialist and qualified staff promote a family atmosphere for the 3-13 age range and prepare children for entry to leading independent schools to which they regularly gain academic, music, art and sports scholarships. We have outstanding facilities with 21 acres of games fields within a 500 acre site,

including a sports hall, indoor 25m swimming pool, tennis courts, art and design studios, ICT suite, new Learning Development Centre (2011) and a superb equestrian school. In addition, we have an 18th century chateau in south-west France where our pupils practise their French. In addition to full boarding and day school, flexi/weekly boarding is a popular choice and we also provide a daily bus service for Hungerford, Ramsbury and district.

At Brockhurst and Marlston House the nursery and pre-prep children have the advantage of a department designed specifically for the age group, adjacent to the main prep school within its own garden and adventure play area. Children join the nursery class following their third birthday and most are introduced to the school day by attending the swimming sessions each Wednesday morning for 'Toddlers and Parents'. These are free sessions for those registered for the nursery class. The curriculum is designed to include the early learning goals, at the Foundation Stage, whilst extending each pupil according to their own pace of learning and individual development as they progress through the school. Much attention is given to social skills and boosting confidence. The pre-prep children use all the facilities of the prep schools and therefore the transition from pre-prep to main school is smooth and automatic.

At the heart of our teaching is the newly-opened (summer 2011) Learning Development Centre, West Berkshire.

Dedicated, trained, experienced staff at the heart of your child's education offer a range of learning experiences including the gifted and talented on extended learning programmes, English as a Foreign Language (EFL) taught in very small groups, or individually and support for pupils with learning difficulties thus meeting the specific needs of each child.

We aim:

- to develop successful, independent learners based on sound assessment and prior knowledge
- to identify strengths and barriers to achievement with each child
- to promote self-esteem, a sense of pride and resilience in each child
- to help children to take responsibility for their learning

The two schools offer a broad curriculum, which includes music, art and drama and an exciting range of extracurricular activities. This breadth is reflected in the range of scholarships achieved by our pupils this year.

However, above all, our children leave us as self-confident, well-mannered and enthusiastic individuals equipped to make the most of the opportunities and challenges ahead of them.

Contact Mrs Rachel Harper on 01635 200293 Email: rachel.harper@brockmarl.org.uk
www.brockmarl.org.uk

Burford School

(Founded 1571)

Lenthall House, Church Lane, Burford, Oxfordshire OX18 4SA
Tel: 01993 823283   Email: boarding.4040@burford.oxon.sch.uk
Fax: 01993 822041   Website: www.burford.oxon.sch.uk

Headteacher: Mrs K Haig BA, MEd
Head of Boarding: Mr P Johnson BEd
School type: Coeducational Boarding & Day
Member of: SBSA, BSA
Age range of pupils: 11–18
No. of pupils enrolled as at 1.9.12: 1184
Boys: 620 Girls: 564 Sixth Form: 230
No. of boarders: 90
Fees per annum as at 1.9.12:
Boarding: £9600
Average size of class: 25

Curriculum

All National Curriculum subjects are taught – the school provides an option choice of 21 GCSEs and 25 AS and A2 subjects.

Entry requirements

Entry is by interview and reference assessments.

The school is a specialist technology and science college offering excellent ICT facilities within eight computer rooms, additionally it is very well resourced in other curriculum areas.

It offers extensive sporting, cultural and extracurricular opportunities including CCF & ACF.

The flourishing boarding community is housed in the original 1571 site of the school in Burford (Lenthall House), the accommodation is of an excellent standard offering a real home from home for approximately 85 boarders.

Burford is quite simply a very happy and successful school.

Burford is a delightful small Cotswold town that lies between Oxford and Cheltenham (A40) within easy reach of London and all major airports.

The only state boarding school in Oxfordshire.

"Life away from home is more than just boarding." – Year 9 boarder.

"I'm so pleased I persuaded Mum and Dad that boarding was a better option than moving. I have enjoyed it immensely and feel so much more confident about university." – Year 13 boarder.

Boarding: 'An outstanding feature of the school.' – Ofsted inspection.

"Our students enjoy genuine success and have a real sense of purpose." – Head of Boarding.

Chafyn Grove School

(Founded 1876)

Bourne Avenue, Salisbury, Wiltshire SP1 1LR
Tel: 01722 333423   Email: office@chafyngrove.co.uk
Fax: 01722 323114   Website: www.chafyngrove.co.uk

Headmaster: E J Newton BA(Hons) (Cantab), PGCE
Appointed: September 2004
School type: Coeducational Day & Boarding
Boarders from 7 years
Age range of pupils: 3–13
No. of pupils enrolled as at 1.9.12: 323
Boys: 217 Girls: 106
No. of boarders: 54
Fees per annum as at 1.9.12: Day: £7335–£14,550
Boarding: £16,215–£19,755
Average size of class: 16–18
Teacher/pupil ratio: 1:10

Whether it's running to their next class, taking part in a gardening activity, or going out to the local arts centre to play in a jazz concert, Chafyn pupils have a full life! We strive to help all our children reach their full potential whether it is on the sports field, on the stage or in the classroom. A huge variety of extracurricular activities, a committed staff, excellent facilities and small class sizes combine to allow us to aim high in every area of school life. At the same time, a friendly environment, supportive parents and a relaxed atmosphere make for happy days at school. It is this combination that makes Chafyn Grove special.

Our boarding enhances the sense of community and is all about making the most of your time at school, developing independence and making friends for life – our aim is to provide a caring and happy environment in which children thrive and grow. Our boarders benefit from a secure and homely atmosphere and are accommodated in cosy, brightly decorated dormitories, often creatively decorated with their own pictures and posters, their own bedding and of course a teddy or two! There is a full weekly activity programme for boarders, as well as a weekend programme, where both boarding and teaching staff are fully involved with the children.

Small class sizes (maximum 18) and a commitment to high standards allow our pupils to perform impressively in the classroom. In recent years all pupils have reached the school of their choice and 14 scholarships is an average annual haul for our pupils going on to Senior Schools. Pupils go on to many well-known schools including Bryanston, Canford, Dauntsey's, Eton, Godolphin, Marlborough, Sherborne and Winchester. Pupils are also prepared for 11+ to the two Grammar Schools in Salisbury – several Year 6 pupils made the grade last year, although some opted to stay at Chafyn, and who can blame them!

EF International Academy Oxford

International Academy

Pullens Lane, Headington, Oxfordshire OX3 0DT
Tel: +41 41 41 74 525   Email: admissionsia@ef.com
Fax: +44 (0) 1865 759661   Website: www.ef.com/academy

Head of School: Ms Ted McGrath
School type: Coeducational Boarding
Age range of pupils: 15–18
No. of pupils enrolled as at 1.1.12: 160
Fees per annum as at 1.1.12:
Boarding: £22,950

EF International Academy is part of EF Education First, the world leader in international education. With over 45 years of experience, EF has helped more than four million students realise their dream of studying abroad.

The School

Our school is situated in the illustrious city of Oxford, renowned for its scholastic tradition and rich cultural and architectural heritage. EF students join Oxford's vibrant academic community, which attracts leading scholars from around the world. Ten minutes from Oxford's centre, the newly renovated campus has multimedia classrooms, a fully-equipped gym, state-of-the-art science and computer labs, wireless internet access, a library, cafeteria and lounge. The school has a truly international atmosphere, with students from over 60 different countries living and studying alongside each other.

Academics

Education at EF is highly personal and a range of internationally acclaimed programmes are offered to meet the individual needs of each student; including IB Diploma and A level, as well as IGCSE and the High School Preparation Programme. Intensive English language courses are also available. EF has a track record of academic excellence with 45% of students receiving A/A* grades at A level, compared with the national average of 27%.

University Placements

Not only have the majority of our students been accepted into top ranked universities such as Oxford, Cambridge and LSE, they have also been admitted to courses that are deemed to be the best in the country for their subject, such as accounting at the University of Warwick, law at University College London, and chemical engineering at the University of Birmingham.

Pastoral Care

Personal tutors provide one-to-one individualised support and guidance. Each student is assigned a personal tutor whose role is to monitor the student's academic progress, university applications and general welfare. Students are encouraged to nurture their talents and develop new skills and confidence.

Scholarships

Scholarships will be awarded to highly talented and ambitious students who can make a positive contribution to the school community. Two students are awarded Founder's scholarships, which will cover 50% of the total fees. Many other general scholarships are also available for students who demonstrate overall excellence.

Residential Life

Accommodation is offered in on-campus dormitories or with host families, where students can benefit from full immersion into British culture and language; both options provide a safe, supportive and comfortable home away from home.

Rye St Antony

(Founded 1930)

Pullens Lane, Oxford, Oxfordshire OX3 0BY
Tel: 01865 762802   Email: enquiries@ryestantony.co.uk
Fax: 01865 763611   Website: www.ryestantony.co.uk

Headmistress: Miss A M Jones BA, PGCE
Appointed: 1990
School type: Girls' Boarding & Day
Boarders from 5 years
Member of: GSA, BSA
Age range of pupils:
Boys: 3–8
Girls: 3–18
No. of pupils enrolled as at 1.9.12: 400
Boys: 20   Girls: 380   Sixth Form: 70
No. of boarders: 70
Fees per annum as at 1.9.12: Day: £8400–£12,780
Weekly Boarding: £16,800–£19,800
Boarding: £17,790–£20,790
Average size of class: 16-20
Teacher/pupil ratio: 1:8

Rye St Antony is an independent boarding and day school for girls aged 3 to 18 (boys 3 to 8). Set in 13 acres of gardens and woodland a mile from the centre of Oxford, Rye is noted for its happy and purposeful atmosphere, its high academic standards, its wide range of extracurricular activities and its strong sense of community.

Early years education at Rye has consistently been judged by Ofsted as outstanding. A secure, supportive and stimulating environment nurtures enthusiasm, confidence and independence. Throughout the junior years specialist teaching is focused on each pupil as an individual, and the aim is to develop bright and enquiring minds, able to think rationally, creatively and independently, in young people growing steadily in their understanding of themselves and others.

In the senior school stimulating teaching across a broad curriculum encourages curiosity, investigation and discovery. Girls value the opportunity for discussion and research, in school and beyond, and the opportunity to be actively engaged in their learning and confident in learning with others and learning independently.

Results are impressive. At GCSE most girls achieve high grades in ten or more subjects, with over half of these grades being A or A*. Almost all girls completing sixth form achieve university places of their first choice, and last year's AS/A level grades gave an average of AAB for each girl. These same girls also achieved significant successes in music, art, drama and sport, the latter including at international level.

At the heart of each girl's programme is its purpose: to help her complete her school years happy, resilient, wise, keen to embark on the future and keen to make her contribution to the world.

Rye St Antony School is a registered charity (No. 309685) to provide education for girls up to the age of 18 years and boys up to the age of 8 years.

St Mary's Calne

(Founded 1873)

Curzon Street, Calne, Wiltshire SN11 0DF
Tel: 01249 857200   Email: office@stmaryscalne.org
Fax: 01249 857207   Website: www.stmaryscalne.org

Headmistress: Dr Helen Wright MA(Oxon), MA(Leics), EdD(Exeter), PGCE(Oxon), FRSA, MIoD
Appointed: April 2003
School type: Girls' Boarding & Day
Age range of pupils: 11–18
No. of pupils enrolled as at 1.9.12: 335
Sixth Form: 110
No. of boarders: 260
Fees per annum as at 1.9.12: Day: £22,539–£23,001
Boarding: £30,870–£31,500
Teacher/pupil ratio: 1:5

St Mary's Calne is a boarding and day school of around 335 girls aged 11-18. Approximately 80% of the girls board and it is a rich boarding life with all girls taking part in the full curriculum and extracurricular activities on offer.

St Mary's is committed to providing a broad and fulfilling education that will challenge and inspire its pupils, as well as helping them to achieve fantastic public examination results. In 2011, 36% of all A level grades were A*s, with over half of the girls achieving all A*-A grades. At GCSE, 63% of girls gained eight or more A*-A grades.

The school is small by design and is renowned for outstanding pastoral care. Every girl is known and cared for as an individual and has a tutor to support and guide her through every aspect of school life; from organisational skills and subject choices through to university application.

All girls go on to higher education (20% to Oxbridge in 2011) and the purpose-built Sixth Form Centre, a tailor-made lecture programme, a women in corporate culture conference, debating competitions, careers advice, leadership roles and much more prepare the girls for university and beyond.

St Mary's sportswomen compete at a national level in several major sports and the school regularly fields a successful team for the British Schoolgirls' Ski Races. All girls work for the Bronze Duke of Edinburgh's Award with large numbers going on to higher levels. 80% of girls play musical instruments and take part in a wide variety of ensembles. Drama productions transfer to the London stage and the Edinburgh Festival Fringe and the department boasts a unique relationship with RADA.

Location
Two hours west of London. Escorted travel to and from London and airports at all holidays and exeats.

Swanbourne House School

(Founded 1920)

Swanbourne, Milton Keynes MK17 0HZ
Tel: 01296 720264   Email: office@swanbourne.org
Fax: 01296 728089   Website: www.swanbourne.org

Joint Heads: Mr S D Goodhart BEd(Hons) & Mrs J S Goodhart BEd
School type: Coeducational Boarding & Day
Boarders from 7
Member of: IAPS, BSA
Age range of pupils: 3–13
No. of pupils enrolled as at 1.9.12:
Boys: 225 Girls: 187
No. of boarders: 70
Fees per annum as at 1.9.12: Day: £7140–£15,255
Boarding: £19,560
Average size of class: 17
Religious denomination: Church of England

Curriculum

Swanbourne House offers a strong academic and scholarship programme by following Common Entrance and also setting our forms for maths, English and French. We have success in preparing children for entry into their chosen public schools.

The school scholarship record is exemplary with 43 scholarships won in the past eight years. Our boarding house was, last year, awarded 'outstanding' in all areas from Ofsted.

Entry requirements

Children may enter the school at any age from 3 years to 11 years. Each child takes a short familiarisation and assessment and then we recommend placement in one of our three, streamed classes. Scholarships are available for highly academic pupils and all-rounders, or for specific talents at 11+. We offer bursaries to forces families. We are keen to meet children who love life and who will thrive through our family care and activity programme.

More information can be gathered from our website: www.swanbourne.org

Swanbourne House School is a registered charity that exists to provide education for children. (No. 310640)

Tudor Hall School

(Founded 1850)

Wykham Park, Banbury, Oxfordshire OX16 9UR
Tel: 01295 263434   Email: admissions@tudorhallschool.com
Fax: 01295 253264   Website: www.tudorhallschool.com

Headmistress: Miss W Griffiths BSc
School type: Girls' Boarding & Day
Boarders from 11
Member of: GSA, AGBIS, ASCL
Age range of pupils: 11–18
No. of pupils enrolled as at 1.4.12: 332
Sixth Form: 88
No. of day girls: 86
No. of boarders: 246
Fees per annum as at 1.4.12: Day: £17,175
Boarding: £26,700
Average size of class: 16
Teacher/pupil ratio: 1:8
Religious denomination: Anglican

Curriculum

The curriculum includes English, mathematics, biology, chemistry, physics, information technology, Latin, French, German or Spanish, history, geography, RS, drama, food & nutrition, dance art, music, textiles and DT. In addition, history of art, government & politics, economics, ancient Greek, drama & theatre studies, photography, PE, further mathematics and business studies may be taken up in the sixth form. Italian, Russian and Mandarin are also available. Sports include netball, hockey, lacrosse, tennis, athletics, swimming and rounders. The wide range of extras includes riding, ballet, speech & drama and most musical instruments.

Entry requirements

11+, 13+ Common Entrance, internal exams and interview, and GCSEs and interview for sixth form.

Tudor Hall is a registered charity existing to provide good, quality education for girls aged 11-18 in a lively, stimulating and friendly boarding environment. (No. 1042783.)

Bedford School

(Founded 1552)

De Parys Avenue, Bedford, Bedfordshire MK40 2TU
Tel: +44 (0)1234 362216 Email: admissions@bedfordschool.org.uk
Fax: +44 (0)1234 362283 Website: www.bedfordschool.org.uk

Head Master: Mr J Moule MA
Appointed: 2008
School type: Boys' Boarding & Day
Age range of pupils: 7–18
No. of pupils enrolled as at 1.9.11: 1090
Sixth Form: 278
No. of boarders: 270
Fees per annum as at 1.9.12: Day: £10,518–£16,227
Weekly Boarding: £17,583–£26,157
Full Boarding: £18,444–£27,051
Average size of class: 15-20
Teacher/pupil ratio: 1:10
Religious denomination: Anglican

Bedford School is an independent boarding and day school for boys aged 7 to 18 years, where fundamental traditions combine with innovative educational thinking. In addition to an established reputation for academic excellence, we are renowned for our strengths in music, the arts and sport. Situated on an extensive parkland estate of 40 acres in the heart of Bedford, the school is a lively community of day boys, weekly and full boarders.

Our highly-qualified teaching staff are selected on their ability to communicate and inspire. The result is a vibrant, stimulating environment, were boys can be happy, grow in self-confidence, thrive academically and make the most of the wide range of opportunities on offer. Our broad curriculum offers boys a varied choice of subjects, and our academic success is demonstrated by a long history of impressive examination results at GCSE, A level, and in the International Baccalaureate Diploma. We also offer an impressive range of extracurricular activities with over 80 clubs and societies.

Our music school is one of the largest in the country and has a full programme of concerts and performances throughout the year. Facilities are virtually unrivalled and include a recreation centre with theatre, large sports hall, squash courts, fitness centre and a 25-metre indoor swimming pool; twin Astroturf pitches; an observatory and planetarium and an impressive library.

We offer a generous Access Award & Scholarship Scheme for talented boys, irrespective of background.

We warmly invite you to join us at one of our open mornings or for a private visit to see the school in action, meet the boys and staff, and get a flavour of life at Bedford School. Please contact Vanessa Hicks, Director of Admissions, for further information on 01234 362216 or email admissions@bedfordschool.org.uk.

Bedford School is part of The Harpur Trust.

Company No. 3475202/Charity no. 1066861.

Berkhamsted School

(Founded 1541)

131 High Street, Berkhamsted, Hertfordshire HP4 2DJ
Tel: 01442 358001   Email: admissions@berkhamstedschool.org
Fax: 01442 358040   Website: www.berkhamstedschool.org

BERKHAMSTED
SCHOOL

Principal: Mr Mark Steed MA(Cantab), MA
Appointed: September 2008
School type: Coeducational & single-sex, day & boarding
Age range of pupils: 3–18
No. of pupils enrolled as at 1.9.12: 1508
Boys: 415 Girls: 316 Sixth Form: 331
Prep: 446
Fees per annum as at 1.9.12: Day: £7770–£17,460
Weekly Boarding: £23,370
Boarding: £27,815
Average size of class: 20

Berkhamsted School offers much to make it worthy of closer consideration: a long-established reputation for excellent educational provision, high-quality facilities and the range of experiences it offers its pupils; an attractive location in a thriving market town with easy access to London; and a range of services that support the lives of busy families.

It is also one of only a small number of schools in the country to offer a 'diamond' structure that combines the best of both single-sex and coeducational teaching. Boys and girls are taught together until the age of 11 (Berkhamsted Pre-Prep and Berkhamsted Prep), separately from 11 – 16 (Berkhamsted Boys and Berkhamsted Girls), before coming back together again in a joint Sixth Form (Berkhamsted Sixth).

Pupils across the School enjoy the benefits of being part of a small, caring community based in an environment appropriate to their specific educational needs, yet with access to the state-of-the-art facilities of a large school; a 550-seat theatre, a six-lane 25m swimming pool and sports centre, spacious, modern dining facilities and one of the best art departments in the country.

Another feature of Berkhamsted is the provision of a range of services that make life easier for parents who are juggling busy schedules; from flexible boarding options that include occasional, weekly or full boarding in high-quality accommodation to a range of coach routes, 'extended day' support, day nursery provision (five months to three years) and wrap-around care 51 weeks of the year.

Academic results are consistently strong with 100% pass rate at A level every year since 2003, and an average of over 85% at A*-B grades in recent years. In 2011, GCSE students achieved a record 69% of grades at A* to A. Thirty six Berkhamsted students have been accepted at Oxford and Cambridge in the past five years and 74% of students achieve places at the top 30 UK universities.

Berkhamsted offers scholarships – academic, art, drama, music and sport – and means-tested bursaries to talented pupils on entry to the school.

Parents are welcome to visit the School at any time: please call 01442 358001 for an appointment and a tour to appreciate what Berkhamsted can offer your child.

Haileybury

(Founded 1862)

Haileybury, Hertford, Hertfordshire SG13 7NU
Tel: +44 (0)1992 706353 Email: registrar@haileybury.com
Fax: +44 (0)1992 470663 Website: www.haileybury.com

The Master: J S Davies MA(Cantab)
Appointed: September 2009
School type: Coeducational Boarding & Day
Age range of pupils: 11–18
No. of pupils enrolled as at 1.9.12: 764
Boys: 458 Girls: 306 Sixth Form: 120
No. of boarders: 483
Fees per annum as at 1.9.12: Day: £13,668–£20,565
Boarding: £17,367–£27,384
Teacher/pupil ratio: 1:7

Make your school days Haileybury days.

All parents want to give their children the best possible start in life and that usually means finding the right school for them. Do they join a new senior school at 11 or at 13? Do they board or not? Thinking ahead means you need to consider whether they would like to opt for A levels or the International Baccalaureate Diploma Programme. Are they passionate about music, drama or art? Do they prefer the sciences or humanities?

Parents should also consider their own needs as well as their children's. If both parents work full-time, perhaps you would like to look at a school that offers a flexible boarding solution, allowing children to be at school uninterrupted during the week but at home for weekends.

If all these options sound impossible to find in a single school on your doorstep, think again! Haileybury, a co-educational, independent boarding school, is only 20 miles north of London in rural Hertfordshire.

Haileybury educates boys and girls aged 11 to 18. As a school, Haileybury has grown, adapted and flourished from its foundation in the 19th century, through the profound changes of the 21st century.

Academic results are most important: we encourage in our pupils a questioning mind and a desire to learn and extend their knowledge and understanding of the world around them. Having offered the International Baccalaureate Diploma Programme most successfully for more than 10 years, we are now widely recognised as one of the leading IB schools in the country and one of the few where pupils can choose between the IB and A levels.

With all this choice on offer, what better incentive is there to come and visit us and see our facilities for yourself? We will be pleased to make an appointment for you to meet The Master, and Housemistresses or Housemasters, and to tour our beautiful site. Please contact Iona Hutchinson, The Registrar, on 01992 706 353 for further information.

Orwell Park School

(Founded 1867)

Nacton, Ipswich, Suffolk IP10 0ER
Tel: 01473 659225   Email: opssecretary@orwellpark.co.uk
Fax: 01473 659822   Website: www.orwellpark.co.uk

Headmaster: Mr Adrian Brown MA(Cantab)
Appointed: September 2011
School type: Coeducational Boarding & Day
Boarders from 7
Member of: IAPS, ISC, BSA
Age range of pupils: 2½–13
No. of pupils enrolled as at 1.9.12: 253
Boys: 150 Girls: 103
No. of boarders: 147
Fees per annum as at 1.9.12:
Pre-Prep (Day): £6045–£9315
Prep (Day): £13,785–£15,285
Prep (Boarding): £17,655–£19,605
Average size of class: 12-14
Teacher/pupil ratio: 1:10
Religious denomination: Interdenominational

Set in more than 100 acres of parkland overlooking the River Orwell in Suffolk, Orwell Park provides a broad and balanced education for boys and girls, boarders and day pupils, between the ages of 3 and 13. A modern, caring and flexible approach to boarding sets Orwell Park apart as a forward-thinking school, which continues to instil traditional values such as commitment, compassion and courtesy in its pupils.

Academically, Orwell Park prides itself on successfully preparing children for entry to senior school at 13+, with more than a third of leavers winning scholarships: for academic excellence or for music, art, sport, design and technology – all to a wide range of senior independent schools. Orwell Park offers academic challenge to all children and learning support for those who need it. In the classroom, a traditional curriculum (including classics) is taught, using the most modern methods. The school employs motivated teachers with a passion for their subject; they will encourage academic self-reliance, helping all children in time to take responsibility for their own learning and personal organisation. The pupil: staff ratio is 10:1.

Extensive grounds provide abundant opportunities for children's games, both formal and informal. Excellent facilities range from assault course to Astroturf, golf course to games pitches, swimming pool to squash courts and sports hall. There is a full fixture list of matches against other schools in which boys and girls of all abilities are selected to play. In addition to sport, an extensive range of activities is also offered.

At Orwell Park, children are encouraged to achieve academic success, to be free to play, explore and learn in one of the most beautiful school settings in England.

St Edmund's College & Prep School

(Founded 1568)

Old Hall Green, Nr Ware, Hertfordshire SG11 1DS
Tel: 01920 824247   Email: admissions@stedmundscollege.org
Fax: 01920 823011   Website: www.stedmundscollege.org

Head: Paulo Durán BA MA
Appointed: September 2012
School type: Coeducational Day & Boarding
(Boarders from 11 years)
Age range of pupils: 3–18
No. of pupils enrolled as at 1.9.12: 823
Boys: 472 Girls: 351 Sixth Form: 145
No. of boarders: 108
Fees per annum as at 1.9.12: Day: £9465–£14,955
Weekly Boarding: £19,830–£22,575
Boarding: £21,855–£24,990
Average size of class: 20
Teacher/pupil ratio: 1:9

When you arrive at St Edmund's College, England's oldest Catholic school, you cannot help but be impressed by the grandeur of its buildings and delightful location: when you leave, however, what you will remember will be its people.

Time and again visitors say how they are struck by the atmosphere of the college that fosters a special sense of community and self awareness amongst the staff and students who work here.

The school combines excellent facilities and teaching standards with a friendly atmosphere and a strong emphasis on learning and mutual respect. The community spirit of the school encourages students to develop as individuals, to pursue their own interests and achieve their goals, both in academic and extracurricular activities and not to be afraid of a challenge.

Scholarship is at the heart of our mission and our students are encouraged to learn, to explore and to ask the difficult questions. Small class sizes ensure that the academic progress of each student is monitored and at every stage we adjust our teaching to suit the ability and needs of each child.

St Edmund's does not turn out stereotypes. By the time they leave school, the students are confident and caring team players, but most importantly they are secure individuals, comfortable in their own skin and ready to contribute to society.

For the younger pupils, St Edmund's Prep, which is located on the same site, offers a sound preparation for the senior school, providing a healthy balance between academic work and recreational activities with plenty of opportunity for creativity and physical exercise. The prep school also includes Cygnets, which is a nurturing nursery featuring dedicated facilities including its own fun and safe outdoor play area.

For further details about St Edmund's College and St Edmund's Prep, please call the Admissions Office on 01920 824247 or visit www.stedmundscollege.org

Tring Park School for the Performing Arts

(Founded 1919)

Tring Park, Tring, Hertfordshire HP23 5LX
Tel: 01442 824255   Email: info@tringpark.com
Fax: 01442 891069   Website: www.tringpark.com

TringPark
School for the   Performing Arts

Principal: Mr Stefan Anderson MA, ARCM, ARCT
Appointed: September 2002
School type: Coeducational Boarding & Day
Age range of pupils: 8–19
No. of pupils enrolled as at 1.9.12: 317
Boys: 88 Girls: 229 Sixth Form: 217
No. of boarders: 197
Fees per annum as at 1.9.12: Day: £12,870–£20,100
Boarding: £21,285–£30,030

Tring Park School for the Performing Arts offers a unique opportunity for gifted young people to specialise in Dance, Drama, Musical Theatre or Music, whilst gaining an excellent academic education to GCSE, IGCSE, BTEC and A level. Recent DCSF figures have shown that our 'Value Added' measure has put us in the top 5% of schools in the entire country.

Tring Park is an independent, co-educational boarding and day school, for up to 320 pupils between the ages of 8-19. The school is housed in a former Rothschild mansion and set in beautiful grounds in Tring, Hertfordshire, only 33 miles from central London with easy access via road and rail.

Pupils perform regularly both in Tring Park's purpose-built Markova Theatre as well as in London, throughout the UK and Europe. Performances have included Gershwin's *Crazy for You*, *The Boy Friend* and *Jesus Christ Superstar* at the Shaw Theatre, London. Tring Park annually provides 25 young ballet dancers to perform in the Christmas production of *Nutcracker* with English National Ballet at the London Coliseum.

Recent successes include three alumni all appearing in principal roles in *Mamma Mia*, former students Amy Nuttall and Jessica Brown Findlay both in major roles in ITV's *Downton Abbey*, plus major roles for former students in *Dirty Dancing*, *Rocky Horror Show* and *Legally Blonde*. Lily James played Desdemona in Shakespeare's *Othello* and now stars in the film *Fast Girls*. Tyrone Singleton and Max Westwell are both Soloists at Birmingham Royal Ballet and the school boasts dancers in companies from English National Ballet to New York City Ballet. See www.tringpark.com/alumni for further information.

For information on forthcoming Open Days or to request a prospectus please contact:

Adelia Wood-Smith

adelia.wood-smith@tringpark.com

Tel. 01442 824255

The AES Tring Park School Trust is a registered charity No. 1040330. Tring Park School exists to promote and provide for the advancement of education.

Ashby School

(Founded 1567)

School House, Leicester Road, Ashby-de-la-Zouch, Leicestershire LE65 1DH
Tel: +44 (0) 1530 413759   Email: schoolhouse@ashbyschool.org.uk
Fax: +44 (0) 1530 415241   Website: www.ashbyschool.org.uk

Headteacher: Mr Eddie Green
Appointed: September 2011
School type: Academy International Status School with Specialisms in Technology & Modern Foreign Language, Senior, Sixth Form
Age range of pupils: 11–19
No. of pupils enrolled as at 1.9.12: 1643
Boys: 852 Girls: 791

Established in 1567, this ancient boarding residence forms part of the large and successful Ashby School in the heart of England. This coeducational school has been awarded two specialisms in technology and modern foreign languages with international school status.

Results for A level are consistently high and GCSE results are also very impressive and above the national average.

The boarding residence is home to a family of boys in an attractive Georgian house, set in its own grounds. Ofsted has classified School House as 'outstanding', stating: 'The atmosphere in the house is extremely positive and reflects the care and support provided... Boys present as really caring about each other and their house, which reflects how well they are cared for.'

In addition, School House has recently invested £2.8million to extend its boarding provision, which provides some of the best accommodation in the UK. We are able to offer individual or twin ensuite rooms to our sixth form students. The new building also provides boarders with an additional computer suite, lounges, a sixth form kitchen and a games room.

Sporting and recreational facilities surround the house with sports fields, a large sports hall and floodlit, all-weather courts. There is also an excellent heated indoor swimming pool. A full programme of sport is available and boarders can also take advantage of professional coaching. The school provides a wide variety of recreational clubs including Duke of Edinburgh's Award Scheme, orienteering and residential/cultural exchange programmes. Opportunities are available to boarders throughout the year including visits to places of historical and cultural interest, theme parks, the theatre, shopping trips, bowling, the cinema and ice skating *etc.*

To find out more about this family of boys in the Heart of England please contact Xenia Elias, Director of Boarding, by email or tel: 00 44 (0) 1530 413759.

The Royal Hospital School

(Crown Charity, founded 1712)

Holbrook, Ipswich, Suffolk IP9 2RX
Tel: +44 (0) 1473 326210   Email: admissions@royalhospitalschool.org
Fax: +44 (0) 1473 326213   Website: www.royalhospitalschool.org

Headmaster: Mr James Lockwood MA
Appointed: September 2012
School type: Coeducational Full Boarding and Day
Member of: HMC, SHMIS, BSA
Age range of pupils: 11–18
No. of pupils enrolled as at 1.9.12: 700
Boys: 410 Girls: 290 Sixth Form: 220
No. of boarders: 290 boys; 220 girls
No. of day pupils: 120 boys; 70 girls
Size of sixth form: 110 boys; 110 girls
No. of boarders: 510
Fees per annum as at 1.9.12: Day: £11,994–£15,672
Weekly Boarding: £19,995–£23,997
Boarding: £19,995–£23,997
Average size of class: 17
Teacher/pupil ratio: 1:8
Religious denomination: Church of England

Founded in 1712 in Greenwich, the Royal Hospital School moved to its present site set in 200 acres of stunning Suffolk countryside overlooking the River Stour, in 1933.

Close pastoral care is at the heart of the school ethos. Every child feels nurtured, supported and encouraged and great emphasis is placed on regular communication between parents, school and pupils. Boarders and day pupils can choose to be members of one of the four girls', five boys' or two coeducational houses and almost all staff live on site, reinforcing the community feel about the school.

Pupils entering the school at 11+ years join a junior house, which aims to help the transition between primary and senior school. The pastoral care and routines are tailored to the needs of younger pupils

and facilities for day pupils to board on an *ad hoc* basis are popular with busy parents. All pupils, whether moving up from the junior houses or entering the school at 13+, are effectively 'new' when they join the senior houses. In the final year of sixth form pupils move into Nelson House with single studies and facilities that encourage more independent living in preparation for university life and beyond.

The curriculum is broad and balanced, combining the best of academic traditions with the latest technologies and with small class sizes, every pupil receives close individual guidance. Supported by high quality enthusiastic teaching, excellent resources and dedicated tutorial support, pupils are encouraged to aim high, attain their personal best and most importantly to enjoy achieving it.

Music, drama and dance play an important part in school life and this is emphasised by the new £3.6 million music school. The art and design technology departments enjoy an outstanding reputation with pupils' work consistently achieving high grades and being exhibited locally and nationally.

Fitness and wellbeing are promoted through the enjoyment of a wide range of sports, from the traditional games of rugby, hockey, cricket and tennis to more specialist pursuits such as water polo, riding, canoeing, golf, shooting and dry skiing. All pupils joining in Year 7 learn to sail and the very enthusiastic can sail up to four times a week to competition level. As well as a fleet of 40 dinghies, the school's own Cornish Shrimpers are used for coastal cruising at the weekends and holidays.

The CCF, Duke of Edinburgh's Award Scheme, Community Action Team and huge range of extracurricular activities, provide a wonderful programme of adventure and self improvement. By the time pupils leave the school, they are well equipped to take responsibility, show initiative, think dynamically and to approach life with an open and receptive mind.

Scholarships, discount and bursaries
Scholarships (Academic, Art, Music, Sport and Sailing).

Seafarer discount: 15% off full boarding fee.

Seafarer bursaries: means-tested through parent charity Greenwich Hospital.

Discounts for services families eligible for MOD Continuity of Education Allowance (CEA).

Sibling discounts: 10% off third and subsequent child.

Stamford Endowed Schools

(Founded 1532)

Brazenose House, St Paul's Street, Stamford, Lincolnshire PE9 2BS
Tel: 01780 750310   Email: ses@ses.lincs.sch.uk
Fax: 01780 750397   Website: www.ses.lincs.sch.uk

Principal: Stephen C Roberts
School type: Coeducational Day & Boarding
Age range of pupils: 2–18
No. of pupils enrolled as at 1.9.12: 1690
Sixth Form: 400
No. of boarders: 106
Fees per annum as at 1.9.12: Day: £12,624
7 day boarding: £23,028
5 day boarding: £20,076
3 day boarding: £17,448
Average size of class: 16-19
Teacher/pupil ratio: 1:11.5

Passion, enthusiasm, commitment and care underlie every aspect of life at the Stamford Endowed Schools. Our children are educated in an environment where learning is regarded as a privilege and key to unlocking all of life's possibilities. Our teachers dedicate themselves to inspiring intellectual curiosity in the students in evermore innovative ways, whilst doing their utmost to promote and protect the wellbeing of the children in their care.

As a community our schools work in harmony, blending students of different backgrounds and broadening their horizons with the many opportunities available in and beyond the classroom. As a result, the students are equipped not only with exceptional exam results, but a wide range of experiences that prepare them for whatever path they choose in life.

The Stamford Endowed Schools are made up of the Stamford Junior School and Earlybird Nursery, Stamford High School, Stamford School and the sixth form. Our children begin their journey at the Earlybird Nursery at age two, progressing to Stamford Junior School at age 4 until 11. The children are taught co-educationally.

At age 11, boys begin at Stamford School and girls at Stamford High School. We accept entry into any year although Years 7 and 9 are the most common entry points. Teaching boys and girls separately provides a proven academic advantage during the period from age 11 to GCSEs. Boys and girls are still able to mix in many extracurricular activities.

Girls and boys remain affiliated with their schools and come back into the classroom together in the sixth form, where study requires a more mature character and attention is given to preparing the students for life beyond the schools. Our sixth form is hugely popular and attracts additional students from across the region.

For more information, please visit our website at www.ses.lincs.sch.uk, call 01780 750310 or email ses@ses.lincs.sch.uk. We have dedicated admissions staff who will guide you through the process of joining our schools and answer any questions you might have, from bursary and scholarship information to details of our bus timetable.

Uppingham School

(Founded 1584)

Uppingham, Rutland LE15 9QE
Tel: 01572 822216   Admissions: 01572 820611
Email: admissions@uppingham.co.uk
Fax: 01572 822332   Website: www.uppingham.co.uk

Headmaster: Mr Richard Harman
Appointed: 2006
School type: Coeducational Boarding
Age range of pupils: 13–18
No. of pupils enrolled as at 1.9.12: 790
Boys: 462 Girls: 328 Sixth Form: 380
No. of boarders: 769
Fees per annum as at 1.9.12: Day: £21,300
Boarding: £30,429
Day: £7,100 per term
Boarding: £10,143 per term
Average size of class: 11-18
Teacher/pupil ratio: 1:7

Why Uppingham?
Full Boarding. Full Stop.
Uppingham is one of few that can declare itself a truly full boarding school. Of the School's roll (790), all but a handful are full boarders. The pupils benefit from a singular focus and an economy of scale that enables a remarkable depth and diversity of curricular and extra-curricular opportunity.

Enriching Mix
A strong academic focus underpins the School which is also renowned for music and strength in the performing arts; there is also a strong sporting tradition, now enhanced by the outstanding new sports centre. Pupils pull together, respecting and enjoying each other's achievements and supporting each other enthusiastically in varied activities.

Finding a Voice
Uppingham is unabashedly a "singing school" and Chapel services provide an exhilarating way for pupils and staff to start most days and generate an unmatchable esprit de corps. The Chapel's pulpit is not the sole preserve of the Chaplain and the School regularly enjoys morning assemblies from a diversity of staff, visiting speakers and well-motivated school orators!

Space to Grow
The boarding house environment is where individual identities are fostered and Uppingham's are smaller than many others. Boys' houses are typically 50 strong whilst girls' houses have a maximum of 60, reflecting the 10 or 12 pupils per year group in each. This affords a high degree of pastoral care in each house.

Together at the Table
House dining is another important feature of life at Uppingham. At meal times, house staff have the chance to catch up with their charges each day whilst the pupils themselves benefit from contact with the constantly changing rotation of staff, and guests, who might dine with them at lunch each day, a feature that strengthens the feeling of community, sharing and social engagement.

Supported and Stretched
With all of the academic staff involved as tutors in houses, the needs and demands of boarders are appreciated and understood by them all. There is a common culture and a superb team in each. Confidence is nurtured, academic curiosity encouraged and challenges made, all of which leads to higher expectations and, ultimately, greater achievement.

Farringtons School

(Founded 1911)

Perry Street, Chislehurst, Kent BR7 6LR
Tel: 020 8467 0256   Email: fvail@farringtons.kent.sch.uk
Fax: 020 8467 5442   Website: www.farringtons.org.uk

Headmistress: Mrs C E James MA
School type: Coeducational Day & Boarding
Member of: SHMIS, AGBIS, BSA
Age range of pupils: 3–18
No. of pupils enrolled as at 1.9.12: 650
Boys: 221 Girls: 429 Sixth Form: 80
No. of boarders: 60
Fees per annum as at 1.9.12: Day: £9060–£12,120
Weekly Boarding: £21,900
Boarding: £23,280
Average size of class: 15-20
Religious denomination: Methodist

Farringtons is a dynamic and inspirational school with outstanding facilities and resources, and is dedicated to providing your child with the best education possible, within a happy, purposeful and stimulating environment. The school offers a broad and balanced academic, sporting and social curriculum that encourages each pupil to fulfil his or her potential.

Conveniently located close to London, on the border of Kent, in 25 acres of attractive leafy grounds, Farringtons has good local and regional transport links and is also easily accessible from the M25, Eurostar terminals and major airports.

Entry requirements

Junior School: interview with Headmistress and a day spent in school.

Senior School: interview with Headmistress and entrance examination.

Examinations offered

A wide range of traditional and modern GCSE and A level subjects (OCR, Edexcel, AQA-SEG, London, Cambridge and AEB). Music and drama examinations also taken.

Academic & leisure facilities

We offer children a stable, stimulating, enjoyable environment, structured to meet their individual needs and ensure that they are happy, secure and reaching their full potential.

Recent refurbishment and development has provided modern, fully-equipped classrooms and science laboratories, designated learning support and careers centres and impressive technology workshops. Members of the sixth form have their own study centre and IT is widely used throughout the school.

Farringtons School Charitable Trust exists solely to provide a high quality, caring education. Registered charity No. 307916.

St James Senior Boys School

(Founded 1975)

Church Road, Ashford, Surrey TW15 3DZ
Tel: 01784 266930   Email: admissions@stjamesboys.co.uk
Fax: 01784 266938   Website: www.stjamesboys.co.uk

Headmaster: Mr David Boddy
Appointed: 2004
School type: Boys' Day & Weekly Boarding
Age range of pupils: 11–18
No. of pupils enrolled as at 1.9.12: 380
Sixth Form: 65
No. of boarders: 26
Fees per annum as at 1.9.12: Day: £12,660
Weekly Boarding: £5400
Average size of class: 22
Teacher/pupil ratio: 1:9

Over recent years, parents have come to appreciate that in future, their sons will need something different to help them live and enjoy life to the full, to be at peace with themselves and of service to all. They will need to be brilliant through their own talents, but they will also need an inner confidence from learning to be still, to know what they stand for, to be able to communicate, lead, and to be able to use a creative approach to problem solving. They will compete against youngsters from all over the world for the best jobs. Their success will depend on the extent to which they can respond freely in all situations.

St James' response to turning boys into men has been to provide a distinctive education, uniting a philosophic approach to the development of life skills, plus the delivery of academic excellence.

The school has experienced unprecedented demand for this philosophically inspired education and this has led to the need to expand into more spacious premises. This year St James is enjoying its second year at Ashford in Surrey. Boys and staff alike are thriving in the magnificent Victorian/Gothic structure set within 32 acres of grounds.

The school has continued its enlightened selective approach, emphasising character along with academic potential, although the entrance exam has been maintained to ensure that the strong academic curriculum can be met, with or without learning support. Sport and extracurricular activities have also flourished.

Every boy is considered unique, but at the same time he comes to know that every human being shares the same essence. Boys meet this in the space of meditation and quiet time, experienced twice daily, and as a silent pause between lessons.

This contemplative approach to modern education is being sought by discerning parents and there is much interest in the St James model. David Boddy, the Headmaster of St James, has recently been elected to become Chairman of the SHMIS organisation and the school is also a member of The International Boys' School Coalition and the ISA.

The Royal Masonic School for Girls

(Founded 1788)

Rickmansworth Park, Rickmansworth, Hertfordshire WD3 4HF
Tel: 01923 773168   Email: enquiries@royalmasonic.herts.sch.uk
Fax: 01923 896729   Website: www.royalmasonic.herts.sch.uk

Headmistress: Mrs Diana Rose MA(Cantab)
School type: Girls' Day & Boarding
(including weekly and flexi boarding) Boarders
from 7 and mixed Pre-school
Age range of pupils: 4–18
Pre-school 2–4
No. of pupils enrolled as at 1.9.12: 917
Boys: 26 Girls: 891 Sixth Form: 175
Pre-school: 83
No. of boarders: 150
Fees per annum as at 1.9.12: Day: £8490–£14,550
Weekly Boarding: £14,850–£23,535
Boarding: £15,105–£24,120
Pre-school fees: Upon application
Average size of class: 20
Teacher/pupil ratio: 1:12
Religious denomination: Non-denominational

At the Royal Masonic School for Girls we enable each girl to fulfil her potential and to find an area in which she can excel. We appreciate that girls have many and varied talents, and we seek to cultivate and foster those talents. RMS girls are socially skilled, courteous and friendly, and they thrive in a school that promotes tolerance and mutual respect.

We offer an exceptionally wide-ranging curriculum in a supportive and friendly environment, where the highest standards prevail. Girls receive individual attention and are given the confidence to succeed. The most notable feature, however, is the distinctive ethos of RMS – we are committed to fostering the achievement of all without undue pressure. Girls are encouraged to focus on stretching themselves in as many fields as possible, not only academically, but also on the sports field and in art, design technology, music and drama. Extracurricular activities abound for girls of all ages, including the Duke of Edinburgh's Award Scheme and Young Enterprise.

The range of 27 subjects in the sixth form enables all pupils to succeed. Our A level pass rate last year was 100% with 86% at grade A or B. 92% of girls gained places at their university of first choice.

Boarding pupils are cared for in well-appointed and spacious houses, with experienced, caring residential staff. We attach a great deal of significance to the quality of our pastoral care for each girl.

The school occupies a stunning site of 315 acres, which creates a serenity rarely found in today's schools, yet we are only 30 minutes from central London by train. Heathrow and Gatwick airports are both serviced by the M25 motorway, which is less than a mile from the school.

Generous open scholarships are available and a discount to HM forces personnel. We also offer a number of means-tested bursaries.

The Royal Masonic School Charitable Trust exists for the advancement of education. Charity No. 276784.

St Paul's Cathedral School

(Founded 12th Century or earlier)

2 New Change, London EC4M 9AD
Tel: 020 7248 5156   Email: admissions@spcs.london.sch.uk
Fax: 020 7329 6568   Website: www.spcslondon.com

Headmaster: Mr Neil Chippington MA, FRCO
Appointed: September 2009
School type: Coeducational Pre-Prep, Day Prep &
Boarding Choir School
Boarders from 7
Member of: IAPS, CSA
Age range of pupils: 4–13
No. of pupils enrolled as at 1.4.12: 250
Boys: 163 Girls: 87
No. of boarders: 33
Fees per annum as at 1.4.12: Day: £11,550–£12,435
Boarding: £7194
Average size of class: 15-20
Teacher/pupil ratio: 1:10
Religious denomination: Church of England,
admits pupils of all faiths

Curriculum

A broad curriculum prepares all pupils for 11+ and
13+ examinations including scholarship and Common
Entrance examinations. There is a strong musical
tradition and choristers' Cathedral choral training is
outstanding. A wide variety of games is offered.

Entry requirements

Entry at 4+ and 7+ years: Pre-prep and day pupils
interview and short test; Choristers voice trials and
tests in October, February and May for boys between
6½-8½ years. Further information from the school.

*St Paul's Cathedral School is a registered charity (No.
312718), which exists to provide education for the
choristers of St Paul's Cathedral and for children living in
the local area.*

Westminster School

(Founded 1560)

17 Dean's Yard, Westminster, London SW1P 3PF
Tel: 020 7963 1003   Email: registrar@westminster.org.uk
Fax: 020 7963 1002   Website: www.westminster.org.uk

Headmaster: Dr Stephen Spurr
Appointed: September 2005
School type: Boys' Boarding & Day
Girls Boarding & Day in Sixth Form
Member of: HMC
Age range of pupils:
Boys: 13–18
Girls: 16–18
No. of pupils enrolled as at 1.9.12: 750
Boys: 615 Girls: 135
No. of boarders: 185
Fees per annum as at 1.9.12: Day: £21,078–£23,538
Boarding: £31,350
Average size of class: 20

Situated next to Westminster Abbey and the Houses of Parliament, Westminster is the only ancient school in London that still occupies its original site. Academically it is one of the most successful schools in the country. In 2011, 55% of A level passes were A* (or Pre-U equivalent) and 98% of grades were A*/A/B. 90 leavers went to Oxford or Cambridge in 2010. The school also has strong traditions in music, drama and sport. Girls were first admitted as full members of the school in 1973. Westminster still operates as a boarding school with many members of staff living on site. For day pupils this means that they are members of a community that does not close down when the ordinary school day finishes – many will remain at school until well into the evening and can join the boarders for supper. Most Westminster boarders live in or close to London and return home at weekends but boarders from overseas are also welcome.

Westminster is an academic school in the 'liberal tradition'. It is an exciting place where individual and collective excellence are expected and promoted. Central to Westminster's ethos is the rapport between teachers and their pupils whether in the classroom or in tutorials. This inspires passion for the subject, conveys knowledge and develops skills of rational, independent thought.

For 13+ entry boys should ideally be registered by the time they enter Year 6 (age 10 or 11). During Year 6 they will be invited to Westminster for tests and interview. Boys who are offered conditional places must still qualify for entry at 13 by taking either Common Entrance or Westminster's scholarship examinations.

Entry at 16+ is by competitive examination. Candidates should register at the start of Year 11 (aged 15).

Boys may enter Westminster Under School at 7+, 8+ or 11+. For information please email: under.school@westminster.org.uk

or telephone: 020 7821 5788.

Westminster School is a registered charity (No. 312728) and a public boarding school for young persons.

Durham School

(Founded 1414)

Durham DH1 4SZ
Tel: 0191 386 4783
Fax: 0191 383 1025
Email: d.woodlands@durhamschool.co.uk
Website: www.durhamschool.co.uk

Headmaster: Mr Martin George
Appointed: April 2009
School type: Coeducational Day & Boarding
Age range of pupils: 3–18
No. of pupils enrolled as at 1.9.12: 590
Boys: 416 Girls: 174 Sixth Form: 143
No. of boarders: 119 (senior school)
Fees per annum as at 1.9.12: Day: £6225–£15,225
Weekly Boarding: £17,175–£20,985
Boarding: £19,497–£23,097
Overseas Boarders (Years 7-13): £20,400–£24,285
(The overseas boarding fee includes Saturday
School where the English language standard is
below: that level normally required for that point
of entry)
Average size of class: 15-20
Teacher/pupil ratio: 1:10
Religious denomination: Church of England

Motto: *Floriat Dunelmia* (Let Durham Flourish)

Confidence for Life

One of the oldest schools in Britain, Durham School
is an independent day and boarding school offering a
complete education for boys and girls from the age of
3-18. It consists of Bow, our own day preparatory
school from 3-11, and the senior school, which offers
both boarding and day education from 11-18.
Founded in 1414, we moved to our present site in
1844, a site that today provides our pupils with the
opportunity for a first class, modern education in a
uniquely beautiful and rural setting in the heart of
this historic and rapidly developing university city.

"At Durham School we see children from the ages of
three to 18 thriving on all fronts; academic, social,
physical, personal and moral. For this to be possible we
need to have first rate staff and facilities, underpinned by
pervasive values of compassion, endeavour, aspiration
and respect. For nearly 600 years Durham School has
helped generations to take their place in the world
equipped with the knowledge, skills, confidence and
principles to succeed. This remains our aim. We provide
a developing blend of tradition and progress, of family
values and a modern outlook, of balanced educational
aims, of high standards and high expectations, of care and
compassion.

"Above all Durham School is a family and from your
very first contact it is our intention to make you feel part
of our community. Our pupils are happy pupils, that is
why they succeed. We want our parents to be happy
parents and to be part of the pupils' success. So please
come and see us to discover why a Durham School
education really is Confidence For Life."

Mr Martin George
Headmaster

*Durham School is a registered charity (No. 1023407),
which exists to advance the education of children and
young people.*

Sedbergh School

(Founded 1525)

Sedbergh, Cumbria LA10 5HG
Tel: 015396 20535   Email: admissions@sedberghschool.org
Fax: 015396 21301   Website: www.sedberghschool.org

SEDBERGH
SCHOOL

Headmaster: Mr A Fleck MA
Appointed: 2010
School type: Coeducational Boarding & Day
Member of: HMC, BSA, IAPS, AGBIS, ASCL, ISC
Age range of pupils: 4–18
No. of pupils enrolled as at 1.9.12: 550
Boys: 387 Girls: 163 Sixth Form: 209
No. of boarders: 470
Fees per annum as at 1.9.12:
Day: £6,774–£20,790
Weekly: £16,062–£17,940 (7-13 only)
Boarding: £16,695–£28,215
Average size of class: 16
Teacher/pupil ratio: 1:9
Religious denomination: Church of England

Sedbergh has faced up to the demands of the 21st century without losing its traditional values and ethos, and today has an excellent reputation for its ability to provide a dynamic and challenging educational environment. Virtually all of the boys and girls at the senior school are seven-day-a-week boarders in a House system providing pastoral care of the highest standard from a resident Housemaster/mistress, tutor and matron. Through living, eating and studying in one of the ten houses (seven boys, three girls), pupils develop a lifelong sense of pride and belonging.

Academic success is taken for granted with nearly 100% pass rates at A level and IGCSE, and the School has close links with several Oxbridge colleges. Most of the pupils leave to go on to the universities of their choice or to gap-year activities. Scholarships and awards are available (academic, music, art, design technology, sport, drama and all rounder). These are offered by examination in Lent term each year and Michaelmas term for sixth form entry. Means-tested bursaries are available for promising individuals who might not otherwise be able to consider the school.

Sedbergh retains its reputation as a formidable force on the sports field but, away from there, enormous opportunities exist for pupils interested in music and drama, art, design technology and the CCF. A school-wide programme of outdoor pursuits ensures everyone has the chance to enjoy the environment that is unique to the school.

Entry requirements are by Common Entrance examination or scholarship/award at 13+, and at 16+ subject to a minimum of five GCSE passes and interview.

Located only ten minutes from the M6 (junction 37) and just over one hour from Manchester Airport, the life-enhancing education offered at Sedbergh is readily accessible from other parts of the UK as well as further afield.

Sedbergh has its own coeducational junior school from ages 4 to 13. SJS offers day, flexi, weekly and full boarding.

Parents can visit Sedbergh School at any time by arrangement. There are formal open days each term at the junior school. Visit the website or telephone for further information.

Sedbergh School is a registered charity, which exists to provide high quality education for boys and girls. (No. 1080672)

Stonyhurst College

(Founded 1593)

Stonyhurst, Clitheroe, Lancashire BB7 9PZ
Tel: 01254 826345   Email: admissions@stonyhurst.ac.uk
Fax: 01254 827131   Website: www.stonyhurst.ac.uk

Headmaster: A Johnson BA
Appointed: 2006
School type: Coeducational Boarding & Day
Age range of pupils: 13–18
No. of pupils enrolled as at 1.9.12: 470
Sixth Form: 221
No. of boarders: 289
Fees per annum as at 1.9.12: Day: £6681–£15,915
Weekly Boarding: £17,289–£23,703
Boarding: £20,406–£28,443
Average size of class: 10-22
Teacher/pupil ratio: 1:8

Stonyhurst takes pupils from 3-18, starting from our pre-prep Hodder House, moving on to our prep school St Mary's Hall and completing their education at Stonyhurst College. We foster and celebrate the talents of each child, helping them to do their best in the extensive range of activities that we provide. Our achievements are confirmed by outstanding inspection reports in all areas of academic, pastoral and extracurricular education and these can be read on our website. Our academic results far outstrip the national average each year and we pride ourselves on the value we can add to child's educational achievements,

helping them to improve on expectations time and time again. Children of all levels achieve more at Stonyhurst than they would have done had they not come to us. Pupils at the end of their time at Stonyhurst go on to top universities across the UK.

Rooted in our Jesuit ethos, Stonyhurst pupils develop lifelong values to become 'men and women for others', so that they can respond to where there is need and serve generously. This means that young people here take part in fundraising for several of our designated charities. Our older pupils are also involved in a programme that takes them out into the community as volunteers.

While at school young people can also take part in the many and varied activities on offer in our extracurricular programme, these include scuba diving, orienteering, dance, car maintenance, essay writing and golf on our own nine hole golf course. The all-round education offered at Stonyhurst is available to all pupils whether they board or are day pupils.

More details are available at www.stonyhurst.ac.uk or from the Admissions Office on 01254 827073/93, admissions@stonyhurst.ac.uk.

Burgess Hill School for Girls

(Founded 1906)

Keymer Road, Burgess Hill, West Sussex RH15 0EG
Tel: 01444 241050   Email: registrar@burgesshill-school.com
Fax: 01444 870314   Website: www.burgesshill-school.com

Headmistress: Mrs Ann Aughwane BSc, CertEd, NPQH
Appointed: 2006
School type: Girls' Day & Boarding
Boarders from 11 years
Member of: GSA, AGBIS
Age range of pupils:
Boys: 2½–4
Girls: 2½–18
No. of pupils enrolled as at 1.9.12: 640
Sixth Form: 65
No. of boarders: 56
Fees per annum as at 1.9.12: Day: £6750–£14,250
Boarding: £25,200
Average size of class: Max 20
Teacher/pupil ratio: 1:17
Religious denomination: Inter-denominational

Burgess Hill School for Girls is an independent day and boarding school for girls aged between 2½ and 18 years. Boarding is offered from the age of 11 years. Boys are accepted in the Nursery.

Burgess Hill School is small enough that children are known as individuals yet large enough to offer breadth, choice and opportunity. The School has high expectations of all its pupils and upholds the best of traditions. Girls are able to strive for excellence wherever their talents lie and the mix of ages, working together on the same site, gives the School a special character. The aim of the School is to provide each girl with the opportunity to realise her potential in every way and the focus is firmly on girls and the way they learn.

The School stands in 14 acres of beautiful grounds close to the centre of Burgess Hill town. The School is a five minute walk from Burgess Hill railway station, which is on the mainline from London to Brighton. Coaches and minibuses also collect girls from outlying areas of East and West Sussex.

Students are encouraged to pursue an active and healthy life with a good balance between work and enrichment. Extracurricular activities cater for all ages and abilities in sports, music, arts and specialist subjects including sailing, golf, horse riding and chess. There are opportunities to go on educational and residential trips and the Duke of Edinburgh Awards are popular. Girls also benefit from the School's links with the local community and they take part in local festivals, competitive events and workshops with other schools. In the Senior School, careers conferences are held with national companies and inspirational speakers to encourage the girls to plan for their futures. In the Sixth Form students take Life Skills lessons and have a networking dinner to build their interpersonal skills and establish key contacts for work experience or careers advice.

Burgess Hill School has three well presented and homely boarding houses. They are ideal for those who live too far away to travel on a daily basis and for international students who are looking for an excellent English education. The boarding community is a caring and supportive extended family unit where experienced housemistresses and

staff know and understand the girls. Extensive refurbishment of the boarding houses took place in 2011. The rooms and common rooms are spacious, light and pleasantly furnished.

The curriculum offers a wide choice of subjects at GCSE and A level. The majority of students take nine GCSEs and go on to study A level qualifications before progressing on to university. The vast majority of the girls go on to universities across the UK, including Exeter, London, Oxford, Cambridge, Cardiff and St Andrews.

Last summer (2011) the school celebrated another successful year of GCSE results. All students passed and over 97% achieved grades A* to C. All students achieved at least five A* to C grades including mathematics and English. The School also celebrated an excellent set of A level results with 84.2% of all A

level results being awarded A* to B grades. Almost two thirds of the year group gained A* to B in all their subjects and a third of the girls gained at least one A*.

Each individual at Burgess Hill School is encouraged to develop her skills to become confident and independent young women. Burgess Hill School consistently 'adds value' to students' academic results by focusing on each individual student, keeping class sizes small, understanding how girls learn and investing in good resources and high quality teaching. In 2011 Burgess Hill School was ranked 5th out of 632 independent and maintained schools in the UK for 'value added' performance by the Centre for Educational Monitoring at University of Durham.

Burgess Hill School for Girls' fees are competitive. Entry to the Junior and Senior School is by the school's own examination. Entry to the infants is by informal activity sessions. Scholarships are awarded each year for academic and/or musical excellence for Years 3, 4, 7, 9 and Lower Sixth. Creative scholarships (including Drama, Sport and Art) are also awarded into Year 9 and Lower Sixth. Parents and students may visit the school by making an appointment with the Head of Admissions or attending the school's Open Days which are held in September, November, March and May.

For more information about Burgess Hill School for Girls and for a copy of the school prospectus, please contact the Head of Admissions by telephone on 01444 241050 or by email at registrar@burgesshill-school.com.

Bradfield College

(Founded 1850)

Bradfield, Reading RG7 6AU
Tel: 0118 964 4500   Email: admissions@bradfieldcollege.org.uk
Fax: 0118 964 4513   Website: www.bradfieldcollege.org.uk

Headmaster: Mr Simon Henderson
Appointed: September 2011
School type: Coeducational Boarding
Age range of pupils: 13–18
No. of pupils enrolled as at 1.4.12: 734
Boys: 483 Girls: 251 Sixth Form: 299
No. of boarders: 619
Fees per annum as at 1.9.12: Day: £24,708
Boarding: £30,885
Average size of class: Max 20
Teacher/pupil ratio: 1:9

A leading coeducational, independent boarding school, Bradfield College provides an outstanding all-round education so as to prepare young people for success in a fast-changing world. The College cares about the individual and prides itself in the warmth of a community in which pupils feel happy and valued. It fosters an environment of high expectations in which all pupils are encouraged to believe in themselves, to be inquisitive, to be resilient and to show ambition within and beyond the classroom. Its all-inclusive ethos embraces the extended 'Bradfield family', which includes pupils past and present and extensive links with the wider community.

The modern College combines values and attributes essential to 21st century life with those of its founder, Thomas Stevens, who established St Andrew's College in 1850. Alongside an excellent academic education, offering both A levels and IB at Sixth Form, all partake of the 'Bradfield experience', which permits each individual to find his or her special niche. The classroom atmosphere engenders a love of learning for its own sake; the participatory culture ensures that expert and enthusiast alike thrive within the broad spectrum of co-curricular activities.

Pastoral care is paramount; boys and girls move on to senior houses after Faulkner's, a coeducational house in which all spend their first year at the College. Each house has a dedicated team of staff and every pupil benefits from the care of a housemaster or housemistress, a personal tutor and a matron.

The superb facilities at Bradfield include modern teaching and learning environments within the beautiful brick-and-flint original buildings. There is a music school, sports complex with indoor swimming pool, a tennis centre and two floodlit all-weather pitches. Alongside these a new state-of-the-art science centre opened its doors to pupils and the local community in September 2010. Set in its own mediaeval village in 250 acres of beautiful Berkshire countryside the College enjoys exceptional playing fields, golf course and stunning views across the Pang valley. All this is within 40 minutes of Heathrow and an hour from central London.

Admission to the College is at both 13+ and into the large and vibrant Sixth Form. Scholarships, exhibitions and awards are available at both levels of entry.

Bradfield College, registered charity No. 309089, is a college for the careful education of boys and girls.

Eagle House School

(Founded 1820)

Sandhurst, Bracknell Forest GU47 8PH

Tel: 01344 772134   Email: info@eaglehouseschool.com

Fax: 01344 779039   Website: www.eaglehouseschool.com

SUBLIMIORA PETAMUS

Headmaster: Mr A P N Barnard BA(Hons), PGCE
Appointed: September 2006
School type: Coeducational Day & Boarding
Boarders from 7 years
Member of: IAPS
Age range of pupils: 3–13
No. of pupils enrolled as at 1.9.12: 360
Boys: 220 Girls: 140
No. of boarders: 65
Fees per annum as at 1.9.12: Day: £9300–£14,850
Boarding: £19,950
Average size of class: 16
Teacher/pupil ratio: 1:8

Eagle House is more than just a school, it is a way of life for all our pupils. In the classroom, on the sports field, in the music or drama halls, on part of our extensive activities programme or just having fun in the wonderful grounds that make up Eagle House, our boys and girls are living life to the full. We believe in a broad education for all our pupils and, as such, offer a huge range of opportunities for all.

Eagle House offers day and boarding for boys and girls aged 3 to 13. The school, located between Sandhurst and Crowthorne, is within easy reach of the M3 and M4 and is served by good rail services as well as being close to Heathrow and Gatwick airports. The school operates morning bus services from surrounding areas. The school has a proud history of producing successful pupils and dates back to 1820. Tradition is important and we are proud of our history but we also realise the need to be at the forefront of modern day education.

The high quality of our teaching and resources mean that all our children achieve to a high standard. A consistent record of academic success as well as frequent achievement in music, drama, art and sports show that we are helping to bring the best out of our boys and girls.

The Eagle House experience begins at aged 3 with our nursery, The Nest, and right from the start we believe in excellence. In a recent Ofsted nursery report our quality of teaching and care in The Nest and reception was given the highest praise. Into the pre-prep with reception and Years 1 and 2, and the learning experience and opportunities continue to help our children to give of their best. The prep school, starting with Year 3 and moving up to Year 8, encourages our boys and girls to grow mentally and physically and helps them to reach their potential in all they do. Our unique Golden Eagle Programme enables every child to develop life skills and take part in a superb range of activities.

The children who leave us in Year 8 are testament to the fact that Eagle House delivers. The school exists to provide a happy, well-balanced education for children and parents; children and staff believe passionately in achieving this goal.

Eagle House caters for all. In the 21st century our school is the right choice for success, happiness and opportunity. With excellent facilities and the flexibility to help with modern day living by offering late stay facilities and flexible boarding, can you afford not to take a look?

Eagle House is a registered charity (No. 309093) for the furtherance of education.

Eastbourne College

(Founded 1867)

Old Wish Road, Eastbourne, East Sussex BN21 4JX
Tel: 01323 452323   Email: admissions@eastbourne-college.co.uk
Fax: 01323 452354   Website: www.eastbourne-college.co.uk

Eastbourne College

Headmaster: Mr S P Davies MA
Appointed: 2005
School type: Co-educational Boarding & Day
Age range of pupils: 13–18
No. of pupils enrolled as at 1.9.11: 621
Boys: 355 Girls: 266 Sixth Form: 273
No. of boarders: 302
Fees per annum as at 1.9.11: Day: £17,985
Boarding: £27,315
Teacher/pupil ratio: 1:9

Eastbourne College is one of only two independent senior schools in the south-east delivering the full boarding experience, seven days a week. For example, every Sunday of term (other than exeat weekends) over 300 boarders enjoy brunch before participating in the wide range of activities on offer at weekends. The vast majority of boarders come from within 90 minutes of the College and the proportion from abroad is notably low.

In the report following the school's 2008 ISI inspection, the value of the extended day and full week for both boarders and day pupils alike was recognised and the college's distinctive co-curricular programme was identified as one of the outstanding features of the school: 'The school succeeds in providing a coherent and excellent co-educational boarding experience for boys and girls, boarders and day pupils. Eastbourne College is a happy and inspiring community that successfully emphasises the key values for which it stands.'

'By giving its pupils a coherent, full and challenging boarding education, Eastbourne College amply fulfils its principal aim. Its day pupils, as much as its boarders, make the most of all that the school offers.'

During 2010, the charities of Eastbourne College and St Andrew's School amalgamated under a single charity, guaranteeing the long-term future of top quality independent education for children aged two to 18 in Eastbourne and beyond. The two schools continue to operate independently with each benefiting from shared expertise and resources.

The Birley Centre, which was completed in September 2011, is one such resource. This initial phase of the College's exciting development programme has provided a first rate facility with an auditorium, exhibition space and a state-of-the-art home for the teaching, performance and recording of music. Completing the cultural quarter of Eastbourne, the Birley Centre is a valuable asset for the town itself.

Gordon's School

(Founded 1885)

West End, Woking, Surrey GU24 9PT
Tel: 01276 858084   Email: registrar@gordons.surrey.sch.uk
Fax: 01276 855335   Website: www.gordons.surrey.sch.uk

Head Teacher: Andrew Moss MEd
School type: Coeducational Boarding & Day
Boarders from 11
Age range of pupils: 11–18
No. of pupils enrolled as at 24.4.12:
Boys: 379 Girls: 348 Sixth Form: 160
Fees per annum as at 5.9.12:
Boarding: £13,083–£14,181
Average size of class: 18

Gordon's is a non-selective state boarding school catering for both boarders and day pupils and is regularly in the top 20 non-selective schools in Britain. As a state school, parents pay for boarding only.

Following a two day inspection of boarding, Ofsted inspectors have described Gordon's as 'outstanding' in all areas. Almost uniquely for any school, Ofsted made no recommendations for action.

Quotes from Ofsted inspections:

'Gordon's is an outstanding school in every respect.'

'The quality of care provided by the school for the pupils is exceptional.'

'Teaching and learning are outstanding.'

'The quality of the extracurricular programme goes beyond excellence.'

'Gordon's provides an outstanding level of care for the pupils who board there.'

'Pupils emerge from the school as articulate, pleasant, well-rounded and confident youngsters.'

At Gordon's, great importance is placed on the quality of teaching in the classroom because we strongly believe that schools are first and foremost centres for learning. Coupled with this is a very firm commitment to traditional values: we insist on high standards, good discipline and the values that parents and society respect.

In 2011, 89.7% of students gained five or more pass grades A* to C at GCSE, (88.8% including English and maths). In value added terms Gordon's attained 1014.8 points, which is significantly above the national average. At GCE A level, 88% of the grades were A* to C, the key grades required to get into the most highly regarded universities.

Such results are, of course, very pleasing. However schools should never be judged on examination results alone. At Gordon's we believe that the only way to gain an accurate picture of a school is to see it in action during a typical working day, to visit lessons and to talk with staff and pupils.

If you would like to visit Gordon's, please contact us on 01276 858084, and ask for our admissions registrar, Mrs Tozer, who will arrange a tour of the school for you and your child.

Gordon's School is a registered charity (No. 312092) to educate or contribute to the education of boys and girls, having particular regard to those with a specific boarding or educational need.

Great Walstead School

(Founded 1925)

East Mascalls Lane, Lindfield, Haywards Heath, West Sussex RH16 2QL
Tel: 01444 483528   Email: admin@greatwalstead.co.uk
Fax: 01444 482122   Website: www.greatwalstead.co.uk

Headmaster: Mr C Baty NPQH, BEd(Waikato NZ)
Appointed: November 2010
School type: Boys' and Girls' Day and Weekly/Flexi
Boarding
Age range of pupils: 2½–13
No. of pupils enrolled as at 1.9.12: 400
Boys: 235 Girls: 165
No. of boarders: 62
Fees per annum as at 1.9.12: Day: £6780–£13,200
Weekly boarding: supplement of £2,655 pa
Average size of class: 16-20
Teacher/pupil ratio: 1:9 + assistants

Where the possibilities and the grounds are endless

Great Walstead School is a coeducational prep school, taking children from 2½ to 13 years. Set in a wonderful location in the heart of the Sussex countryside, Great Walstead provides a full, rich and varied education.

With over 270 acres, the surrounding grounds play a big part in the learning and development of the children at the school. Pupils use the outdoor facilities daily to explore, learn and take part in educational activities.

Here at Great Walstead our teachers are leaders in their field. They combine excellence in education with teaching pupils fundamental lessons in life, such as kindness and good manners, and help to prepare them for the outside world.

Great Walstead's five core values are Christian faith, dedication, success, the environment and communication, all of which our children adopt in everything they do. But above all else we take academic subjects very seriously.

This year, Great Walstead has once again seen great success with over half of the school's Year 8s leaving with a scholarship or an award to the senior school of their choice.

As Colin Baty, Headmaster, comments: "Here at Great Walstead we are very proud of the results our pupils achieve each year with all children gaining entry to the school of their choice and a high percentage of scholarships and awards to a number of senior schools both locally and further afield. These exceptional results demonstrate that we individually prepare our pupils to the highest levels."

Alongside the academic work the children enjoy fabulous opportunities in sports and visual and performing arts. From singing at the O2 to a cricket tour in South Africa, Great Walstead offers a varied and inspirational school life for all its pupils whatever their interests and abilities.

For more information or to come and see what makes Great Walstead such a special place visit www.greatwalstead.co.uk; we would love to show you around anytime.

Hurstpierpoint College

(Founded 1849)

Hassocks, West Sussex BN6 9JS
Tel: 01273 833636
Fax: 01273 835257   Website: www.hppc.co.uk

Headmaster: Mr T J Manly BA, MSc
School type: Coeducational Boarding & Day
Age range of pupils: 4–18
No. of pupils enrolled as at 1.9.12: 1030
Fees per annum as at 1.9.12: Day: £19,785
Weekly Boarding: £24,945
Boarding: £27,885–£29,430
Boarding is only available in the Senior School:
Flexiboarding: £23,385

Hurstpierpoint College offers outstanding day and boarding education for boys and girls aged 4 to 18 years. Set in Sussex countryside just north of the Downs, its 140-acre campus provides superb academic, sporting and cultural facilities.

The core belief at Hurst is that education is all about pupils' achievement of personal bests – academic, extracurricular and in their relationships with others.

Every child has access to all the opportunities at Hurst, whether sporting, creative, activity or community related. For example, every child has the chance to be in a sports team, join a choir or musical ensemble, tackle the Duke of Edinburgh Silver award and participate in one or more of over 20 different theatrical productions a year.

Alongside this commitment to inclusion and real engagement, Hurst seeks to achieve true excellence. In 2011/12, a large academic cohort headed off to Oxford and other first rate universities, athletes competed regionally and nationally, the outstanding Cadet Force numbered over 250, a Young Enterprise team swept the prizes locally and 20 Duke of Edinburgh Gold Award winners are to collect their awards at Buckingham Palace.

"A school which is going from strength to strength under the strong leadership of its dynamic headmaster. It is now the first choice for many parents who would traditionally have sent their children further afield. Fantastic value added, where each child is tracked and challenged to reach their full potential in all areas of their lives, and where they are encouraged to push themselves beyond their comfort zone." *The Good Schools Guide's report on Hurstpierpoint College, June 2012*

To find out what Hurstpierpoint College can offer your child, we invite you to arrange a personal family visit or to attend one of our open mornings.

Kent College Pembury

(Founded 1886)

Old Church Road, Pembury, Tunbridge Wells, Kent TN2 4AX
Tel: 01892 822006   Email: admissions@kentcollege.kent.sch.uk
Fax: 01892 820221   Website: www.kent-college.co.uk

Headmistress: Mrs Sally-Anne Huang MA(Oxon), MSc, PGCE
Head of Prep: Mrs Ann Lawson BEd Hons
School type: Girls' Day & Boarding
Boarders from 10
Age range of pupils: 3–18
Prep School 3–11
No. of pupils enrolled as at 1.9.12: 600
Sixth Form: 102
No. of boarders: 90
Fees per annum as at 1.9.12: Day: £7584–£18,156
Boarding: £20,646–£26,850
Day: £7047–£10,611
Boarding: £12,788
Flexi-boarding: £35 per night
Average size of class: 16
Teacher/pupil ratio: 1:9

Set in 75 acres of parkland, Kent College is an idyllic oasis, providing a safe, natural environment where girls enjoy living and learning. The thriving school is a happy, caring home for boarders who can join at age ten. The Christian ethos gives a clear moral framework; pupils are well mannered, tolerant and respectful of one another. It is a busy, vibrant school where we enjoy doing things as a whole community, be it a barbecue lunch, arts festival or theatre trip to London's West End.

A broad and balanced approach

Academic standards are high, with excellent GCSE and A level results, and pupils gain places at top universities to do a variety of courses, from medicine to engineering. The curriculum and approach is broad and balanced. Success is achieved by nurturing the girls' confidence and inspiring a love of learning. The school has a reputation for excellence in performing arts and sport.

Exciting opportunities

An impressive and diverse range of 140 activities enables students to discover new talents and nurture existing ones. Exciting exchanges to Australia, Europe and America, and international sport, music and drama tours are an important part of school life. Along with the school's thriving Gymnastics Academy which competes to a very high standard at national competitions, and Swimming Academy, the school is set to launch an exciting new Theatre Academy from September 2012 which will deliver workshops in drama, dance & singing.

Facilities and location

Modern, architect-designed facilities include homely boarding houses, a state-of-the-art theatre, large sports hall, music school, dance studio, on-site outdoor 'adventure course', science laboratories and an indoor swimming pool. Sixth formers benefit from their own study centre. An iconic library and art centre will be opened in 2013. The school is only three miles from the town of Royal Tunbridge Wells, 15 minutes from the M25 and 40 minutes from London by train.

Scholarships and admissions

Main intakes for boarders are at age 10, 11, 13 and 16. Academic, music, drama, sport and art scholarships and bursaries are available.

The Oratory School

(Founded 19th Century)

Woodcote, Reading RG8 OPJ
Tel: 01491 683500   Email: enquiries@oratory.co.uk
Fax: 01491 680020   Website: www.oratory.co.uk

Head Master: Mr C I Dytor MC, KHS, MA(Cantab), MA(Oxon)
Appointed: August 2000
School type: Boys' Boarding & Day
Boarders from 11 years
Age range of pupils: 11–18
No. of pupils enrolled as at 1.9.12: 420
Sixth Form: 120
No. of boarders: 220
Fees per annum as at 1.9.12: Day: £14,835–£20,565
Boarding: £19,920–£28,395
Teacher/pupil ratio: 1:8

The Oratory School is the UK's only All Boys' Independent Catholic Senior Boarding and Day School with 420 boys aged from 11-18yrs with Catholic and non-Catholic families. Set in acres of beautiful Chiltern countryside in South Oxfordshire, the School is within easy reach of Heathrow and other major airports and the M4.

Founded in 1859 by Blessed John Henry Newman, a brilliant original man, who combined two traditions: Academic excellence with Christian pastoral care for the individual boy. He believed in an education system based on sound moral principles, a scientific and methodical approach to academic study and a personal concern for the welfare of every pupil. Newman's personal motto became the School's: '*Cor ad Cor Loquitur*' ('Heart speaking to Heart'), and this continues to flow through the life of the School. Oratory boys are known for their spirit and 'can-do' attitude to life.

The Head Master believes that this focus on body, mind and spirit, so vital for success and happiness, is at the heart of Catholic education and of the School today.

The School ensures there is a close monitoring of work, with an academic timetable designed to provide the widest choice possible. Boys are encouraged to achieve the highest standards in every area of school life and the development of leadership skills play an important part in this grounding. The School has excellent sporting facilities. Along with rugby and football pitches, cricket squares and tennis courts, there is also a golf course, Real Tennis court, indoor shooting range and a boathouse on the River Thames. The award-winning Art & Design department offers Foundation Course status and the arts in general flourish assisted by the Hopkins Society, which takes boys on visits to literary festivals, concerts, plays, the opera and ballet.

The Oratory is now entering into its second 10-year development phase with a new 'cutting edge' performing arts centre to be ready for September 2012 and a massive new sports centre complex planned to be developed over the next two years, with new swimming pool and café facilities.

Clive Dytor, the Head Master, is determined to keep The Oratory at the forefront of boys' education.

Royal Alexandra and Albert School
under the patronage of Her Majesty the Queen

(Founded 1758)

Gatton Park, Reigate, Surrey RH2 0TD
Tel: 01737 649 000   Email: admissions@gatton-park.org.uk
Fax: 01737 649 002   Website: www.raa-school.co.uk

Headmaster: P Spencer Ellis BA, MPhil, NPQH
Appointed: 2001
School type: State Maintained, Preparatory, Senior, Sixth Form
Age range of pupils: 7–18
No. of pupils enrolled as at 1.4.12: 1000
Boys: 510 Girls: 490 Sixth Form: 200
No. of boarders: 450
Teacher/pupil ratio: 1:11-8
Religious denomination: Church of England

The Royal Alexandra and Albert School has experienced extraordinary success over the last few years. Excellent results combined with affordable fees (around £4000/term for full boarding) have made us the first choice for many parents who are looking for a top quality, well-rounded education. This is a true boarding school with Saturday morning lessons, longer holidays and a vast range of sporting and other activities in the afternoons, evenings and at weekends. Set in 260 acres of parkland, yet close to London, we are convenient for families who live in the UK and overseas.

Curriculum
The National Curriculum is followed in the primary school and for Key Stage 3 (Years 7-9). Pupils then take a wide range of GCSE and vocational courses in Key Stage 4. Our Sixth Form offers the widest possible range of courses and subjects.

Sixth Form
The strong ethos of the secondary school is carried through to the Sixth Form. Many of our Sixth Formers choose to board and there are 42 brand new study bedrooms with en suite shower rooms providing university standard accommodation.

The new purpose-built Sixth Form Centre has a spacious common room, café, study and resource rooms together with a fully equipped computer suite.

Advice on academic work, pastoral matters and careers is provided by a tutor, who remains the student's tutor for the full two years of the Sixth Form.

Sixth Form students are very much part of the whole school and are expected to mentor younger pupils, help run clubs and activities and lead school projects.

Boarding ethos
With up to 450 boarding pupils, we are one of the largest boarding schools in the country. All children, including those who are not full boarders, enjoy an extended day at the school, which includes all meals, activities and support in the boarding houses. We have maintained the atmosphere and traditions of a boarding school, but have kept pace with the changing needs and expectations of young people and their parents.

Staffing levels in our nine boarding houses are high, with an average of six staff in each house.

Study bedrooms for two, three or four pupils provide a comfortable, modern home-from-home atmosphere for our older pupils.

We are the only state boarding school to offer boarding to junior pupils and we have up to 60 boarders aged 7-11.

Our purpose-built health centre staffed by qualified nurses provides round the clock high quality medical care for pupils.

The school community

For over 250 years this school has been transforming the lives of young people and we are proud of our heritage. The world has moved on since 1758 but we still aim to nurture and develop the children who come to this school so that they enter the adult world fully prepared to meet any challenge.

We are a church school and are committed to fostering Christian principles within a caring community, where people of all faiths and beliefs are made welcome. Whilst we encourage pupils to strive to do their best we also expect them to be tolerant and sensitive to the needs of others.

Entry requirements

Entry is by confidential reference from the current school and interview, to assess suitability for boarding. No EAL provision is available. Only UK/EU passport holders and those with a right of residence in the UK are eligible for places.

Examinations offered

Key Stage 2 and 3 tests; GCSEs; GCE A levels and vocational qualifications in the Sixth Form.

Academic & leisure facilities

Purpose-built teaching facilities include state-of-the art ICT systems providing internet and intranet access for all staff and pupils. Sports facilities are exceptional and include our own riding school with indoor and outdoor sand school, indoor swimming pool, dance studio and flood-lit all weather pitches. Scouts, cadets and Duke of Edinburgh's Award Scheme are popular; music and dance are outstanding.

Religious activities

The school has its own chapel and a full-time Anglican Chaplain.

Scholarships

Means-tested bursaries are available to children whose home circumstances make a boarding education desirable.

The Royal Alexandra & Albert School Foundation, a registered charity (No. 311945) provides boarding, pastoral care and bursary support for pupils at the Royal Alexandra & Albert School.

Seaford College

(Founded 1884)

Lavington Park, Petworth, West Sussex GU28 0NB
Tel: 01798 867392   Email: admissions@seaford.org
Fax: 01798 867606   Website: www.seaford.org

Headmaster: T J Mullins MBA, BA
School type: Coeducational Boarding & Day
Member of: SHMIS, HMC, BSA, IAPS
Age range of pupils: 7–18
No. of pupils enrolled as at 1.9.12: 621
Boys: 436 Girls: 185 Sixth Form: 143
No. of boarders: 137
Fees per annum as at 1.9.12: Day: £8100–£16,890
Weekly Boarding: £17,400–£22,500
Boarding: £16,440–£26,700
Average size of class: 15-20
Teacher/pupil ratio: 1:9
Religious denomination: Church of England

Seaford College is a coeducational independent day and boarding school for pupils aged 7 to 18, situated amid 400 acres of picturesque, rolling parkland in West Sussex. The college, with its excellent amenities and outstanding panoramic views, offers an inspirational environment that nurtures academic excellence, sporting success and creative talent.

Seaford College aims to provide a distinctive and inclusive educational experience in which individual pupils are known, have the opportunity to discover themselves and are valued for their contribution to school life.

The college uses its resources to provide and enhance educational, cultural, spiritual and social opportunities within the local community so that students leave school as confident, articulate and well-rounded individuals.

The college has an excellent record for academic achievement, sport, art and music. Past pupils have obtained music scholarships to some of the country's leading music schools, including the Royal College of Music and Oxford and Cambridge universities, and art scholarships to Central St Martin's College of Art and Design and other leading UK art colleges.

Seaford College offers outstanding sports facilities, including an all-weather water-based Astroturf hockey pitch, golf course and driving range. Students regularly play at county level, with the opportunity to explore action and adventure with the CCF in a lively programme of outdoor pursuits.

Pupils in the recently-opened Preparatory school at Seaford College share the superb facilities with the senior school and enjoy a seamless education from 7 to 18.

The prep school prides itself on its friendly atmosphere and all pupils are encouraged to develop their skills of tolerance and an understanding of others. Weekly chapel services, conducted by the school Chaplain, encourage the strong Christian ethos of the school and pupils participate in weekday assemblies.

The school has a proud record in supporting local charities through its many fundraising activities. Strong emphasis is placed on a disciplined framework where good manners and a smart appearance are expected and where staff and parents work closely together for the common good of the children.

Boarding is offered to students from the age of 10 and around 40% of pupils at Seaford College elect to board, in order to take full advantage of the social, sporting and extracurricular activities on offer. The college offers not only full boarding, but also weekly and flexible boarding in order to meet the needs of pupils and their parents.

Traditional buildings blend beautifully with the recent 21st century improvements: a new boys' boarding house, accommodating 90 students in individual and twin bedrooms, opened in summer 2011, and work is shortly due to commence on a new indoor swimming pool and sports centre.

Other recent developments include an exciting new music suite, which consists of individual teaching and practice rooms, a computer and keyboard room, with large flexible teaching and performance space, a sound-proofed band practice room and outdoor concert arena.

A state-of-the-art maths and science block offers the latest technologies and facilities, while the college has long been recognised as a centre of excellence for art and design. A specialist art library and large exhibition gallery are incorporated into the purpose-built arts faculty, which offers options in fine art, photography and ceramics, as well as design and technology.

All the usual academic subjects are taught, with 24 subjects available to students at GCSE and 28 at A level. The college also offers preparation for the Cambridge Pre-U.

Overseas students are expected to study English as a foreign language and study for the International Language Testing System, which is a requirement for UK university entrance.

Seaford sees its sixth form very much as a transitional stage between school and university or the workplace and treats its students as young adults. They have their own social centre – The Hollington Centre –

which has facilities for individual study, a coffee bar with internet cafe, a lounge area and several classrooms where subjects such as economics, business studies, media studies and politics are taught.

Sixth form boarders have individual study bedrooms, as well as their own common room and dining room. Students are divided into small tutor groups but most commonly meet on a 1-1 basis with their tutors to discuss aspects of their work and progress.

Most of Seaford's sixth formers go on to university or higher education – all are equipped with self-confidence and entrepreneurial skills, as well as a passion for life and a willingness to succeed.

Entry to the college is by test and Trial Day and, although intake is non-selective, expectations are high. If your child is talented and enthusiastic, the college offers a range of scholarships at 11+, 13+ and sixth form, including academic studies, music, art and sport.

The college has its own dedicated learning support unit, catering for pupils with dyslexia, dyscalculia and dyspraxia.

Whatever their chosen path, Seaford College seeks to prepare young people for adult life so that they have the personal skills, confidence and enthusiasm to make it a success.

Seaford College is a registered charity that exists to enhance children's educational opportunities. The Johnson Trust. Registered charity no. 277439.

Vinehall School

(Founded 1938)

Robertsbridge, East Sussex TN32 5JL
Tel: 01580 880413   Email: registrar@vinehallschool.com
Fax: 01580 882119   Website: www.vinehallschool.com

Vinehall School

Headmaster: Richard Follett
Appointed: January 2011
School type: Coeducational Day & Boarding
Member of: IAPS, BSA, ISBA, ISC
Age range of pupils: 2–13
No. of pupils enrolled as at 1.9.12: 270
Boys: 146 Girls: 124
No. of boarders: 35
Fees per annum as at 1.9.12: Day: £1035–£15,180
Boarding: £19,440–£26,400
Average size of class: 18
Teacher/pupil ratio: 1:10

Vinehall School is a traditional Prep School with a 21st century approach, combining a noticeably friendly and happy atmosphere with impressive achievements in academics, music, art, sport and drama. Set within 47 acres of beautiful countryside on the East Sussex/Kent border, Vinehall offers an extensive range of excellent modern facilities which enhance both the curricular and extra-curricular opportunities for the pupils. These include:

- An attractive, modern and spacious Pre Prep School within the grounds
- A magnificent Millennium Building, comprising classrooms, a dedicated IT suite, numerous additional computers and a Library
- A science block
- A dedicated music building
- An art, design and technology centre
- An excellent purpose-built theatre with seating for 250
- A sports hall with adjoining indoor swimming pool

- An all weather Astroturf pitch
- An adventure playground, extensive playing fields and a nine hole golf course

The curriculum is based on the National Curriculum but extends far beyond, for example, the innovative 'Learning Journey' curriculum (which begins in Year 3), stimulates enquiring young minds. In Years 7 and 8, Vinehall prepares its pupils for Common Entrance, local grammar school entrance and scholarship entrance to a variety of independent senior schools at 13+ including Battle Abbey, Benenden, Brighton College, Charterhouse, Cranbrook, Eastbourne College, Eton, King's Canterbury, Millfield, Sevenoaks, St Bedes, St Leonards-Mayfield, Tonbridge, Winchester and Worth.

We are selective but not academically 'elitist'. Our intake is broad and one of our strengths is working with each individual child to encourage them to make the most of every opportunity, to develop self confidence and self belief and to help them achieve the very best of which they are capable.

Games and the arts are an integral part of the Vinehall timetable. Pupils participate in all major team sports and everyone has a chance to represent the School. Creative arts are also strong, with flourishing art, music and drama departments, all of which exhibit/perform regularly both inside and outside School. Carpentry and wood-turning are also offered.

Boarding is at the very heart of the School and Vinehall has a well established boarding community, the majority being from Sussex, Kent and London. Junior Boarding is offered in Years 3-6 (four nights per week) with children moving on to full boarding in Years 7 and 8. There are regular exeat weekends and a full and varied programme of weekend activities. Pastoral care is excellent. Our February 2012 ISI Inspection report said: 'Pupils' personal development, including their spiritual, moral, social and cultural development is excellent. Thanks to the excellent relationships and the warm, caring atmosphere, pupils thrive and develop faith in their abilities. Pupils are exceptionally well looked after and arrangements for safeguarding are exemplary'.

Vinehall School is an educational charity No. 307014.

West Hill Park Preparatory School

(Founded 1910)

Titchfield, Fareham, Hampshire PO14 4BS
Tel: 01329 842356   Email: admissions@westhillpark.com
Fax: 01329 842911   Website: www.westhillpark.com

Headmaster: A P Ramsay BEd(Hons), MSc
Appointed: September 2009
School type: Coeducational Boarding & Day
Age range of pupils: 2–13
No. of pupils enrolled as at 1.9.12: 288
Boys: 180 Girls: 108
No. of boarders: 35
Fees per annum as at 1.9.12: Day: £8985–£14,985
Boarding: £13,785–£19,785
Average size of class: 10 -18
Teacher/pupil ratio: 1:14

At West Hill Park School, your child will be welcomed into a happy, supportive community in which everyone is valued and where we encourage everyone to show respect and care for one another.

Excellent academic performance is central to the school's ethos. However, we are careful not to measure children by academic achievement alone and place real value on the breadth of experience they gain. Effort, enthusiasm and conduct are highly esteemed and the resulting growth in confidence is the key to unlocking other accomplishments.

Up to Year 5, our classes are currently taught in mixed ability groups with differentiation to at least three levels. From Year 6, pupils are streamed and set for Maths, English and Science. In this way, each child's individual strengths and weaknesses are catered for both academically and socially.

Art, Design and Technology, ICT, Music, Dance and Drama all stimulate creativity and imagination.

Boarding (judged by Ofsted to be 'outstanding') has to be appealing to children and here, boarding is very much based on feeling happy and safe, and having a lot of fun. There is a firm but fair routine; time set aside for study, music practice and quiet relaxation as well as regular fun nights and special weekend activities. We offer full, weekly, flexible or a one night boarding experience to suit your family.

Extensive games and athletics fields, an astro hockey surface, heated indoor swimming pool, netball and tennis courts all provide the necessary facilities to allow us to compete at a high level with independent schools locally, and also at County and National levels.

Breadth and diversity are crucial to the philosophy of West Hill Park. We encourage children to take every opportunity life brings and to appreciate the world around them. The comprehensive activities programme epitomises the school's attitude that 'children are capable of anything, if only we let them try'.

As children progress through the school, they are encouraged to take more responsibility for their learning, and their contribution to school life. They grow to understand their importance in the community, both through instruction and example. This provides them with a strong platform from which they can confidently move into their senior school as independent, self-reliant individuals.

www.winchestercollege.org

Winchester College (boarding school for boys age 13 – 18, 690 pupils)
One of the most distinguished schools in the World
Admissions: Tel +44 (0)1962 621247

Winchester College is a registered charity – No. 1139000

EF International Academy Torbay

EF House, Castle Road, Torquay, Torbay TQ1 3BG
Tel: +41 41 41 74 525   Email: admissionsia@ef.com
Fax: +44 1803 202 943   Website: www.ef.com/academy

International Academy

Head of School: David Davies
School type: Coeducational Boarding
Accommodation in home-stays
Age range of pupils: 14–18
No. of pupils enrolled as at 1.1.12: 150
Fees per annum as at 1.1.12:
Boarding: £19,950

EF International Academy is part of EF Education First, the world leader in international education. With over 45 years of experience, EF has helped more than four million students realise their dream of studying abroad.

The School
The EF International Academy campus is situated in the heart of Torbay, a popular tourist destination on England's scenic south-west coast. London, Oxford and Stonehenge are a train-ride away. The school is housed in a fully modernised historic building, which provides a safe, comfortable learning environment, complete with state-of-the-art science and language labs, wireless internet, library facilities, a dining area and lounge.

Academics
Education at EF is highly personal and a range of internationally renowned programmes are offered to meet the individual needs of each student; including IB Diploma and A level, as well as IGCSE and the High School Preparation programme. Intensive English language courses are also available. EF has a track record of academic excellence with 45% of students receiving A/A* grades at A level, compared with the national average of 27%.

University Placements
The EF International Academy class of 2011 is on course for another year of success. Our students have been accepted on to courses that are deemed to be the best in the country for their subject, such as medicine at the University of Leicester and mathematics at the University of Oxford. 36% of our students have been admitted into one of the top ten UK universities for their chosen subject.

Pastoral Care
Personal tutors provide one-to-one individualised support and guidance. Each student is assigned a personal tutor whose role is to monitor the student's academic progress, university applications and general welfare. Students are encouraged to nurture their talents and develop new skills and confidence.

Scholarships
Scholarships will be awarded to highly talented and ambitious students who can make a positive contribution to the school community. Two students are awarded Founder's scholarships, which will cover 50% of total fees. Many other general scholarships are also available for students who demonstrate overall excellence.

Residential Life
Students stay with host families and benefit from full immersion into British culture and language. Host families are rigorously vetted and many have years of experience in offering a safe, supportive home away from home to EF Torbay students.

Kingsley School

(Founded 2009)

Northdown Road, Bideford, Devon EX39 3LY
Tel: 01237 426200   Email: admissions@kingsleyschoolbideford.co.uk
Fax: 01237 425981   Website: www.kingsleyschoolbideford.co.uk

KINGSLEY SCHOOL
BIDEFORD

Headmaster: Mr Andy Waters BEd, MA
Appointed: September 2006
School type: Coeducational Boarding & Day
Boarders from age 8
Age range of pupils: 3 months–18 years
No. of pupils enrolled as at 1.1.12: 400
Sixth Form: 80
No. of boarders: 70
Fees per annum as at 1.9.11: Day: £5010–£11,640
Boarding: £14,430–£22,200
Average size of class: 12
Teacher/pupil ratio: 1:9

Kingsley School Bideford, a single campus co-educational boarding and day school for pupils aged 3 to 18, is committed to discovering, nurturing and celebrating the talents and achievements of each and every one of its pupils. Set in 25 acres of playing fields, gardens and woods, the school is a stone's throw from North Devon's stunning surf beaches and within easy reach of Exmoor and Dartmoor national parks.

Kingsley students consistently achieve excellent results in public examinations. GCSE results are 50% higher than the UK national average and more than 90% of Kingsley sixth formers go on to the university of their choice. The academic curriculum is broad and includes sports and creative subjects such as music, drama and art.

Matching the breadth of the academic subjects is the exceptional range of sports and other activities available to every student of every ability level. Many of the outdoor activities take advantage of the school's wonderful location – surfing and rowing are extremely popular, while Dartmoor provides the dramatic setting for the annual Ten Tors Challenge. Kingsley's gymnastics squad consistently wins major competitions. The Judo Academy has a unique partnership with the University of Bath, enabling Kingsley's elite players to benefit from the renowned Team Bath training resources. Kingsley's drama and music departments stage a series of outstanding performances throughout the year in our purpose-designed theatre, while the Duke of Edinburgh Awards programme is always popular.

Kingsley boarders enjoy excellent accommodation, good food, a secure, happy environment and a well-planned programme of social activities. Free transport is provided to and from Heathrow Airport. Everything is supervised by our enthusiastic and committed team of houseparents and resident staff, all of whom are dedicated to providing an 'extended family' atmosphere.

Milton Abbey School

(Founded 1954)

Blandford Forum, Dorset DT11 0BZ
Tel: 01258 880484   Email: admissions@miltonabbey.co.uk
Fax: 01258 881194   Website: www.miltonabbey.co.uk

MILTON ABBEY

Headmaster: G E Doodes MA
Appointed: 2010
School type: Coeducational Boarding & Day
Age range of pupils: 13–18
No. of pupils enrolled as at 1.9.12: 228
Boys: 201 Girls: 27 Sixth Form: 106
No. of boarders: 221
Fees per annum as at 1.9.12: Day: £21,300
Boarding: £28,350
Average size of class: 12

Milton Abbey is a small co-educational boarding and day school committed to the individual, and delivers an education that is meant to challenge, stretch and develop young men and women into leaders and assured adults who possess confidence without arrogance. At Milton Abbey's heart is a philosophy of developing each and every girl and boy into fully rounded people academically, culturally, spiritually, and within a caring, supportive environment.

Milton Abbey is inclusive and ambitious for every pupil. Success, in whatever form, is celebrated. No one is overlooked. The small size allows for a level of care that is unsurpassed in bigger schools. However, our size does not diminish from our expectations of pupils – we want them to have big achievements, big ambitions and big hearts.

Throughout their time at Milton Abbey, our main responsibility to pupils is to find a spark that will light a passion. This may be in the classroom, as academic excellence is promoted thoroughly throughout the school. It could be on the games field, or in the theatre or concert hall, where we endeavour to engender a sense of pride in teamwork and individual performance. It could be on the school farm, the pheasant pens, the school shoot or in the ferret shed, as environmental awareness and a passion for the outdoors is a key feature of our life here.

Recent investment has seen the building of two new boarding houses and the renovation and opening of a new girl's 13-18 house in September 2012.

We warmly welcome you to visit us. For further details please contact The Admissions Office on 01258 882182 / admissions@miltonabbey.co.uk or visit our website www.miltonabbey.co.uk.

Abbots Bromley School

(Founded 1875)

High Street, Abbots Bromley, Rugeley, Staffordshire WS15 3BW
Tel: 01283 840232   Email: enquiries@abbotsbromley.net
Fax: 01283 840988   Website: www.abbotsbromley.net

Abbots Bromley School

Headmistress: Mrs J Dowling MA(Cantab), PGCE, NPQH
School type: Co-educational Pre-prep & Prep Girls Senior Boarding and Day
Age range of pupils:
Boys: 3–11
Girls: 3–18
No. of pupils enrolled as at 1.9.12: 251
Boys: 4 Girls: 247 Sixth Form: 54
No. of boarders: 59
Fees per annum as at 1.9.12: Day: £4386–£14,910
Weekly Boarding: £16,545–£20,925
Boarding: £20,295–£24,975

At Abbots Bromley School, there is so much on offer to suit a wide variety of individuals. Our friendly boarding community caters for weekly, flexi or occasional boarders. The safe haven of Abbots Bromley allows our pupils to grow up in beautiful natural surroundings, but at the same time we are never too far from locations where the students may benefit from cultural and intellectual experiences.

In Roch House Preparatory School, we educate boys and girls from Kindergarten to Year 6. This coeducational school sits within the main site with its own dedicated facilities. There is a happy friendly atmosphere in Roch House. The small class sizes, broad and stimulating curriculum, lively extracurricular programme and experienced staff all contribute to making Roch House a place for children to thrive and succeed.

In the Senior School, we offer a girls-only programme from the age of 11. Alongside our academic programme, our students are able to take a variety of qualifications to a high level in areas such as riding, dance and musical theatre without jeopardising any future plans they may have too early in their careers. We are lucky to have our own equestrian centre on site, fabulous dance facilities and a newly-refurbished theatre, where pupils can display their talents.

We offer excellent sporting facilities for budding sports women in a variety of disciplines including swimming and the opportunities for musicians are enhanced with an annual overseas tour to share their music with different communities.

Academic, art, dance, music, riding and sport scholarships are available as well as bursaries.

For students wishing to join us from overseas three airports lie within close proximity: East Midlands, Birmingham and Manchester.

We enjoy showing visitors all that we have to offer and invite you to come and see for yourself the wealth of opportunities available to your child.

Malvern St James

(Founded 1893)

Avenue Road, Great Malvern, Worcestershire WR14 3BA
Tel: 01684 584624   Email: registrar@malvernstjames.co.uk
Fax: 01684 566204   Website: www.malvernstjames.co.uk

Head Teacher: Mrs Patricia Woodhouse
BMus(Hons)
Appointed: September 2010
School type: Girls' Boarding & Day
Age range of pupils: 4–18
No. of pupils enrolled as at 1.9.12: 400
Fees per annum as at 1.9.12: Day: £7095–£15,645
Weekly Boarding: £15,240–£27,030
Boarding: £16,935–£29,955
Average size of class: 12-16
Teacher/pupil ratio: 1:7

"...an environment in which pupils can grow in self-esteem, self-confidence and respect." ISI 2011.

Malvern St James Girls' School is a leading boarding and day school that presents an imaginative vision of education for girls from the age of 4 through to 18, taught within a positive, purposeful atmosphere. 'MSJ' fosters creativity and bold-thinking; we challenge and encourage every girl to extend her personal horizons and realise her full potential. The school is home to a warm and welcoming community with a buoyant atmosphere of shared celebration, extolling personal success in every field of endeavour.

Curriculum and facilities
Small classes, led by dedicated and dynamic teachers, provide a first class education tailored to the individual. Our teaching facilities include a state-of-the-art science centre, multimedia language centre and new sports centre with fitness suite, all of which provide the best in 21st century teaching facilities. We offer a busy and varied weekend programme of activities to suit all interests, including watersports, rock climbing, abseiling, music, drama and expeditions leading to the Duke of Edinburgh's Award.

Scholarships
Academic, music, art, riding and sport scholarships are available for middle school entry; academic, music, art, riding, drama and sport scholarships for sixth form entry.

A scholarship is worth up to a maximum of 20% of annual fees and an exhibition is worth up to a maximum of 10% of the current fees. In both cases, means-tested top up bursaries can be awarded.

Entrance examinations
Prep and Pre-prep: informal assessment.

Middle School: cognitive ability tests (CAT 3) and a comprehension examination or the Common Entrance examination.

Sixth Form: subject entrance paper and general essay.

Location
Situated at the foot of the beautiful Malvern Hills in the heart of Worcestershire. InterCity trains run from Great Malvern, the M5 and M50 are nearby and London, Birmingham and Manchester airports are within easy reach.

Malvern St James is a registered charity (No. 527513) that exists to support excellent education for girls.

Packwood Haugh School

(Founded 1892)

Ruyton XI Towns, Shrewsbury, Shropshire SY4 1HX
Tel: 01939 260217 Email: enquiries@packwood-haugh.co.uk
Fax: 01939 262077 Website: www.packwood-haugh.co.uk

Headmaster: Clive Smith-Langridge BA (Hons), PGCE
Appointed: September 2012
School type: Coeducational Day & Boarding
Boarders from 7 years
Age range of pupils: 4–13
No. of pupils enrolled as at 1.9.12: 240
Boys: 160 Girls: 80
No. of boarders: 128
Fees per annum as at 1.9.12: Day: £6669–£14,919
Boarding: £18,645
Average size of class: 13.5
Teacher/pupil ratio: 1:7

Packwood Haugh has a national reputation for achievement and for providing an education tailored to the needs of pupils, in an environment where each child is happy. Happy to strive for excellence in the classroom and on the games field, happy to contribute selflessly to the community, and happy to enjoy everything that the school offers.

The school is well-equipped with an outstanding theatre which is used daily for assemblies as well as for full scale productions, superb sports fields and well-equipped classrooms; a new sports hall complex was completed in 2007 which includes extensive facilities for art and craft design and technology teaching. Each form has time in the computer suite, and children use the school's network and the internet.

Quality teaching inspires children of all abilities to aim high and the infectious Packwood 'work ethic' ensures that potential is fulfilled. Packwood Haugh pupils regularly secure places at senior schools including Downe House, Eton, Gordonstoun, Harrow, Malvern, Oundle, Radley, Rugby, Shrewsbury, Uppingham, Winchester and Wycombe Abbey and a 100% pass rate at Common Entrance is usual. The school has a strong record of sporting achievement.

Pastoral care from staff, and from the older children to the younger, creates a friendly, and positive 'home from home' in which to live, learn and grow... There are 50 clubs on offer with a wide choice of activities from archery to xylophones.

Most pupils board, with girls and boys living in separate houses. Boarding facilities are continually improved and children often choose to board to enjoy the fun. The school offers a full boarding routine in term time with fixed exeats and half term and escorted travel to and from London.

Quote: "No one could ever suffer from boredom in this boarding school; this is very much acknowledged by the pupils who appreciate all the opportunities available to them." (ISI inspection report)

Packwood Haugh is a Registered Charity (No. 528411) and exists to educate children and serve the community.

Rugby School

(Founded 1567)

Rugby School

Rugby, Warwickshire CV22 5EH
Tel: 01788 556274   Email: admissions@rugbyschool.net
Fax: 01788 556277   Website: www.rugbyschool.net

Headmaster: P S J Derham
Appointed: September 2001
School type: Coeducational Boarding & Day
Age range of pupils: 11–18
No. of pupils enrolled as at 1.9.12: 792
Boys: 442 Girls: 350 Sixth Form: 344
No. of boarders: 647
Fees per annum as at 1.9.12: Day: £15,165
Weekly Boarding: £17,700
Boarding: £27,225
Average size of class: 15
Teacher/pupil ratio: 1:8.2

In truth, most schools can say most of the following. But only one school can say it all.

We're an all round coeducational school, where pupils are actively encouraged to develop their own individual skills and talents. Every child has something special inside them; it's our job to find out what that is.

We're a school which values outstanding academic performance – but never at the expense of achieving excellence in other fields. In our experience, a hothouse isn't necessarily a place where many pupils will blossom.

We're a school located in the Midlands, and we're often noted for our remarkably unsnobby atmosphere. But amongst pupils and teachers alike, you'll detect a fierce pride about being here.

We're a school with a strong sense of service to the community. We're blessed with some marvellously well-equipped facilities, and we think it's only fair we afford wider access to them whenever we can.

We also think it's fair to give children a chance to come here who couldn't otherwise afford to do so. Our aim is to have 1 in 10 of our pupils granted full Arnold Foundation bursaries by the year 2020.

We're a true 7-day a week school with a strong boarding ethos. The place doesn't empty at weekends for the simple reason that there's so much going on here.

We're a school that loves to innovate and try out new things. Just because 'it's never been done before' doesn't mean we shouldn't give it a go now.

Without being over-pious about it, we're a Christian foundation, where tolerance and understanding are taught with just the same skill and dedication as English and maths.

We're a school with a strong House structure, and a long tradition of in-house dining. This means there's an unusual emphasis on individual pastoral care, so being here really is the next best thing to being back home.

After five years of receiving one of the best school educations in the world, all of our pupils finally leave Rugby.

But Rugby never, ever leaves them.

Fulneck School

(Founded 1753)

Fulneck, Pudsey, Leeds, West Yorkshire LS28 8DS
Tel: 0113 2570235   Email: enquiries@fulneckschool.co.uk; admissions@fulneckschool.co.uk
Fax: 0113 2557316   Website: www.fulneckschool.co.uk

Principal: Mrs Deborah Newman
Appointed: 2012
School type: Coeducational Day & Boarding
Age range of pupils: 3–18
No. of pupils enrolled as at 1.9.12: 440
Sixth Form: 67
No. of boarders: 89
Fees per annum as at 1.9.12: Day: £6210–£11,010
Weekly Boarding: £15,390–£18,585
Boarding: £16,725–£20,700
Average size of class: Av 15
Teacher/pupil ratio: 1:8

Fulneck School is an outstanding day and boarding school, located in Leeds. We educate boys and girls between the ages of 3 and 18; boarders are accepted from the age of 9.

Fulneck School provides an all-round education of exceptional quality (Best Sixth Form in Leeds, 2010 and 2011) and 'an excellent learning experience for all its pupils' (ISI Inspection Report Dec 2010) who thrive in the stimulating and challenging yet caring environment. The school has a strong system of pastoral care in which pupils feel valued whilst at the same time 'achieving outstanding personal development' (ISI 2010).

Fulneck's exceptional teaching and learning environment was confirmed recently by three outstanding inspection reports. In addition to the The Independent School Inspectorate (ISI), Ofsted also awarded Fulneck an 'outstanding' mark for the boarding provision and the Council for the Registration of Schools Teaching Dyslexic Pupils (CReSTeD) inspection re-confirmed the prestigious DU status, the highest grade awarded for a mainstream school. Furthermore, Fulneck School received the highest accolade of Ofsted Outstanding Provider.

The inspection report praised Fulneck's tailored teaching and highlighted that the 'outcomes for children are outstanding. Children reach exceptional levels of achievement in all areas of learning' (ISI 2010).

Entry requirements
Entry by assessment at all ages commensurate with expected National Curriculum levels. Consideration is given to pupils with special needs/dyslexia.

Academic & leisure facilities
Fulneck offers modern facilities within historic Grade I listed buildings. There are well equipped ICT suites, modern junior and senior libraries, a professional theatre, art studio, gymnasia, science laboratories, separate sixth form centre, designated common rooms, sports fields, tennis and netball courts, adjacent golf course and nearby full length swimming pool, fitness club and horsing riding school and livery.

Fulneck provides early and late care in addition to an exciting Holiday Club for junior pupils.

Children with learning difference can access the outstanding CReSTeD DU category Learning Support Unit. Fulneck also has a dedicated specialist English as Additional Language unit for students from overseas.

Fulneck School provides an outstanding education experience for boys and girls between the ages of 3 and 18. Registered charity no. 251211.

Woodhouse Grove School

(Founded 1812)

Apperley Bridge, Bradford, West Yorkshire BD10 0NR
Tel: 0113 250 2477   Email: gilks.tv@woodhousegrove.co.uk
Fax: 0113 250 5290   Website: www.woodhousegrove.co.uk

Headmaster: David C Humphreys BA
Appointed: 1996
School type: Coeducational Day & Boarding
Member of: HMC
Age range of pupils: 11–18
No. of pupils enrolled as at 1.9.12: 718
Boys: 437 Girls: 281 Sixth Form: 176
No. of boarders: 103
Fees per annum as at 1.9.12: Day: £10,650–£10,920
Weekly Boarding: £20,550–£20,850
Boarding: £22,080–£22,200
Average size of class: 20
Teacher/pupil ratio: 1:10

Situated on a 70 acre campus with extensive grounds yet conveniently located close to major air, railway and motorway networks, the Grove provides a first class all round education for boys and girls, day and boarders alike. Our Junior School, Bronte House, lays excellent foundations from 3-11; however we welcome 50% of the Grove's pupils from other schools at 11, 13 and 16.

Our outstanding facilities, excellent academic results, wide range of extracurricular activities and a

beautiful setting ensure that we can provide your child with the best opportunities and the preparation for a life beyond the classroom. Our boarders enjoy modern, well equipped boarding houses, a secure and caring environment, a 'home from home' atmosphere, and an ever changing list of activities which contribute to the fun and enjoyment of being a boarder at the Grove.

The school's Christian foundation and forward thinking combine with excellent facilities that include an impressive 25m competition swimming pool, state-of-the-art sports and performing arts centre and a purpose-built music and drama facility.

We are a school with traditional values but ambitions for the future, an unpretentious school that seeks to nurture all. Visitors to Woodhouse Grove often comment on our warm and friendly atmosphere – come and see! Meet the pupils and talk to the Headmaster. You will find a friendly welcome and a school with a proud past and an exciting future.

Woodhouse Grove School is a registered charity (No. 529205), which exists to provide education for children.

Kilgraston School
NURSERY • PREP • SENIOR • SIXTH FORM

(Founded 1931)

Winner
The
**Independent School
Awards** 2011

*Independent School
of the Year 2011*

Bridge of Earn, Perth, Perth & Kinross PH2 9BQ
Tel: 01738 812257   Email: headoffice@kilgraston.com
Fax: 01738 813410   Website: www.kilgraston.com

Principal: Mr Frank Thompson MA, MPhil, PGCE
Appointed: September 2012
School type: Girls' Day & Boarding
Age range of pupils:
Boys: 2½–9
Girls: 2½–18
No. of pupils enrolled as at 1.9.12: 321
Boys: 4 Girls: 317 Sixth Form: 91
No. of boarders: 132
Fees per annum as at 1.9.12: Day: £8265–£14,490
Boarding: £19,620–£24,705
Average size of class: Av 15
Teacher/pupil ratio: 1:9

Kilgraston is a girls boarding and day school set in 54 acres of pristine Scottish parkland in Bridge of Earn, just south of Perth. It has recently won the prestigious prize of 'Independent School of the Year' at the Independent School Awards.

The school was nominated for the Outstanding Strategic Initiative Award in recognition of the changes the school has made to achieve a 55% growth over the last five years. It also received the Outstanding Financial/Commercial Initiative prize for the ongoing multi-million pound investment in facilities and the introduction of new sports academies developed to nurture young sporting talent. The judges also took into account the recent excellent HMIe inspection and the most successful examination results to date with an exceptional 57% A grades (95% A-C) for Higher and an outstanding 54% A grades (92% A-C) at Advanced Higher. The culmination of these led to the nomination for Independent School of the Year and eventual success.

Kilgraston has pushed its academic capabilities over the last decade and often has the highest grades in Scotland being in the top three for Advanced Highers in the past four years. Kilgraston's academic record is helped due to the small class sizes; the sixth form often has less than 10 pupils per class and the lower ages with around 15.

With an equestrian centre with 60m x 40m floodlit arena (only school in Scotland with this facility on site), a new international-sized all-weather hockey pitch, 8 all-weather tennis courts, sports hall with climbing wall and fitness suite and a new 25m indoor swimming pool there is enough to keep the girls occupied!

Means-tested scholarships and bursaries are available on top of a 10% discount for armed forces families. Please visit our website or contact Mrs Linda-Anne Drane, Principal's PA, for more information or to arrange a visit.

Merchiston Castle School

(Founded 1833)

294 Colinton Road, Edinburgh EH13 0PU
Tel: 0131 312 2200   Email: admissions@merchiston.co.uk
Fax: 0131 441 6060   Website: www.merchiston.co.uk

MERCHISTON
EDINBURGH | Boys first

Headmaster: Mr A R Hunter BA
Appointed: September 1998
School type: Boys' Boarding & Day
Age range of pupils: 8–18
No. of pupils enrolled as at 1.9.12: 470
Sixth Form: 157
No. of boarders: 330
Fees per annum as at 1.9.12: Day: £12,120–£19,545
Boarding: £17,070–£26,655
Teacher/pupil ratio: 1:9

Merchiston is set in 100 acres of beautiful parkland, four miles from the centre of Edinburgh and just 20 minutes from Edinburgh's international airport, which has over 100 direct routes. Only an hour's flight from London, Edinburgh's rich culture offers stimulation and excitement to the boys, whether they are visiting an art gallery or attending an international rugby fixture.

With an ethos based on traditional values, Merchiston encourages self-reliance and independence, as well as respect and tolerance for others. The School's goal is to help every boy reach his full potential and leave Merchiston ready for the world. Merchiston has strong and effective approaches to develop each boy's personal achievement and boasts an impressive record of helping boys excel far beyond their expected results at GCSE and A level. Merchiston was named the Top Scottish School for A levels in 2011 (Daily Telegraph and The Herald) and has an unrivalled reputation for providing a first rate all-round education. Merchiston was rated 'Excellent' for the Quality of Care and Support and Quality of Environment by The Care Inspectorate in 2010.

"My time at Merchiston allowed me to develop into a young man who was ready to head into further education and on into the real world. The combination of first class pastoral care, a style and standard of teaching which allowed a smooth transition into university, with a co-curricular programme second to none and the friendships built up along the way made my time at Merchiston some of the best of my life so far."
Merchistonian

There is a long and successful tradition of sport at Merchiston, with equal emphasis on recreation and excellence. Within fantastic facilities, there are over 20 sports on offer which cater for all interests and levels of ability. As one of the leading innovators of sports education in the UK, the School established Scotland's first tennis academy in 2007 and more recently its own golf academy. The School is currently represented at national and international level in many sports including athletics, cricket and rugby.

"The school provided excellent opportunities and activities for me to participate in, which catered for my interests, as well as giving me the best teaching and tuition, which led to my gaining a place at Cambridge."
Merchistonian

"Our main objective is to motivate pupils to try their hardest and to strive to achieve the highest levels possible in all areas, whilst living as part of a community. Whilst we are concentrating on the academic platform of each boy, alongside the importance of co-curricular activities, we also try to focus on developing boys who are all-rounders with a sense of values."

Andrew Hunter, Headmaster

Queen Victoria School

(Founded 1908)

Dunblane, Perth & Kinross FK15 0JY
Tel: 0131 310 2927   Email: admissions@qvs.org.uk
Fax: 0131 310 2926   Website: www.qvs.org.uk

Head: Mrs W Bellars MA(Hons), PGCE, DipEd, MA(Ed Man)
Appointed: January 2007
School type: Coeducational Boarding
Age range of pupils: 11–18
No. of pupils enrolled as at 21.8.12: 270
Boys: 141 Girls: 129 Sixth Form: 28
No. of boarders: 270
Fees per annum as at 21.8.12:
Boarding: £1179
Religious denomination: Inter-denominational

Queen Victoria School (QVS) is a non-academically selective, fully boarding, coeducational school for the children of Armed Forces personnel who are Scottish or who have served in Scotland.

A small parental contribution (currently around £1179 a year) is levied, but there are no fees. Tuition, boarding, uniform, books and most other costs are met by the Ministry of Defence. In cases of need, the parental contribution can sometimes be paid by one of the Services' Benevolent Funds or similar.

Entry to QVS is decided on the basis of need. Our reason for existing is to provide continuity and stability of education for children who would otherwise be moved around the country, and perhaps the world, several times in the course of their school careers, as a result of their serving parent's postings. We are also tasked by the Ministry of Defence with providing for those families who could not otherwise afford boarding education.

Children can come to QVS from Primary 7, around the age of ten-and-a-half, and this is our main point of entry: this is where most places are available. Children who come into Primary 7 have a year of adjusting to boarding school life before moving into the senior school. The P7 year also allows a year-group who will be at different stages in their academic development when they arrive (as a result of being educated in different schools and different education systems) to achieve some shared level of attainment and content covered, before moving into the senior school. Some QVS students have been to as many as 11 different primary schools before coming to us!

Because all QVS entrants are the children of serving personnel, there is a very special kind of support provided by them for one another. Nowadays, when many parents are on unaccompanied tours, it is particularly reassuring to our children and to their families to know that they are not unusual here. Everyone knows what it is like to be part of a Service family. Several staff have Service experience too, and all are committed to the unique requirement of looking after Services children in a fully boarding environment.

Academic
We offer a range of subject choices and consistently achieve pass rates well above the Scottish national averages.

Sport
These are a very important part of QVS life. Rugby, hockey and football are the main team sports, with very high standards being achieved by both teams and individuals.

Ceremonial
The pipes, drums and dancers of Queen Victoria School have earned an international reputation. Piping,

drumming or dancing lessons are compulsory for every younger pupil, and many maintain their interest and commitment through to Secondary 6 and beyond.

Extracurricular activities

A wide range of hobbies is on offer. Pupils are encouraged to take up at least one each season, and some do several each week.

QVS has a lively Combined Cadet Force (CCF) and all S2 pupils are given an induction year in which they spend time with each of the three Service sections – Navy, Army and Air Force.

The Duke of Edinburgh's Award Scheme operates at all three levels – bronze, silver and gold – at QVS.

Application to join QVS

In February/March each year the admissions board will interview eligible candidates for places in August of that year. The closing date for applications is January 15th in the same year. This is a deadline that we have to adhere to firmly, because of the need to obtain reports on the candidates before the admissions board sits. Applications can be made at any time before January 15th, with most being made in the autumn of the preceding year. An open morning is held for prospective applicants and their families in September of each year, but visits to the school can be made at any time by contacting the admissions secretary. We do not however recommend that visits are made during QVS holidays.

There are more places available in P7 each year than in any other year, although it is possible for older

© Simon Williams

children to apply. Each year a small number of places is offered in older year-groups, according to the availability of bed space.

Although the school prospectus and DVD can give you a hint of what we offer, there is no substitute for visiting the school and talking with current pupils and staff. Our pupils are the best ambassadors for the school, and current and past parents can also be very helpful in telling prospective QVS parents what the experience is like. If you are a serving parent, it is very possible that someone on your unit will have experience of QVS, so do ask around!

If you would like to visit the school or find out more, please contact the admissions secretary on +44 (0) 131 310 2927 or military 94745 2927.

Strathallan School

(Founded 1913)

STRATHALLAN
Opportunities *for all* to excel

Forgandenny, Perth, Perth & Kinross PH2 9EG
Tel: 01738 812546   Email: admissions@strathallan.co.uk
Fax: 01738 812549   Website: www.strathallan.co.uk

Headmaster: Mr B K Thompson MA(Oxon)
Appointed: 2000
School type: Coeducational Boarding & Day
Age range of pupils: 9–18
No. of pupils enrolled as at 1.9.12: 567
Boys: 318 Girls: 249 Sixth Form: 200
No. of boarders: 368
Fees per annum as at 1.9.12: Day: £4044–£6163
Boarding: £6479–£9083
Average size of class: 11
Teacher/pupil ratio: 1:7

Holding an international reputation within its own portfolio of achievements, Strathallan School in Perthshire needs little introduction to those seeking a high-quality boarding and day establishment for their sons and daughters aged nine to 18.

Reputation is one thing, the means by which it is earned is, perhaps, less well appreciated. Looking at academic performance first, there are two key aspects for success:

- A nurturing environment.
- Support from teachers who are passionate about their subjects as well as being high quality practitioners.

Each pupil receives support from an academic tutor and there is also a full-time careers advisor to help with opportunities beyond School.

Central to this is accomplishment:

- 82% of this year's A level entries were graded A*/B.

Strathallan achieves this, it contends, by tailoring work to individual needs. 'We prepare pupils for entry to top universities.'

Certainly the location offers pupils every advantage:

- Set in glorious countryside on a site of 153 acres.
- Offering a safe and secure environment for children to grow and develop.
- It is still within easy reach of the City of Perth and Scotland's International Airports, Edinburgh 40mins & Glasgow (1hour). This makes the commute to London Heathrow less than two hours and considerably more accessible for those living around the world.

The serious business of excellence in academic outcome is but one aspect of independent education. Strathallan prides itself on being friendly and welcoming with a strong sense of community, the aim being to support and to motivate each individual to realise potential in all areas. "We celebrate what pupils achieve and strive to create an ethos which demonstrates that with hard work and expert tuition, they can achieve."

- There is wireless broadband throughout the school.
- Senior Houses feature individual study bedrooms for privacy, and common room and leisure facilities for socialising and relaxation.
- The Junior House is designed to cater for children who wish to enter the School at ages nine to 13 and is situated within its own campus, as well as enjoying the facilities of the main School.

"We are convinced that we made the right decision in placing our son at Strathallan. The School has been instrumental in his achieving his highest academic potential and ultimately gaining a place at Cambridge, quite apart from having a wonderful time which I know he will look back on with great fondness for the rest of his life." a former parent.

Rydal Penrhos School

(Founded 1880)

Pwllycrochan Avenue, Colwyn Bay, Conwy LL29 7BT
Tel: +44 (0)1492 530155 Email: info@rydal-penrhos.com
Fax: +44 (0)1492 531872 Website: www.rydalpenrhos.com

RYDAL PENRHOS SCHOOL

Headmaster: Mr P A Lee-Browne MA
Appointed: April 2008
School type: Coeducational Day & Boarding plus flexi and weekly boarding
Member of: HMC, IAPS, SHMIS, ARS, IB
Affiliations: BSA
Age range of pupils: 2½–18
No. of pupils enrolled as at 1.6.12: 617
Boys: 355 Girls: 262
No. of boarders: 148
Fees per annum as at 1.6.12: Day: £5970–£14,055
Weekly Boarding: £20,460–£25,245
Boarding: £22,740–£28,020
Teacher/pupil ratio: 1:8

Location

Rydal Penrhos School is in a wonderful safe and unique location, nestled on the North Wales coast in Colwyn Bay, but also on the doorstep of the Snowdonia National Park. It is also within easy reach of Manchester and Liverpool airports, with London less than three hours away, via an express rail link.

Ethos

Rydal Penrhos School plays a huge part in our pupils' journey from youth into adulthood. As well as providing scholarship and intellectual fulfilment, we also tend to an individual's spiritual and personal wellbeing, all within a powerful framework of Christian values provided by the school's Methodist foundation. Achievement is the primary goal, but in a spirit of community, tolerance and respect, to ensure that every pupil leaving Rydal has a set of qualities, values and skills to last a lifetime.

School life: inside the classroom and out
Small class sizes, coupled with an individual tutor system, mean we can tailor the learning process to our pupils' individual intellectual needs and capabilities. We set great store by self-development through independent reflection and learning. We have a culture that embraces drama, music and the visual arts and the facilities to support them.

Rydal Penrhos School has the on-campus facilities to offer sports such as rugby (2010 saw the opening of a new rugby academy in partnership with the WRU), hockey, cricket, netball and swimming, as well as squash, tennis, basketball and even Eton Fives. However, it also runs a vast array of other outdoor activities that exploit Snowdonia and the Irish Sea: for example, sailing (the school is a Royal Yacht Association training centre), kayaking, golf, climbing, gorge scrambling, orienteering, mountain biking and skiing.

Curriculum

The school has offered the IB diploma since 2003, and has produced excellent results from the outset. We provide the full range of subjects at GCSE and a wide choice for IB (or A level) in the sixth form as well as a pre-sixth/pre IB course.

Boarding

There are five well-established boarding houses, each looked after by experienced house parents and matrons who lead a team of tutors drawn from academic staff. The Health Centre and the central care team provide further support. There is a full and well-supported out of hours and weekend activity programme for boarders and day pupils to ensure good integration of all pupils and a real sense of belonging.

St John's-on-the-Hill

(Founded 1923)

Tutshill, Chepstow, Monmouthshire NP16 7LE
Tel: 01291 622045   Email: registrar@stjohnsonthehill.co.uk
Fax: 01291 623932   Website: www.stjohnsonthehill.co.uk

Headmaster: Mr N Folland BSc
Appointed: 2011
School type: Coeducational Day & Boarding
Boarders from 7 years; Pre-Prep & Day Nursery
Age range of pupils: 3 months–13 years
No. of pupils enrolled as at 1.9.12: 302
Fees per annum as at 1.9.12: Day: £6675–£11,025
Weekly Boarding: £15,525
Boarding: £15,525
Average size of class: 16
Teacher/pupil ratio: 1:10

St John's-on-the-Hill is situated in extensive, attractive grounds on the border of Monmouthshire and Gloucestershire, overlooking Chepstow Castle and the beautiful Wye Valley. Served by an excellent motorway system, just three miles from the old Severn Bridge, St John's provides a consistently high standard of care and education.

Discovering and developing individual talent
The family atmosphere ensures that even the youngest child feels a sense of belonging. A high standard of teaching and small class sizes, combined with first-class facilities, ensure boys and girls can develop both their academic ability and character to the full. Emphasis is on mutual respect, integrity and the need to discover and develop individual talents, whether they are creative, intellectual or athletic.

Celebrating achievement
Children are encouraged to develop skills and achieve success across the curriculum. Sport, art, design technology, music and performing arts are therefore an important part of school life. Children are encouraged to be creative from an early age and to take part in regular drama productions, either front or backstage. Traditional and modern choral music is a particular strength within the school.

Scholarships and bursaries
Scholarships and awards are made for academic, music, sporting and dramatic ability. HM Forces bursaries are also available.

Boarding at St John's
Children can board from the age of seven on a full, weekly, or 'flexi' basis. The boarding house is family-run and has a friendly, homely atmosphere with spacious accommodation.

Creating the future
On leaving St John's, children enter a wide range of senior schools of their choice and with more than 100 senior school scholarships awarded to St John's children in the last five years, the school is justifiably proud of its scholarship record and senior school links.

St John's-on-the-Hill and Brightlands School Trust Limited is a registered charity (No. 312953) founded for the education of children.

Overseas Schools

Ecole Active Bilingue Jeannine Manuel

(Founded 1954)

70 rue du Théâtre, Paris, 75015 France
Tel: +33 1 44 37 00 80   Email: admissions@eabjm.net
Fax: +33 1 45 79 06 66   Website: www.eabjm.org

Principal: Elisabeth Zéboulon
School type: Coeducational Day
Member of: ECIS, IB, ELSA, CIS
Age range of pupils: 4–18
No. of pupils enrolled as at 1.9.12: 2395
Boys: 1150 Girls: 1245
Fees per annum as at 1.9.12: Day: €4740–€5010
€1580–€1670 per term
IB Classes: €15,600
Average size of class: 27

EABJM is a non-profit pre-K-12 coeducational school founded in 1954 with the mission to develop international understanding through bilingual (French/English) education. An associated UNESCO school, EABJM has become the largest non-denominational independent school in France, with 2300 pupils representing over 66 nationalities and every major cultural tradition. The school's academic excellence matches its diversity: EABJM is regularly ranked among the top five of all 121 Paris high schools (state and independent) for its overall academic performance.

Each year, EABJM welcomes more than 100 new non-French speaking pupils who enrol in 'adaptation' classes where they follow a French immersion programme. A senior advisor follows them closely and, the following year, they join the mainstream where they continue to be supported with a special French programme, which involves three weekly hours of special French classes over and above the standard French curriculum.

THE LOWER AND MIDDLE SCHOOL follow the National Curriculum with several exceptions: English is taught every day and, in middle school, sciences, history and geography are taught in English. The curriculum is enriched at all levels, not only with a more advanced English language and literature curriculum, but also, for example, with Chinese language instruction (compulsory in grades 3-4-5), an integrated science programme in lower school, and independent research projects in middle school.

IN UPPER SCHOOL, tenth graders follow the National Curriculum. In 11th grade, pupils choose between the standard French Baccalaureate, the French OIB (International Option within the French Baccalaureate) and the International Baccalaureate. Out of the last three graduating classes, 16% followed the standard French track, 59% opted for the French OIB and 25% chose the IB. (As the IB is not subsidized, its tuition is more than three times the French curriculum tuition.)

Over the past three years, approximately 23% of our students have gone to US colleges or universities, 39% chose the UK or Canada, 36% entered the French higher education system, and the balance pursued their education all over the world.

Admission

Although admission is competitive and applications typically exceed available spaces by a ratio of 5:1, every effort is made to reserve space for international applicants, including children of families who expect to remain in France for a limited period of time and wish to combine a cultural immersion in French education with the ability to re-enter their own school systems and excel.

Oporto British School

(Founded 1894)

Rua da Cerca 326, 4150-201 Porto, Portugal
Tel: +351 22 616 6660   Email: school@obs.edu.pt
Fax: +351 22 616 6668   Website: www.obs.edu.pt

Head Master: Mr Michael William Clack
School type: Coeducational Day
Age range of pupils: 3–18
No. of pupils enrolled as at 1.9.12: 404
Fees per annum as at 1.9.12: Day: £6572–£9657
Average size of class: 16
Teacher/pupil ratio: 1:9

The Oporto British School is proud of the fact that it is the oldest British School in mainland Europe, having been established in 1894.

At the Oporto British School we aim to be a vibrant and challenging school which opens the minds and hearts of our pupils. We seek to engender a stimulating and inspirational environment in which all our pupils learn and develop. Our objective is to guide and encourage our pupils to develop and progress spiritually, academically and communally, enabling them to take their place in society as responsible citizens.

We believe that every pupil should strive for success whether that is in mathematics, English, science, sport or the performing arts. Fundamentally, our aim is to instil in our pupils a sense of mutual respect, tolerance, leadership and service. Our pupils are well-mannered, friendly, bilingual and engaging.

We follow a British-style curriculum until the completion of the IGCSE years. The most senior pupils then study the IB Diploma curriculum. The Form 12 pupils have achieved very good IB Diploma results in recent years, which have been amongst the best in Portugal. The school, while being conscious of its British foundation and traditions, is very much an international school of the 21st century.

The school is open and friendly. Excellent relationships are evident throughout its close knit, supportive community, which is often described as being 'like one big family'.

A major feature of the school is the quality of teaching, which occurs in classes with favourable teacher-pupil ratios. Maximum class sizes are 20.

The best way to gauge our unique atmosphere is to come and visit us. I shall be delighted to welcome you and talk about my vision for the School.

St. George's School in Switzerland

(Founded 1927)

Chemin de St Georges 19, CH 1815 Clarens/Montreux, Switzerland
Tel: +41 21 964 3411   Email: office@st-georges.ch
Fax: +41 21 964 4932   Website: www.st-georges.ch

Head of School: Dr Ilya Eigenbrot
School type: Coeducational Day & Boarding School
Age range of pupils: 3–18
Teacher/pupil ratio: 1:5

Almost 100 years of academic excellence

Reflecting back on 85 years of exciting activity at St. George's School, we can proudly say that we have successfully provided our students with the best international education in Switzerland while retaining the excellence of a British school.

Under an hour's drive from Geneva, our 12-acre campus is located in the residential suburb of Clarens, near Montreux, overlooking the lake and the Alps.

St. George's opened a day campus in Verbier for juniors aged 3 to 10.

The high quality of our staff and the outstanding on-campus sport facilities ensure that students benefit from academic achievement as well as emphasis on their physical skills and development.

Academia - *Levavi Occulos*

Our mission is to provide a global sense of excellence in education, reaching the perfect balance between intellectual stimulation, physical activity and the development of social skills. Our academic programmes give access to the worldwide renowned IGCSE and IB diploma. They guarantee a solid learning base including science, social skills, liberal and performing arts, foreign languages preparing your children for a bright and strong academic future.

We aim to provide the students with a sense of initiative and the self-confidence needed to help them become worldly, reliable, caring and responsible adults.

Boarders

St. George's has proved to be a 'home away from home' for thousands of young women and men giving them the chance to experience a unique way of life. Everything at the school is designed to help students adapt easily and quickly to their second home. In 2007, to celebrate the school decided to open the boarding section to boys. The school in Clarens now welcomes boys and girls from 10 to 18.

By enrolling your children at St. George's, you are giving them a chance to understand different cultures, instill in them the need for daily discipline, the values of respect, and monitor their development into mature, caring achievers.

Summer camp

Since the 1980s, St. George's School Summer Camps have been known as an ongoing success story, welcoming boys and girls aged 10 to 17 from over 20 countries throughout July and August. We provide our summer campers with a safe, happy stimulating atmosphere in a beautiful environment. Campers are given the opportunity to improve their language skills while making friends from around the world. Excursions, sports and outdoor entertainment remain a major part of the programme to guarantee exciting lifelong memories.

Specialist & Sixth Form Schools & Colleges

Leiths School of Food & Wine

(Founded 1975)

16-20 Wendell Road, Shepherd's Bush, London W12 9RT
Tel: 020 8749 6400   Email: info@leiths.com
Website: www.leiths.com

Managing Director: Camilla Schneideman
School type: Coeducational Day
Age range of pupils: 17–99
No. of pupils enrolled as at 1.9.12: 96
Fees per annum as at 1.9.12:
Essential Certificate: £3,035
Two Term Diploma: £15,250
Three Term Diploma: £19,850
Average size of class: 16
Teacher/pupil ratio: 1:8

Leiths School of Food and Wine is a leading London cookery school for professional and amateur cooks. Established by Prue Leith and Caroline Waldegrave in 1975, Leiths' culinary qualifications are highly regarded in the food industry, with graduates going on to work in Michelin-starred kitchens, star in cooking shows and work for top food magazines. If you have a keen interest in cooking and want to learn an essential skill that will serve you for life, Leiths runs a four-week Essential Certificate each year, as well as a ten-week course in September. Both courses are exam based certificate courses that include a food hygiene certificate as well as offering budgeting, healthy eating and menu planning advice and are designed to build your cookery skills and confidence. Leiths List, our agency for cooks, can help place you in a suitable job once qualified. Leiths also run one week cookery classes throughout the year that are ideal for university survival, teaching you to cook delicious simple food on any budget. Whether you are an aspiring professional or enthusiastic amateur, you will leave Leiths armed with the essential skills and confidence necessary to be a culinary success.

Contact Leiths for a prospectus now on +44 (0) 20 8749 6400 or view all our courses at www.leiths.com alternatively for any other questions please email us info@leiths.com

Westminster Tutors

(Founded 1934)

86 Old Brompton Road, South Kensington, London SW7 3LQ
Tel: 020 7584 1288   Email: info@westminstertutors.co.uk
Fax: 020 7584 2637   Website: www.westminstertutors.co.uk

Principal: Virginia Maguire BA, MLitt
School type: Coeducational Day
Age range of pupils: 14–mature
No. of pupils enrolled as at 1.9.12:
Boys: 25 Girls: 25 Sixth Form: 40
Fees per annum as at 1.9.12: Day: £6300–£20,400
Average size of class: 2
Teacher/pupil ratio: 1:1

Established in 1934, Westminster Tutors has been providing top-flight tuition for over 75 years. We are a small coeducational college with a friendly, informal atmosphere and excellent examination results in a wide range of subjects. The small size of the teaching groups allows a great deal of attention to be paid to the individual needs of students, helping them to achieve their full potential. Each student has a personal tutor who monitors academic progress and general wellbeing, and all students receive personal higher education and career guidance from the Principal. We keep in close contact with parents and send regular reports on each student's progress and achievements. Students have access at all times to computing facilities, including the use of the internet, and are encouraged to develop their IT skills wherever possible. Both traditional and modern methods of research and study are encouraged.

Westminster Tutors specialises in A level courses taken over one or two years or, for intensive re-take courses, as little as three months. We also offer revision courses and private tuition throughout the year. Students do not always require five GCSE passes to be accepted onto our A level courses; nonetheless, 70% of the grades achieved by recent A level students have been A* to B grade. Nearly all our students go on to higher education, and we have been preparing students for Oxford and Cambridge entrance for over 75 years with outstanding success. We also provide specialist tuition for all university admissions tests.

All our tutors have excellent degrees from top universities, and many are graduates from Oxford and Cambridge. Our links with these, and many other universities, ensure that our students are best placed to make strong applications to higher education.

Westminster Tutors is in attractive premises on Old Brompton Road, close to South Kensington underground station and Hyde Park.

Geographical directory of schools in the United Kingdom

Please note the following:
The user will find Essex and Hertfordshire in **Greater London** and **East of England**; Kent and Surrey in **Greater London** and **South-East**. When seeking schools in any of these counties, therefore, the user is advised to check both regional sections.

Directory regions contents page

© MAPS IN MINUTES ™ (2012)

Scotland
D365

Northern
Ireland
D361

North-
East
D301

Isle of Man
D311

Yorkshire &
Humberside
D353

North-
West
D305

East Midlands
D269

West
Midlands
D343

East of
England
D257

Wales
D371

Central
& West
D245

South-East
D315

South-West
D335

Channel Islands
D243

Greater London &
London D277

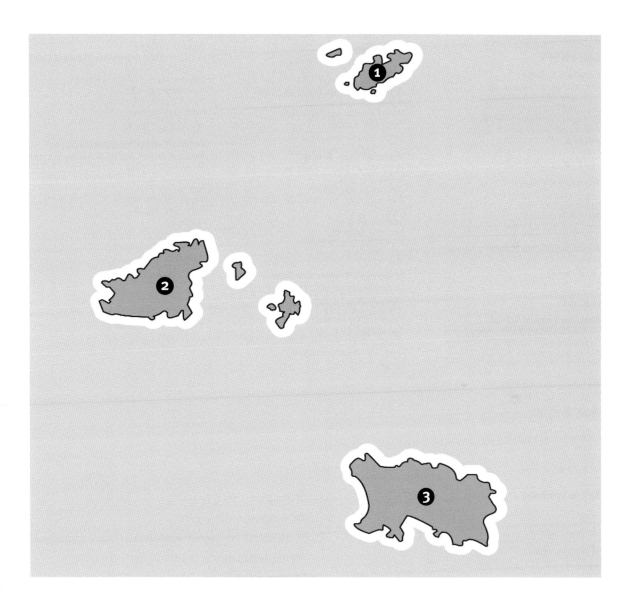

Key and page index:

ALDERNEY

Ormer House Preparatory School
La Vallee, Alderney GY9 3XA
Tel: 01481 823287
Head: Mrs M J Burridge
Age range: 3–13
No. of pupils: B20 G14
Fees: Day £5055

GUERNSEY

Elizabeth College
The Grange, St Peter Port,
Guernsey GY1 2PY
Tel: 01481 726544
Principal: G J Hartley MA, MSc
Age range: 16–18 B3–16 G3–11
No. of pupils: 712 VIth115
Fees: Day £6633–£7250

The Ladies' College
Les Gravees, St Peter Port,
Guernsey GY1 1RW
Tel: 01481 721602
Principal: Mrs J Riches
Age range: 4–18
No. of pupils: 555 VIth100
Fees: Day £5385–£5964

JERSEY

Beaulieu Convent School
Wellington Road, Saint Helier,
Jersey JE2 4RJ
Tel: 01534 731280
Headmaster: Mr C Beirne
Age range: 4–18
No. of pupils: 760 VIth120
Fees: Day £4584

De La Salle College
Wellington Road, St Saviour,
Jersey JE2 7TH
Tel: 01534 754100
Heads: Mr John Sankey MA(Oxon),
DipEd & Mr M Hebden
Age range: 4–18
No. of pupils: 752 VIth34
Fees: Day £2040

FCJ Primary School
Deloraine Road, St Saviour,
Jersey JE2 7XB
Tel: 01534 723063
Headmistress: Ms Maureen Doyle
Age range: 4–11
No. of pupils: 290 B110 G180
Fees: Day £2820

Helvetia House School
14 Elizabeth Place, Saint Helier,
Jersey JE2 3PN
Tel: 01534 724928
Headmistress: Mrs Ann Atkinson BA,
DipEd
Age range: 4–11
No. of pupils: 82
Fees: Day £2226–£2307

St George's Preparatory School
La Hague Manor, Rue de la Hague, St
Peter, Jersey JE3 7DB
Tel: 01534 481593
Headmaster: Mr Colin Moore
Age range: 3–11
No. of pupils: 210 B94 G116
Fees: Day £4260–£11,970

St Michael's Preparatory School
La Rue de la Houguette, St Saviour,
Jersey JE2 7UG
Tel: 01534 856904
Headmaster: R de Figueiredo BA(Hons),
PGCE
Age range: 3–13
No. of pupils: 348 B201 G147
Fees: Day £8049–£12,348

Victoria College
Le Mont Millais, St Helier, Jersey JE1 4HT
Tel: 01534 638200
Headmaster: Mr Alun Watkins
Age range: 11–18
No. of pupils: 730 VIth200
Fees: Day £4194

Victoria College Preparatory School
Pleasant Street, St Helier, Jersey JE2 4RR
Tel: 01534 723468
Headmaster: Russell Price BSc, MPhil
Age range: 7–11
No. of pupils: 300
Fees: Day £1440

Key to symbols

⚥ Boys' school

⚥ Girls' school

🌐 International school

16 Tutorial or sixth form college

Ⓐ A levels

🏫 Boarding accommodation

£ Bursaries

IB International Baccalaureate

✎ Learning support

16 Entrance at 16+

⚘ Vocational qualifications

IAPS Member of Independent Association of Preparatory Schools

HMC The Headmasters' & Headmistresses' Conference

ISA Independent Schools Association

GSA Girls' School Association

BSA Boarding Schools' Association

Ⓢ SHMIS

Unless otherwise indicated, all schools are coeducational day schools. Single-sex and boarding schools will be indicated by the relevant icon.

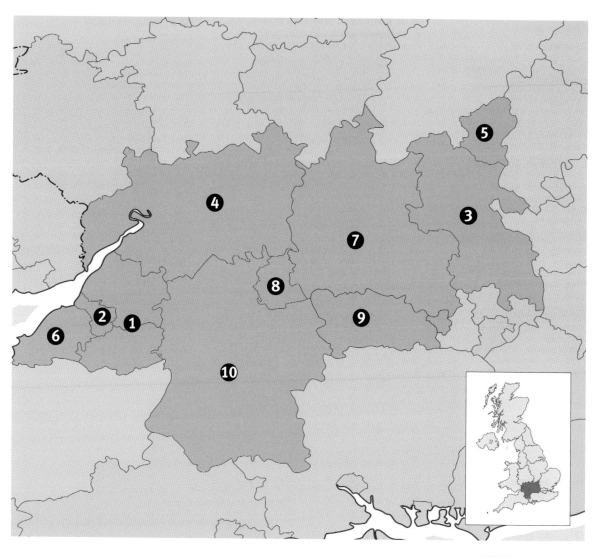

Key and page index:

1 Bath & North-East Somerset: D246

2 Bristol: D247

3 Buckinghamshire: D248

4 Gloucestershire: D249

5 Milton Keynes: D250

6 North Somerset: D251

7 Oxfordshire: D251

8 Swindon: D254

9 West Berkshire: D254

10 Wiltshire: D254

BATH & NORTH-EAST SOMERSET

Bath Academy
27 Queen Square, Bath, Bath & North-East Somerset BA1 2HX
Tel: 01225 334577
Age range: 16–20+
No. of pupils: 160 B80 G80 Vlth120
Fees: Day £8450–£9700 FB £15,000

Downside School
Stratton-on the-Fosse, Radstock, Bath, Bath & North-East Somerset BA3 4RJ
Tel: 01761 235103
Head Master: Fr Leo Maidlow Davis
Age range: 11–18
No. of pupils: 458 B286 G172 Vlth140
Fees: Day £12,900–£14,352
FB £20,940–£26,361

King Edward's Junior School
North Road, Bath, Bath & North-East Somerset BA2 6JA
Tel: 01225 463218
Head of the Junior School: Mr Greg Taylor
Age range: 7–11
No. of pupils: 174 B108 G66
Fees: Day £8386

King Edward's Pre-Prep School
Weston Lane, Bath, Bath & North-East Somerset BA1 4AQ
Tel: 01225 421681
Head: Mr Stuart Andrews
Age range: 3–7
No. of pupils: 110 B69 G41
Fees: Day £4230–£4800

King Edward's Senior School
North Road, Bath, Bath & North-East Somerset BA2 6HU
Tel: 01225 464313
Head: Mr Martin Boden
Age range: 11–18
No. of pupils: 207 B144 G63 Vlth207
Fees: Day £6150–£10,260

Kingswood Preparatory School
College Road, Lansdown, Bath, Bath & North-East Somerset BA1 5SD
Tel: 01225 734460
Headmaster: Mr Marcus E Cornah
Age range: 3–11
No. of pupils: 335 B185 G150
Fees: Day £7125–£8250 WB £14,118
FB £16,806–£17,808

Kingswood School
Lansdown, Bath, Bath & North-East Somerset BA1 5RG
Tel: 01225 734210
Headmaster & Principal: Mr Simon Morris MA
Age range: 11–18
No. of pupils: 642 B260 G193 Vlth189
Fees: Day £9789 WB £15,918–£19,722
FB £18,222–£21,828

Monkton Prep School
Combe Down, Bath, Bath & North-East Somerset BA2 7ET
Tel: 01225 837912
Headmaster: Mr C J Stafford BA, CertEd
Age range: 2–13
No. of pupils: B211 G139
Fees: Day £9999–£13,794
WB £16,050–£17,583
FB £18,366–£19,464

Monkton Senior School
Bath, Bath & North-East Somerset BA2 7HG
Tel: 01225 721133
Principal: Richard Backhouse MA
Age range: 11–19
No. of pupils: 375 B239 G136 Vlth148
Fees: Day £12,753–£16,572
WB £14,998–£21,885
FB £17,997–£24,534

Norland College
York Place, London Road, Bath, Bath & North-East Somerset BA1 6AE
Tel: 01225 904040
Principal: Mrs Liz Hunt
Age range: 17+
No. of pupils: 93

Prior Park College
Ralph Allen Drive, Bath, Bath & North-East Somerset BA2 5AH
Tel: 01225 831000
Head: Mr James Murphy-O'Connor
Age range: 11–18
No. of pupils: 580 B310 G270 Vlth180
Fees: Day £11,736–£13,077 WB £18,687
FB £23,583

The Paragon School
Lyncombe House, Lyncombe Vale, Bath, Bath & North-East Somerset BA2 4LT
Tel: 01225 310837
Headmaster: Mr Titus Mills BA
Age range: 3–11
No. of pupils: 252 B149 G103
Fees: Day £5835–£6504

Key to symbols

(♦) Boys' school

(♣) Girls' school

(🌐) International school

(16▸) Tutorial or sixth form college

(A) A levels

(⊞) Boarding accommodation

(£) Bursaries

(IB) International Baccalaureate

(✐) Learning support

(16▸) Entrance at 16+

(🎥) Vocational qualifications

(IAPS) Member of Independent Association of Preparatory Schools

(HMC) The Headmasters' & Headmistresses' Conference

(ISA) Independent Schools Association

(GSA) Girls' School Association

(BSA) Boarding Schools' Association

(S) SHMIS

Unless otherwise indicated, all schools are coeducational day schools. Single-sex and boarding schools will be indicated by the relevant icon.

The Royal High School, Bath
Lansdown Road, Bath, Bath & North-East Somerset BA1 5SZ
Tel: +44 (0)1225 313877
Head: Mrs Rebecca Dougall BA, MA
Age range: 3–18
No. of pupils: 680 VIth190
Fees: Day £7650–£11,225
FB £18,630–£21,300

BRISTOL

Badminton Junior School
Westbury-on-Trym, Bristol BS9 3BA
Tel: 0117 905 5200
Head of the Junior School: Mrs E Davies
Age range: 3–11
No. of pupils: 125
Fees: Day £6900–£10,200 WB £19,020
FB £19,020

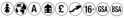

Badminton School
Westbury-on-Trym, Bristol BS9 3BA
Tel: 0117 905 5200
Headmistress: Mrs Jan Scarrow BA, FRSA
Age range: 4–18
No. of pupils: 441
Fees: Day £6900–£15,360
FB £18,120–£27,330

Bristol Grammar School
University Road, Bristol BS8 1SR
Tel: 0117 973 6006
Headmaster: R I Mackinnon
Age range: 4–18
No. of pupils: 1137 B715 G422 VIth288
Fees: Day £5700–£10,590

Bristol Steiner School
Redland Hill House, Redland,
Bristol BS6 6UX
Tel: 0117 933 9990
Age range: 3–16
No. of pupils: B99 G114
Fees: Day £1728–£4800

Carmel Christian School
817A Bath Road, Brislington,
Bristol BS4 5NL
Tel: 0117 977 5533
Headteacher: Mr David Owens
Age range: 5–16
No. of pupils: 28 B13 G15
Fees: Day £480–£720

Cleve House School
254 Wells Road, Bristol BS4 2PN
Tel: 0117 977 7218
Heads: D Lawson BA(Hons), MA & Mrs E Lawson BEd, MA
Age range: 2–11
No. of pupils: 110 B55 G55
Fees: Day £5685

Clifton College
32 College Road, Clifton, Bristol BS8 3JH
Tel: 0117 315 7000
Headmaster: Mr Mark J Moore
Age range: 3–18
No. of pupils: 1330 B845 G485 VIth280
Fees: Day £5460–£16,245
WB £16,305–£21,645
FB £17,070–£24,075

Clifton College Preparatory School
The Avenue, Clifton, Bristol BS8 3HE
Tel: 0117 3157 502
Headmaster: J E Milne
Age range: 3–13
No. of pupils: 400 B250 G150
Fees: Day £6000–£12,000
WB £16,305–£16,920
FB £17,070–£17,700

Clifton High School
College Road, Clifton, Bristol BS8 3JD
Tel: 0117 973 0201
Head: Dr Alison M Neill BSc, PhD, PGCE
Age range: 4–18
No. of pupils: 527
Fees: Day £7605–£10,905 FB £19,605

Clifton Tutors Limited
31 Pembroke Road, Clifton,
Bristol BS8 3BE
Tel: 0117 973 8376
Director of Studies: William P Shaw BA
Age range: 7–19

Colston's School
Stapleton, Bristol BS16 1BJ
Tel: 0117 965 5207
Headmaster: Peter Fraser
Age range: 3–18
No. of pupils: B408 G173 VIth138
Fees: Day £5160–£7110 FB £15,045

Fairfield PNEU School
Fairfield Way, Backwell,
Bristol BS48 3PD
Tel: 01275 462743
Headmistress: Mrs Lesley Barton
Age range: 3–11
No. of pupils: B52 G58
Fees: Day £1850–£7300

Gracefield Preparatory School
266 Overndale Road, Fishponds,
Bristol BS16 2RG
Tel: 0117 956 7977
Headmistress: Mrs E Morgan
Age range: 4–11
No. of pupils: 90 B45 G45
Fees: Day £2725

Mount Zion School
6 Gloucester Street, Eastville,
Bristol BS5 6QE
Tel: 07890 623366
Headteacher: Mrs S M Houghton
Age range: 4–11
No. of pupils: B5 G2

Overndale School
19 Chapel Lane, Old Sodbury,
Bristol BS17 6NQ
Tel: 01454 310332
Headmistress: Mrs K Winstanley
Age range: 3 months–11 years
No. of pupils: B56 G43
Fees: Day £3300

Prospect School
Tramway Road, Brislington,
Bristol BS4 3DS
Tel: 0117 9772271
Headteacher: Mrs Lucy Sherrin
Age range: 11–16
No. of pupils: 41 B21 G20

Queen Elizabeth's Hospital
Berkeley Place, Clifton, Bristol BS8 1JX
Tel: 0117 930 3040
Head: Mr S W Holliday MA
Age range: 7–18
No. of pupils: 640 VIth140
Fees: Day £7359–£11,259

Redland High School for Girls
Redland Court, Redland, Bristol BS6 7EF
Tel: 0117 924 5796
Headmistress: Mrs Caroline Bateson BA(Hons)
Age range: 3–18
No. of pupils: 450 VIth90
Fees: Day £5760–£9600

Silverhill School
Swan Lane, Winterbourne,
Bristol BS36 1RL
Tel: 01454 772156
Co-Principals: Mr J Capper MA(Cantab) & Mrs J Capper BA(London)
Age range: 2–11
No. of pupils: 185 B95 G90
Fees: Day £4800–£6255

The Downs School
Wraxall, Bristol BS48 1PF
Tel: 01275 852008
Head: M A Gunn MA(Ed), BA, PGCE
Age range: 4–13
No. of pupils: 262 B173 G89

The Red Maids' Junior School
Grange Court Road, Westbury-on-Trym,
Bristol BS9 4DP
Tel: 0117 962 9451
Headteacher: Mrs G B Rowcliffe BEd
Age range: 7–11
No. of pupils: 120
Fees: Day £6630

The Red Maids' School
Westbury Road, Westbury-on-Trym,
Bristol BS9 3AW
Tel: +44 (0)117 962 2641
Headmistress: Mrs Isabel Tobias BA
Age range: 7–18
No. of pupils: 594 VIth100
Fees: Day £10,440

Tockington Manor School
Tockington, Bristol BS32 4NY
Tel: 01454 613229
Headmaster: Mr R G Tovey CertEd
Age range: 2–14
No. of pupils: B153 G97
Fees: Day £7650–£12,510 FB £17,070

Torwood House School
8, 27-29 Durdham Park, Redland,
Bristol BS6 6XE
Tel: 0117 9735620
Headmistress: Mrs D Seagrove
Age range: 0–11
No. of pupils: 70
Fees: Day £1964–£2049

BUCKINGHAMSHIRE

Akeley Wood School
Akeley Wood, Buckingham,
Buckinghamshire MK18 5AE
Tel: 01280 814110
Headmaster: Dr Jerry Grundy BA, PhD
Age range: 12 months–18 years
No. of pupils: 833 B500 G333 VIth119
Fees: Day £7185–£10,575

Ashfold School
Dorton House, Dorton, Aylesbury,
Buckinghamshire HP18 9NG
Tel: 01844 238237
Headmaster: Mr M O M Chitty BSc
Age range: 3–13
No. of pupils: B172 G108 VIth28
Fees: Day £7320–£12,900 WB £15,084

Caldicott
Crown Lane, Farnham Royal,
Buckinghamshire SL2 3SL
Tel: 01753 649301
Headmaster: Mr S J G Doggart
BA(Cantab)
Age range: 7–13
No. of pupils: 256
Fees: Day £13,080–£14,148 FB £19,227

CHESHAM PREPARATORY SCHOOL
For further details see p. 50
Two Dells Lane, Chesham,
Buckinghamshire HP5 3QF
Tel: 01494 782619
Email: secretary@cheshamprep.co.uk
Website: www.cheshamprep.co.uk
Headmaster: Mr Michael Davies BA,
PGCE
Age range: 3–13
No. of pupils: B194 G156
Fees: Day £8124–£11,931

Crown House School
19 London Road, High Wycombe,
Buckinghamshire HP11 1BJ
Tel: 01494 529927
Headmaster: Ali Khan BSc(Hons), MBA
Age range: 4–11
No. of pupils: 120 B71 G40
Fees: Day £5985–£6570

Dair House School
Bishops Blake, Beaconsfield Road,
Farnham Royal,
Buckinghamshire SL2 3BY
Tel: 01753 643964
Headmaster: Mr Terry Wintle BEd(Hons)
Age range: 3–11
No. of pupils: 104 B64 G40
Fees: Day £2907–£8526

Davenies School
Station Road, Beaconsfield,
Buckinghamshire HP9 1AA
Tel: 01494 685400
Headmaster: C Watson MA, BEd(Hons)
Age range: 4–13
No. of pupils: 325
Fees: Day £10,035–£11,955

Gateway School
1 High Street, Great Missenden,
Buckinghamshire HP16 9AA
Tel: 01494 862407
Headteacher: Mr S J Y Wade MA, PGCE
Age range: 2–12
No. of pupils: 342 B197 G145
Fees: Day £8748

Gayhurst School
Bull Lane, Gerrards Cross,
Buckinghamshire SL9 8RJ
Tel: 01753 882690
Headmaster: A J Sims MA(Cantab)
Age range: 4–13
No. of pupils: 265
Fees: Day £7089–£9009

Godstowe Preparatory School
Shrubbery Road, High Wycombe,
Buckinghamshire HP13 6PR
Tel: 01494 529273
Headmaster: Mr David Gainer
Age range: B3–7 G3–13
No. of pupils: B19 G390
Fees: Day £8505–£13,245 WB £19,455
FB £19,455

Heatherton House School
Copperkins Lane, Chesham Bois,
Amersham, Buckinghamshire HP6 5QB
Tel: 01494 726433
Headmaster: Mr Peter Rushforth
Age range: 3–11
No. of pupils: 165
Fees: Day £930–£10,800

High March School
23 Ledborough Lane, Beaconsfield,
Buckinghamshire HP9 2PZ
Tel: 01494 675186
Headmistress: Mrs S J Clifford
Age range: 3–11
No. of pupils: 292 B8 G284
Fees: Day £798–£11,025

Holy Cross Convent School
The Grange, Chalfont St Peter, Gerrards
Cross, Buckinghamshire SL9 9DW
Tel: 01753 895600
Headmistress: Mrs Margaret Shinkwin
BA, MA(Ed), NPQH
Age range: 3–18
No. of pupils: 255
Fees: Day £752–£6186 FB £9000

Kingscote Pre-Preparatory School
Oval Way, Gerrards Cross,
Buckinghamshire SL9 8PZ
Tel: 01753 885535
Headmistress: Mrs Fiona Davies BEd, MBA
Age range: 3–7
No. of pupils: 100
Fees: Day £3900–£8145

Ladymede School
Little Kimble, Aylesbury,
Buckinghamshire HP17 0XP
Tel: 01844 346154
Headmistress: Carole Hawkins
Age range: 3–11
No. of pupils: 100 B45 G55
Fees: Day £2592–£8040

Maltman's Green School
Maltman's Lane, Gerrards Cross,
Buckinghamshire SL9 8RR
Tel: 01753 883022
Headmistress: Mrs Joanna Pardon MA,
BSc(Hons), PGCE
Age range: 3–11
No. of pupils: 420
Fees: Day £7110–£11,070

Pipers Corner School
Pipers Lane, Great Kingshill, High
Wycombe, Buckinghamshire HP15 6LP
Tel: 01494 718 255
Headmistress: Mrs H J Ness-Gifford
BA(Hons), PGCE
Age range: 3–18
No. of pupils: 526 VIth62
Fees: Day £6945–£13,470
WB £18,030–£21,960
FB £18,270–£22,200

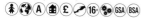

Ravenstone House Aylesbury
Green End, off Rickford's Hill, Aylesbury,
Buckinghamshire HP20 2SA
Tel: 01296 392516
Registrar: Mrs Carole Angood
Age range: 2 months–7 years
No. of pupils: B40 G40
Fees: Day £6276

Sefton Park School
School Lane, Stoke Poges,
Buckinghamshire SL2 4QA
Tel: 01753 662167
Headteacher: Mr Timothy Thorpe
Age range: 11–16
No. of pupils: 120 B72 G48

St Mary's School
94 Packhorse Road, Gerrards Cross,
Buckinghamshire SL9 8JQ
Tel: 01753 883370
Headmistress: Mrs J A Ross BA(Hons),
NPQH
Age range: 3–18
No. of pupils: 320 VIth38
Fees: Day £3420–£12,155

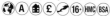

**St Teresa's Catholic Independent
School & Nursery**
Aylesbury Road, Princes Risborough,
Buckinghamshire HP27 0JW
Tel: 01844 345005
Head: Mrs T Milton
Age range: 3–11
No. of pupils: 132
Fees: Day £5775–£7308

Stowe School
Buckingham,
Buckinghamshire MK18 5EH
Tel: 01280 818000
Headmaster: Dr Anthony Wallersteiner
Age range: 13–18
No. of pupils: 740 B500 G230 VIth350
Fees: Day £19,860 FB £26,850

The Beacon School
Chesham Bois, Amersham,
Buckinghamshire HP6 5PF
Tel: 01494 433654
Headmaster: P Brewster BSc(Hons),
PGCE
Age range: 3–13
No. of pupils: 470 B470
Fees: Day £4695–£13,200

Thorpe House School
Oval Way, Gerrards Cross,
Buckinghamshire SL9 8QA
Tel: 01753 882474
Headmaster: Mr Anthony Lock
MA(Oxon), PGCE
Age range: 7–16
No. of pupils: 240
Fees: Day £10,575–£12,675

Wycombe Abbey School
High Wycombe,
Buckinghamshire HP11 1PE
Tel: 01494 520381
Headmistress: Mrs Cynthia Hall
MA(Oxon)
Age range: 11–18
No. of pupils: 559 VIth172
Fees: Day £22,950 FB £30,600

GLOUCESTERSHIRE

Airthrie School
29 Christchurch Road, Cheltenham,
Gloucestershire GL50 2NY
Tel: 01242 512837
Principal: Mrs A E Sullivan DipEd, DipIM,
CertCounselling
Age range: 3–11
No. of pupils: 168 B62 G106
Fees: Day £5280–£7494

Beaudesert Park School
Minchinhampton, Stroud,
Gloucestershire GL6 9AF
Tel: 01453 832072
Headmaster: Mr J P R Womersley BA,
PGCE
Age range: 4–13
No. of pupils: B223 G178
Fees: Day £2200–£4295
WB £4900–£5620

Berkhampstead School
Pittville Circus Road, Cheltenham,
Gloucestershire GL52 2QA
Tel: 01242 523263
Head: R P Cross BSc(Hons)
Age range: 3–11
No. of pupils: 215 B98 G117
Fees: Day £2793–£7470

Bredon School
Pull Court, Bushley, Tewkesbury,
Gloucestershire GL20 6AH
Tel: 01684 293156
Headmaster: Mr John Hewitt MBA, BA
Age range: 4–18
No. of pupils: 240 B177 G63 VIth33
Fees: Day £5835–£15,855
WB £17,115–£24,405
FB £17,565–£24,870

Cheltenham College
Bath Road, Cheltenham,
Gloucestershire GL53 7LD
Tel: 01242 265600
Headmaster: Dr Alex Peterken
Age range: 13–18
No. of pupils: 600 B390 G210 VIth250
Fees: Day £22,275–£23,175
FB £29,727–£30,627

Cheltenham College Junior School
Thirlestaine Road, Cheltenham,
Gloucestershire GL53 7AB
Tel: 01242 522697
Headmaster: Mr Scott Bryan
Age range: 3–13
No. of pupils: 420 B210 G210
Fees: Day £6150–£14,760
FB £15,075–£19,665

Cheltenham Ladies' College
Bayshill Road, Cheltenham,
Gloucestershire GL50 3EP
Tel: +44 (0)1242 520691
Principal: Eve Jardine-Young MA
Age range: 11–18
No. of pupils: 855 VIth300
Fees: Day £19,365–£22,020
FB £28,845–£32,493

Dean Close Preparatory School
Lansdown Road, Cheltenham,
Gloucestershire GL51 6QS
Tel: 01242 512217
Head: Rev Leonard Browne MA
Age range: 2+–13
No. of pupils: 434 B234 G200
Fees: Day £6210–£12,930
FB £14,610–£18,495

Dean Close School
Shelburne Road, Cheltenham,
Gloucestershire GL51 6HE
Tel: 01242 258044
Headmaster: Jonathan Lancashire
Age range: 13–18
No. of pupils: 494 B258 G236 VIth216
Fees: Day £20,370 FB £28,845

Dormer House School
High Street, Moreton-in-Marsh,
Gloucestershire GL56 0AD
Tel: 01608 650758
Headmistress: Mrs C May
Age range: 2–11
No. of pupils: 102
Fees: Day £6900

Eastbrook College
7a Eastbrook Education Trust,
Gloucester, Gloucestershire GL4 3DB
Tel: 01452 417722
Age range: 11–16
No. of pupils: 59 B28 G31

Gloucestershire Islamic Secondary School for Girls
Sinope Street, off Widden Street,
Gloucester, Gloucestershire GL1 4AW
Tel: 01452 300465
Head: Mr Abdullah Patel
Age range: 11–16
No. of pupils: 67
Fees: Day £900–£1000

Hatherop Castle Preparatory School
Hatherop, Cirencester,
Gloucestershire GL7 3NB
Tel: 01285 750206
Headmaster: P Easterbrook BEd
Age range: 2–13
No. of pupils: 190
Fees: Day £6285–£10,455
FB £15,270–£16,110

Hopelands School
38 Regent Street, Stonehouse,
Gloucestershire GL10 2AD
Tel: 01453 822164
Headmistress: Mrs S Bradburn
Age range: 3–11
No. of pupils: 59 B20 G39
Fees: Day £4479–£5322

Ingleside School
Beeches Road, Cirencester,
Gloucestershire GL7 1BN
Tel: 01285 654046
Headteacher: Mr Anderson
Age range: 2 years 9 months–11 years
No. of pupils: 106 B50 G56
Fees: Day £3225–£3597

Kitebrook House
Little Compton, Moreton-in-Marsh,
Gloucestershire GL56 0RP
Tel: 01608 674350
Head: Ms Pippa Quarrell
Age range: 3–13
No. of pupils: 134 B64 G70
Fees: Day £8790–£11,200 WB £14,940

Querns Westonbirt Preparatory School
Tetbury, Gloucestershire GL8 8QG
Tel: 01666 881390
Headmistress: Miss V James
Age range: 4–11
No. of pupils: B35 G60
Fees: Day £5712–£8472

Rendcomb College
Rendcomb, Cirencester,
Gloucestershire GL7 7HA
Tel: 01285 831213
Headmaster: Mr R Martin BA
Age range: 3–18
No. of pupils: 405 B219 G189 VIth75
Fees: Day £6000–£18,885
FB £19,170–£25,350

Rose Hill School
Alderley, Wotton-under-Edge,
Gloucestershire GL12 7QT
Tel: 01453 843196
Headmaster: Mr Paul Cawley-Wakefield
BEd
Age range: 2¹⁄₂–13
No. of pupils: 135 B84 G51
Fees: Day £6147–£12,150

School of the Lion
Beauchamp House, Churcham,
Gloucester, Gloucestershire GL2 8AA
Tel: 01452 750253
Headmaster: Mr Nigel Steele
Age range: 3–18
No. of pupils: 11 B6 G5 VIth2
Fees: Day £1362–£1800

St Anthony's Convent School
91-93 Belle Vue Road, Cinderford,
Gloucestershire GL14 2AA
Tel: 01594 823558
Headteacher: Mrs J James
Age range: 3–11
No. of pupils: B37 G35
Fees: Day £5220–£5280

St Edward's Junior School
London Road, Charlton Kings,
Cheltenham, Gloucestershire GL52 6NR
Tel: 01242 538900
Headmaster: Mr Stephen McKernan
BA(Hons) MEd NPQH
Age range: 1–11
No. of pupils: B195 G177
Fees: Day £5667–£8775

St Edward's School
Cirencester Road, Cheltenham,
Gloucestershire GL53 8EY
Tel: 01242 538600
Headmaster: Dr A J Nash MA, PhD
Age range: 11–18
No. of pupils: B225 G225 VIth89
Fees: Day £2240–£2620

The Acorn School
Church Street, Nailsworth,
Gloucestershire GL6 0BP
Tel: 01453 836508
Headmaster: Mr Graeme E B Whiting
Age range: 3–19
No. of pupils: B50 G80 VIth30
Fees: Day £3800–£6000

The King's School
Pitt Street, Gloucester,
Gloucestershire GL1 2BG
Tel: 01452 337337
Headmaster: Alistair K J Macnaughton
Age range: 3–18
No. of pupils: 509 B286 G223 VIth100
Fees: Day £5985–£15,960

The Richard Pate School
Southern Road, Cheltenham,
Gloucestershire GL53 9RP
Tel: 01242 522086
Headmaster: Mr Robert MacDonald
Age range: 3–11
No. of pupils: B154 G128
Fees: Day £2370–£7110

Westonbirt School
Westonbirt, Tetbury,
Gloucestershire GL8 8QG
Tel: 01666 880333
Headmistress: Mrs Mary Henderson MA
Age range: 11–18
No. of pupils: 240 VIth80
Fees: Day £15,645–£18,816
WB £22,992–£27,990
FB £22,992–£27,990

Wycliffe Preparatory & Senior School
Bath Road, Stonehouse,
Gloucestershire GL10 2JQ
Tel: 01453 822432
Senior School Head: Mrs M E Burnet
Ward MA(Hons)
Age range: 2–18
No. of pupils: B370 G240 VIth178
Fees: Day £5295–£15,870
FB £13,620–£25,800

Wynstones School
Whaddon Green, Gloucester,
Gloucestershire GL4 0UF
Tel: 01452 429220
Chair of the College of Teachers:
Marianna Law-Lindberg
Age range: 3–18
No. of pupils: B127 G143 VIth9
Fees: Day £4956–£7236 FB £4835

MILTON KEYNES

Broughton Manor Preparatory School
Newport Road, Broughton, Milton
Keynes MK10 9AA
Tel: 01908 665234
Headmaster: Mr Ross Urquhart
Age range: 2 months–11 years
No. of pupils: B125 G125
Fees: Day £9600

Fernwood School
Church Road, Aspley Heath, Milton
Keynes MK17 8TJ
Tel: 01908 583541
Head: Mrs M E Denyer
Age range: 1–9
No. of pupils: 75

Filgrave School
Filgrave Village, Newport Pagnell,
Milton Keynes MK16 9ET
Tel: 01234 711534
Headteacher: Mrs H Schofield BA(Hons),
MA, PGCE
Age range: 2–7
No. of pupils: 27
Fees: Day £5160

Milton Keynes Preparatory School
Tattenhoe Lane, Milton Keynes MK3 7EG
Tel: 01908 642111
Headmistress: Mrs Hilary Pauley BEd
Age range: 0–11
No. of pupils: 500 B250 G250
Fees: Day £10,374

SWANBOURNE HOUSE SCHOOL
For further details see p. 55
Swanbourne, Milton Keynes MK17 0HZ
Tel: 01296 720264
Email: office@swanbourne.org
Website: www.swanbourne.org
Joint Heads: Mr S D Goodhart
BEd(Hons) & Mrs J S Goodhart BEd
Age range: 3–13
No. of pupils: B225 G187
Fees: Day £7140–£15,255 FB £19,560

THE GROVE INDEPENDENT SCHOOL
For further details see p. 56
Redland Drive, Loughton, Milton
Keynes MK5 8HD
Tel: 01908 690590
Email: office@groveschool.co.uk
Website: www.groveschool.co.uk
Principal: Mrs Deborah Berkin
Age range: 3 months–13 years
No. of pupils: 210 B107 G103
Fees: Day £10,876

The Webber Independent School
Soskin Drive, Stantonbury Fields, Milton
Keynes MK14 6DP
Tel: 01908 574740
Principal: Sue Vig
Age range: 3–18
No. of pupils: 300 B177 G123 VIth15
Fees: Day £3894–£10,371

Thornton College
Thornton, Milton Keynes MK17 0HJ
Tel: 01280 812610
Headmistress: Miss Agnes T Williams
Age range: B2½–4+ G2½–16
No. of pupils: 370 G370
Fees: Day £6300–£10,095
WB £10,500–£13,305
FB £13,305–£16,545

**Walton Pre-Preparatory School &
Nursery**
The Old Rectory, Walton Drive, Milton
Keynes MK7 6BB
Tel: 01908 678403
Headmistress: Mrs M Ramsbotham
CertEd
Age range: 2 months–7 years
No. of pupils: 120 B60 G60
Fees: Day £8316

NORTH SOMERSET

Ashbrooke House School
9 Ellenborough Park North, Weston-
Super-Mare, North Somerset BS23 1XH
Tel: 01934 629515
Headteacher: Ruth Thomas
Age range: 3–11
No. of pupils: B50 G50
Fees: Day £1962–£3948

Lancaster House School
38 Hill Road, Weston-Super-Mare,
North Somerset BS23 2RY
Tel: 01934 624116
Headmistress: Mrs Susan Lewis
BA(Hons), CertEd
Age range: 4–11
No. of pupils: 32 B10 G22
Fees: Day £3600

Sidcot School
Oakridge Lane, Winscombe,
North Somerset BS25 1PD
Tel: 01934 843102
Head: Mr John Walmsley BSc, PGCE
Age range: 3–18
No. of pupils: 515 B290 G225 VIth170
Fees: Day £6150–£14,250
FB £22,050–£27,750

OXFORDSHIRE

**Abacus College & Oxford Language
Centre**
Threeways House, George Street,
Oxford, Oxfordshire OX1 2BJ
Tel: 01865 240111
Principal: Robert Swan
Age range: 13–19+
No. of pupils: B50 G40 VIth90
Fees: Day £9500–£10,500

Abingdon Preparatory School
Josca's House, Frilford, Abingdon,
Oxfordshire OX13 5NX
Tel: 01865 391570
Headmaster: Mr C Hyde-Dunn
Age range: 4–13
No. of pupils: 250

Abingdon School
Park Road, Abingdon,
Oxfordshire OX14 1DE
Tel: 01235 521563
Head: Felicity Lusk
Age range: 11–18
No. of pupils: 860 VIth270
Fees: Day £15,141 WB £26,760
FB £31,050

Bellerbys College
Trajan House, Mill Street, Oxford,
Oxfordshire OX2 0DJ
Tel: 01865 263 400
Principal: Julia Southby
Age range: 15–19
No. of pupils: 72 B43 G29
Fees: FB £15,500–£21,000

BLOXHAM SCHOOL
For further details see p. 44
Bloxham, Banbury,
Oxfordshire OX15 4PE
Tel: 01295 720222
Email: registrar@bloxhamschool.com
Website: www.bloxhamschool.com
Headmaster: Mr Mark E Allbrook MA
Age range: 11–18
No. of pupils: 424 B270 G154 VIth140
Fees: Day £15,750–£22,320 WB £20,460
FB £28,845

BURFORD SCHOOL
For further details see p. 48
Lenthall House, Church Lane, Burford,
Oxfordshire OX18 4SA
Tel: 01993 823283
Email:
boarding.4040@burford.oxon.sch.uk
Website: www.burford.oxon.sch.uk
Headteacher: Mrs K Haig BA, MEd
Age range: 11–18
No. of pupils: 1184 B620 G564 VIth230
Fees: FB £9600

Carrdus School
Overthorpe Hall, Banbury,
Oxfordshire OX17 2BS
Tel: 01295 263733
Head: Mr Edward Way
Age range: B3–8 G3–11
No. of pupils: 149 B30 G119
Fees: Day £1182–£9300

Chandlings
Bagley Wood, Kennington, Oxford,
Oxfordshire OX1 5ND
Tel: 01865 730771
Head: Mrs S Ashworth Jones
Age range: 2–11
No. of pupils: B248 G174
Fees: Day £9540–£12,540

Cherwell College
Greyfriars, Paradise Street, Oxford,
Oxfordshire OX1 1LD
Tel: 01865 242670
Principal: Andy Thompson MA(Cantab)
Age range: 15–21
No. of pupils: 150 B80 G70 VIth145
Fees: Day £15,000–£17,000
WB £22,000–£24,000
FB £23,000–£25,000

Christ Church Cathedral School
3 Brewer Street, Oxford,
Oxfordshire OX1 1QW
Tel: 01865 242561
Headmaster: Martin Bruce MA, BA, FCollP
Age range: B3–13 G3–4
No. of pupils: 159 B154 G5
Fees: Day £5409–£12,123 FB £7560

Cokethorpe School
Witney, Oxfordshire OX29 7PU
Tel: 01993 703921
Headmaster: Mr D Ettinger BA, MA, PGCE
Age range: 4–18
No. of pupils: 666 B427 G239 VIth133
Fees: Day £10,275–£14,925

Cothill House
Abingdon, Oxfordshire OX13 6JL
Tel: 01865 390800
Headmaster: Mr D M Bailey
Age range: 8–13
No. of pupils: 250
Fees: FB £19,260

Cranford House School
Moulsford, Wallingford,
Oxfordshire OX10 9HT
Tel: 01491 651218
Headmistress: Mrs Claire Hamilton
MA(Cantab)
Age range: B3–7 G3–16
No. of pupils: 377 B51 G326
Fees: Day £4350–£12,975

d'Overbroeck College
The Swan Building, 111 Banbury Road,
Oxford, Oxfordshire OX2 6JX
Tel: 01865 310000
Principals: Mr S Cohen BSc & Dr R
Knowles MA, DPhil(Oxon)
Age range: 11–19
No. of pupils: 270 B130 G140 VIth230
Fees: Day £15,345–£19,440
FB £20,430–£27,090

Dragon School
Bardwell Road, Oxford,
Oxfordshire OX2 6SS
Tel: 01865 315405
Head: Mr John R Baugh BEd
Age range: 4–13
No. of pupils: 836 B543 G293
Fees: Day £8850–£16,320 FB £23,370

EF INTERNATIONAL ACADEMY OXFORD
For further details see p. 51
Pullens Lane, Headington,
Oxfordshire OX3 0DT
Tel: +41 41 41 74 525
Head of School: Ms Ted McGrath
Age range: 15–18
No. of pupils: 160
Fees: FB £22,950

Emmanuel Christian School
Sandford Road, Littlemore, Oxford,
Oxfordshire OX4 4PU
Tel: 01865 395236
Headmistress: Miss Jean Dandy BSc, PGCE
Age range: 3–11
No. of pupils: 51 B30 G21
Fees: Day £3540

Ferndale Preparatory School
5-7 Bromsgrove, Faringdon,
Oxfordshire SN7 7JF
Tel: 01367 240618
Headmaster: Andrew Mersh BEd(Hons)
Age range: 3–11
No. of pupils: 100
Fees: Day £6465–£7245

Greene's Tutorial College
45 Pembroke Street, Oxford,
Oxfordshire OX1 1BP
Tel: 01865 248308
Senior Tutor: Matthew Uffindell MA,
DipEd
No. of pupils: 213 VIth160

Headington Preparatory School
26 London Road, Oxford,
Oxfordshire OX3 7PB
Tel: +44 (0)1865 759411
Head: Miss Andrea Bartlett BEd (Hons),
University of London
Age range: 3–11
No. of pupils: 270

Headington School
London Road, Oxford,
Oxfordshire OX3 7TD
Tel: +44 (0)1865 759100
Headmistress: Mrs Caroline Jordan
MA(Oxon)
Age range: 11–18
No. of pupils: 780
Fees: Day £7002–£14,403
WB £19,287–£25,143
FB £20,937–£27,885

Kingham Hill School
Kingham, Chipping Norton,
Oxfordshire OX7 6TH
Tel: 01608 658999
Headmaster: Mr Nick Seward BEng, MA
Age range: 11–18
No. of pupils: 285 B182 G103 VIth54
Fees: Day £13,230–£15,126
FB £19,110–£23,520

King's School, Oxford
New Yatt Road, Witney, Oxford,
Oxfordshire OX29 6TA
Tel: 01993 778463
Principal: Mr John Ellwood
Age range: 16+
No. of pupils: 140
Fees: Day £7000

Magdalen College School
Cowley Place, Oxford,
Oxfordshire OX4 1DZ
Tel: 01865 242191
Master: Dr Tim Hands
Age range: 7–18
No. of pupils: 669 VIth161
Fees: Day £8018–£9880

Modes Study Centre
73/75 George Street, Oxford,
Oxfordshire OX1 2BQ
Tel: 01865 245172/249349
Principal: Dr Stephen C R Moore
MA(Oxon), DPhil(Oxon)
Age range: 16+
No. of pupils: 61 B30 G31
Fees: Day £9396–£14,040
FB £13,716–£18,360

Moulsford Preparatory School
Moulsford, Wallingford,
Oxfordshire OX10 9HR
Tel: 01491 651438
Headmaster: M J Higham BA, CertEd
Age range: 4–13
No. of pupils: B300
Fees: Day £8550–£12,810 WB £16,050

New College School
2 Savile Road, Oxford,
Oxfordshire OX1 3UA
Tel: 01865 243657
Headmaster: Mr N R Gullifer MA
Age range: 4–13
No. of pupils: 130
Fees: Day £7413–£11,985

Our Lady's Abingdon School
Radley Road, Abingdon,
Oxfordshire OX14 3PS
Tel: 01235 524658
Principal: Mr Stephen Oliver
Age range: 3–18
Fees: Day £6648–£11,268

Overthorpe Preparatory School
Blacklocks Hill, Banbury,
Oxfordshire OX17 2BS
Tel: 01295 262144
Joint Heads: Mr & Mrs T G Gormley
Age range: 3–12
Fees: Day £2325–£4050

Oxford High School GDST
Belbroughton Road, Oxford,
Oxfordshire OX2 6XA
Tel: 01865 559888
Head: Mrs Judith Carlisle BA(Hons)
Age range: B6–7 G3–18
No. of pupils: B11 G908 VIth143
Fees: Day £2585–£3567

Oxford Montessori School
Forest Farm, Elsfield, Oxford,
Oxfordshire OX3 9UW
Tel: 01865 358210
Principal: Judith Walker Mont Dip, NNEB
Age range: 5–10
No. of pupils: 169 B87 G82

Oxford Tutorial College
12 King Edward Street, Oxford,
Oxfordshire OX1 4HT
Tel: 01865 793333
Principal: Fiona Pocock MA, PGCE
Age range: 16–25
No. of pupils: 120 B64 G56
Fees: Day £8000–£16,000

Radley College
Radley, Abingdon, Oxfordshire OX14 2HR
Tel: 01235 543000
Warden: A W McPhail MA
Age range: 13–18
No. of pupils: 636 VIth250
Fees: FB £27,345

Ravenstone House Pre-Preparatory School & Nursery
32 Launton Road, Bicester,
Oxfordshire OX26 6PY
Tel: 01869 323730
Headmistress: Miss J Fowler BA(Hons), QTS
Age range: 2 months–7 years
Fees: Day £7500

Rupert House School
90 Bell Street, Henley-on-Thames,
Oxfordshire RG9 2BN
Tel: 01491 574263
Headmistress: Mrs N J Gan MA(Ed), FRSA
Age range: B4–7 G4–11
No. of pupils: 214 B45 G169
Fees: Day £3810–£9150

RYE ST ANTONY
For further details see p. 52
Pullens Lane, Oxford,
Oxfordshire OX3 0BY
Tel: 01865 762802
Email: enquiries@ryestantony.co.uk
Website: www.ryestantony.co.uk
Headmistress: Miss A M Jones BA, PGCE
Age range: B3–8 G3–18
No. of pupils: 400 B20 G380 VIth70
Fees: Day £8400–£12,780
WB £16,800–£19,800
FB £17,790–£20,790

Shifa School
Merton Street, Banbury,
Oxfordshire OX16 4RP
Tel: 01295 279954
Headteacher: Mr F Aslam
Age range: 11–16
No. of pupils: 23
Fees: Day £1500

Shiplake College
Henley-on-Thames, Oxfordshire RG9 4BS
Tel: 0118 940 2455
Headmaster: Mr A G S Davies BSc(St Andrews)
Age range: B11–18 G16–18
No. of pupils: 385 B355 G30 VIth140
Fees: Day £17,220 WB £25,530
FB £25,530

Sibford School
Sibford Ferris, Banbury,
Oxfordshire OX15 5QL
Tel: 01295 781200
Head: Michael Goodwin BA
Age range: 3–18
No. of pupils: 454 B278 G176 VIth70
Fees: Day £7663–£16,589
WB £20,802–£21,093
FB £22,206–£22,650

St Clare's, Oxford
139 Banbury Road, Oxford,
Oxfordshire OX2 7AL
Tel: +44 (0)1865 552031
Principal: Mrs Paula Holloway BSc, PGCE, MSc(Oxon), DipPM
Age range: 15–19
No. of pupils: 260
Fees: Day £17,846 WB £29,804
FB £30,161

St Edward's, Oxford
Woodstock Road, Oxford,
Oxfordshire OX2 7NN
Tel: +44 (0)1865 319200
Warden: Stephen Jones
Age range: 13–18
No. of pupils: 667 B435 G232 VIth276
Fees: Day £23,844 FB £29,805

St Hugh's School
Carswell Manor, Faringdon,
Oxfordshire SN7 8PT
Tel: 01367 870700
Headmaster: A J P Nott BA(Hons), PGCE
Age range: 3–13
No. of pupils: B179 G125
Fees: Day £8505–£14,430
WB £16,200–£17,280

St John's Priory School
St John's Road, Banbury,
Oxfordshire OX16 5HX
Tel: 01295 259607
Headmaster: Nick Leiper
Age range: 2–11
No. of pupils: 139 B78 G61
Fees: Day £3240–£6990

St Mary's School
13 St Andrew's Road, Henley-on-Thames, Oxfordshire RG9 1HS
Tel: 01491 573118
Headmistress: Mrs S Bradley BSc(Hons)
Age range: 2–11
No. of pupils: 143 B72 G71
Fees: Day £1152–£6210

The European School
Culham, Abingdon,
Oxfordshire OX14 3DZ
Tel: 01235 522621
Head: Mr S Sharron
Age range: 4–18
No. of pupils: 839 B396 G443
Fees: Day £1918–£3596

The King's School
12 Wesley Walk, High Street, Witney,
Oxfordshire OX8 6ZJ
Tel: 01993 709985
Headteacher: K Elmitt
Age range: 5–16
No. of pupils: B106 G90
Fees: Day £2940

The Manor Preparatory School
Faringdon Road, Abingdon,
Oxfordshire OX13 6LN
Tel: 01235 858458
Headmaster: Mr Piers Heyworth MA, PGCE
Age range: B2–7 G2–11
No. of pupils: 373 B48 G325
Fees: Day £9420–£12,150

The School of St Helen & St Katharine
Faringdon Road, Abingdon,
Oxfordshire OX14 1BE
Tel: 01235 520173
Headmistress: Miss R Edbrooke
Age range: 9–18
No. of pupils: 650 VIth170
Fees: Day £11,235

The Unicorn School for the Dyslexic Child
20 Marcham Road, Abingdon,
Oxfordshire OX14 1AA
Tel: 01235 530222
Headteacher: Mrs J Vaux BA(Hons)Oxon,
PGCE, OxCertSpLD, BScPsychol
Age range: 6–13
No. of pupils: 70

TUDOR HALL SCHOOL
For further details see p. 57
Wykham Park, Banbury,
Oxfordshire OX16 9UR
Tel: 01295 263434
Email: admissions@tudorhallschool.com
Website: www.tudorhallschool.com
Headmistress: Miss W Griffiths BSc
Age range: 11–18
No. of pupils: 332 Vlth88
Fees: Day £17,175 FB £26,700

Windrush Valley School
The Green, London Lane, Ascott-under-Wychwood, Oxfordshire OX7 6AN
Tel: 01993 831793
Headmaster: Mr Alan Wood MEd, TCert,
DipSpEd, ACP, FCollP
Age range: 3–11
No. of pupils: 205
Fees: Day £3900–£4260

Wychwood School
74 Banbury Road, Oxford,
Oxfordshire OX2 6JR
Tel: 01865 557976
Headmistress: Mrs S Wingfield Digby
BA(Hons)Oxon, PGCE(London),
MA(Oxon)
Age range: 11–18
No. of pupils: 150 Vlth40
Fees: Day £8925 WB £13,800
FB £14,400

SWINDON

Maranatha Christian School
Queenlaines Farm, Sevenhampton,
Swindon SN6 7SQ
Tel: 01793 762075
Headteacher: Mr Paul Medlock
Age range: 3–18
No. of pupils: 57 B35 G22
Fees: Day £1935–£7470

Pinewood School
Bourton, Swindon SN6 8HZ
Tel: 01793 782205
Headmaster: Mr P J Hoyland
Age range: 3–13
No. of pupils: 313 B165 G148
Fees: Day £6485–£13,410
WB £13,800–£14,670
FB £14,310–£15,210

WEST BERKSHIRE

BROCKHURST & MARLSTON HOUSE SCHOOLS
For further details see p. 46
Hermitage, Thatcham,
West Berkshire RG18 9UL
Tel: 01635 200293
Email: info@brockmarl.org.uk
Website: www.brockmarl.org.uk
Heads: David Fleming MA(Oxon), MSc &
Mrs C E Riley MA, BEd,
CertEd(Southampton)
Age range: 3–13
No. of pupils: 275
Fees: Day £7410–£12,450 WB £16,530
FB £16,530

Cedars School
Church Road, Aldermaston,
West Berkshire RG7 4LR
Tel: 0118 971 4251
Headteacher: Mrs P J O'Halloran
Age range: 4–11
No. of pupils: 50 B25 G25
Fees: Day £6570

Cheam School
Headley, Newbury,
West Berkshire RG19 8LD
Tel: 01635 268381
Headmaster: Mr Mark Robin Johnson
BEd
Age range: 3–13
No. of pupils: 401 B207 G194
Fees: Day £9585–£16,755 FB £22,650

Downe House School
Cold Ash, Thatcham,
West Berkshire RG18 9JJ
Tel: 01635 200286
Headmistress: Mrs E McKendrick
BA(Liverpool)
Age range: 11–18
No. of pupils: 565 Vlth167
Fees: Day £20,895 FB £28,875

Horris Hill
Newtown, Newbury,
West Berkshire RG20 9DJ
Tel: 01635 40594
Headmaster: J H L Phillips BEd
Age range: 8–13
No. of pupils: 120
Fees: Day £14,250 FB £19,680

Marlston House Preparatory School
Hermitage, Newbury,
West Berkshire RG18 9UL
Tel: 01635 200293
Headmistress: Mrs Caroline Riley MA,
BEd
Age range: 3–13
No. of pupils: 110
Fees: Day £7410–£12,450 WB £16,530

St Gabriel's
Sandleford Priory, Newbury,
West Berkshire RG20 9BD
Tel: 01635 555680
Principal: Alun S Jones LTCL, LWCMD
Age range: B3–7 G3–18
No. of pupils: 462 B2 G460 Vlth59
Fees: Day £9255–£13,230

St Michael's School
Harts Lane, Burghclere, Newbury,
West Berkshire RG20 9JW
Tel: 01635 278137
Headmaster: Rev Patrick Summers
Age range: B4–18 G4–11
No. of pupils: 57
Fees: Day £2250 WB £4500–£7000
FB £4500–£7500

Thorngrove School
The Mount, Highclere, Newbury,
West Berkshire RG20 9PS
Tel: 01635 253172
Joint Heads: Mr N J Broughton BSc &
Mrs C B Broughton BA(Hons)
Age range: 2½–13
No. of pupils: B135 G97
Fees: Day £8475–£11,130

WILTSHIRE

Avondale School
High Street, Bulford, Salisbury,
Wiltshire SP4 9DR
Tel: 01980 632387
Joint Headteachers: Mr R McNeall
BA(Hons) PGCE & Mrs S McNeall
BEd(Hons)
Age range: 3–11
No. of pupils: B58 G54
Fees: Day £5625–£5685

CHAFYN GROVE SCHOOL
For further details see p. 49
Bourne Avenue, Salisbury,
Wiltshire SP1 1LR
Tel: 01722 333423
Email: office@chafyngrove.co.uk
Website: www.chafyngrove.co.uk
Headmaster: E J Newton
BA(Hons)(Cantab), PGCE
Age range: 2½–13
No. of pupils: 323 B217 G106
Fees: Day £7125–£14,130
FB £15,750–£19,185

Dauntsey's School
High Street, West Lavington, Devizes,
Wiltshire SN10 4HE
Tel: 01380 814500
Head: Mr Stewart B Roberts MA
Age range: 11–18
No. of pupils: 800 B440 G360 Vlth270
Fees: Day £15,060 FB £28,500

Emmaus School
School Lane, Staverton, Trowbridge,
Wiltshire BA14 6NZ
Tel: 01225 782684
Head: Mrs M Wiltshire
Age range: 5–16
No. of pupils: 54
Fees: Day £2900

Godolphin Preparatory School
Laverstock Road, Salisbury,
Wiltshire SP1 2RB
Tel: 01722 430 652
Headmistress: Mrs P White
BEd(Winchester)
Age range: 3–11
No. of pupils: 85
Fees: Day £5535–£10,692

Grittleton House School
Grittleton, Chippenham,
Wiltshire SN14 6AP
Tel: 01249 782434
Headmaster: Mr N J Dawes
Age range: 2–16
No. of pupils: 283 B173 G110
Fees: Day £6375–£9570

Heywood Preparatory School
The Priory, Corsham, Wiltshire SN13 0AP
Tel: 01249 713379
Principals: Mr Michael Hall BSc(Hons) &
Mrs Pamela Hall BA(Hons)
Age range: 3–11
No. of pupils: 180 B100 G80
Fees: Day £5430–£6225

Leaden Hall School
70 The Close, Salisbury,
Wiltshire SP1 2EP
Tel: 01722 334700
Head: Mrs Julia Eager
Age range: 3–11
No. of pupils: 250
Fees: Day £2400–£4050
FB £4280–£5150

Leehurst Swan
Campbell Road, Salisbury,
Wiltshire SP1 3BQ
Tel: 01722 333094
Headmaster: Mr R N Leake
Age range: 2–16
No. of pupils: B194 G160
Fees: Day £6855–£11,985

Marlborough College
Marlborough, Wiltshire SN8 1PA
Tel: 01672 892300
the Master: Mr Nicholas Sampson MA
Age range: 13–18
No. of pupils: 878 B548 G330 Vlth388
Fees: Day £21,180 FB £28,245

Meadowpark Nursery & Pre-Preparatory
Calcutt Street, Cricklade,
Wiltshire SN6 6BA
Tel: 01793 752600
Headteacher: Mrs R Kular
Age range: 0–11
No. of pupils: B90 G85
Fees: Day £4900

Milford Park School
White Hill, Pitton, Salisbury,
Wiltshire SP5 1DU
Tel: 01722 712482
Head: Melanie Sweeney
Age range: 7–11

Norman Court Preparatory School
West Tytherley, Salisbury,
Wiltshire SP5 1NH
Tel: 01980 862345
Headmaster: Mr Patrick Savage
Age range: 3–13
No. of pupils: 206 B145 G61
Fees: Day £7275–£14,775 WB £19,005
FB £19,005

Prior Park Preparatory School
Calcutt Street, Cricklade,
Wiltshire SN6 6BB
Tel: 01793 750275
Headteacher: M A Pearce
Age range: 3–13
No. of pupils: 275 B154 G121
Fees: Day £10,212–£12,804
FB £15,009–£17,898

Salisbury Cathedral School
The Old Palace, 1 The Close, Salisbury,
Wiltshire SP1 2EQ
Tel: 01722 555300
Headmaster: Mr P M Greenfield BEd
Age range: 3–13
No. of pupils: 200 B120 G80
Fees: Day £6450–£12,510 FB £18,270

Sandroyd School
Rushmore, Tollard Royal, Salisbury,
Wiltshire SP5 5QD
Tel: 01725 516264
Headmaster: Martin J Harris BSc(Hons),
PGCE
Age range: 5–13
No. of pupils: 225 B164 G61
Fees: Day £7470–£17,505
FB £16,650–£20,940

South Hills School
Home Farm Road, Wilton, Salisbury,
Wiltshire SP2 8PJ
Tel: 01722 744971
Principal: Mrs A Proctor
Age range: 3 months–7 Years
No. of pupils: B58 G61

St Francis School
Marlborough Road, Pewsey,
Wiltshire SN9 5NT
Tel: 01672 563228
Acting Headmaster: Mr N J Brodrick
Age range: 2–13
No. of pupils: 314 B158 G156
Fees: Day £208–£3095

ST MARGARET'S PREPARATORY SCHOOL
For further details see p. 53
Curzon Street, Calne, Wiltshire SN11 0DF
Tel: 01249 857220
Email: office@stmargaretsprep.org.uk
Website: www.stmargaretsprep.org.uk
Headmistress: Karen Cordon
Age range: 3–11
No. of pupils: 220 B95 G125
Fees: Day £4674–£10,950

ST MARY'S CALNE
For further details see p. 54
Curzon Street, Calne, Wiltshire SN11 0DF
Tel: 01249 857200
Email: office@stmaryscalne.org
Website: www.stmaryscalne.org
Headmistress: Dr Helen Wright
MA(Oxon), MA(Leics), EdD(Exeter),
PGCE(Oxon), FRSA, MIoD
Age range: 11–18
No. of pupils: 335 Vlth110
Fees: Day £22,539–£23,001
FB £30,870–£31,500

Stepping Stones Nursery & Pre-Prep School
Froxfield, Marlborough,
Wiltshire SN8 3JT
Tel: 01488 681067
Head of Pre-Prep School: Mrs Sarah Pitt
Age range: 2–8+
No. of pupils: 50 B30 G20
Fees: Day £4625–£5325

Stonar School
Cottles Park, Atworth, Melksham,
Wiltshire SN12 8NT
Tel: 01225 701740
Head: Mrs Elizabeth Thomas
Age range: B2–11 G2–18
No. of pupils: 309 B23 G286 Vlth46
Fees: Day £900–£13,365
WB £16,350–£19,050
FB £15,825–£23,550

The Godolphin School
Milford Hill, Salisbury, Wiltshire SP1 2RA
Tel: 01722 430511
Headmistress: Mrs Samantha Price
Age range: 11–18
No. of pupils: 400 Vlth128
Fees: Day £17,262 FB £24,819

Tisbury School
Weaveland Road, Tisbury,
Wiltshire SP3 6HJ
Tel: 01747 873077
Head: Mr Alan Simons
Age range: 11–16
No. of pupils: 100 B54 G46

Warminster School
Church Street, Warminster,
Wiltshire BA12 8PJ
Tel: +44 (0)1985 210160
Headmaster: Martin Priestley
Age range: 3–18
No. of pupils: 640 B375 G265 VIth150
Fees: Day £13,020 FB £23,430
A £ IB 16+ IAPS HMC BSA S

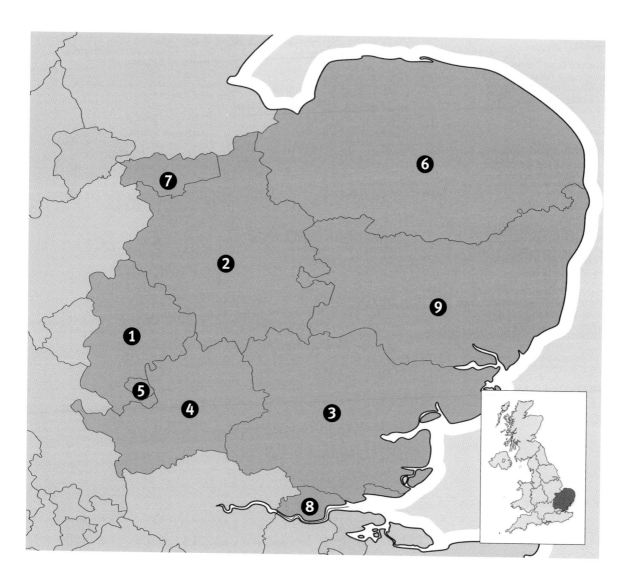

Key and page index:

BEDFORDSHIRE

Bedford Girls' School
Cardington Road, Bedford,
Bedfordshire MK42 0BX
Tel: 01234 361900
Headmistress: Miss Jo MacKenzie BSc,
MSc
Age range: 7–18
No. of pupils: 1200

Bedford Girls' School
Cardington Road, Bedford,
Bedfordshire MK42 0BX
Tel: 01234 361900
Headmistress: Miss Jo MacKenzie BSc,
MSc
Age range: 7–18
No. of pupils: 1200
Fees: Day £7602–£10,683

Bedford Modern School
Manton Lane, Bedford,
Bedfordshire MK41 7NT
Tel: 01234 332500
Headmaster: Mr M Hall BA(Hons) MA
Age range: 7–18
No. of pupils: 1195 B904 G291
Fees: Day £7500–£10,296

(A)(£)(✎)(16⁺)(IAPS)(HMC)

Bedford Preparatory School
De Parys Avenue, Bedford,
Bedfordshire MK40 2TU
Tel: 01234 362271/362274
Headmaster: Mr C Godwin BSc, MA
Age range: 7–13
No. of pupils: 438
Fees: Day £9312–£12,204
WB £14,694–£17,586
FB £15,414–£18,306

(♟)(♠)(✎)(IAPS)

BEDFORD SCHOOL
For further details see p. 60
De Parys Avenue, Bedford,
Bedfordshire MK40 2TU
Tel: +44 (0)1234 362216
Email:
admissions@bedfordschool.org.uk
Website: www.bedfordschool.org.uk
Head Master: Mr J Moule MA
Age range: 7–18
No. of pupils: 1090 VIth278
Fees: Day £10,518–£16,227
WB £17,583–£26,157
FB £18,444–£27,051

(♟)(🌐)(A)(♠)(£)(IB)(✎)(16⁺)(HMC)(BSA)

Dame Alice Harpur School (now known as Bedford Girls' School)
Cardington Road, Bedford,
Bedfordshire MK42 0BX
Tel: 01234 361900
Headmistress: Miss Jo MacKenzie BSc,
MSc
Age range: 7–18
No. of pupils: 1200
Fees: Day £7602–£10,683

(♟)(A)(£)(16⁺)(GSA)

Luton Pentecostal Church Christian Academy
15 Church Street, Luton,
Bedfordshire LU1 3JE
Tel: 01582 412276
Head: Rev C Oakey
Age range: 3–13
Fees: Day £2400

(£)

Orchard School & Nursery
High Gobion Road, Barton-le-Clay,
Bedford, Bedfordshire MK45 4LT
Tel: 01582 882054
Headteacher: Mrs A Burton
Age range: 0–6
No. of pupils: 127 B61 G66

(IAPS)

Pilgrims Pre-Preparatory School
Brickhill Drive, Bedford,
Bedfordshire MK41 7QZ
Tel: 01234 369555
Head: Mrs J Webster BEd(Hons), EYPS
Age range: 3 months–8 years
No. of pupils: 385 B194 G191
Fees: Day £2795–£7590

(IAPS)(ISA)

Polam Oaks with Little Acorns Nursery
43-45 Lansdowne Road, Bedford,
Bedfordshire MK40 2BU
Tel: 01234 261864
Principal: Mrs Margaret Mason
Age range: 2½–9
No. of pupils: 120 B60 G60
Fees: Day £5550

Rushmoor School
58-60 Shakespeare Road, Bedford,
Bedfordshire MK40 2DL
Tel: 01234 352031
Headteacher: Ian Daniel BA, NPQH
Age range: B3–16 G3–11
No. of pupils: B301 G10
Fees: Day £4890–£8985

(£)(✎)(ISA)

Sceptre School
Ridgeway Avenue, Dunstable,
Bedfordshire LU5 4QL
Tel: 01582 665676
Headteacher: Mr Peter Hayman
Age range: 11–16
No. of pupils: 77 B35 G42

St Andrew's School
78 Kimbolton Road, Bedford,
Bedfordshire MK40 2PA
Tel: 01234 267272
Headmistress: Mrs J E Marsland
BPhil(Ed)
Age range: B3–9 G3–16
No. of pupils: 385 B33 G352
Fees: Day £5205–£8505

(♟)(✎)(GSA)

Key to symbols

(♟) Boys' school

(♀) Girls' school

(🌐) International school

(16⁺) Tutorial or sixth form college

(A) A levels

(♠) Boarding accommodation

(£) Bursaries

(IB) International Baccalaureate

(✎) Learning support

(16⁺) Entrance at 16+

(💼) Vocational qualifications

(IAPS) Member of Independent Association of Preparatory Schools

(HMC) The Headmasters' & Headmistresses' Conference

(ISA) Independent Schools Association

(GSA) Girls' School Association

(BSA) Boarding Schools' Association

(S) SHMIS

Unless otherwise indicated, all schools are coeducational
day schools. Single-sex and boarding schools will be
indicated by the relevant icon.

St George's School
28 Priory Road, Dunstable,
Bedfordshire LU5 4HR
Tel: 01582 661471
Headmistress: Mrs Plater
Age range: 3–11
No. of pupils: 120 B60 G60
Fees: Day £4020–£4560

CAMBRIDGESHIRE

Abbey College - Cambridge
17 Station Road, Cambridge,
Cambridgeshire CB1 2JB
Tel: 01223 578280
Principal: Dr Julian Davies
Age range: 14–21
No. of pupils: B130 G130
Fees: Day £21,000 FB £33,000

Beechwood School
Cherry Hinton Road, Shelford Bottom,
Cambridge, Cambridgeshire CB22 3BF
Tel: 01223 400190
Headteacher: Mr M T Drake
Age range: 11–16
No. of pupils: 29 B17 G12

Bellerbys College
Queens Campus, Bateman Street,
Cambridge, Cambridgeshire CB2 1LU
Tel: 01223 363159
Principal: John Rushton
Age range: 15–25
No. of pupils: B163 G181
Fees: FB £15,300

Cambridge Centre for Sixth-form Studies
1 Salisbury Villas, Station Road,
Cambridge, Cambridgeshire CB1 2JF
Tel: 01223 716890
Principal: Mr Stuart Nicholson
MA(Oxon), MBA, PGCE, NPQH, CPhys
Age range: 15–21
No. of pupils: 200 B108 G92
Fees: Day £6285–£16,530 FB £10,740

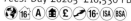

Cambridge International School
Cherry Hinton Hall, Cherry Hinton Road,
Cambridge, Cambridgeshire CB1 8DW
Tel: 01223 416938
Principal: Dr Harriet Sturdy
Age range: 4–16
No. of pupils: 225
Fees: Day £8115–£9645

Cambridge Seminars Tutorial College
Logic House, 143-147 Newmarket Road,
Cambridge, Cambridgeshire CB5 8HA
Tel: 01223 313464
Principal: M R Minhas BSc, CEng
Age range: 16–20
Fees: Day £12,000

Cambridge Steiner School
Hinton Road, Fulbourn, Cambridge,
Cambridgeshire CB21 5DZ
Tel: 01223 882727
Chair of Faculty: Faculty of Teachers
Age range: 2½–11
No. of pupils: 100
Fees: Day £1500–£5500

CATS Cambridge
13-15 Round Church Street, Cambridge,
Cambridgeshire CB5 8AD
Tel: 01223 314431
Principal: Dr Glenn Hawkins
Age range: 14–19+
No. of pupils: 352
Fees: Day £14,480–£23,850
FB £20,270–£33,150

Kimbolton School
Kimbolton, Huntingdon,
Cambridgeshire PE28 0EA
Tel: 01480 860505
Headmaster: Jonathan Belbin BA
Age range: 4–18
No. of pupils: B486 G439 VIth170
Fees: Day £8115–£12,645 FB £20,925

King's Acremont, The King's School Ely Nursery & Pre-Prep
Egremont Street, Ely,
Cambridgeshire CB6 1AE
Tel: 01353 662978
Head: Mrs F A Blake BA, PGCE
Age range: 2–6
No. of pupils: B79 G75
Fees: Day £5835–£6300

King's College School
West Road, Cambridge,
Cambridgeshire CB3 9DN
Tel: 01223 365814
Headmaster: Mr Nicholas Robinson BA,
PGCE, FRSA
Age range: 4–13
No. of pupils: 417 B238 G179
Fees: Day £9510–£12,270 WB £19,020

Madingley Pre-Preparatory School
Cambridge Road, Madingley, Cambridge,
Cambridgeshire CB23 8AH
Tel: 01954 210309
Headteacher: Mrs Penelope Evans
CertEd, AdvDip
Age range: 3–8
No. of pupils: 60 B30 G30
Fees: Day £8550

Mander Portman Woodward - Cambridge
3-4 Brookside, Cambridge,
Cambridgeshire CB2 1JE
Tel: 01223 350158
Principal: Dr Nick Marriott
Age range: 15–19
No. of pupils: 130 B65 G65 VIth100
Fees: Day £2925–£15,975
FB £7425–£20,475

Perse Girls Senior School
Union Road, Cambridge,
Cambridgeshire CB2 1HF
Tel: 01223 454700
head of School: Miss P M Kelleher
MA(Oxon), MA(Sussex)
Age range: 11–18
No. of pupils: 585 VIth150
Fees: Day £13,155

Phoenix School Cambridge
50 Church Street, Willingham,
Cambridge, Cambridgeshire CB24 5HT
Tel: 01954 263113
Headteacher: Mrs Jackie Daire
Age range: 3–11
No. of pupils: 11

Sancton Wood School
2 St Paul's Road, Cambridge,
Cambridgeshire CB1 2EZ
Tel: 01223 471703
Headmaster: The Reverend Dr Jack
McDonald
Age range: 3–16
No. of pupils: 193 B103 G90
Fees: Day £5220–£6510

St Andrew's Cambridge
2A Free School Lane, Cambridge,
Cambridgeshire CB2 3QA
Tel: 01223 360040
Principal: Mrs A Collins
Age range: 14–20
No. of pupils: B67 G63 VIth130
Fees: FB £15,000–£17,000

St Faith's
Trumpington Road, Cambridge,
Cambridgeshire CB2 8AG
Tel: 01223 352073
Headmaster: Mr N L Helliwell
Age range: 4–13
No. of pupils: 539 B317 G222
Fees: Day £9735–£12,270

St John's College School
73 Grange Road, Cambridge,
Cambridgeshire CB3 9AB
Tel: 01223 353532
Headmaster: Mr K L Jones MA(Cantab)
Age range: 4–13
No. of pupils: 466 B264 G202
Fees: Day £10,197–£12,318
FB £19,455–£19,455

St Mary's School
Bateman Street, Cambridge,
Cambridgeshire CB2 1LY
Tel: 01223 353253
Headmistress: Miss Charlotte Avery
Age range: 4–18
No. of pupils: 650 G650 VIth105
Fees: Day £12,465 WB £23,100
FB £26,862

The King's School Ely
Ely, Cambridgeshire CB7 4DB
Tel: 01353 660700
Head: Mrs Susan Freestone MEd, GRSM,
LRAM, ARCM, FRSA
Age range: 13–18
No. of pupils: 471 B283 G188 VIth168
Fees: Day £15,570 WB £22,530
FB £22,530

The King's School Ely Junior School
Ely, Cambridgeshire CB7 4DB
Tel: 01353 660732
Head: Mr R J Whymark
Age range: 7–13
No. of pupils: 343 B204 G139
Fees: Day £9855–£14,865
FB £15,720–£21,510

The Leys School
Cambridge, Cambridgeshire CB2 2AD
Tel: 01223 508900
Headmaster: Mark Slater
Age range: 11–18
No. of pupils: B330 G210 VIth200

The Perse Girls Junior School
St Eligius Street, Cambridge,
Cambridgeshire CB2 1HX
Tel: 01223 346 140
Head: Miss K Milne
Age range: 7–11
No. of pupils: 135
Fees: Day £11,610

The Perse Pelican Nursery and Pre-Preparatory School
Northwold House, 92 Glebe Road,
Cambridge, Cambridgeshire CB1 7TD
Tel: 01223 403940
Headmistress: Mrs S C Waddington MA
Age range: 3–7
No. of pupils: 152 B82 G68
Fees: Day £10,740

The Perse Preparatory School
Trumpington Road, Cambridge,
Cambridgeshire CB2 8EX
Tel: 01223 403920
Head: Gareth Jones BMus, PGCE
Age range: 7–11
No. of pupils: 261
Fees: Day £12,153

The Perse School
Hills Road, Cambridge,
Cambridgeshire CB2 8QF
Tel: 01223 403800
Head: Mr E C Elliott
Age range: 11–18
No. of pupils: 851 B686 G165 VIth250
Fees: Day £13,263

Whitehall School
117 High Street, Somersham,
Cambridgeshire PE17 3EH
Tel: 01487 840966
Headteacher: Mr Sean Peace
Age range: 3–11
No. of pupils: 109 B53 G56
Fees: Day £1510–£1953

Wisbech Grammar School
North Brink, Wisbech,
Cambridgeshire PE13 1JX
Tel: 01945 583631
Headmaster: Mr N J G Hammond
Age range: 13–18
No. of pupils: 662 B313 G349 VIth120
Fees: Day £6870–£9990

ESSEX

Braeside School for Girls
130 High Road, Buckhurst Hill,
Essex IG9 5SD
Tel: 020 8504 1133
Head Teacher: Mrs G Haddon BA(Hons),
PGCE
Age range: 3–16
No. of pupils: 199
Fees: Day £4950–£10,359

Brentwood Preparatory School
Middleton Hall Lane, Brentwood,
Essex CM15 8EQ
Tel: 01277 243333
Headmaster: Mr N L Helliwell MA,
BEd(Hons)
Age range: 7–11
No. of pupils: 240 B131 G109
Fees: Day £10,251

Brentwood Pre-Preparatory School
Shenfield Road, Brentwood,
Essex CM15 8BD
Tel: 01277 243239
Headmistress: Mrs S E Wilson BEd,
CertEd
Age range: 3–7
No. of pupils: B77 G75
Fees: Day £5130

Brentwood School
Ingrave Road, Brentwood,
Essex CM15 8AS
Tel: 01277 243243
Headmaster: Mr D I Davies
Age range: 11–18
No. of pupils: B468 G237 VIth334
Fees: Day £13,560 FB £24,345

Chigwell School
High Road, Chigwell, Essex IG7 6QF
Tel: 020 8501 5700
Headmaster: Mr M E Punt MA, MSc
Age range: 7–18
No. of pupils: 740 VIth273
Fees: Day £8391–£12,903
WB £17,493–£18,567 FB £19,611

Colchester High School
Wellesley Road, Colchester,
Essex CO3 3HD
Tel: 01206 573389
Principal: David Young BA(Hons) PGCE
Age range: 2½–16
No. of pupils: 486 B403 G83
Fees: Day £5184–£8106

Coopersale Hall School
Flux's Lane, off Stewards Green Road,
Epping, Essex CM16 7PE
Tel: 01992 577133
Headmistress: Miss Kaye Lovejoy
Age range: 2½–11
No. of pupils: 275 B135 G140
Fees: Day £3645–£7275

Dame Bradbury's School
Ashdon Road, Saffron Walden,
Essex CB10 2AL
Tel: 01799 522348
Headmistress: Mrs J Crouch
Age range: 3–11
No. of pupils: 250
Fees: Day £1890–£9600

Elm Green Preparatory School
Parsonage Lane, Little Baddow,
Chelmsford, Essex CM3 4SU
Tel: 01245 225230
Principal: Ms Ann Milner
Age range: 4–11
No. of pupils: 220 B118 G102
Fees: Day £7197

Felsted Preparatory School
Felsted, Great Dunmow, Essex CM6 3JL
Tel: 01371 822610
Headmistress: Mrs Jenny Burrett
BA(Dunelm), MEd(Cantab), PGCE
Age range: 4–13
No. of pupils: 460 B261 G199
Fees: Day £6390–£13,965 FB £17,850

Felsted School

Felsted, Great Dunmow, Essex CM6 3LL
Tel: +44 (0) 1371 822605
Headmaster: Dr Michael Walker
Age range: 13–18
No. of pupils: 516 B294 G222 VIth236
Fees: Day £18,480 WB £22,377
FB £24,705

FKS Schools

Edwards House, Braintree Road, Felsted,
Essex CM6 3DS
Tel: 01371 820638
Headmistress: Mrs A Woods
Age range: 4–11
No. of pupils: 161
Fees: Day £6219–£6864

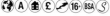

Friends' School

Mount Pleasant Road, Saffron Walden,
Essex CB11 3EB
Tel: 01799 525351
Head: Graham Wigley BA, MA
Age range: 3–18
No. of pupils: 390 B200 G190 VIth60
Fees: Day £2195–£4980
WB £6045–£6990 FB £6550–£7800

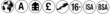

Gosfield School

Cut Hedge Park, Halstead Road,
Gosfield, Halstead, Essex CO9 1PF
Tel: 01787 474040
Principal: Dr Sarah Welch
Age range: 4–18
No. of pupils: B110 G70 VIth12
Fees: Day £7440–£12,540
WB £10,860–£12,720
FB £14,490–£20,985

Great Warley School

Warley Street, Great Warley, Brentwood,
Essex CM13 3LA
Tel: 01277 233288
Head: Mrs B Harding
Age range: 3–11
No. of pupils: B70 G56
Fees: Day £2250–£3500

Guru Gobind Singh Khalsa College

Roding Lane, Chigwell, Essex IG7 6BQ
Tel: 020 8559 9160
Principal: Mr Amarjit Singh Toor
BSc(Hons), BSc, BT
Age range: 3–17
No. of pupils: B88 G122
Fees: Day £3900

Heathcote School

Eves Corner, Danbury, Chelmsford,
Essex CM3 4QB
Tel: 01245 223131
Head Teacher: Miss H Petersen
Age range: 2–11
No. of pupils: 74 B39 G35
Fees: Day £466–£6990

Herington House School

1 Mount Avenue, Hutton, Brentwood,
Essex CM13 2NS
Tel: 01277 211595
Principal: Mr R Dudley-Cooke
Age range: 3–11
No. of pupils: 129
Fees: Day £4365–£8670

Holmwood House Preparatory School

Chitts Hill, Lexden, Colchester,
Essex CO3 9ST
Tel: 01206 574305
Headmaster: Alexander Mitchell
Age range: 4–13
No. of pupils: 302 B198 G104
Fees: Day £7920–£14,079 WB £18,258

Hutton Manor School

428 Rayleigh Road, Hutton, Brentwood,
Essex CM13 1SD
Tel: 01277 245585
Head: Mr P Pryke
Age range: 3–11
No. of pupils: B73 G73
Fees: Day £2975–£3995

Littlegarth School

Horkesley Park, Nayland, Colchester,
Essex CO6 4JR
Tel: 01206 262332
Headmaster: Mr Peter Jones
Age range: 2½–11
No. of pupils: 308 B153 G155
Fees: Day £1860–£8400

Loyola Preparatory School

103 Palmerston Road, Buckhurst Hill,
Essex IG9 5NH
Tel: 020 8504 7372
Headmaster: Mr P G M Nicholson
CertEd, BEd(Hons)
Age range: 3–11
No. of pupils: 182
Fees: Day £4482–£7470

Maldon Court Preparatory School

Silver Street, Maldon, Essex CM9 4QE
Tel: 01621 853529
Headteacher: Mrs L Guest
Age range: 3–11
No. of pupils: 124 B62 G62
Fees: Day £6579

New Hall School

The Avenue, Boreham, Chelmsford,
Essex CM3 3HS
Tel: 01245 467588
Principal: Mrs Katherine Jeffrey MA, BA,
PGCE, MA(Ed Mg), NPQH
Age range: 3–18
No. of pupils: 1132 B478 G654 VIth166
Fees: Day £7392–£15,225
FB £16,110–£22,860

Oaklands School

8 Albion Hill, Loughton, Essex IG10 4RA
Tel: 020 8508 3517
Headmistress: Mrs Pam Simmonds
MA(Oxon), BSc
Age range: B2½–7 G2½–11
No. of pupils: 243 B62 G181
Fees: Day £3795–£7650

Oxford House School

2-4 Lexden Road, Colchester,
Essex CO3 3NE
Tel: 01206 576686
Principal: Mr D Wood
Age range: 2½–11
No. of pupils: 130 B65 G65
Fees: Day £1140–£2270

Peniel Academy

Brizes Park, Ongar Road, Kelvedon
Hatch, Brentwood, Essex CM15 0DG
Tel: 01277 374123
Headmaster: Reverend M S B Reid BD
Age range: 4–18

St Anne's Preparatory School

New London Road, Chelmsford,
Essex CM2 0AW
Tel: 01245 353488
Headmistress: Mrs Fiona Pirrie
BEd(Hons)
Age range: 3–11
No. of pupils: 160 B70 G90
Fees: Day £6300–£6600

St Cedd's School

178 New London Road, Chelmsford,
Essex CM2 0AR
Tel: 01245 354380
Head: Dr P Edmonds
Age range: 3–11
No. of pupils: B229 G240
Fees: Day £7320–£7875

St John's School

Stock Road, Billericay, Essex CM12 0AR
Tel: 01277 623070
Head Teacher: Mrs F Armour BEd(Hons)
Age range: 3–16
No. of pupils: 392 B237 G155
Fees: Day £5106–£9660

St Margaret's Preparatory School

Gosfield Hall Park, Gosfield, Halstead,
Essex CO9 1SE
Tel: 01787 472134
Principal: Mrs E Powling
Age range: 2–11
No. of pupils: 250 B123 G127
Fees: Day £46–£2975

St Mary's School

Lexden Road, Colchester, Essex CO3 3RB
Tel: 01206 572544
Principal: Mrs H K Vipond MEd,
BSc(Hons), NPQH
Age range: 4–16
No. of pupils: 424
Fees: Day £6180–£8610

St Nicholas School

Hillingdon House, Hobbs Cross Road,
Harlow, Essex CM17 0NJ
Tel: 01279 429910
Headmaster: Mr K M Knight BEd, MA,
NPQH
Age range: 4–16
No. of pupils: 400 B200 G200
Fees: Day £6780–£8850

St Philomena's Preparatory School

Hadleigh Road, Frinton-on-Sea,
Essex CO13 9HQ
Tel: 01255 674492
Headmistress: Mrs B McKeown DipEd
Age range: 3–11
No. of pupils: B48 G56
Fees: Day £4920–£6210

The Daiglen School

68 Palmerston Road, Buckhurst Hill,
Essex IG9 5LG
Tel: 020 8504 7108
Headteacher: Mrs M Bradfield
Age range: 3–11
No. of pupils: 130 B100 G30
Fees: Day £6360

Ursuline Preparatory School

Old Great Ropers, Great Ropers Lane,
Warley, Brentwood, Essex CM13 3HR
Tel: 01277 227152
Headmistress: Mrs Pauline Wilson MSc
Age range: 3–11
No. of pupils: B79 G86
Fees: Day £2610–£4950

Widford Lodge School

Widford Road, Chelmsford,
Essex CM2 9AN
Tel: 01245 352581
Headmaster: Mr Simon Trowell
Age range: 2–11
No. of pupils: B99 G72
Fees: Day £5400–£7050

HERTFORDSHIRE

Abbot's Hill School

Bunkers Lane, Hemel Hempstead,
Hertfordshire HP3 8RP
Tel: 01442 240333
Headmistress: Mrs K Lewis MA(Cantab),
BSc(Open), PGCE, FRSA, MIMgt
Age range: B3–5 G3–16
No. of pupils: 472
Fees: Day £8205–£14,640

Aldenham School

Elstree, Hertfordshire WD6 3AJ
Tel: 01923 858122
Headmaster: James C Fowler MA
Age range: 3–18
No. of pupils: 700 B515 G185 VIth158
Fees: Day £12,750–£18,249
FB £19,101–£26,580

Aldwickbury School

Wheathampstead Road, Harpenden,
Hertfordshire AL5 1AD
Tel: 01582 713022
Headmaster: Mr V W Hales
Age range: 4–13
No. of pupils: 310
Fees: Day £2002–£3012
WB £3800–£3884

Beechwood Park School

Markyate, St Albans,
Hertfordshire AL3 8AW
Tel: 01582 840333
Headmaster: Mr P C E Atkinson
BSc(Hons), MIBiol, PGCE
Age range: 2½–13
No. of pupils: 495 B294 G201
Fees: Day £8844–£12,096 WB £15,375

BERKHAMSTED SCHOOL

For further details see p. 61
131 High Street, Berkhamsted,
Hertfordshire HP4 2DJ
Tel: 01442 358001
Email: admissions@berkhamsted-
school.org
Website: www.berkhamstedschool.org
Principal: Mr Mark Steed MA(Cantab),
MA
Age range: 3–18
No. of pupils: 1508 B415 G316 VIth331
Fees: Day £7770–£17,460 WB £23,370
FB £27,815

Bhaktivedanta Manor School

Hilfield Lane, Aldenham, Watford,
Hertfordshire WD25 8EZ
Tel: 01923 851000 Ext241
Administrator: Mrs Wendy Harrison
Age range: 4½–12
No. of pupils: 30 B15 G15
Fees: Day £1200

Bishop's Stortford College

10 Maze Green Road, Bishop's Stortford,
Hertfordshire CM23 2PJ
Tel: 01279 838575
Headmaster: Mr Jeremy Gladwin
Age range: 13–18
No. of pupils: 578 B315 G263 VIth240
Fees: Day £15,567–£15,660
WB £22,218–£22,326
FB £22,440–£23,316

Bishop's Stortford College Junior School

Maze Green Road, Bishop's Stortford,
Hertfordshire CM23 2PH
Tel: 01279 838607
Head of Junior School: J A Greathead
BEd
Age range: 4–13
No. of pupils: 565 B305 G260
Fees: Day £7200–£12,453
WB £15,501–£16,839
FB £15,672–£17,622

C K H R Immanuel College

87/91 Elstree Road, Bushey,
Hertfordshire WD23 4BE
Tel: 020 8950 0604
Headmaster: Mr Philip Skelker MA
Age range: 11–18
No. of pupils: 520 B263 G257 VIth127
Fees: Day £10,995

Charlotte House Preparatory School

88 The Drive, Rickmansworth,
Hertfordshire WD3 4DU
Tel: 01923 772101
Headmistress: Mrs S J Hayes BA(Hons)
Age range: 3–11
No. of pupils: 104
Fees: Day £2610–£9000

Duncombe School

4 Warren Park Road, Bengeo, Hertford,
Hertfordshire SG14 3JA
Tel: 01992 414100
Headmistress: Mrs Verity White MEd
Age range: 2–11
No. of pupils: 322 B166 G156
Fees: Day £3546–£10,455

Edge Grove School

Aldenham Village,
Hertfordshire WD2 8NL
Tel: 01923 855724
Headmaster: Mr Ian Elliott
Age range: 3–13
No. of pupils: 320 B207 G113
Fees: Day £9450–£13,875
WB £4056–£5085 FB £14,025–£17,115

Egerton Rothesay School
Durrants Lane, Berkhamsted,
Hertfordshire HP4 3UJ
Tel: 01442 877060
Headteacher: Mrs N I Boddam-Whetham
BA(Hons), PGTC
Age range: 5–16
No. of pupils: 167
Fees: Day £10,725–£22,170

Francis House Preparatory School
Aylesbury Road, Tring,
Hertfordshire HP23 4DL
Tel: 01442 822315
Head: Mrs Janice Hiley
Age range: 2–11
No. of pupils: 117 B57 G60
Fees: Day £650–£2470

Haberdashers' Aske's School
Butterfly Lane, Elstree, Borehamwood,
Hertfordshire WD6 3AF
Tel: 020 8266 1700
Headmaster: Mr P B Hamilton MA
Age range: 5–18
No. of pupils: 1402 VIth310
Fees: Day £10,641–£14,103

Haberdashers' Aske's School for Girls
Aldenham Road, Elstree, Borehamwood,
Hertfordshire WD6 3BT
Tel: 020 8266 2300
Headmistress: Mrs E J Radice MA(Oxon)
Age range: 4–18
No. of pupils: 1180
Fees: Day £9468–£11,490

HAILEYBURY
For further details see p. 62
Haileybury, Hertford,
Hertfordshire SG13 7NU
Tel: +44 (0)1992 706353
Email: registrar@haileybury.com
Website: www.haileybury.com
The Master: J S Davies MA(Cantab)
Age range: 11–18
No. of pupils: 764 B458 G306 VIth120
Fees: Day £13,668–£20,565
FB £17,367–£27,384

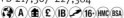

Haresfoot School
Chesham Road, Berkhamsted,
Hertfordshire HP4 2SZ
Tel: 01442 872742
Principal: Mrs Carole Hawkins BA, PGCE
Age range: 0–11
No. of pupils: B98 G90
Fees: Day £1845–£7770

Heath Mount School
Woodhall Park, Watton-at-Stone,
Hertford, Hertfordshire SG14 3NG
Tel: 01920 830230
Headmaster: Mr R Middleton MSc,
BEd(Hons)
Age range: 3–13
No. of pupils: B207 G153
Fees: Day £2715–£9315
WB £12,630–£12,960

High Elms Manor School
High Elms Manor, High Elms Lane,
Watford, Hertfordshire WD25 0JX
Tel: 01923681103
Headmistress: Mrs Sheila O'Neill
MontDipDist, TCert, BA, AMI Dip
Age range: 0–12
No. of pupils: 90 B45 G45
Fees: Day £11,136

Howe Green House School
Great Hallingbury, Bishops Stortford,
Hertfordshire CM22 7UF
Tel: 01279 657706
Headmaster: Mr Graham R Gorton
BA(Hons), PGCE
Age range: 2–11
No. of pupils: B82 G72
Fees: Day £5745–£9126

Immanuel College
87-91 Elstree Road, Bushey,
Hertfordshire WD23 4EB
Tel: 020 8950 0604
Head Master: Mr Phillip Skelker
Age range: 16–18 B11–16 G11–16
No. of pupils: 480 VIth120
Fees: Day £12,450

Justin Craig Education
Craig House, 13 High Street, Colney
Heath, St Albans, Hertfordshire AL4 0NS
Tel: 01727 827000
Director of Courses: Mrs M Craig
Age range: 15+

Kingshott
St Ippolyts, Hitchin,
Hertfordshire SG4 7JX
Tel: 01462 432009
Headmaster: Mr Iain Gilmour
Age range: 3–13
No. of pupils: 384 B232 G152
Fees: Day £4770–£10,350

Little Acorns Montessori School
Lincolnsfield Centre, Bushey Hall Drive,
Bushey, Hertfordshire WD23 2ER
Tel: 01923 230705
Head of School: Lola Davies BPA,
AMIDip
Age range: 2½–6
No. of pupils: 28
Fees: Day £2120

Lochinver House School
Heath Road, Little Heath, Potters Bar,
Hertfordshire EN6 1LW
Tel: 01707 653064
Headmaster: Ben Walker BA(Hons),
PGCE, CELTA
Age range: 4–13
No. of pupils: 330
Fees: Day £8700–£11,397

Lockers Park School
Lockers Park Lane, Hemel Hempstead,
Hertfordshire HP1 1TL
Tel: 01442 251712
Headmaster: Mr D S Farquharson
Age range: 5–13
No. of pupils: 140
Fees: Day £8385–£14,985 FB £18,840

Longwood School
Bushey Hall Drive, Bushey,
Hertfordshire WD23 2QG
Tel: 01923 253715
Head Teacher: Mrs Muriel Garman
Age range: 3–11
No. of pupils: B56 G44
Fees: Day £4590–£5790

Manor Lodge School
Rectory Lane, Ridge Hill, Shenley,
Hertfordshire WD7 9BG
Tel: 01707 642424
Headmaster: Mr G Dunn CertEd
Age range: 3–11
No. of pupils: 406 B193 G213
Fees: Day £8100–£9990

Northwood Preparatory School
Moor Farm, Sandy Lodge Road,
Rickmansworth, Hertfordshire WD3 1LW
Tel: 01923 825648
Headmaster: Dr T D Lee BEd(Hons)
Age range: 4–13
No. of pupils: 300
Fees: Day £2613–£9414

Princess Helena College
Preston, Hitchin, Hertfordshire SG4 7RT
Tel: 01462 432100
Headmistress: Mrs Jo-Anne Duncan
Age range: 11–18
No. of pupils: 194
Fees: Day £19,275–£24,618
FB £22,740–£28,065

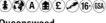

Queenswood
Shepherd's Way, Brookmans Park,
Hatfield, Hertfordshire AL9 6NS
Tel: 01707 602500
Principal: Mrs P C Edgar
BA(Hons)London, PGCE
Age range: 11–18
No. of pupils: 400 VIth120
Fees: Day £19,485–£21,825
FB £26,295–£28,665

Radlett Preparatory School
Kendal Hall, Watling Street, Radlett,
Hertfordshire WD7 7LY
Tel: 01923 856812
Principal: Mr W N Warren BEd(Hons),
FCollP
Age range: 4–11
No. of pupils: B240 G225
Fees: Day £7140–£7250

Redemption Academy
PO Box 352, Stevenage,
Hertfordshire SG1 9AG
Tel: 01438 727370
Headteacher: Mrs S J Neale
Age range: 2–16
No. of pupils: 41 B16 G25
Fees: Day £2400–£2880

Rudolf Steiner School
Langley Hill, Kings Langley,
Hertfordshire WD4 9HG
Tel: 01923 262505
Age range: 3–19
No. of pupils: 405
Fees: Day £2985–£7800

(A)(£)(✎)(16+)

Sherrardswood School
Lockleys, Welwyn, Hertfordshire AL6 0BJ
Tel: 01438 714282
Headmistress: Mrs L Corry
Age range: 2–18
No. of pupils: 357 B220 G175
Fees: Day £6720–£12,750

(A)(£)(✎)(16+)(ISA)

St Albans High School for Girls
Townsend Avenue, St Albans,
Hertfordshire AL1 3SJ
Tel: 01727 853800
Headmistress: Mrs Rosemary Martin
MEd, NPQH, FRSA
Age range: 4–18
No. of pupils: 940 Vlth170
Fees: Day £9660–£12,285

(👧)(A)(£)(✎)(16+)(IAPS)(GSA)

ST ALBANS SCHOOL
For further details see p. 64
Abbey Gateway, St Albans,
Hertfordshire AL3 4HB
Tel: 01727 855521
Email: hm@st-albans-school.org.uk
Website: www.st-albans.herts.sch.uk
Headmaster: Mr A R Grant MA(Cantab),
FRSA
Age range: B11–18 G16–18
No. of pupils: 820 B745 G75 Vlth300
Fees: Day £14,736

(👦)(A)(£)(✎)(16+)(HMC)

St Albans Tutors
69 London Road, St Albans,
Hertfordshire AL1 1LN
Tel: 01727 842348
Joint Principals: Assim Jemal BA(Hons) &
Lucy Webster BA(Hons), PGCE
Age range: 15+
No. of pupils: B28 G16
Fees: Day £3400

(16+)(A)(✎)

St Christopher School
Barrington Road, Letchworth,
Hertfordshire SG6 3JZ
Tel: 01462 650 850
Head: Richard Palmer
Age range: 3–18
No. of pupils: 511 B294 G217 Vlth78
Fees: Day £3375–£14,505
FB £15,600–£25,470

 (🌐)(A)(⚖)(£)(✎)(16+)(❋)(BSA)(S)

St Columba's College
King Harry Lane, St Albans,
Hertfordshire AL3 4AW
Tel: 01727 855185
Headmaster: David R Buxton
Age range: 11–18
No. of pupils: Vlth150
Fees: Day £8235–£10,416

(👦)(A)(£)(✎)(16+)(HMC)(S)

St Columba's College Prep School
King Harry Lane, St Albans,
Hertfordshire AL3 4AW
Tel: 01727 862616
Head of Prep: Mrs Ruth Loveman
Age range: 4–11
Fees: Day £8550–£9714

 (👦)(£)(IAPS)

ST EDMUND'S COLLEGE & PREP SCHOOL
For further details see p. 65
Old Hall Green, Nr Ware,
Hertfordshire SG11 1DS
Tel: 01920 824247
Email:
admissions@stedmundscollege.org
Website: www.stedmundscollege.org
Head: Paulo Dur·n BA MA
Age range: 3–18
No. of pupils: 823 B472 G351 Vlth145
Fees: Day £9465–£14,955
WB £19,830–£22,575
FB £21,855–£24,990

(🌐)(A)(⚖)(£)(✎)(16+)(HMC)

St Edmund's Prep
Old Hall Green, Ware,
Hertfordshire SG11 1DS
Tel: 01920 824239
Head: Mr L J Blom BEd(Hons), BA,
NPQH, HDE PhysEd
Age range: 3–11
No. of pupils: 150 B92 G58
Fees: Day £2540–£3715

(✎)

St Francis' College
Broadway, Letchworth Garden City,
Hertfordshire SG6 3PJ
Tel: 01462 670511
Headmistress: Mrs D MacGinty BEd,
NPQH, DipMontEd
Age range: 3–18
No. of pupils: 460 Vlth75
Fees: Day £8370–£11,385
WB £15,555–£18,630
FB £19,140–£22,155

(👧)(🌐)(A)(⚖)(£)(16+)(GSA)(BSA)

St Hilda's School
High Street, Bushey,
Hertfordshire WD23 3DA
Tel: 020 8950 1751
Headmistress: Mrs Tracy Handford MA
Age range: B3–5 G3–11
No. of pupils: 142 B6 G136
Fees: Day £4635–£8685

(👦)(✎)(IAPS)

St Hilda's School
28 Douglas Road, Harpenden,
Hertfordshire AL5 2ES
Tel: 01582 712307
Headmistress: Mrs C Godlee
Age range: 3–11
No. of pupils: 170
Fees: Day £5205–£9090

(👦)(✎)(ISA)

St John's Preparatory School
The Ridgeway, Potters Bar,
Hertfordshire EN6 5QT
Tel: 01707 657294
Headmistress: Mrs C Tardios BA(Hons)
Age range: 4–11
No. of pupils: 184 B93 G91
Fees: Day £8190–£8730

(✎)

St Joseph's In The Park
St Mary's Lane, Hertingfordbury,
Hertford, Hertfordshire SG14 2LX
Tel: 01992 581378
Headmaster: Mr Neil Jones
Age range: 3–11
No. of pupils: 161 B89 G72
Fees: Day £5298–£14,247

(£)(✎)(IAPS)

St Margaret's School, Bushey
Merry Hill Road, Bushey,
Hertfordshire WD23 1DT
Tel: 020 8416 4400
Head: Mrs Lynne Crighton BA(Hons)
Age range: 4–18
No. of pupils: 427 Vlth90
Fees: Day £8940–£13,500
WB £18,225–£21,330 FB £25,050

(👧)(🌐)(A)(⚖)(£)(✎)(16+)(GSA)(BSA)

Stanborough School
Stanborough Park, Garston, Watford,
Hertfordshire WD25 9JT
Tel: 01923 673268
Head: Mr Roger Murphy
Age range: 3–19
No. of pupils: 300 B128 G172 Vlth20
Fees: Day £3660–£5500
WB £12,834–£15,846

(🌐)(⚖)(IB)(16+)(ISA)(BSA)

Stormont
The Causeway, Potters Bar,
Hertfordshire EN6 5HA
Tel: 01707 654037
Headmistress: Mrs M E Johnston
BA(Hons), PGCE
Age range: 4–11
No. of pupils: 166
Fees: Day £9825–£10,275

(👦)(£)(✎)(IAPS)

The Christian School (Takeley)
Dunmow Road, Brewers End, Takeley,
Bishop's Stortford,
Hertfordshire CM22 6QH
Tel: 01279 871182
Headmaster: M E Humphries
Age range: 5–16
No. of pupils: B23 G22
Fees: Day £3720

The King's School
Elmfield, Ambrose Lane, Harpenden,
Hertfordshire AL5 4DU
Tel: 01582 767566
Principal: Mr Clive John Case BA, HDE
Age range: 5–16
No. of pupils: B101 G94
Fees: Day £4380

The Purcell School, London
Aldenham Road, Bushey,
Hertfordshire WD2 3TS
Tel: 01923 331100
Headmaster: Mr Peter Crook MA, BMus,
ARAM, ARCO
Age range: 8–18
No. of pupils: 167 B57 G110 VIth70
Fees: WB £22,452 FB £28,716

**TRING PARK SCHOOL FOR THE
PERFORMING ARTS**
For further details see p. 68
Tring Park, Tring,
Hertfordshire HP23 5LX
Tel: 01442 824255
Email: info@tringpark.com
Website: www.tringpark.com
Principal: Mr Stefan Anderson MA,
ARCM, ARCT
Age range: 8–19
No. of pupils: 317 B88 G229 VIth217
Fees: Day £12,870–£20,100
FB £21,285–£30,030

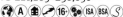

Wellgrove Primary School
Littlebury, College Road, Cheshunt,
Hertfordshire EN8 9NQ
Tel: 01992 624 141
Headteacher: Mrs Janice Tew-Cragg
Age range: 7–11
No. of pupils: B14 G22

WESTBROOK HAY PREP SCHOOL
For further details see p. 69
London Road, Hemel Hempstead,
Hertfordshire HP1 2RF
Tel: 01442 256143
Email: admin@westbrookhay.co.uk
Website: www.westbrookhay.co.uk
Headmaster: Keith D Young BEd(Hons)
Age range: 3–13
No. of pupils: 290 B190 G100
Fees: Day £8610–£12,390

York House School
Redheath, Sarratt Road, Croxley Green,
Rickmansworth, Hertfordshire WD3 4LW
Tel: 01923 772395
Headmaster: Jon Gray BA(Ed)
Age range: 3–13
No. of pupils: 240
Fees: Day £10,845

LUTON

Moorlands School & Nursery
Leagrave Hall, High Street,
Luton LU4 9LE
Tel: 01582 573376
Head Teacher: Mrs D Attias
Age range: 2–11
No. of pupils: 261 B132 G129
Fees: Day £2484–£5379

Rabia Girls School
12-16 Portland Road, Luton LU4 8AX
Tel: 01582 493239
Headteacher: Mrs F Shaikh
Age range: 4–16
No. of pupils: 265 B77 G188

NORFOLK

All Saints School
School Road, Lessingham, Norwich,
Norfolk NR12 0DJ
Tel: 01692 582083
Headmistress: J N Gardiner
Age range: 3–16
No. of pupils: B47 G41
Fees: Day £2736–£4455

Beeston Hall School
West Runton, Cromer, Norfolk NR27 9NQ
Tel: 01263 837324
Headmaster: Mr R C Gainher BSc(Hons)
Age range: 7–13
No. of pupils: 159 B98 G61
Fees: Day £15,033 FB £20,304

Breckland Park School
Turbine Way, Swaffham,
Norfolk PE37 7XD
Tel: 01760 336939
Headteacher: Mrs Sally Garrett
Age range: 7–18
No. of pupils: 143 B72 G71 VIth27

**Downham Preparatory School &
Montessori Nursery**
The Old Rectory, Stow Bardolph, Kings
Lynn, Norfolk PE34 3HT
Tel: 01366 388066
Headmistress: Mrs E Laffeaty-Sharpe
MontDip
Age range: 2–11
No. of pupils: 170 B86 G84
Fees: Day £4959–£6702

Glebe House School
2 Cromer Road, Hunstanton,
Norfolk PE36 6HW
Tel: 01485 532809
Headmaster: Mr Crofts
Age range: 0–13
No. of pupils: 110 B58 G52
Fees: Day £7200–£10,800
WB £9180–£12,780

Gresham's
Cromer Road, Holt, Norfolk NR25 6EA
Tel: +44 (0) 1263 714500
Headmaster: Mr Philip John
Age range: 3–18
No. of pupils: 878 B497 G381 VIth197
Fees: Day £20,925 FB £27,300

Gresham's Preparatory School
Cromer Road, Holt, Norfolk NR25 6EY
Tel: 01263 714600
Headmaster: Mr J H W Quick BA, PGCE
Age range: 8–13
No. of pupils: 373 B203 G170
Fees: Day £15,720–£13,800 FB £20,625

Gresham's Pre-Prep School
Market Place, Holt, Norfolk NR25 6BB
Tel: 01263 714563
Headmistress: Janette Davidson
Age range: 3–8
No. of pupils: 134 B76 G58
Fees: Day £7860–£8715

Hethersett Old Hall School
Hethersett, Norwich, Norfolk NR9 3DW
Tel: 01603 810390
Headmaster: Mr S Crump
Age range: B3–11 G3–18
No. of pupils: 197 B24 G173 VIth29
Fees: Day £5850–£12,450
WB £13,395–£17,850
FB £15,585–£23,175

Langley School
Langley Park, Loddon, Norwich,
Norfolk NR14 6BJ
Tel: 01508 520210
Headmaster: Dominic Findlay
Age range: 10–18
No. of pupils: 461 B295 G166 VIth97
Fees: Day £10,320 WB £17,490
FB £20,985

Norwich High School for Girls GDST
95 Newmarket Road, Norwich,
Norfolk NR2 2HU
Tel: 01603 453265
Headmaster: Mr J J Morrow BA(Oxon),
MA
Age range: 3–18
No. of pupils: 840 VIth120
Fees: Day £6420–£10,260

Norwich School

70 The Close, Norwich, Norfolk NR1 4DD
Tel: 01603 728430
Head Master: Steffan D A Griffiths
Age range: 7–18
No. of pupils: 1000 B687 G313 Vlth294
Fees: Day £11,088–£12,174

(A) (£) (16+) (IAPS) (HMC)

Norwich Steiner School

302A Bowthorpe Road, Guardian Road,
Norwich, Norfolk NR5 8AB
Tel: 01603 503795
Headteacher: Mr Andrew Vestrini
Age range: 3–11
No. of pupils: 31 B18 G13
Fees: Day £2160–£3000

Notre Dame Preparatory School

147 Dereham Road, Norwich,
Norfolk NR2 3TA
Tel: 01603 625593
Headmaster: Mr K O'Herlihy
Age range: 2–11
No. of pupils: 140 B70 G70
Fees: Day £810–£5445

 (£) (ISA)

Riddlesworth Hall Preparatory School

Garboldisham, Diss, Norfolk IP22 2TA
Tel: 01953 681 246
Headmaster: Paul Cochrane
Age range: 2–13
No. of pupils: 137 B75 G62
Fees: Day £10,470 WB £16,500
FB £17,535

(箕) (£) (IAPS) (BSA)

Sacred Heart Convent School

17 Mangate Street, Swaffham,
Norfolk PE37 7QW
Tel: 01760 721330/724577
Headmistress: Sr Francis Ridler FDC,
BEd(Hons), EYPS
Age range: 3–16
No. of pupils: 156 B33 G109
Fees: Day £7005–£10,425
WB £14,850–£15,975 FB £19,350

 (ISA) (BSA)

St Nicholas House School

Yarmouth Road, North Walsham,
Norfolk NR28 9AT
Tel: 01692 403143
Headteacher: Mr C J A Wardle
Age range: 3–11
No. of pupils: 65 B37 G28
Fees: Day £4260

 (ISA)

Stretton School

West Lodge, Albemarle Road, Norwich,
Norfolk NR2 2DF
Tel: 01603 451285
Principal: Mrs Y D Barnett
Age range: 1–8
No. of pupils: 80 B45 G35
Fees: Day £1020–£7500

Taverham Hall School

Taverham, Norwich, Norfolk NR8 6HU
Tel: 01603 868206
Headmaster: Mr Mike A Crossley NPQH,
BEd(Hons)
Age range: 1–13
Fees: Day £2856–£12,510 WB £16,200

 (IAPS)

The New Eccles Hall School

Quidenham, Norwich, Norfolk NR16 2NZ
Tel: 01953 887217
Headmaster: Richard Allard
Age range: 2–16
No. of pupils: 170
Fees: Day £4110–£6825
FB £10,845–£12,870

(地) (箕) (£) (⚽) (ISA) (BSA)

Thetford Grammar School

Bridge Street, Thetford,
Norfolk IP24 3AF
Tel: 01842 752840
Headmaster: Mr G J Price MA
Age range: 4–18
No. of pupils: 308 B169 G139 Vlth44
Fees: Day £9072–£10,971

(A) (£) (16+) (S)

Thorpe House Langley Preparatory School

7 Yarmouth Road, Norwich,
Norfolk NR7 0EA
Tel: 01603 433055
Headmaster: Simon Marfleet
Age range: 2–11
No. of pupils: 144 B89 G55
Fees: Day £2100–£2540

(£)

Town Close House Preparatory School

14 Ipswich Road, Norwich,
Norfolk NR2 2LR
Tel: 01603 620180
Headmaster: Mr Graeme Lowe BEd
Age range: 3–13
No. of pupils: 455 B275 G180
Fees: Day £7080–£11,085

(£) (IAPS)

PETERBOROUGH

Kirkstone House School

Main Street, Baston,
Peterborough PE6 9PA
Tel: 01778 560350
Head: Mrs C Jones BSocSc
Age range: 5–16
No. of pupils: 234 B150 G84
Fees: Day £5688–£8493

(£) (⚽) (ISA)

The Peterborough School

Thorpe Road, Peterborough PE3 6AP
Tel: 01733 343357
Headmaster: Mr A M Meadows
BSc(Hons)
Age range: 6 weeks–18 years
No. of pupils: 350 B120 G230 Vlth52
Fees: Day £8454–£11,958

(🎿) (地) (A) (箕) (£) (⚽) (16+) (BSA) (S)

SOUTHEND-ON-SEA

Alleyn Court Preparatory School

Wakering Road, Southend-on-
Sea SS3 0PW
Tel: 01702 582553
Headmaster: Mr Gareth Davies
BA(Hons), PGCE
Age range: 2½–11
No. of pupils: B173 G127
Fees: Day £2160–£9255

(£) (⚽) (IAPS) (ISA)

Crowstone Preparatory School

121-123 Crowstone Road, Westcliff-on-
Sea, Southend-on-Sea SS0 8LH
Tel: 01702 346758
Headmaster: J P Thayer
Age range: 3–11
No. of pupils: 133
Fees: Day £2655

(ISA)

Saint Pierre School

16 Leigh Road, Leigh-on-Sea, Southend-
on-Sea SS9 1LE
Tel: 01702 474164
Headmaster: Kurt Davies
Age range: 2½–11+
No. of pupils: B59 G36
Fees: Day £2062–£6186

(£)

St Hilda's School

15 Imperial Avenue, Westcliff-on-Sea,
Southend-on-Sea SS0 8NE
Tel: 01702 344542
Headmistress: Mrs Susan O'Riordan
BA(Hons), PGCE
Age range: B3–11 G3–16
Fees: Day £6336–£9450

(🏃) (£) (⚽) (ISA)

St Michael's Church Of England Preparatory School

198 Hadleigh Road, Leigh-on-Sea,
Southend-on-Sea SS9 2LP
Tel: 01702 478719
Head: Steve Tompkins BSc(Hons), PGCE,
MA, NPQH
Age range: 3–11
No. of pupils: 271 B140 G131
Fees: Day £3510–£6990

(£) (⚽) (IAPS)

Thorpe Hall School

Wakering Road, Southend-on-
Sea SS1 3RD
Tel: 01702 582340
Headmaster: Mr Andrew Hampton
Age range: 2–16
No. of pupils: B210 G140
Fees: Day £3339–£4821

(⚽) (ISA)

SUFFOLK

Arbor Preparatory School & Cherry Trees Montessori Nursery
Flempton Road, Risby, Bury St Edmunds, Suffolk IP28 6QJ
Tel: 01284 760531
Headmistress: Mrs W E S Compson BSc(Hons), MontDipAdv
Age range: 0–11
No. of pupils: 240 B125 G115
Fees: Day £4800–£5850

Barnardiston Hall Prep School
Barnardiston, Haverhill, Suffolk CB9 7TG
Tel: 01440 786316
Headmaster: Lt Col K A Boulter MA(Cantab), PGCE
Age range: 2–13
No. of pupils: 250 B125 G125
Fees: Day £8925–£11,430 WB £15,810 FB £17,145

Culford Preparatory School
Culford, Bury St Edmunds, Suffolk IP28 6TX
Tel: 01284 385383
Headmaster: Mr Mike Schofield
Age range: 7–13
No. of pupils: 214
Fees: Day £9030–£12,660 FB £17,340–£18,600

Culford Pre-Preparatory School
Fieldgate House, Bury St Edmunds, Suffolk IP28 6TX
Tel: 01284 729358
Headmistress: Mrs Sarah Preston BA
Age range: 3–7
Fees: Day £1440–£7605

Culford School
Culford, Bury St Edmunds, Suffolk IP28 6TX
Tel: 01284 728615
Headmaster: Mr J F Johnson-Munday MA, MBA
Age range: 13–18
No. of pupils: 635 B340 G295 VIth140
Fees: Day £15,240 FB £22,740–£24,660

Fairstead House School
Fordham Road, Newmarket, Suffolk CB8 7AA
Tel: 01638 662318
Headmaster: Gareth Williams
Age range: 3–11
No. of pupils: 118 B63 G55
Fees: Day £2256–£8130

Felixstowe International College
Maybush Lane, Felixstowe, Suffolk IP11 7NA
Tel: 01394 282388
Principal: Mrs J S Lee
Age range: 10–17
No. of pupils: 20 B12 G8
Fees: FB £19,500

Finborough School
The Hall, Great Finborough, Stowmarket, Suffolk IP14 3EF
Tel: 01449 773600
Principal: Mr J Sinclair
Age range: 2–18
No. of pupils: 226 B123 G103 VIth20
Fees: Day £5220–£8580 WB £10,860–£14,280 FB £13,200–£17,010

Framlingham College
Framlingham, Suffolk IP13 9EY
Tel: 01728 723789
Headmaster: Mr P B Taylor BA(Hons)
Age range: 13–18
No. of pupils: 418 VIth195
Fees: Day £15,237 WB £23,706 FB £23,706

Ipswich High School GDST
Woolverstone, Ipswich, Suffolk IP9 1AZ
Tel: 01473 780201
Head: Ms Elaine Purves BA
Age range: 3–18
No. of pupils: 650 VIth100
Fees: Day £6987–£9627

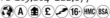

Ipswich Preparatory School
3 Ivry Street, Ipswich, Suffolk IP1 3QW
Tel: 01473 281302
Headteacher: Mrs A H Childs
Age range: 3–11
No. of pupils: 311 B182 G129
Fees: Day £8358–£9201

Ipswich School
Henley Road, Ipswich, Suffolk IP1 3SG
Tel: 01473 408300
Headmaster: Mr Nicholas Weaver MA
Age range: 11–18
No. of pupils: 785 B483 G302 VIth216
Fees: Day £11,175–£12,252 WB £18,264–£20,544 FB £19,264–£22,677

Larchcroft School
32 Larchcroft Road, Ipswich, Suffolk IP1 6AR
Tel: 01473 464975
Headteacher: Mr Alan Webber
Age range: 11–16
No. of pupils: 54 B26 G28

Moreton Hall Preparatory School
Mount Road, Bury St Edmunds, Suffolk IP32 7BJ
Tel: 01284 753532
Headmaster: Mr Simon Head MA, PGCE
Age range: 2½–13
No. of pupils: 104 B59 G45
Fees: Day £7035–£11,715 WB £15,735 FB £17,595

Old Buckenham Hall School
Brettenham, Ipswich, Suffolk IP7 7PH
Tel: 01449 740252
Headmaster: Mr J A Brett MA
Age range: 3–13
No. of pupils: 228
Fees: Day £15,300 WB £20,070 FB £20,070

Old School Henstead
Toad Row, Beccles, Suffolk NR34 7LG
Tel: 01502 741150
Headmaster: Mr M J Hewett BA, CertEd, MCollP
Age range: 4½–11
No. of pupils: 123 B65 G58
Fees: Day £4500–£6300

ORWELL PARK SCHOOL
For further details see p. 63
Nacton, Ipswich, Suffolk IP10 0ER
Tel: 01473 659225
Email: opssecretary@orwellpark.co.uk
Website: www.orwellpark.co.uk
Headmaster: Mr Adrian Brown MA(Cantab)
Age range: 2½–13
No. of pupils: 253 B150 G103

Saint Felix School
Halesworth Road, Southwold, Suffolk IP18 6SD
Tel: 01502 722175
Headmaster: Dr Simon Letman
Age range: 1–18
No. of pupils: 464 B220 G244 VIth74
Fees: Day £6000–£12,900 WB £14,440–£18,300 FB £18,900–£22,800

South Lee Preparatory School
Nowton Road, Bury St Edmunds, Suffolk IP33 2BT
Tel: 01284 754654
Headmaster: Mr Derek Whipp MA, CertEd
Age range: 2–13
No. of pupils: 327 B162 G158
Fees: Day £5850–£8550

St Joseph's College
Birkfield, Belstead Road, Ipswich,
Suffolk IP2 9DR
Tel: 01473 690281
Principal: Mrs S Grant BMus(Hons)
Age range: 3–18
No. of pupils: 560 B403 G157 VIth109
Fees: Day £5634–£9510
WB £14,475–£15,825
FB £15,150–£16,500

Stoke College
Stoke-by-Clare, Sudbury,
Suffolk CO10 8JE
Tel: 01787 278141
Head: Mr John Gibson BA, CertEd
Age range: 3–16
No. of pupils: B143 G98
Fees: Day £6732–£10,482
WB £14,586–£16,926

Summerhill School
Leiston, Suffolk IP16 4HY
Tel: 01728 830540
Principal: Mrs Z S Readhead
Age range: 5–17
No. of pupils: B37 G32
Fees: Day £3735–£8931
FB £8568–£14,889

The Hollies Preparatory School
Snape Road, Sudbourne, Woodbridge,
Suffolk IP12 2AT
Tel: 01394 450146
Head: Mr T McNeil
Age range: 5–11
No. of pupils: 105 B46 G59
Fees: Day £5210–£10,650

THE ROYAL HOSPITAL SCHOOL
For further details see p. 66
Holbrook, Ipswich, Suffolk IP9 2RX
Tel: +44 (0) 1473 326210
Email: admissions@royalhospi-
talschool.org
Website: www.royalhospitalschool.org
Headmaster: Mr James Lockwood MA
Age range: 11–18
No. of pupils: 700 B410 G290 VIth220
Fees: Day £11,994–£15,672
WB £19,995–£23,997
FB £19,995–£23,997

Woodbridge School
Woodbridge, Suffolk IP12 4JH
Tel: 01394 615000
Headmaster: Mr S H Cole MA,
MA(EdMgt), CPhys, MInstP, PGCE
Age range: 4–18
No. of pupils: B380 G380 VIth200
Fees: Day £6600–£11,994 FB £21,192

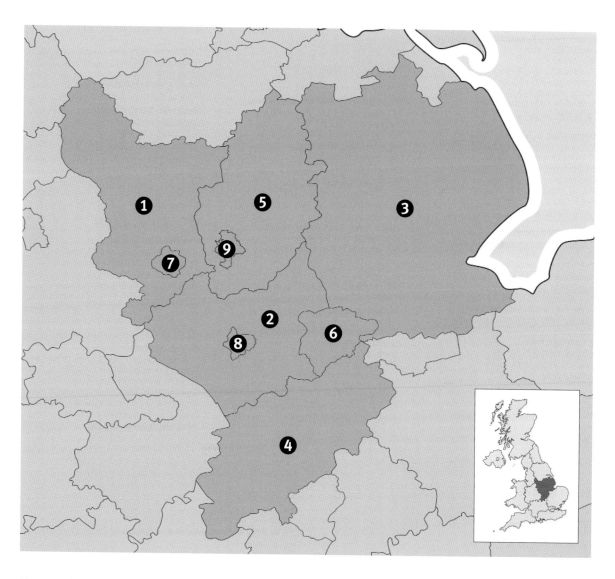

Key and page index:

DERBY

Dame Catherine Harpur's School
Rose Lane, Ticknall, Derby DE73 1JW
Tel: 01332 862792
Head: Ms Whyte
Age range: 3–11
No. of pupils: 28 B12 G16
Fees: Day £3275

Derby Grammar School
Rykneld Hall, Rykneld Road, Littleover,
Derby DE23 4BX
Tel: 01332 523027
Headmaster: Mr Richard D Paine
Age range: B7–18 G16–18
No. of pupils: 298 B284 G14 VIth66
Fees: Day £7779–£10,779

 (A) (£) (16+) (ISA)

Derby High School
Hillsway, Littleover, Derby DE23 7DT
Tel: 01332 514267
Headmaster: Mr C T Callaghan
Age range: B3–11 G3–18
No. of pupils: 576 B90 G486 VIth74
Fees: Day £7050–£9510

(A) (£) (16+) (GSA)

Emmanuel School
Juniper Lodge, 43 Kedleston Road,
Derby DE22 1FP
Tel: 01332 340505
Headteacher: Mrs C Pearson
Age range: 3–16
No. of pupils: 65 B38 G27
Fees: Day £1698–£2706

Foremarke Hall
Milton, Derby DE65 6EJ
Tel: 01283 703269
Headmaster: Mr P Watson MA(Hons),
PGCE
Age range: 3–13
No. of pupils: B291 G196
Fees: Day £6831–£13,221 WB £17,556
FB £17,556

(♠) (£) (IAPS) (BSA)

Friar Gate House School
Friar Gate, Derby DE1 1DJ
Tel: 01332 342765
Headmistress: Mrs S Williams
Age range: 3–16
No. of pupils: 60

Morley Hall Preparatory School
Hill House, Morley Road, Chaddesden,
Derby DE21 4QZ
Tel: 01332 674501
Principal: Mrs R N Bowater
Age range: 3–11
No. of pupils: 74 B36 G38
Fees: Day £3678–£5289

Normanton House Primary School
Normanton House, Village Street,
Derby DE23 8DF
Tel: 01332 769333
Headteacher: Mr Nighat Sultana Khan
Age range: 5–10
No. of pupils: 97 B52 G45

Ockbrook School
The Settlement, Ockbrook,
Derby DE7 3RJ
Tel: 01332 673532
Head Teacher: Mrs Alison Steele
Age range: B2–11 G2–18
No. of pupils: 500 B42 G355 VIth61
Fees: Day £6690–£9825
WB £5685–£5685 FB £8835–£8835

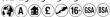 (A) (♠) (£) (16+) (GSA) (BSA)

DERBYSHIRE

Barlborough Hall School
Barlborough, Chesterfield,
Derbyshire S43 4TJ
Tel: 01246 810511
Headteacher: Mrs Wanda E Parkinson
BEd
Age range: 3–11
No. of pupils: 236 B120 G116
Fees: Day £6420–£8553

(£) (IAPS)

Gateway Christian School
Moor Lane, Dale Abbey, Ilkeston,
Derbyshire DE7 4PP
Tel: 0115 9440609
Head Teacher: Mrs Corinna Walters
Age range: 3–11
No. of pupils: 31 B18 G13
Fees: Day £2400

Michael House Steiner School
The Field, Shipley, Heanor,
Derbyshire DE75 7JH
Tel: 01773 718050
Age range: 3–16
No. of pupils: 150 B81 G69
Fees: Day £1500–£4200

Mount St Mary's College
Spinkhill, Derbyshire S21 3YL
Tel: 01246 433388
Headmaster: Mr Laurence McKell MA,
MEd, PGCE
Age range: 11–18
No. of pupils: 389 B241 G148 VIth96
Fees: Day £9963–£11,448
WB £15,246–£19,623
FB £18,300–£24,375

 (A) (♠) (£) (16+) (HMC) (BSA)

Old Vicarage School
11 Church Lane, Darley Abbey, Derby,
Derbyshire DE22 1EW
Tel: 01332 557130
Headmaster: Mr M J Adshead
Age range: 3–13
No. of pupils: 95 B49 G46
Fees: Day £6135–£6810

(£)

Repton School
The Hall, Repton, Derbyshire DE65 6FH
Tel: 01283 559222
Head: R A Holroyd MA
Age range: 13–18
No. of pupils: 658 B375 G283 VIth284
Fees: Day £20,940 FB £28,221

(🌐) (A) (♠) (£) (16+) (HMC) (BSA)

Key to symbols

(♠) Boys' school

(♀) Girls' school

(🌐) International school

(16+) Tutorial or sixth form college

(A) A levels

(♠) Boarding accommodation

(£) Bursaries

(IB) International Baccalaureate

(✎) Learning support

(16+) Entrance at 16+

(🍀) Vocational qualifications

(IAPS) Member of Independent Association of Preparatory Schools

(HMC) The Headmasters' & Headmistresses' Conference

(ISA) Independent Schools Association

(GSA) Girls' School Association

(BSA) Boarding Schools' Association

(S) SHMIS

Unless otherwise indicated, all schools are coeducational
day schools. Single-sex and boarding schools will be
indicated by the relevant icon.

S Anselm's School
Stanedge Road, Bakewell,
Derbyshire DE45 1DP
Tel: 01629 812734
Headmaster: S C Northcott MA
Age range: 3–13
No. of pupils: 226 B123 G103
Fees: Day £7680–£14,940 FB £17,550

St Peter & St Paul School
Brambling House, Hady Hill,
Chesterfield, Derbyshire S41 0EF
Tel: 01246 278522
Headmaster: Mr Andrew Lamb
Age range: 3 months–11 years
No. of pupils: 129 B74 G58
Fees: Day £6132–£6432

St Wystan's School
High Street, Repton,
Derbyshire DE65 6GE
Tel: 01283 703258
Headmaster: Phillip Soutar
Age range: 2½–11
No. of pupils: B59 G63

Tissington Pre-Preparatory & Kindergarten School
The Old Stable Block, Tissington,
Ashbourne, Derbyshire DE6 1RA
Tel: 01335 350123
Headmistress: Lady Caroline Fitzherbert
Age range: 2½–8
No. of pupils: B36 G42
Fees: Day £6450

LEICESTER

Al-Aqsa Schools Trust
The Wayne Way, Leicester LE5 4PP
Tel: 0116 2760953
Headteacher: Mrs Amina Wiltshire
Age range: 5–16
No. of pupils: 231 B101 G130

Brooke House Day School
Croft Road, Cosby, Leicester LE9 1SE
Tel: 0116 286 7372
Head: Mrs Joy Parker
Age range: 3–14

Darul Arqam Educational Institute
2 Overton Road, Leicester LE5 0JA
Tel: 0116 2741626
Headteacher: Mr Ahmed Abdul Dadipatel
Age range: 5–16
No. of pupils: 75 B73 G2

Darul Uloom Leicester
119 Loughborough Road,
Leicester LE4 5LN
Tel: 0116 2668922
Headteacher: Mr Harun Musa
Age range: 11–25
No. of pupils: 140 B140
Fees: Day £1560 FB £2280

Irwin College
164 London Road, Leicester LE2 1ND
Tel: 0116 255 2648
Principal: Mr A J Elliott BA(Oxon),
MPhil(Cantab), TEFL
Age range: 14–20
No. of pupils: 100 B50 G50 VIth60
Fees: Day £6200 FB £12,600

Jameah Academy
33 Woodhill, Leicester LE5 3SP
Tel: 0116 2627745
Headteacher: Mrs S Patel
Age range: 6–16
No. of pupils: 142

Leicester Grammar Junior School
London Road, Grea Glen,
Leicester LE8 9FL
Tel: 0116 259 1950
Headteacher: Mrs M Redfearn
Age range: 3–11
No. of pupils: 405 B221 G184
Fees: Day £8625

Leicester Grammar School
London Road, Great Glen,
Leicester LE8 9FL
Tel: 0116 259 1900
Head & Chief Executive: C P M King MA
Age range: 10–18
No. of pupils: 704 B402 G302 VIth188
Fees: Day £7905

Leicester High School for Girls
454 London Road, Leicester LE2 2PP
Tel: 0116 2705338
Headmistress: Mrs J Burns BA
Age range: 3–18
No. of pupils: 435 VIth60
Fees: Day £2250–£3100

Leicester Islamic Academy
320 London Road, Leicester LE2 2PP
Tel: 0116 2705343
Principal: Dr M H Mukadam FRSA,
BEd(Hons), PhD
Age range: 3–16
No. of pupils: B265 G435
Fees: Day £1300–£1400

Leicester Montessori Grammar School
58 Stoneygate Road, Leicester LE2 2BN
Tel: 0116 2706667
Headteacher: Mr Leyton De Henton
Smith
Age range: 4–14
No. of pupils: 84 B50 G34
Fees: Day £10,200

Leicester Montessori Sixth Form College
140 Regent Road, Leicester LE1 7PA
Tel: 0845 2300222
Head Teacher: Geraldine Lauriston
Age range: 14–18+
No. of pupils: 65
Fees: Day £7398–£7884

Leicester Prep School
2 Albert Road, Leicester LE2 2AA
Tel: 0116 2707414
Headmaster: Christopher J Cann
MA(Oxon)
Age range: 3–11
No. of pupils: 130 B60 G70
Fees: Day £1530–£5820

Ratcliffe College
Fosse Way, Ratcliffe on the Wreake,
Leicester LE7 4SG
Tel: 01509 817000
Head: Mr G Lloyd BA, MSc, FMusTCL
Age range: 3–18
No. of pupils: 689 B392 G297 VIth154
Fees: Day £7392–£13,644 FB £20,862

Sathya Sai School
Shree Sanathan Centre, Belper Street,
Leicester LE4 6ED
Tel: 07929 660 098
Principal: Mrs Lim
Age range: 5–8
No. of pupils: 35 B17 G18
Fees: Day £500

St Crispin's School
6 St Mary's Road, Leicester LE2 1XA
Tel: 0116 2707648
Head: Mrs D Lofthouse
Age range: 2–16
No. of pupils: B89 G39

Stoneygate School
254 London Road, Leicester LE2 1RP
Tel: 0116 259 2282
Headmaster: J H Morris MA(Cantab)
Age range: 3–13
No. of pupils: B250 G160
Fees: Day £4800–£6100

Tiny Tots Pre-School & Primary
16-20 Beal Street, Leicester LE2 0AA
Tel: 0116 2515345
Principle: Mr N Hussein
Age range: 2½–11
No. of pupils: 104 B60 G44

LEICESTERSHIRE

ASHBY SCHOOL
For further details see p. 72
School House, Leicester Road, Ashby-de-la-Zouch, Leicestershire LE65 1DH
Tel: +44 (0) 1530 413759
Email: schoolhouse@ashbyschool.org.uk
Website: www.ashbyschool.org.uk
Headteacher: Mr Eddie Green
Age range: 11–19
No. of pupils: 1643 B852 G791

Brooke House College
Leicester Road, Market Harborough, Leicestershire LE16 7AU
Tel: 01858 462452
Principal: Mr G E I Williams
Age range: 14–20
No. of pupils: B100 G100 Vlth73
Fees: FB £21,750

Burleigh Community College
Thorpe Hill, Loughborough, Leicestershire LE11 4SQ
Tel: 01509 554400
Principal: John Smith MSc
Age range: 14–19
No. of pupils: 1359 B688 G671 Vlth464
Fees: FB £7863

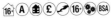

Fairfield Preparatory School
Leicester Road, Loughborough, Leicestershire LE11 2AE
Tel: 01509 215172
Headmaster: Mr R Outwin-Flinders BEd(Hons)
Age range: 4–11
No. of pupils: 489 B252 G237
Fees: Day £7083

Grace Dieu Manor School
Grace Dieu, Coalville, Leicestershire LE67 5UG
Tel: 01530 222276
Headmaster: Mr C E Foulds BA
Age range: 3–13
No. of pupils: 315 B165 G150
Fees: Day £5415–£9456

Loughborough Grammar School
6 Burton Walks, Loughborough, Leicestershire LE11 2DU
Tel: 01509 233233
Headmaster: P B Fisher MA
Age range: 10–18
No. of pupils: 1010 Vlth270

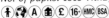

Loughborough High School
Burton Walks, Loughborough, Leicestershire LE11 2DU
Tel: 01509 212348
Headmistress: Mrs G Byrom
Age range: 11–18
No. of pupils: 605 Vlth170
Fees: Day £9798

Manor House School
South Street, Ashby-de-la-Zouch, Leicestershire LE65 1BR
Tel: 01530 412932
Headteacher: Mrs E A Scrine
Age range: 4–16
No. of pupils: B75 G72
Fees: Day £4302–£5700

Our Lady's Convent School
Gray Street, Loughborough, Leicestershire LE11 2DZ
Tel: 01509 263901
Headteacher: Mrs P Hawley
Age range: B3–11 G3–18
No. of pupils: 332 B5 G327 Vlth54
Fees: Day £7116–£9723

The Dixie Grammar School
Station Road, Market Bosworth, Leicestershire CV13 0LE
Tel: 01455 292244
Headmaster: J Wood MA
Age range: 3–18
No. of pupils: 520 B282 G267 Vlth71
Fees: Day £5760–£7920

LINCOLNSHIRE

Ayscoughfee Hall
Welland Hall, London Road, Spalding, Lincolnshire PE11 2TE
Tel: 01775 724733
Headmaster: Mr B G Chittick MA, BEd(Hons)
Age range: 3½–11
No. of pupils: 152 B68 G84
Fees: Day £3240–£5220

Bicker Preparatory School & Early Years
School Lane, Bicker, Boston, Lincolnshire PE20 3DW
Tel: 01775 821786
Proprietor & Principal: Mrs S A Page CertEdDist, SMPS
Age range: 3–11
No. of pupils: 80 B40 G40
Fees: Day £4680–£4785

Copthill Independent Day School
Barnack Road, Uffington, Stamford, Lincolnshire PE9 3AD
Tel: 01780 757506
Headmaster: Mr J A Teesdale BA(Hons), PGCE
Age range: 2–11
No. of pupils: 309 B152 G157
Fees: Day £6885–£7290

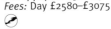

Dudley House School
1 Dudley Road, Grantham, Lincolnshire NG31 9AA
Tel: 01476 400184
Headmistress: Mrs Jenny Johnson
Age range: 3–11
No. of pupils: 50
Fees: Day £3960

Excell International School
Tunnard Street, Boston, Lincolnshire PE21 6PL
Tel: 01205 363 150
Principal: Dr A Omokhodion
Age range: 3–18
No. of pupils: 39
Fees: Day £4950–£6000
FB £9450–£10,500

Greenwich House School
106 High Holme Road, Louth, Lincolnshire LN11 0HE
Tel: 01507 609252
Headmistress: Mrs J Brindle
Age range: 9 months–11 years
No. of pupils: 50 B28 G22
Fees: Day £5100

Handel House Preparatory School
Northolme Road, Gainsborough, Lincolnshire DN21 2JB
Tel: 01427 612426
Headmistress: Mrs Victoria Haigh
Age range: 2–11
No. of pupils: B32 G27
Fees: Day £2580–£3075

Lincoln Minster Preparatory School
Eastgate, Lincoln, Lincolnshire LN2 1QG
Tel: 01522 523769
Headteacher: Mrs Karen Maltby BEd, MEd
Age range: 2½–11
No. of pupils: 270 B146 G124
Fees: Day £6201–£9210
WB £13,608–£16,140
FB £14,682–£17,415

Lincoln Minster Senior School
The Prior Building, Upper Lindum Street, Lincoln, Lincolnshire LN2 5RW
Tel: 01522 551300
Principal: Mr Clive Rickart
Age range: 2½–18
No. of pupils: 840 B423 G417 Vlth144
Fees: Day £6510–£9672
WB £14,289–£16,947
FB £15,417–£18,285

Locksley Christian School
Bliney House, Manby Park, Manby,
Lincolnshire LN11 8UT
Tel: 01507 327859
Headteacher: Mrs A Franklin BSc
Age range: 3–18
No. of pupils: B32 G34
Fees: Day £2004

St Hugh's School
Cromwell Avenue, Woodhall Spa,
Lincolnshire LN10 6TQ
Tel: 01526 352169
Head: S Greenish BEd
Age range: 2–13
No. of pupils: 194 B108 G86
Fees: Day £6300–£11,670
FB £15,285–£15,570

St Mary's Preparatory School
5 Pottergate, Lincoln,
Lincolnshire LN2 1PH
Tel: 01522 524622
Headmaster: Andrew Salmond Smith
BA(Hons), PGCE
Age range: 2¹⁄₂–11
No. of pupils: 212 B96 G116
Fees: Day £1140–£8136

STAMFORD ENDOWED SCHOOLS
For further details see p. 75
Brazenose House, St Paul's Street,
Stamford, Lincolnshire PE9 2BS
Tel: 01780 750310
Email: ses@ses.lincs.sch.uk
Website: www.ses.lincs.sch.uk
Principal: Stephen C Roberts
Age range: 2–18
No. of pupils: 1690 Vlth400
Fees: Day £12,624

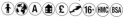

Stamford High School
St Martin's, Stamford,
Lincolnshire PE9 2LL
Tel: 01780 428200
Principal: Mr S C Roberts
Age range: 11–18
No. of pupils: 633 G633 Vlth201
Fees: Day £12,252 WB £16,932–£19,488
FB £22,356

Stamford Junior School
Kettering Road, Stamford,
Lincolnshire PE9 2LR
Tel: 01780 484400
Principal: Mr S C Roberts
Age range: 2–11
No. of pupils: 344 B160 G184
Fees: Day £8580 WB £17,436
FB £17,544

The Grantham Preparatory School
Gorse Lane, Grantham,
Lincolnshire NG31 7UF
Tel: 01476 593293
Headmistress: Mrs K A Korcz
Age range: 3–11
No. of pupils: 124 B65 G59
Fees: Day £5265–£7470

Viking School
140 Church Road North, Skegness,
Lincolnshire PE25 2QJ
Tel: 01754 765749
Principal: Mrs S J Barker
Age range: 3–11
No. of pupils: 100
Fees: Day £1085

Witham Hall
Witham-on-the-Hill, Bourne,
Lincolnshire PE10 0JJ
Tel: 01778 590222
Joint Heads: D Telfer BA, CertEd & Mrs S
Telfer CertEd
Age range: 4–13
No. of pupils: 228 B121 G107
Fees: Day £6645–£10,875 FB £14,850

NORTHAMPTONSHIRE

Beachborough School
Westbury, Brackley,
Northamptonshire NN13 5LB
Tel: 01280 700071
Headmaster: Mr J F Whybrow BEd
Age range: 2–13
No. of pupils: 260
Fees: Day £570–£10,485

Bosworth Independent College
Nazareth House, Barrack Road,
Northampton,
Northamptonshire NN2 6AF
Tel: 01604 235090
Principal: Mr Michael W McQuin MEd
Age range: 14–University
No. of pupils: B157 G147 Vlth250
Fees: Day £9840 WB £18,925–£21,450
FB £19,975–£22,500

Great Houghton School
Great Houghton Hall, Northampton,
Northamptonshire NN4 7AG
Tel: 01604 761907
Head: Mrs J Lancaster-Adlam
Age range: 3–16
No. of pupils: 331 B202 G122
Fees: Day £6738–£11,331

LAXTON JUNIOR SCHOOL
For further details see p. 73
East Road, Oundle, Peterborough,
Northamptonshire PE8 4BX
Tel: 01832 277275
Email: info@laxtonjunior.org.uk
Website: www.laxtonjunior.org.uk
Head: Mr Mark Potter BEd(Hons)
Age range: 4–11
No. of pupils: 244 B127 G117
Fees: Day £9270–£10,185

Maidwell Hall
Maidwell, Northampton,
Northamptonshire NN6 9JG
Tel: 01604 686234
Headmaster: R A Lankester MA, PGCE
Age range: 7–13
No. of pupils: 114 B96 G18
Fees: Day £13,500 WB £21,900
FB £21,900

Northampton Christian School
The Parish Rooms, Park Avenue North,
Northampton,
Northamptonshire NN3 2HT
Tel: 01604 715900
Headmistress: Mrs Zoe Blakeman
Age range: 4–18
No. of pupils: B11 G8
Fees: Day £1890–£2205

NORTHAMPTON HIGH SCHOOL GDST
For further details see p. 74
Newport Pagnell Road, Hardingstone,
Northampton,
Northamptonshire NN4 6UU
Tel: 01604 765765
Email: nhsadmin@nhs.gdst.net
Website:
www.northamptonhigh.gdst.net
Headmistress: Mrs S Dixon BA
Age range: 3–18
No. of pupils: 680 Vlth110
Fees: Day £8680–£11,865

Oundle School
Oundle, Peterborough,
Northamptonshire PE8 4GH
Tel: 01832 277125
Headmaster: Mr C M P Bush
Age range: 11–18
No. of pupils: 1104 B650 G454 Vlth423
Fees: Day £18,480 FB £28,590

Overstone Park School
Overstone Park, Overstone,
Northampton,
Northamptonshire NN6 0AD
Tel: 01604 643787
Principal: Mrs M F Brown BA(Hons),
PGCE
Age range: 0–18
No. of pupils: 106 B65 G41
Fees: Day £2628–£3105

Pitsford School
Pitsford Hall, Pitsford, Northampton,
Northamptonshire NN6 9AX
Tel: 01604 880306
Headmaster: N R Toone BSc, MInstP
Age range: 3–18
No. of pupils: 360 B220 G140 VIth63
Fees: Day £6990–£11,781

Quinton House School
Upton Hall, Upton, Northampton,
Northamptonshire NN5 4UX
Tel: 01604 752050
Headteacher: Mr G Jones BA(Hons)
Age range: 2–18
No. of pupils: 350 B154 G167 VIth43
Fees: Day £2325–£2710

Ravenstone House Northampton
Moulton Lodge, Moulton Way North,
Moulton, Northampton,
Northamptonshire NN3 7RW
Tel: 01604 790440
Headmistress: Mrs Mary Heal
BA(Hons)Ed
Age range: 2 months–7 years
No. of pupils: B50 G50
Fees: Day £6255

Spratton Hall
Smith Street, Spratton, Northampton,
Northamptonshire NN6 8HP
Tel: 01604 847292
Head Master: Mr Stephen Player
Age range: 4–13
No. of pupils: 407 B205 G202
Fees: Day £8400–£11,400

St Peter's Independent School
Lingswood Park, Blackthorn,
Northampton,
Northamptonshire NN3 8TA
Tel: 01604 411745
Head Master: G J Smith BA, CertEd
Age range: 4–18
No. of pupils: 130
Fees: Day £3600

St Peter's School
52 Headlands, Kettering,
Northamptonshire NN15 6DJ
Tel: 01536 512066
Headmistress: Mrs Maria Chapman
Age range: 2½–11
No. of pupils: 161 B79 G82
Fees: Day £3765–£6795

Wellingborough School
Wellingborough,
Northamptonshire NN8 2BX
Tel: 01933 222427
Headmaster: Mr G R Bowe MA
Age range: 3–18
No. of pupils: B492 G396 VIth145
Fees: Day £6522–£11,004

Winchester House
High Street, Brackley,
Northamptonshire NN13 7AZ
Tel: 01280 702483
Headmaster: Mark Seymour BA
Age range: 3–13
No. of pupils: 325 B200 G125
Fees: Day £636–£15,435
WB £16,155–£20,385 FB £16,065

NOTTINGHAM

Colston Bassett Preparatory School
School Lane, Colston bassett,
Nottingham NG12 3FD
Tel: 01949 81118
Headteacher: Mrs Julie Hunt
Age range: 4–11
Fees: Day £5925

Coteswood House School
19 Thackeray's Lane, Woodthorpe,
Nottingham NG5 4HT
Tel: 0115 9676551
Head: Mrs S M Fernley
Age range: 3–11
No. of pupils: 40 B20 G20
Fees: Day £4200

Dagfa Nottingham School
Broadgate, Beeston,
Nottingham NG9 2FU
Tel: 0115 913 8330
Head: Mrs J Le Poidevin BEd(Hons)
NPQH
Age range: 3–16
No. of pupils: 220 B140 G80
Fees: Day £5430–£6585

Grosvenor School
218 Melton Road, Edwalton,
Nottingham NG12 4BS
Tel: 0115 9231184
Headmaster: Mr C G J Oldershaw BEd
Age range: 4–13
No. of pupils: 112 B70 G42
Fees: Day £8505–£9435

Hazel Hurst School
400 Westdale Lane, Mapperley,
Nottingham NG3 6DG
Tel: 0115 9606759
Headteacher: Mrs Rosemary Eache
Age range: 2–8
No. of pupils: B25 G31
Fees: Day £4680–£5250

Hollygirt School
Elm Avenue, Nottingham NG3 4GF
Tel: 0115 9580596
Headmistress: Mrs Pam Hutley
BA(Hons), PGCE, MSc
Age range: 3–16
No. of pupils: 240
Fees: Day £6879–£9219

Iona School
310 Sneinton Dale,
Nottingham NG3 7DN
Tel: 0115 9415295
Chair of College: Richard Moore
Age range: 3–11
No. of pupils: B39 G46
Fees: Day £3816

Jamia Al-Hudaa Residential College
Forest House, Berkeley Avenue,
Mapperley Park, Nottingham NG3 5TT
Tel: 0115 9690800
Principal: Raza ul-Haq Siakhvy
Age range: 5–19
No. of pupils: 224

Jubilee House Christian School
166-168 Pasture Road, Stapleford,
Nottingham NG9 8GQ
Tel: 0115 939 5552
Headteacher: Mrs J Marks
Age range: 3–16
No. of pupils: 70 B31 G39

Nottingham High Junior School
Waverley Mount, Nottingham NG7 4ED
Tel: 0115 845 2214
Headmaster: A Earnshaw
Age range: 7–11
No. of pupils: 155
Fees: Day £8658

Nottingham High School
Waverley Mount, Nottingham NG7 4ED
Tel: 0115 9786056
Headmaster: K D Fear BA
Age range: 11–18
No. of pupils: 761 VIth227
Fees: Day £11,478

Nottingham High School for Girls GDST
9 Arboretum Street,
Nottingham NG1 4JB
Tel: 0115 9417663
Headmistress: Mrs S M Gorham
Age range: 4–18
No. of pupils: 1117 VIth239
Fees: Day £6978–£9627

Nottingham Islamia School
30 Bentinck Road, Hyson Green,
Nottingham NG7 4AF
Tel: 0115 970 5858
Head: Dr Musharraf Hussain
Age range: 5–11

Plumtree School
Church Hill, Plumtree,
Nottingham NG12 5ND
Tel: 0115 937 5859
Headmaster: N White CertEd
Age range: 3–11
No. of pupils: B60 G50
Fees: Day £5250

Salterford House School
Salterford Lane, Calverton,
Nottingham NG14 6NZ
Tel: 0115 9652127
Headmistress: Mrs Marlene Venables
CertEd
Age range: 2–11
No. of pupils: 124 B61 G63
Fees: Day £5250–£5310

St Joseph's School
33 Derby Road, Nottingham NG1 5AW
Tel: 0115 9418356
Headmaster: Mr D L St J Crawley BA
Age range: 1–11
No. of pupils: B102 G54
Fees: Day £3900

Trent College
Derby Road, Long Eaton,
Nottingham NG10 4AD
Tel: 0115 849 4949
Head: Mrs G Dixon BSc, MBA
Age range: 11–18
No. of pupils: 1117 B650 G467 VIth200
Fees: Day £7200–£13,500
WB £16,305–£17,685
FB £19,020–£20,625

NOTTINGHAMSHIRE

Al Karam Secondary School
Eaton Hall, Retford,
Nottinghamshire DN22 0PR
Tel: 01777 706441
Headteacher: Mr Ahmed
Age range: 11–16
No. of pupils: 132

Highfields School
London Road, Newark,
Nottinghamshire NG24 3AL
Tel: 01636 704103
Headteacher: Mrs C L Fraser BEd(Hons)
Age range: 3–11
No. of pupils: 140 B76 G64
Fees: Day £7470

Saville House School
11 Church Street, Mansfield Woodhouse,
Mansfield, Nottinghamshire NG19 8AH
Tel: 01623 625068
Head: Mrs S Hagues
Age range: 3–11
No. of pupils: 89 B36 G53
Fees: Day £4125

The Lammas School
Lammas Road, Sutton-in-Ashfield,
Nottinghamshire NG17 2AD
Tel: 01623 516879
Head: C M Peck BEd(Hons), CertEd
Age range: 4–16
No. of pupils: B80 G70
Fees: Day £3975–£4800

The Orchard School
South Leverton, Retford,
Nottinghamshire DN22 0DJ
Tel: 01427 880395
Principal: Mrs S M Fox BA, PGCE
Age range: 5–16
No. of pupils: 200
Fees: Day £3795–£6180

Wellow House School
Wellow, Newark,
Nottinghamshire NG22 0EA
Tel: 01623 861054
Headmaster: Peter Cook BEd(Hons)
Age range: 3–13
No. of pupils: 131 B78 G53
Fees: Day £6210–£10,695 WB £13,440

Worksop College
Worksop, Nottinghamshire S80 3AP
Tel: 01909 537155
Headmaster: G W Horgan MA
Age range: 13–18
No. of pupils: 398 B214 G154
Fees: Day £15,345 FB £23,520

**Worksop College Preparatory School,
Ranby House**
Retford, Nottinghamshire DN22 8HX
Tel: 01777 703138
Headmaster: C S J Pritchard MA, BA
(Hons), QTS
Age range: 3–13
No. of pupils: 244 B129 G115
Fees: Day £561–£11,610 FB £16,800

RUTLAND

Brooke Priory School
Station Approach, Oakham,
Rutland LE15 6QW
Tel: 01572 724778
Headmistress: Mrs E Bell BEd
Age range: 3–11
No. of pupils: 230 B115 G115
Fees: Day £5085–£6360

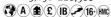

Oakham School
Chapel Close, Oakham,
Rutland LE15 6DT
Tel: 01572 758758
Headmaster: Nigel M Lashbrook BA
Age range: 10–18
No. of pupils: 1050 B545 G505 VIth396
Fees: Day £15,150–£17,100
WB £18,300–£25,650
FB £23,250–£28,500

UPPINGHAM SCHOOL
For further details see p. 76
Uppingham, Rutland LE15 9QE
Tel: 01572 822216 Admissions: 01572
820611
Email: admissions@uppingham.co.uk
Website: www.uppingham.co.uk
Headmaster: Mr Richard Harman
Age range: 13–18
No. of pupils: 790 B462 G328 VIth380
Fees: Day £21,300 FB £30,429

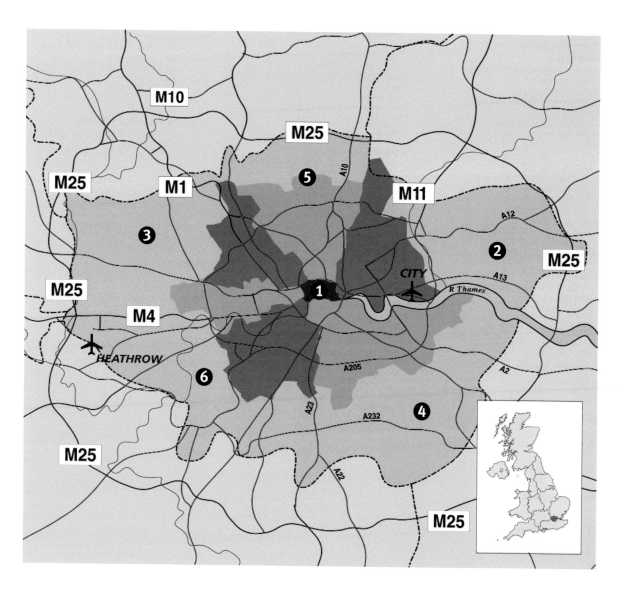

Key and page index:

1 London: D285

2 Essex: D278

3 Hertfordshire: D279

4 Kent: D279

5 Middlesex: D280

6 Surrey: D282

ESSEX

Al-Noor Primary School
619-625 Green Lane, Goodmayes, Ilford,
Essex IG3 9RP
Tel: 020 8597 7576
Head: Mrs Someera Butt
Age range: 4–10
No. of pupils: 175
Fees: Day £2550–£2750

Avon House
490-492 High Road, Woodford Green,
Essex IG8 0PN
Tel: 020 8504 1749
Headteacher: Mrs A Campbell
Age range: 3–11
No. of pupils: B100 G80
Fees: Day £7020–£7380

Bancroft's School
High Road, Woodford Green,
Essex IG8 0RF
Tel: 020 8505 4821
Head: Mary E Ireland
Age range: 7–18
No. of pupils: 1089 B562 G527 VIth234
Fees: Day £10,626–£13,188

Beehive Preparatory School
233 Beehive Lane, Redbridge, Ilford,
Essex IG4 5ED
Tel: 020 8550 3224
Headmaster: Mr C J Beasant BEd
Age range: 4–11
No. of pupils: 95 B47 G48
Fees: Day £4350

Cranbrook College
Mansfield Road, Ilford, Essex IG1 3BD
Tel: 020 8554 1757
Head: Mr A Moss
Age range: 4–16
No. of pupils: 200
Fees: Day £6405–£8235

Eastcourt Independent School
1 Eastwood Road, Goodmayes, Ilford,
Essex IG3 8UW
Tel: 020 8590 5472
Headmistress: Mrs Christine Redgrave
BSc(Hons),DipEd,MEd
Age range: 3–11
No. of pupils: B165 G166
Fees: Day £5070

Gidea Park College
2 Balgores Lane, Gidea Park, Romford,
Essex RM2 5JR
Tel: 01708 740381
Headmistress: Mrs Susan-Jayne Gooding
BA
Age range: 3–11
No. of pupils: 177 B88 G89
Fees: Day £1275–£2500

Glenarm College
20 Coventry Road, Ilford, Essex IG1 4QR
Tel: 020 8554 1760
Principal: Mrs V Mullooly
Age range: 3–11
No. of pupils: B53 G80
Fees: Day £4755–£5055

Goodrington School
17 Walden Road, Hornchurch,
Essex RM11 2JT
Tel: 01708 448349
Head Teacher: Mrs J R Ellenby
Age range: 3–11
No. of pupils: 79 B30 G49
Fees: Day £4650

Ilford Grammar School
785 High Road, Seven Kings, Ilford,
Essex IG3 8RW
Tel: 020 8599 8822
Headmistress: B P M Wiggs BSc(Hons),
PGCE
Age range: 3–16
No. of pupils: B114 G80
Fees: Day £5250–£7200

Ilford Ursuline R C Preparatory School
2 Coventry Road, Ilford, Essex IG1 4QR
Tel: 020 8518 4050
Headmistress: Mrs C Spinner
Age range: 3–11
No. of pupils: 159
Fees: Day £5697

Immanuel School
Havering Grange Centre, Havering Road
North, Romford, Essex RM1 4HR
Tel: 01708 764449
Principal: Miss Norcross
Age range: 3–16
No. of pupils: B71 G57

Maytime Preparatory School
87 York Road, Ilford, Essex IG1 3AF
Tel: 020 8553 1524
Headteacher: Mrs M O'Mahoney
Age range: 0–6

Oakfields Montessori School
Harwood Hall, Harwood Hall Lane,
Corbets Tey, Essex RM14 2YG
Tel: 01708 220117
Headmistress: Mrs K Malandreniotis
Age range: 2½–11
Fees: Day £2508–£4260

Park School for Girls
20 Park Avenue, Ilford, Essex IG1 4RS
Tel: 020 8554 2466
Headmistress: Mrs N O'Brien BA
Age range: 7–18
No. of pupils: 230 VIth19
Fees: Day £4755–£6285

Raphael Independent School
Park Lane, Hornchurch, Essex RM11 1XY
Tel: 01708 744735
Headmistress: Mrs J Lawrence
BEd(Hons)
Age range: 4–16
No. of pupils: 135 B75 G60
Fees: Day £4020–£7200

Key to symbols

(♦) Boys' school

(♣) Girls' school

(🌐) International school

(16·) Tutorial or sixth form college

(A) A levels

(⚫) Boarding accommodation

(£) Bursaries

(IB) International Baccalaureate

(✐) Learning support

(16·) Entrance at 16+

(🎓) Vocational qualifications

(IAPS) Member of Independent Association of Preparatory Schools

(HMC) The Headmasters' & Headmistresses' Conference

(ISA) Independent Schools Association

(GSA) Girls' School Association

(BSA) Boarding Schools' Association

(S) SHMIS

Unless otherwise indicated, all schools are coeducational
day schools. Single-sex and boarding schools will be
indicated by the relevant icon.

St Aubyn's School
Bunces Lane, Woodford Green,
Essex IG8 9DU
Tel: 020 8504 1577
Head: Gordon James MA(Oxon)
Age range: 3–13
No. of pupils: 500 B290 G210
Fees: Day £4200–£9990

£ / (IAPS)

St Mary's Hare Park School & Nursery
South Drive, Gidea Park, Romford,
Essex RM2 6HH
Tel: 01708 761220
Head Teacher: Mrs K Karwacinski
Age range: 2½–11
No. of pupils: 180 B80 G100
Fees: Day £4485

Woodford Green Preparatory School
Glengall Road, Snakes Lane, Woodford
Green, Essex IG8 0BZ
Tel: 020 8504 5045
Headmaster: Mr A J Blackhurst
BA(Hons), AdvDipEd
Age range: 3–11
No. of pupils: 384 B197 G187
Fees: Day £4155–£6405

 £ /

HERTFORDSHIRE

LYONSDOWN SCHOOL TRUST
For further details see p. 82
3 Richmond Road, New Barnet, Barnet,
Hertfordshire EN5 1SA
Tel: 020 8449 0225
Email:
enquiries@lyonsdownschool.co.uk
Website: www.lyonsdownschool.co.uk
Head: Mrs L Maggs-Wellings BEd
Age range: B3–7 G3–11
No. of pupils: 214 B31 G183
Fees: Day £3189–£8103

 / (ISA)

Norfolk Lodge Montessori Nursery & Pre-Prep School
Dancers Hill Road, Barnet,
Hertfordshire EN5 4RP
Tel: 020 8447 1565
Head Teacher: Mrs Mary Wales
Age range: 6 months–7 years
No. of pupils: 140
Fees: Day £2200–£2400

 /

St Martha's Senior School
Camlet Way, Hadley, Barnet,
Hertfordshire EN4 0NJ
Tel: 020 8449 6889
Headmaster: Mr James Sheridan
Age range: 11–18
No. of pupils: 265 VIth32
Fees: Day £3720

(符) (A) £ / (16+) (ISA) (GSA)

Susi Earnshaw Theatre School
68 High Street, Barnet,
Hertfordshire EN5 5SJ
Tel: 020 8441 5010
Headteacher: Mr David Earnshaw
Age range: 10–16
No. of pupils: 59 B19 G40
Fees: Day £6000–£6600

£

THE ROYAL MASONIC SCHOOL FOR GIRLS
For further details see p. 89
Rickmansworth Park, Rickmansworth,
Hertfordshire WD3 4HF
Tel: 01923 773168
Email:
enquiries@royalmasonic.herts.sch.uk
Website: www.royalmasonic.herts.sch.uk
Headmistress: Mrs Diana Rose
MA(Cantab)
Age range: 4–18
No. of pupils: 917 B26 G891 VIth175
Fees: Day £8490–£14,550
WB £14,850–£23,535
FB £15,105–£24,120

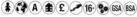

KENT

Ashgrove School
116 Widmore Road, Bromley,
Kent BR1 3BE
Tel: 020 8460 4143
Principal: Patricia Ash CertEd,
BSc(Hons), PhD, CMath, FIMA
Age range: 3–11
No. of pupils: B52 G54
Fees: Day £7065

Babington House School
Grange Drive, Chislehurst, Kent BR7 5ES
Tel: 020 8467 5537
Headteacher: Miss D Leek-Bailey
Age range: B3–7 G3–16
No. of pupils: 262 B65 G197
Fees: Day £1230–£4140

Benedict House Preparatory School
1-5 Victoria Road, Sidcup,
Kent DA15 7HD
Tel: 020 8300 7206
Head Teacher: Mr T Brogan
Age range: 3–11
No. of pupils: B70 G70
Fees: Day £3135–£7185

Bickley Park School
24 Page Heath Lane, Bickley, Bromley,
Kent BR1 2DS
Tel: 020 8467 2195
Headmaster: Mr Paul Ashley
Age range: B3–13 G3–4
No. of pupils: 370 B350 G20
Fees: Day £6525–£11,925

Bishop Challoner School
228 Bromley Road, Shortlands, Bromley,
Kent BR2 0BS
Tel: 020 8460 3546
Headteacher: Karen Barry
Age range: 3–18
No. of pupils: 412 B287 G125 VIth32
Fees: Day £6441–£9036

(A) £ / (16+) (ISA)

Breaside Preparatory School
41-43 Orchard Road, Bromley,
Kent BR1 2PR
Tel: 020 8460 0916
Headmistress: Mrs Karen Nicholson BEd,
NPQH, Diploma in Early Years
Age range: 2½–11
No. of pupils: 304 B157 G147
Fees: Day £9450–£9525

(IAPS)

Bromley High School
Blackbrook Lane, Bickley, Bromley,
Kent BR1 2TW
Tel: 020 8781 7000
Head: Ms Louise Simpson BSc (UCW)
Age range: 4–18
No. of pupils: 912 VIth125
Fees: Day £9996–£12,606

(符) (A) £ / (16+) (GSA)

Darul Uloom London
Foxbury Avenue, Perry Street,
Chislehurst, Kent BR7 6SD
Tel: 020 8295 0637
Principal: Mufti Mustafa
Age range: 11–18
No. of pupils: 160
Fees: FB £2400

FARRINGTONS SCHOOL
For further details see p. 78
Perry Street, Chislehurst, Kent BR7 6LR
Tel: 020 8467 0256
Email: fvail@farringtons.kent.sch.uk
Website: www.farringtons.org.uk
Headmistress: Mrs C E James MA
Age range: 3–18
No. of pupils: 650 B221 G429 VIth80
Fees: Day £9060–£12,120 WB £21,900
FB £23,280

(符) (A) (符) £ / (16+)

Harenc Preparatory School for Boys
Church House, 167 Rectory Lane, Foots
Cray, Sidcup, Kent DA14 5BU
Tel: 020 8309 0619
Headmistress: Miss S J Woodward BA,
FRSA
Age range: 3–11
No. of pupils: 108
Fees: Day £6285–£8241

Merton Court Preparatory School
38 Knoll Road, Sidcup, Kent DA14 4QU
Tel: 020 8300 2112
Headmaster: Mr Dominic Price BEd,
MBA
Age range: 3–11
No. of pupils: B141 G127
Fees: Day £8115–£8910

St Christopher's School
49 Bromley Road, Beckenham,
Kent BR3 2PA
Tel: 020 8650 2200
Headmaster: Mr A Velasco MEd,
BH(Hons), PGCE
Age range: 3–11
No. of pupils: 305 B160 G145
Fees: Day £2250–£6630

St David's College
Beckenham Road, West Wickham,
Kent BR4 0QS
Tel: 020 8777 5852
Principal: Mrs A Wagstaff BA(Hons)
Age range: 4–11
No. of pupils: 155 B93 G62
Fees: Day £6015–£6165

West Lodge School
36 Station Road, Sidcup, Kent DA15 7DU
Tel: 020 8300 2489
Head Teacher: Mrs Susan Webb
Age range: 3–11
No. of pupils: 164 B60 G104
Fees: Day £4740–£7950

Wickham Court School
Schiller International, Layhams Road,
West Wickham, Kent BR4 9HW
Tel: 020 8777 2942
Head: Mrs Barbara Hunter
Age range: 2–16
No. of pupils: 121 B50 G71
Fees: Day £4481–£6900

MIDDLESEX

Acorn Independent College
39-47 High Street, Southall,
Middlesex UB1 3HF
Tel: 020 8571 9900
Principal: Mrs Gladys Watt
Age range: 13–19
No. of pupils: 115
Fees: Day £9500–£12,950

ACS Hillingdon International School
Hillingdon Court, 108 Vine Lane,
Hillingdon, Uxbridge,
Middlesex UB10 0BE
Tel: +44 (0) 1895 259 771
Head of School: Ginger G Apple
Age range: 4–18
No. of pupils: 642
Fees: Day £9170–£19,490

Alpha Preparatory School
21 Hindes Road, Harrow,
Middlesex HA1 1SH
Tel: 020 8427 1471
Head: P J Wylie BA(Hons), CertEd
Age range: 3–11
No. of pupils: 177 B98 G79
Fees: Day £2640–£8430

Ashton House School
50-52 Eversley Crescent, Isleworth,
Middlesex TW7 4LW
Tel: 020 8560 3902
Headteacher: Mrs M Grundberg MA,
PGCE
Age range: 3–11
No. of pupils: B70 G60
Fees: Day £7900–£8600

Athelstan House School
36 Percy Road, Hampton,
Middlesex TW12 2LA
Tel: 020 8979 1045
Headmistress: Elsa Woolf
Age range: 3–7
No. of pupils: 65

Buckingham College Preparatory School
458 Rayners Lane, Pinner,
Middlesex HA5 5DT
Tel: 020 8866 2737
Headmaster: Mr L S Smith BA(Hons),
MSc, LCP, PGDE, CertEd
Age range: 4–11
No. of pupils: 110 B110
Fees: Day £7338–£9606

Buckingham College School
11-17 Hindes Road, Harrow,
Middlesex HA1 1SH
Tel: 020 8427 1220
Headmaster: Mr S Larter BA(Hons),
PGCE, JP
Age range: B11–18 G16–18
No. of pupils: 150 VIth27
Fees: Day £8763–£10,161

Buxlow Preparatory School
5/6 Castleton Gardens, Wembley,
Middlesex HA9 7QJ
Tel: 020 8904 3615
Headmistress: Mrs Ann Baines
Age range: 4–11
No. of pupils: B46 G42
Fees: Day £6885

Denmead School
41-43 Wensleydale Road, Hampton,
Middlesex TW12 2LP
Tel: 020 8979 1844
Headmaster: Mr M T McKaughan BEd
Age range: 3–11
No. of pupils: B213 G10
Fees: Day £4575–£10,590

HALLIFORD SCHOOL
For further details see p. 79
Russell Road, Shepperton,
Middlesex TW17 9HX
Tel: 01932 223593
Email: registrar@halliford.net
Website: www.hallifordschool.co.uk
Head: Mr Philip V Cottam MA(Oxon), FRGS
Age range: B11–18 G16–18
No. of pupils: B433 G10
Fees: Day £12,000

Hampton School
Hanworth Road, Hampton,
Middlesex TW12 3HD
Tel: 020 8979 5526
Headmaster: Mr B R Martin MA(Cantab),
MBA, FCMI, FRSA
Age range: 11–18
No. of pupils: 1130 VIth330
Fees: Day £12,870

Harrow School
5 High Street, Harrow on the Hill,
Middlesex HA1 3HT
Tel: 020 8872 8007
Head Master: Mr Jim Hawkins
Age range: 13–18
No. of pupils: 800 VIth320
Fees: FB £29,670

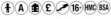

Heathfield School GDST
Beaulieu Drive, Pinner,
Middlesex HA5 1NB
Tel: 020 8868 2346
Head: Mrs Anne Stevens BA(Hons)
Durham, PGCE Cambridge, NPQH, NCSL
Age range: 3–18
No. of pupils: 486 VIth77
Fees: Day £8000–£13,000

Holland House School
1 Broadhurst Avenue, Edgware,
Middlesex HA8 8TP
Tel: 020 8958 6979
Headmistress: Mrs Irinia Tyk BA(Hons)
Age range: 4–11
No. of pupils: B70 G70
Fees: Day £3120

Jack and Jill School
30 Nightingale Road, Hampton,
Middlesex TW12 3HX
Tel: 020 8979 3195
Principal: Miss K Papirnik BEd(Hons)
Age range: B2–5 G2–7
No. of pupils: 155 B37 G118
Fees: Day £2409–£9597

Lady Nafisa Independent Secondary School for Girls
83A Sunbury Road, Feltham,
Middlesex TW13 4PH
Tel: 020 8751 5610
Headteacher: Ms Fouzia Butt
Age range: 11–16

Menorah Grammar School
Abbots Road, Edgware,
Middlesex HA8 0QS
Tel: 020 8906 9756
Headteacher: Rabbi A M Goldblatt
Age range: 11–17
No. of pupils: 203

Merchant Taylors' School
Sandy Lodge, Northwood,
Middlesex HA6 2HT
Tel: 01923 820644
Head Master: Mr S N Wright MA(Cantab)
Age range: 11–18
No. of pupils: 865 VIth275
Fees: Day £16,020

Newland House School
32-34 Waldegrave Park, Twickenham,
Middlesex TW1 4TQ
Tel: 020 8865 1234
Headmaster: Mr D A Alexander
Age range: B4–13 G4–11
No. of pupils: B274 G149
Fees: Day £9300–£10,440

North London Collegiate School
Canons, Canons Drive, Edgware,
Middlesex HA8 7RJ
Tel: +44 (0)20 8952 0912
Headmistress: Mrs Bernice McCabe
Age range: 4–18
No. of pupils: 1080
Fees: Day £11,472–£14,523

Northwood College
Maxwell Road, Northwood,
Middlesex HA6 2YE
Tel: 01923 825446
Head Mistress: Miss Jacqualyn Pain MA,
MA, MBA
Age range: 3–18
No. of pupils: 750 VIth100
Fees: Day £8250–£13,050

Oak Heights
3 Red Lion Court, Alexandra Road,
Hounslow, Middlesex TW3 1JS
Tel: 020 8577 1827
Head: Mr S Dhillon
Age range: 11–16
No. of pupils: 48
Fees: Day £6000

Orley Farm School
South Hill Avenue, Harrow,
Middlesex HA1 3NU
Tel: 020 8869 7600
Headmaster: Mark Dunning
Age range: 4–13
No. of pupils: 505 B340 G165
Fees: Day £3835–£4432

Peterborough & St Margaret's School
Common Road, Stanmore,
Middlesex HA7 3JB
Tel: 020 8950 3600
Headmistress: Mrs Susan Watts
Age range: 4–16
No. of pupils: 170
Fees: Day £5847–£8691

Quainton Hall School & Nursery
91 Hindes Road, Harrow,
Middlesex HA1 1RX
Tel: 020 8427 1304
Headmaster: E F Brown BEd, MA
Age range: B2.6–13 G2.6–11
Fees: Day £8250–£9150

Reddiford School
36-38 Cecil Park, Pinner,
Middlesex HA5 5HH
Tel: 020 8866 0660
Headteacher: Mrs J Batt CertEd, NPQH
Age range: 3–11
No. of pupils: 320 B194 G126
Fees: Day £3480–£8340

Regent College
Sai House, 167 Imperial Drive, Harrow,
Middlesex HA2 7HD
Tel: 020 8966 9900
Principal: Mr Selva Pankaj MBA, FCMA
Age range: 11–19
No. of pupils: 167 B103 G64
Fees: Day £2745–£12,995

Roxeth Mead School
Buckholt House, 25 Middle Road,
Harrow, Middlesex HA2 0HW
Tel: 020 8422 2092
Headmistress: Mrs A Isaacs
Age range: 3–7
No. of pupils: 57 B28 G29
Fees: Day £6970

Sefton Harrow Primary School
51 Sheepcote Road, Harrow,
Middlesex HA1 2JL
Tel: 020 84273876
Age range: 7–11
No. of pupils: B23 G16

ST CATHERINE'S SCHOOL
For further details see p. 84
Cross Deep, Twickenham,
Middlesex TW1 4QJ
Tel: 020 8891 2898
Email:
admissions@stcatherineschool.co.uk
Website: www.stcatherineschool.co.uk
Headmistress: Sister Paula Thomas
BEd(Hons), MA
Age range: 3–18
No. of pupils: 390
Fees: Day £8190–£11,460

St Christopher's School
71 Wembley Park Drive, Wembley,
Middlesex HA9 8HE
Tel: 020 8902 5069
Headteacher: Mrs Alison McNeill
Age range: 4–11
No. of pupils: 72 B45 G27
Fees: Day £2435–£2560

ST HELEN'S COLLEGE
For further details see p. 85
Parkway, Hillingdon, Uxbridge,
Middlesex UB10 9JX
Tel: 01895 234371
Email: info@sthelenscollege.com
Website: www.sthelenscollege.com
Joint Headteachers: Mr D A Crehan
ARCS, BA, BSc, MSc, CPhys & Mrs G R
Crehan BA, MA, PGCE
Age range: 3–11
No. of pupils: 351 B177 G174
Fees: Day £4725–£7785

ST HELEN'S SCHOOL
For further details see p. 86
Eastbury Road, Northwood,
Middlesex HA6 3AS
Tel: +44 (0)1923 843210
Email: enquiries@sthn.co.uk
Website: www.sthn.co.uk
Headmistress: Dr Mary Short BA, PhD
Age range: 3–18
No. of pupils: 1122 VIth155
Fees: Day £9516–£13,830

St John's School
Potter Street Hill, Northwood,
Middlesex HA6 3QY
Tel: 020 8866 0067
Headmaster: C R Kelly BA
Age range: 3–13
No. of pupils: 392
Fees: Day £7970–£11,750

St John's Senior School
North Lodge, The Ridgeway, Enfield,
Middlesex EN2 8BE
Tel: 020 8366 0035
Headmaster: Mr A Tardios LLB(Hons),
BA(Hons), CertEd
Age range: 11–18
No. of pupils: 238 B142 G96 VIth32
Fees: Day £9660

St Martin's School
40 Moor Park Road, Northwood,
Middlesex HA6 2DJ
Tel: 01923 825740
Headmaster: Mr D T Tidmarsh
BSc(Wales)
Age range: 3–13
No. of pupils: 400
Fees: Day £1450–£4066

STAINES PREPARATORY SCHOOL TRUST
For further details see p. 88
3 Gresham Road, Staines upon Thames,
Middlesex TW18 2BT
Tel: 01784 450909
Email: registrar@stainesprep.co.uk
Website: www.stainesprep.co.uk
Headmaster: Peter Roberts BSc
Age range: 3–11
No. of pupils: 342 B195 G147
Fees: Day £7950–£9150

Tashbar of Edgware
Yeshurun Federation Synagogue,
Fernhurst Gardens, Edgware,
Middlesex HA8 7PH
Tel: 020 8951 0239
Headteacher: Mr N Jaffe
Age range: 3–11
No. of pupils: 8

The Falcons Preparatory School for Boys
41 Few Foot Road, Richmond,
Middlesex TW9 2SS
Tel: 0844 225 2211
Headmaster: Mr A P Shawyer
Age range: 7–13
No. of pupils: 100
Fees: Day £12,660

The Hall Pre-Preparatory School
The Grange, Rickmansworth Road,
Northwood, Middlesex HA6 2RB
Tel: 01923 822807
Headmistress: Mrs D E Wesson
Age range: 2–7
No. of pupils: B35 G23
Fees: Day £1950–£5850

The John Lyon School
Middle Road, Harrow,
Middlesex HA2 0HN
Tel: 020 8872 8400
Head: Miss Katherine Haynes BA, MEd
Age range: 11–18
No. of pupils: 575 VIth150
Fees: Day £13,770

The Lady Eleanor Holles School
Hanworth Road, Hampton,
Middlesex TW12 3HF
Tel: 020 8979 1601
Head: Mrs Gillian Low MA(Oxon)
Age range: 7–18
No. of pupils: 875 VIth176
Fees: Day £11,460–£14,700

The Mall School
185 Hampton Road, Twickenham,
Middlesex TW2 5NQ
Tel: 020 8977 2523
Email: admissions@themallschool.org.uk
Website: www.themallschool.org.uk
Headmaster: Mr D C Price BSc, MA
Age range: 4–13
No. of pupils: 316
Fees: Day £9195–£10,680

The Noam Primary School
8-10 Forty Avenue, Wembley,
Middlesex HA9 8JW
Tel: 020 8908 9491
Headteacher: Mrs S Simmonds
Age range: 3–11
No. of pupils: 154

The St Michael Steiner School
Park Road, Hanworth, Feltham,
Middlesex TW13 6PN
Tel: 020 8870 0500
Age range: 3–15
No. of pupils: 101
Fees: Day £5800–£8900

Twickenham Preparatory School
Beveree, 43 High Street, Hampton,
Middlesex TW12 2SA
Tel: 020 8979 6216
Head: D Malam
BA(Hons)(Southampton),
PGCE(Winchester)
Age range: B4–13 G4–11
No. of pupils: 276 B153 G123
Fees: Day £8490–£9180

SURREY

Al-Khair School
109-117 Cherry Orchard Road, Croydon,
Surrey CR0 6BE
Tel: 020 8662 8664
Headteacher: Mr Usman Qureshi
Age range: 5–16
No. of pupils: 126 B86 G40

Broomfield House School
Broomfield Road, Kew Gardens,
Richmond, Surrey TW9 3HS
Tel: 020 8940 3884
Headteacher: Mr N O York BA(Hons),
MA, MPhil, FRSA
Age range: 3–11
No. of pupils: 160 B70 G90
Fees: Day £5054–£11,787

Cambridge Tutors College
Water Tower Hill, Croydon,
Surrey CR0 5SX
Tel: 020 8688 5284/7363
Principal: Mr M Di Clemente
Age range: 15–19
No. of pupils: 217 B113 G104 VIth208
Fees: Day £18,360

Canbury School
Kingston Hill, Kingston upon Thames,
Surrey KT2 7LN
Tel: 020 8549 8622
Headmaster: R F Metters BEd
Age range: 11–16
No. of pupils: 65 B48 G17
Fees: Day £13,320

Collingwood School
3 Springfield Road, Wallington,
Surrey SM6 0BD
Tel: 020 8647 4607
Headmaster: Mr Chris Fenwick
Age range: 3–11
No. of pupils: 120
Fees: Day £3600–£6750

Croydon High School GDST
Old Farleigh Road, Selsdon, South
Croydon, Surrey CR2 8YB
Tel: 020 8260 7500
Headmistress: Mrs Debbie Leonard MEd
Age range: 3–18
No. of pupils: 665 VIth90
Fees: Day £7578–£12,609

Cumnor House School
168 Pampisford Road, South Croydon,
Surrey CR2 6DA
Tel: 020 8660 3445
Head: Mr P J Clare-Hunt MA, CertEd
Age range: B2–13 G2–4
No. of pupils: 414 B409 G5
Fees: Day £2680–£3460

Cumnor House School for Girls
1 Woodcote Lane, Purley,
Surrey CR8 3HB
Tel: 020 8660 3445
Headmaster: Mr Peter Kelly
Age range: B2–4 G2–11
Fees: Day £2680–£3460

Educare Small School
12 Cowleaze Road, Kingston upon
Thames, Surrey KT2 6DZ
Tel: 020 8547 0144
Head: Mrs E Steinthal
Age range: 3–11
No. of pupils: 32 B18 G14
Fees: Day £3900

Elmhurst School
44-48 South Park Hill Rd, South
Croydon, Surrey CR2 7DW
Tel: 020 8688 0661
Headmaster: Mr M J Apsley BA(Hons),
PGCE
Age range: 4–11
No. of pupils: 207
Fees: Day £6300–£7545

Folly's End Christian School

Folly's End Church, 5-9 Surrey Street,
Croydon, Surrey CR0 1RG
Tel: 020 8649 9121
Senior Leaders: Dave & Ze Markee
Age range: 3–11
No. of pupils: B27 G26
Fees: Day £4740

Holy Cross Preparatory School

George Road, Kingston upon Thames,
Surrey KT2 7NU
Tel: 020 8942 0729
Headteacher: Mrs S Hair BEd(Hons)
Age range: 4–11
No. of pupils: 250
Fees: Day £9960

HOMEFIELD SCHOOL

For further details see p. 80
Western Road, Sutton, Surrey SM1 2TE
Tel: 020 8642 0965
Email: administration@homefield.sutton.sch.uk
Website: www.homefield.sutton.sch.uk
Headteacher: Mr P R Mowbray MA(Cantab)
Age range: 3–13
No. of pupils: 400
Fees: Day £4290–£9975

Kew College

24-26 Cumberland Road, Kew,
Surrey TW9 3HQ
Tel: 020 8940 2039
Headmistress: Mrs Anne Dobell MA(Oxon), PGCE
Age range: 3–11
No. of pupils: B123 G137
Fees: Day £4275–£8025

Kew Green Preparatory School

Layton House, Ferry Lane, Kew Green,
Richmond, Surrey TW9 3AF
Tel: 020 8948 5999
Headmaster: Mr J Peck
Age range: 4–11
No. of pupils: 260 B130 G130
Fees: Day £13,305

KING'S HOUSE SCHOOL

For further details see p. 81
68 King's Road, Richmond,
Surrey TW10 6ES
Tel: 020 8940 1878
Email: schooloffice@kingshouseschool.org
Website: www.kingshouseschool.org
Head: Mr Mark Turner BA PGCE NPQH
Age range: B3–13 G3–4
No. of pupils: 450 B430 G20
Fees: Day £1750–£4250

Kingston Grammar School

70 London Road, Kingston upon
Thames, Surrey KT2 6PY
Tel: 020 8546 5875
Head: Mrs S K Fletcher MA(Oxon)
Age range: 11–18
No. of pupils: 812 B459 G353 VIth121
Fees: Day £14,835–£14,835

Laleham Lea School

29 Peaks Hill, Purley, Surrey CR8 3JJ
Tel: 020 8660 3351
Headteacher: Mrs J Staunton
Age range: 3–11
No. of pupils: 70 B35 G35
Fees: Day £2128–£6405

Linley House

6 Berrylands Road, Surbiton,
Surrey KT5 8RA
Tel: 020 8399 4979
Principal: Mrs S M Mallin CertEd(Bristol)
Age range: 3–7
No. of pupils: 32 B18 G14
Fees: Day £3528–£7149

Marymount International School London

George Road, Kingston upon Thames,
Surrey KT2 7PE
Tel: +44 (0)20 8949 0571
Headmistress: Ms Sarah Gallagher MA, HDip in Ed
Age range: 11–18
No. of pupils: 240 VIth50
Fees: Day £17,050–£19,480
WB £28,950–£31,380
FB £30,340–£32,770

New Life Christian Primary School

Cairo New Road, Croydon,
Surrey CR0 1XP
Tel: 020 8680 7671 ext 327
Headteacher: Mrs S Kehinde
Age range: 4–11
No. of pupils: B63 G45
Fees: Day £4032

£

NZO Academy of London & Surrey

121 Lombard House, Lombard Business
Park, 2 Purley Way, Croydon,
Surrey CR0 3JP
Tel: 020 8648 2020
Headteacher: Mr Horace Amkrah
Age range: 14–16
No. of pupils: 6

Oakwood Independent School

Godstone Road, Purley, Surrey CR8 2AN
Tel: 020 8668 8080
Headmaster: Mr Ciro Candia BA(Hons), PGCE
Age range: 2–11
No. of pupils: 188 B83 G105
Fees: Day £4314–£6870

£ (IAPS)

Old Palace of John Whitgift School

Old Palace Road, Croydon,
Surrey CR0 1AX
Tel: 020 8688 2027
Head: Dr J Harris
Age range: B3 months–4 years G3 months–19 years
No. of pupils: 850 VIth160
Fees: Day £6846–£9159

Old Vicarage School

48 Richmond Hill, Richmond,
Surrey TW10 6QX
Tel: 020 8940 0922
Headmistress: Mrs G D Linthwaite
Age range: 4–11
No. of pupils: 180
Fees: Day £6030–£6690

Park Hill School

8 Queens Road, Kingston upon Thames,
Surrey KT2 7SH
Tel: 020 8546 5496
Principal: Mrs Marie Christie
Age range: 2½–7
No. of pupils: 100 B40 G60
Fees: Day £4320–£8130

Reedham Park School

71A Old Lodge Lane, Purley,
Surrey CR8 4DN
Tel: 020 8660 6357
Headteacher: Ms L Shaw BA(Hons), DipEurHum
Age range: 4–11
No. of pupils: 105 B55 G50
Fees: Day £2460–£2850

ROKEBY SCHOOL

For further details see p. 83
George Road, Kingston upon Thames,
Surrey KT2 7PB
Tel: 020 8942 2247
Email: hmsec@rokeby.org.uk
Website: www.rokebyschool.co.uk
Head: J R Peck
Age range: 4–13
No. of pupils: 370
Fees: Day £9387–£13,659

Royal Russell Junior School

Coombe Lane, Croydon, Surrey CR9 5BX
Tel: 020 8651 5884
Junior School Headmaster: Mr James C Thompson
Age range: 3–11
No. of pupils: 300 B170 G130
Fees: Day £3660–£10,155

Royal Russell School
Coombe Lane, Croydon, Surrey CR9 5BX
Tel: 020 8657 3669
Headmaster: Christopher Hutchinson
Age range: 11–18
No. of pupils: 590 B310 G280 VIth180
Fees: Day £13,740 FB £20,100–£27,180

Seaton House School
67 Banstead Road South, Sutton,
Surrey SM2 5LH
Tel: 020 8642 2332
Headmistress: Mrs V Rickus MA, BEd
Age range: B3–5 G3–11
No. of pupils: 155 B3 G152
Fees: Day £3240–£8118

Shrewsbury House School
107 Ditton Road, Surbiton,
Surrey KT6 6RL
Tel: 020 8399 3066
Headmaster: Mr K Doble BA, PDM, PGCE
Age range: 7–13
No. of pupils: 320
Fees: Day £13,680

St David's School
23/25 Woodcote Valley Road, Purley,
Surrey CR8 3AL
Tel: 020 8660 0723
Headmistress: Mrs Lindsay Nash
BEd(Hons)
Age range: 3–11
No. of pupils: 167 B84 G83
Fees: Day £2985–£5940

ST JAMES SENIOR BOYS SCHOOL
For further details see p. 87
Church Road, Ashford, Surrey TW15 3DZ
Tel: 01784 266930
Email: admissions@stjamesboys.co.uk
Website: www.stjamesboys.co.uk
Headmaster: Mr David Boddy
Age range: 11–18
No. of pupils: 380 VIth65
Fees: Day £12,660 WB £5400

Surbiton High School
13-15 Surbiton Crescent, Kingston upon
Thames, Surrey KT1 2JT
Tel: 020 8546 5245
Principal: Ann Haydon BSc(Hons)
Age range: 4–18
No. of pupils: 1210 B135 G1075 VIth186
Fees: Day £6390–£10,857

Sutton High School GDST
55 Cheam Road, Sutton,
Surrey SM1 2AX
Tel: 020 8642 0594
Headteacher: Mr Stephen Callaghan
Age range: 3–18
No. of pupils: 766 G766 VIth106
Fees: Day £6285–£10,470

The Royal Ballet School
White Lodge, Richmond,
Surrey TW10 5HR
Tel: 020 7836 8899
Director: Ms Gailene Stock AM
Age range: 11–19
No. of pupils: B54 G68 VIth80
Fees: Day £14,394–£18,946
FB £17,709–£25,588

The Study School
57 Thetford Road, New Malden,
Surrey KT3 5DP
Tel: 020 8942 0754
Head Teacher: Miss Joanne Knight
Age range: 3–11
No. of pupils: 134 B78 G56
Fees: Day £3984–£8973

Trinity School
Shirley Park, Croydon, Surrey CR9 7AT
Tel: 020 8656 9541
Headmaster: M J Bishop MA, MBA
Age range: 10–18
No. of pupils: 890 B830 G65 VIth220
Fees: Day £12,462

Unicorn School
238 Kew Road, Richmond,
Surrey TW9 3JX
Tel: 020 8948 3926
Headmistress: Mrs Roberta Linehan
Age range: 3–11
No. of pupils: 169 B83 G86
Fees: Day £5685–£10,425

Westbury House
80 Westbury Road, New Malden,
Surrey KT3 5AS
Tel: 020 8942 5885
Principal: Mrs M T Morton CertEd
Age range: 3–11
No. of pupils: B80 G75
Fees: Day £1045–£2507

Whitgift School
Haling Park, South Croydon,
Surrey CR2 6YT
Tel: +44 (0)20 8688 9222
Headmaster: Dr Christopher Barnett
Age range: 10–18
No. of pupils: 1300
Fees: Day £14,424

Wick School
25A Hardman Road, Kingston upon
Thames, Surrey KT2 6RH
Tel: 020 8123 4815
Headmistress: Mrs J Evans
Age range: 6–18
No. of pupils: 310

LONDON

CENTRAL LONDON

CATS College
53-55 Bloomsbury Square,
London WC1A 2RA
Tel: 01223 778129
Director: Dr Glenn Hawkins
Age range: 15–20
Fees: Day £15,800 FB £23,310

CITY OF LONDON SCHOOL
For further details see p. 91
Queen Victoria Street, London EC4V 3AL
Tel: 020 7489 0291
Email: admissions@clsb.org.uk
Website: www.clsb.org.uk
Headmaster: Mr D Levin MA
Age range: 10–18
No. of pupils: 920 VIth250
Fees: Day £13,401

City of London School for Girls
St Giles' Terrace, Barbican,
London EC2Y 8BB
Tel: 020 7847 5500
Headmistress: Miss D Vernon
Age range: 7–18
No. of pupils: 710
Fees: Day £13,527

Dallington School
8 Dallington Street, Islington,
London EC1V 0BQ
Tel: 020 7251 2284
Headteacher: Mrs M C Hercules
Age range: 3–11
No. of pupils: 140 B70 G70
Fees: Day £8000–£10,200

HULT-International Business School
46-47 Russell Square, Bloomsbury,
London WC1B 4JP
Tel: 020 7584 9696
Provost: Mr Ray Hilditch BA, MBA, PGCE,
FRSA
Age range: 17–60
No. of pupils: 300 B130 G170
Fees: Day £4000 FB £10,260

Italia Conti Academy of Theatre Arts
Italia Conti House, 23 Goswell Road,
London EC1M 7AJ
Tel: 020 7608 0047
Principal: Anne Sheward
Age range: 10–21

ST PAUL'S CATHEDRAL SCHOOL
For further details see p. 107
2 New Change, London EC4M 9AD
Tel: 020 7248 5156
Email: admissions@spcs.london.sch.uk
Website: www.spcslondon.com
Headmaster: Mr Neil Chippington MA,
FRCO
Age range: 4–13
No. of pupils: 250 B163 G87
Fees: Day £11,550–£12,435 FB £7194

The Charterhouse Square School
40 Charterhouse Square,
London EC1M 6EA
Tel: 020 7600 3805
Head Mistress: Mrs J Malden MA,
BEd(Hons)
Age range: 4–11
No. of pupils: B90 G80
Fees: Day £8250

The College of Central London
73 Great Eastern Street,
London EC2A 3HR
Tel: 020 7739 5555
Director of Studies: Barry Culverwell
Fees: Day £3300

The Lyceum
Kayham House, 6 Paul Street,
London EC2A 4JH
Tel: 020 7247 1588
Joint Headteachers: Mr Jeremy Rowe &
Mrs Lynn Hannay
Age range: 4–11
No. of pupils: 100 B50 G50
Fees: Day £10,500

The Urdang Academy of Ballet
20-22 Shelton Street, Covent Garden,
London WC2H 9JJ
Tel: 0207 713 7710
Principal: Mrs J Crowther BA(Hons)
Age range: 10–16
No. of pupils: B3 G20
Fees: Day £6600

EAST LONDON

Al-Falah Primary School
48 Kenninghall Road, Clapton,
London E5 8BY
Tel: 020 8985 1059
Headteacher: Mr Khalil Goddard
Age range: 5–11
No. of pupils: 83 B53 G30
Fees: Day £1600

Al-Mizan School
46 Whitechapel Road, London E1 1JX
Tel: 020 7650 3070
Head: Mr Musleh Faradhi
Age range: 7–18
No. of pupils: 200 VIth13
Fees: Day £2400

Azhar Academy
235A Romford Road, Forest Gate,
London E7 9HL
Tel: 020 8534 5959
Headteacher: Mrs R Rehman
Age range: 11–16
No. of pupils: 189

Key to symbols

(Boys) Boys' school

(Girls) Girls' school

(International) International school

(16) Tutorial or sixth form college

(A) A levels

(Boarding) Boarding accommodation

(£) Bursaries

(IB) International Baccalaureate

(Learning) Learning support

(16) Entrance at 16+

(Vocational) Vocational qualifications

(IAPS) Member of Independent Association of Preparatory Schools

(HMC) The Headmasters' & Headmistresses' Conference

(ISA) Independent Schools Association

(GSA) Girls' School Association

(BSA) Boarding Schools' Association

(S) SHMIS

Unless otherwise indicated, all schools are coeducational day schools. Single-sex and boarding schools will be indicated by the relevant icon.

Faraday School
Trinity Buoy Wharf, 64 Orchard Place,
London E14 0JW
Tel: 020 8965 7374
Head Teacher: Mr M McElhone
Age range: 4–11
Fees: Day £6480

Forest School
College Place, Snaresbrook,
London E17 3PY
Tel: 020 8520 1744
Warden: Mrs S J Kerr-Dineen MA
Age range: 4–18
No. of pupils: 1232 B617 G615 VIth250
Fees: Day £9435–£13,950

Gatehouse School
Sewardstone Road, Victoria Park,
London E2 9JG
Tel: 020 8980 2978
Headmistress: Mrs Belinda Canham JP,
BA(Hons), PGCE(Froebel)
Age range: 3–11
No. of pupils: 320 B158 G162
Fees: Day £6920–£8502

Grangewood Independent School
Chester Road, Forest Gate,
London E7 8QT
Tel: 020 8472 3552
Headteacher: Mrs C A Adams
Age range: 3–11
No. of pupils: 75

Green Gables Montessori Primary School
The Institute, 302 The Highway,
Wapping, London E1W 3DH
Tel: 020 7488 2374
Head: Mrs V Hunt
Age range: 0–8
No. of pupils: 45 B25 G20
Fees: Day £740–£10,480

Hyland House School
896 Forest Road, Walthamstow,
London E17 4AE
Tel: 020 8520 4186
Headmistress: Mrs T Thorpe
Age range: 3–11
No. of pupils: B50 G52
Fees: Day £2520

London East Academy
46-80 Whitechapel Road, London E1 1JX
Tel: 020 7650 3070
Headteacher: Musleh Faradhi
Age range: 11–18
No. of pupils: B151 VIth18
Fees: Day £3000

Lubavitch House School (Junior Boys)
135 Clapton Common, London E5 9AE
Tel: 020 8800 1044
Head: Rabbi D Golomb
Age range: 5–11
No. of pupils: 101
Fees: Day £520–£3100

Madani Girls School
Myrdle Street, London E1 1HL
Tel: 020 7377 1992
Headteacher: Mrs F Liyawdeen
Age range: 11–18
No. of pupils: 248 VIth11
Fees: Day £1900

Normanhurst School
68-74 Station Road, Chingford,
London E4 7BA
Tel: 020 8529 4307
Headmistress: Mrs Claire Osborn
Age range: 2½–16
No. of pupils: 250 B146 G104
Fees: Day £7470–£11,235

Paragon Christian Academy
233-241 Glyn Road, London E5 0JP
Tel: 020 8985 1119
Headteacher: Mrs J A Lynch
Age range: 5–16
No. of pupils: 34 B19 G15

Pillar Box Montessori Nursery & Pre-Prep School
107 Bow Road, London E3 2AN
Tel: 020 8980 0700
Headmistress: Ms Lorraine Redknapp
Age range: 0–7
Fees: Day £250–£500

Promised Land Academy
St Cedds Hall, Webb Gardens, Plaistow,
London E13 8SR
Tel: 020 84713939
Head: Mr A Coote
Age range: 4–16

Quwwat-ul Islam Girls School
16 Chaucer Road, Forest Gate,
London E7 9NB
Tel: 020 8548 4736
Headteacher: Mrs B Khan
Age range: 4–11
No. of pupils: 150

River House Montessori School
3-4 Shadwell Pierhead, Glamis Road,
London E1W 3TD
Tel: 020 7538 9886
Headmistress: Miss S Greenwood
Age range: 3–12
No. of pupils: B55 G45
Fees: Day £2700–£9000

Snaresbrook College
75 Woodford Road, South Woodford,
London E18 2EA
Tel: 020 8989 2394
Head Mistress: Mrs L J Chiverrell CertEd
Age range: 3–11
No. of pupils: 164 B84 G80
Fees: Day £6696–£8952

St Joseph's Convent School For Girls
59 Cambridge Park, Wanstead,
London E11 2PR
Tel: 020 8989 4700
Headteacher: Ms C Glover
Age range: 3–11
No. of pupils: 171
Fees: Day £5355

Talmud Torah Machikei Hadass School
96-98 Clapton Common, London E5 9AL
Tel: 020 8800 6599
Headteacher: Rabbi C Silbiger
Age range: 4–11
No. of pupils: 271

Winston House Preparatory School
140 High Road, London E18 2QS
Tel: 020 8505 6565
Head Teacher: Mrs Marian Kemp
Age range: 3–11
Fees: Day £5850–£7050

NORTH LONDON

Annemount School
18 Holne Chase, Hampstead Garden
Suburb, London N2 0QN
Tel: 020 8455 2132
Principal: Mrs G Maidment BA(Hons),
MontDip
Age range: 2–7
No. of pupils: 100
Fees: Day £2375–£4250

Avenue Nursery & Pre-Preparatory School
2 Highgate Avenue, London N6 5RX
Tel: 020 8348 6815
Headteacher: Mrs Mary Fysh
Age range: 2½–7
No. of pupils: 79 B37 G42

Beehive School
Ground Floor, Arkansas House, New
Orleans Walk, London N19 3SZ
Tel: 020 7686 7514
Head: Mr Paul Kelly
Age range: 3–11
No. of pupils: 34

Beis Aharon School
97-99 Bethune Road, London N16 5ED
Tel: 020 88007 368
Head: Y Pomerantz
Age range: 2–12
No. of pupils: 177

Beis Chinuch Lebonos Girls School
Woodberry Down Centre, Woodberry Down, London N4 2SH
Tel: 020 8807 737
Headmistress: Mrs Bertha Schneck
Age range: 2–16
No. of pupils: 421

Beis Malka Girls School
93 Alkham Road, London N16 6XD
Tel: 020 8806 2070
Headmaster: M Dresdner
Age range: 5–16
No. of pupils: 339

Beis Rochel D'Satmar Girls School
51-57 Amhurst Park, London N16 5DL
Tel: 020 8800 9060
Headmistress: Mrs A Scher
Age range: 2–17
No. of pupils: 788

Beis Trana Girls' School
21 Northfield Road, London N16 5RL
Tel: 020 8809 7737
Age range: 2–13

Bnois Jerusalem School
79-81 Amhurst Park, London N16 5DL
Tel: 020 8802 7470
Head: Mrs Sonnenschein
Age range: 3–16

Channing School
Highgate, London N6 5HF
Tel: 020 8340 2328
Head: Mrs B Elliott MA(Cantab)
Age range: 4–18
No. of pupils: 638 VIth88
Fees: Day £12,375–£13,395

DWIGHT SCHOOL LONDON
For further details see p. 94
6 Friern Barnet Lane, London N11 3LX
Tel: +44 (0)20 8920 0600
Email: admissions@nlis.org
Website: www.dwightlondon.org
Head: Mr David Rose MA(Ed), BA, CertEd, FRSA
Age range: 2–18
No. of pupils: 356
Fees: Day £3390–£16,290 FB £10,000

Excel Preparatory School
The Annex, Selby Centre, Off Whitehart Lane, Tottenham, London N17 8JL
Tel: 020 8493 8906
Head: Mrs M Jean-Marie
Age range: 1–13
No. of pupils: 23 B14 G9

Finchley & Acton Yochien School
6 Hendon Avenue, Finchley, London N3 1UE
Tel: 020 8343 2191
Headteacher: Mr Katsumasa Kitagaki
Age range: 2–6
No. of pupils: 145 B72 G73

Getters Talmud Torah
86 Amhurst Park, London N16 5AR
Tel: 020 8802 2512
Headteacher: Mr David Kahana
Age range: 4–11
No. of pupils: 171

Grange Park Preparatory School
13 The Chine, Grange Park, Winchmore Hill, London N21 2EA
Tel: 020 8360 1469
Headteacher: Mrs B McLaughlin
Age range: 4–11
No. of pupils: 95
Fees: Day £8340

Greek Secondary School of London
Avenue Lodge, Bounds Green Road, London N22 7EU
Tel: 020 8881 9320
Age range: 13–18
No. of pupils: 200

Highgate Junior School
Cholmeley House, 3 Bishopswood Road, London N6 4PL
Tel: 020 8340 9193
Principal: Mr S M James BA
Age range: 7–11
No. of pupils: B388 G223
Fees: Day £10,695–£11,955

Highgate Pre-Preparatory School
7 Bishopswood Road, London N6 4PH
Tel: 020 8340 9196
Principal: Mrs Diane Hecht
Age range: 3½–7

HIGHGATE SCHOOL
For further details see p. 99
North Road, Highgate, London N6 4AY
Tel: 020 8340 1524
Email: office@highgateschool.org.uk
Website: www.highgateschool.org.uk
Head Master: Mr A S Pettitt MA
Age range: 3–18
No. of pupils: 1492 B827 G665 VIth305
Fees: Day £14,565–£16,815

Holly Park Montessori School
The Holly Park Methodist Church Hall, Crouch Hill, London N4 4BY
Tel: 020 7263 6563
Headmistress: Mrs A Lake AMI Montessori Dip, BEd(Hons)
Age range: 2–7
No. of pupils: 60 B30 G30
Fees: Day £1400–£2320

Keble Preparatory School
Wades Hill, London N21 1BG
Tel: 020 8360 3359
Headmaster: Mr G McCarthy
Age range: 4–13
No. of pupils: B200
Fees: Day £9390–£11,670

Lubavitch House School (Senior Girls)
107-115 Stamford Hill, Hackney, London N16 5RP
Tel: 020 8800 0022
Headmaster: Rabbi Shmuel Lew FRSA
Age range: 11–17
No. of pupils: 102
Fees: Day £3900

Montessori House
5 Princes Avenue, Muswell Hill, London N10 3LS
Tel: 020 8444 4399
Head: Ms Lisa Christoforou
Age range: 6 months–7 years
No. of pupils: 100 B50 G50
Fees: Day £5355–£9450

Mustard School
Parish Hall, Nuttall Street, London N1 5LR
Tel: 020 7739 3499
Headteacher: Mr A F Johnson
Age range: 3–18
No. of pupils: 47 B32 G15 VIth3
Fees: Day £3060

Norfolk House School
10 Muswell Avenue, Muswell Hill, London N10 2EG
Tel: 020 8883 4584
Head Teacher: Ms Sam Habgood
Age range: 4–11
No. of pupils: 130 B65 G65
Fees: Day £9855

North London Muslim School
131-133 Fore Street, Edmonton, London N18 2XF
Tel: 020 8345 7008
Headteacher: Mr W Abdulla
Age range: 4–10
No. of pupils: 21 B14 G7

North London Rudolf Steiner School
1-3 The Campsbourne, London N8 7PN
Tel: 020 8341 3770
Age range: 2½–7
No. of pupils: 40 B20 G20

Palmers Green High School
Hoppers Road, Winchmore Hill,
London N21 3LJ
Tel: 020 8886 1135
Headmistress: Mrs Christine Edmundson
BMus(Hons), MBA, PGCE, LRAM, ARCM
Age range: 3–16
No. of pupils: 300
Fees: Day £5985–£10,785

Pardes House Grammar School
Hendon Lane, Finchley, London N3 1SA
Tel: 020 8349 4222
Headteacher: Rabbi D Dunner
Age range: 10–16
No. of pupils: 222

Phoenix Academy
85 Bounces Road, Edmonton,
London N9 8LD
Tel: 020 8887 6888
Headteacher: Mr A Hawkes
Age range: 11–16
No. of pupils: 19 B9 G10

Rosemary Works Independent School
1 Branch Place, London N1 5PH
Tel: 020 7739 3950
Head: Dorothy Davey
Age range: 3–11
No. of pupils: 104 B60 G44
Fees: Day £6195

Salcombe Preparatory School
Green Road, Southgate, London N14 4PL
Tel: 020 8441 5282
Headmaster: Mr B Curzon
Age range: 4–11
No. of pupils: 236 B140 G96
Fees: Day £7890

St Paul's Steiner School
1 St Paul's Road, Islington,
London N1 2QH
Tel: 020 7226 4454
College of Teachers: College of Teachers
Age range: 2–14
No. of pupils: 136 B69 G67

Sunrise Day Nursery
1 Cazenove Road, Hackney,
London N16 6PA
Tel: 020 8806 6279/8885 3354
Principal: Didi Ananda Manika
Age range: 2–11
No. of pupils: 50
Fees: Day £3900–£4976

Sunrise Primary School
55 Coniston Road, Tottenham,
London N17 0EX
Tel: 020 8806 6279 (Office); 020 8885
3354 (School)
Head: Mrs Mary-Anne Lovage
MontDipEd, BA
Age range: 2–11
No. of pupils: 30 B15 G15
Fees: Day £3900

Talmud Torah Bobov Primary School
87 Egerton Road, London N16 6UE
Tel: 020 8809 1025
Headteacher: Rabbi A Just
Age range: 3–13
No. of pupils: 320 B302 G18

Talmud Torah Chaim Meirim School
26 Lampard Grove, London N16 6XB
Tel: 020 8806 0898
Principal: Rabbi S Hoffman
Age range: 6–13

Talmud Torah School
122 Bethune Road, London N16 5DU
Tel: 020 8802 2512
Age range: 3–11
No. of pupils: 60

Talmud Torah Yetev Lev School
111-115 Cazenove Road, London N16 6AX
Tel: 020 8806 3834
Headteacher: Mr J Stauber
Age range: 2–11
No. of pupils: 567

Tawhid Boys School
21 Cazenove Road, London N16 6PA
Tel: 020 8806 2999
Headteacher: Mr Usman Mapara
Age range: 10–15
No. of pupils: 115
Fees: Day £2000

Tayyibah Girls School
88 Filey Avenue, Stamford Hill,
London N16 6JJ
Tel: 020 8880 0085
Headmistress: Mrs N B Qureishi MSc
Age range: 5–15
No. of pupils: 270
Fees: Day £1630

The Children's House Upper School
King Henry's Walk, London N1 4PB
Tel: 020 7249 6273
Headteacher: Mrs J Rothwell
Age range: 4–7
No. of pupils: 60 B29 G31
Fees: Day £3250

The Gower School
Montessori Primary School, 10 Cynthia
Street, Barnsbury, London N1 9JF
Tel: 020 7278 2020
Principal: Emma Gowers
Age range: 4–11

The Kerem School
Norrice Lea, London N2 0RE
Tel: 020 8455 0909
Headteacher: Mr Richard Felsenstein
Age range: 3–11
No. of pupils: B125 G114
Fees: Day £8250–£6675

TTTYY School
14 Heathland Road, London N16 5NH
Tel: 020 8802 1348
Headmaster: Mr S B Gluck
Age range: 2–13
No. of pupils: 187

Vita et Pax School
Priory Close, Southgate,
London N14 4AT
Tel: 020 8449 8336
Headmistress: Mrs M O'Connor
BEd(Hons)
Age range: 3–11
No. of pupils: B90 G84
Fees: Day £6150

Wellgrove School
4 Well Grove, Whetstone,
London N20 9EQ
Tel: 020 84468855
Headteacher: Mr W Jones
Age range: 11–16
No. of pupils: 75 B32 G43

Wisdom Secondary School
336 Philip Lane, London N15 4AB
Tel: 020 8880 9070
Headteacher: Ramazan G̦veli BA, MSc
Age range: 11–16
Fees: Day £4400–£5400

Yesodey Hatorah School
2-4 Amhurst Park, London N16 5AE
Tel: 020 8826 5500
Headteacher: Rabbi Pinter
Age range: 3–16
No. of pupils: 920 B249 G671

NORTH-WEST LONDON

Abercorn School
Infant Department, 28 Abercorn Place,
London NW8 9XP
Tel: 020 7286 4785
High Mistress: Mrs Andrea Greystoke
BA(Hons)
Age range: 2½–13½
No. of pupils: 360 B180 G180
Fees: Day £7245–£13,425

Al-Sadiq & Al-Zahra Schools
134 Salusbury Road, London NW6 6PF
Tel: 020 7372 7706
Headteacher: Dr M Movahedi
Age range: 4–16
No. of pupils: 389 B185 G204

Arnold House School
1 Loudoun Road, St John's Wood,
London NW8 0LH
Tel: 020 7266 4840
Headmaster: Mr Vivian Thomas
Age range: 5–13
No. of pupils: 250
Fees: Day £5300

Ayesha Community Education
133 West Hendon, Broadway,
London NW9 7DY
Tel: 0208 203 8446
Headteacher: Mrs Sadiya Hadadi
Age range: 4–18
No. of pupils: B30 G220 VIth16
Fees: Day £3000

Beis Hamedrash Elyon
211 Golders Green Road,
London NW11 9BY
Tel: 020 8201 8668
Headteacher: Mr C Steinhart
Age range: 11–14
No. of pupils: 45

Beis Soroh Schneirer
Arbiter House, Wilberforce Road,
London NW9 6AT
Tel: 020 8343 1190
Head: Mrs R Weiss
Age range: 2–11
No. of pupils: 150

Belmont, Mill Hill Preparatory School
The Ridgeway, London NW7 4ED
Tel: 020 8906 7270
Head: Mrs L C Duncan BSc, PGCE
Age range: 7–13
No. of pupils: 407 B238 G169
Fees: Day £14,205

Beth Jacob Grammar School for Girls
Stratford Road, Hendon,
London NW4 2AT
Tel: 020 8203 4322
Headteacher: Mrs D Steinberg
Age range: 11–17
No. of pupils: 264

Brampton College
Lodge House, Lodge Road, Hendon,
London NW4 4DQ
Tel: 020 8203 5025
Principal: Bernard Canetti BA(Hons),
MSc
Age range: 16–18
No. of pupils: 250

Brondesbury College for Boys
8 Brondesbury Park, London NW6 7BT
Tel: 020 8830 4522
Headteacher: Mr Dan Salahuddin Clifton
Age range: 11–16
No. of pupils: 93

Chalcot Montessori School AMI
9 Chalcot Gardens, London NW3 4YB
Tel: 020 7722 1386
Principal: Ms Joanna Morfey AMI Dip
Age range: 2–6
No. of pupils: 24 B12 G12
Fees: Day £6450–£6750

DEVONSHIRE HOUSE PREPARATORY SCHOOL
For further details see p. 92
2 Arkwright Road, Hampstead,
London NW3 6AE
Tel: 020 7435 1916
Email: enquiries@devonshirehouseprep-school.co.uk
Website:
www.devonshirehouseschool.co.uk
Headmistress: Mrs S Piper BA(Hons)
Age range: B2½–13 G2½–11
No. of pupils: 600 B324 G276
Fees: Day £7650–£14,000

Fine Arts College, Hampstead
24 Lambolle Place, Belsize Park,
London NW3 4PG
Tel: 020 7586 0312
Co Principals: Candida Cave CFA(Oxon)
& Nicholas Cochrane CFA(Oxon)
Age range: 13–19
No. of pupils: 115
Fees: Day £6000–£15,600

FRANCIS HOLLAND SCHOOL, REGENT'S PARK, NW1
For further details see p. 96
Clarence Gate, Ivor Place, Regent's Park,
London NW1 6XR
Tel: 020 7723 0176
Email: registrar@fhs-nw1.org.uk
Website: www.francisholland.org.uk
Head: Mrs Vivienne Durham MA(Oxon)
Age range: 11–18
No. of pupils: 450 VIth120
Fees: Day £15,000

Golders Hill School
666 Finchley Road, London NW11 7NT
Tel: 020 8455 2589
Headmistress: Mrs A T Eglash BA(Hons)
Age range: 2–7
No. of pupils: 180 B100 G80
Fees: Day £831–£6870

Goodwyn School
Hammers Lane, Mill Hill,
London NW7 4DB
Tel: 020 8959 3756
Principal: Struan Robertson
Age range: 3–11
No. of pupils: 223 B104 G119
Fees: Day £3645–£7673

Gower House School & Nursery
Blackbird Hill, London NW9 8RR
Tel: 020 8205 2509
Headmaster: Mr M Keane
Age range: 2–11
No. of pupils: 200 B110 G90
Fees: Day £5010–£5835

Grimsdell, Mill Hill Pre-Preparatory School
Winterstoke House, Wills Grove, Mill
Hill, London NW7 1QR
Tel: 020 8959 6884
Head: Mrs Pauline E R Bennett-Mills
CertEd
Age range: 3–7
No. of pupils: 182 B105 G77
Fees: Day £1793–£3897

Hampstead Hill Pre-Prep & Nursery School
St Stephen's Hall, Pond Street,
Hampstead, London NW3 2PP
Tel: 020 7435 6262
Principal: Mrs Andrea Taylor
Age range: B2–7+ G2–7+
No. of pupils: B200 G150
Fees: Day £11,000–£14,000

Heathside Preparatory School
16 New End, Hampstead,
London NW3 1JA
Tel: 020 7794 5857
Heads: Ms Melissa Remus MA & Ms Jill
White MA
Age range: 2–11
No. of pupils: B113 G118
Fees: Day £9000–£10,800

Hendon Preparatory School
20 Tenterden Grove, Hendon,
London NW4 1TD
Tel: 020 8203 7727
Headmaster: Mr David Baldwin
Age range: 2–13
No. of pupils: B170 G81
Fees: Day £7650–£9945

Hereward House School
14 Strathray Gardens, London NW3 4NY
Tel: 020 7794 4820
Headmaster: Mr T W Burden
Age range: 4–13
No. of pupils: B170
Fees: Day £11,250–£13,050

International Community School
4 York Terrace East, Regents Park,
London NW1 4PT
Tel: +44 20 7935 1206
Head of School: Mr Philip D M Hurd
Age range: 3–18
No. of pupils: 260 B140 G120 VIth30
Fees: Day £14,100–£19,275

Islamia Girls' High School
129 Salusbury Road, London NW6 6PE
Tel: 020 7372 3472
Headteacher: Miss Asmat Ali
Age range: 11–16
No. of pupils: 120
Fees: Day £6100

L'Ile Aux Enfants
22 Vicar's Road, London NW5 4NL
Tel: 020 7267 7119
Headmistress: Mrs Chailleux
Age range: 3–11
No. of pupils: 192
Fees: Day £3270

London Jewish Girls' High School
18 Raleigh Close, Hendon,
London NW4 2TA
Tel: 020 8203 8618
Headteacher: Mr Joel Rabinowitz
Age range: 11–16

LYNDHURST HOUSE PREP SCHOOL
For further details see p. 102
24 Lyndhurst Gardens, Hampstead,
London NW3 5NW
Tel: 020 7435 4936
Email: pmg@lyndhursthouse.co.uk
Website: www.lyndhursthouse.co.uk
Headmaster: Andrew Reid MA(Oxon)
Age range: 4–13
No. of pupils: 165
Fees: Day £14,460–£16,110

Maple Walk School
62A Crownhill Road, London NW10 4EB
Tel: 020 8963 3890
Headteacher: Sarah Knollys
Age range: 4–11
Fees: Day £6300

Maria Montessori Institute
26 Lyndhurst Gardens, Hampstead,
London NW3 5NW
Tel: 020 7435 3646
Director of Training & School: Mrs Lynne
Lawrence BA, Mont Int Dip(AMI)
Age range: 18+
No. of pupils: 50
Fees: Day £7100

Maria Montessori School - Hampstead
26 Lyndhurst Gardens,
London NW3 5NW
Tel: 020 7435 3646
Director of School: Mrs L Lawrence
Age range: 2½–11
No. of pupils: 60 B30 G30
Fees: Day £5400

Mill Hill School
The Ridgeway, Mill Hill Village,
London NW7 1QS
Tel: 020 8959 1176
Head: Dr Dominic Luckett
Age range: 13–18
No. of pupils: 689 B492 G197 VIth259
Fees: Day £13,860 FB £21,900

Naima Jewish Preparatory School
21 Andover Place, London NW6 5ED
Tel: 020 7328 2802
Headteacher: Mr Michael Cohen MA,
NPQH
Age range: 3–11
No. of pupils: B83 G82
Fees: Day £5997–£7470

Nancy Reuben Primary School
Finchley Lane, Hendon, London NW4 1DJ
Tel: 020 82025646
Head: D A David
Age range: 3–11
No. of pupils: 207

North Bridge House Junior School
8 Netherhall Gardens, London NW3 5RR
Tel: 020 7435 2884
Head: Mrs A Allsopp
Age range: 5–8
No. of pupils: 186
Fees: Day £13,560

North Bridge House Prep School
1 Gloucester Avenue, London NW1 7AB
Tel: 020 7267 6266
Head: Mr B Bibby
Age range: B8–13 G8–11
No. of pupils: 280
Fees: Day £12,390

North Bridge House School
1 Gloucester Avenue, London NW1 7AB
Tel: 020 7267 6266
Head of Senior School: Miss A Ayre
Age range: 2½–16
No. of pupils: 860 B518 G342
Fees: Day £3375–£12,930

North Bridge House Senior School
1 Gloucester Avenue, London NW1 7AB
Tel: 020 7267 6266
Head: Ms A Ayre
Age range: 11–16
No. of pupils: 195
Fees: Day £13,560

OYH Primary School
Finchley Lane, Hendon, London NW4 1DJ
Tel: 020 8202 5646
Headteacher: D A David
Age range: 3–11
No. of pupils: 180 B89 G91

Rainbow Montessori School
13 Woodchurch Road, Hampstead,
London NW6 3PL
Tel: 020 7328 8986
Principal: Linda Madden MontDipAdv
Age range: 5–12
No. of pupils: B60 G60
Fees: Day £3097–£3140

Sarum Hall
15 Eton Avenue, London NW3 3EL
Tel: 020 7794 2261
Headmistress: Mrs Christine Smith
Age range: 3–11
No. of pupils: 170 G170
Fees: Day £6048–£10,065

South Hampstead High School GDST
3 Maresfield Gardens, London NW3 5SS
Tel: 020 7435 2899
Headmistress: Mrs J E Stephen BSc
Age range: 4–18
No. of pupils: 852 VIth162
Fees: Day £9342–£12,006

Southbank International School - Hampstead
16 Netherhall Gardens,
London NW3 5TH
Tel: 020 7243 3803
Principal: Helen O'Donoghue
Age range: 3–11
No. of pupils: 205 B104 G101
Fees: Day £13,200–£20,550

St Anthony's School
90 Fitzjohn's Avenue, Hampstead,
London NW3 6NP
Tel: 020 7431 1066
Headmaster: Chris McGovern
Age range: 5–13
No. of pupils: 295 B295
Fees: Day £12,345–£12,690

St Christina's R C Preparatory School
25 St Edmunds Terrace, Regent's Park,
London NW8 7PY
Tel: 020 7722 8784
Headteacher: Miss N Clyne-Wilson
Age range: B3–7 G3–11
No. of pupils: 220 B45 G175
Fees: Day £9594

St Christopher's School
32 Belsize Lane, Hampstead,
London NW3 5AE
Tel: 020 7435 1521
Head: Mrs S A West BA(Hons), PGCE,
MA
Age range: 4–11
No. of pupils: 235
Fees: Day £10,950

St Johns Wood Pre-Preparatory School
St Johns Hall, Lords Roundabout, Prince
Albert Road, London NW8 7NE
Tel: 020 7722 7149
Headmistress: Ms D Louskas
Age range: 3–7
No. of pupils: 70 B45 G25
Fees: Day £7620–£12,090

St Margaret's School
18 Kidderpore Gardens, Hampstead,
London NW3 7SR
Tel: 020 7435 2439
Principal: Mr M Webster BSc, PGCE
Age range: 4–16
No. of pupils: 152
Fees: Day £8778–£10,116

St Martin's School
22 Goodwyn Avenue, Mill Hill,
London NW7 3RG
Tel: 020 8959 1965
Head: Mrs Angela Wilson DipEd
Age range: 3–11
No. of pupils: 100
Fees: Day £6369

ST MARY'S SCHOOL HAMPSTEAD
For further details see p. 106
47 Fitzjohn's Avenue, Hampstead,
London NW3 6PG
Tel: 020 7435 1868
Email: enquiries@stmh.co.uk
Website: www.stmh.co.uk
Head: Miss Angela Rawlinson BA,
MA(1st Class Honours), DipTchng, NPQH
No. of pupils: 300 B17 G283
Fees: Day £6312–£11,700

St Nicholas School
22 Salmon Street, London NW9 8PN
Tel: 020 8205 7153
Headmistress: Mrs Alyce Gregory CertEd
Age range: 5–11
No. of pupils: 80 B40 G40
Fees: Day £5760

Swaminarayan School
260 Brentfield Road, Neasden,
London NW10 8HE
Tel: 020 8965 8381
Headteacher: Mr Mahendra Savjani
Age range: 2–18
No. of pupils: 452 B242 G210 VIth36
Fees: Day £7818–£10,707

Sylvia Young Theatre School
1 Nutford Place, London W1M 5YZ
Tel: 020 7258 2330
Headteacher: Ms Frances Chave BSc,
PGCE, NPQH
Age range: 10–16
No. of pupils: B83 G153
Fees: Day £9360–£12,690
WB £15,800–£16,500
FB £18,300–£19,500

Talmud Torah Torat Emet
27 Green Lane, London NW4 2NL
Tel: 020 8201 7770
Headteacher: Rabbi M Nissim
Age range: 5–9

The Academy School
2 Pilgrim's Place, Rosslyn Hill,
London NW3 1NG
Tel: 020 7435 6621
Headteacher: Mr Evans
Age range: 6–14

The American School in London
One Waverley Place, London NW8 0NP
Tel: 020 7449 1221
Head: Mrs Coreen Hester
Age range: 4–18
No. of pupils: 1352 B698 G654
Fees: Day £19,350–£22,550

The Cavendish School
31 Inverness Street, Camden Town,
London NW1 7HB
Tel: 020 7485 1958
Headmistress: Mrs T Dunbar BSc(Hons),
PGCE, NPQH
Age range: G3–11
No. of pupils: 218
Fees: Day £11,550

The Hall School
23 Crossfield Road, Hampstead,
London NW3 4NU
Tel: 020 7722 1700
Headmaster: P Lough MA
Age range: 4–13
No. of pupils: 440
Fees: Day £9300–£11,400

The Islamia Schools' Trust
129 Salusbury Road, London NW6 6PE
Tel: 020 7372 3472
Age range: 11–16
No. of pupils: 124
Fees: Day £4200

The King Alfred School
Manor Wood, North End Road,
London NW11 7HY
Tel: 020 8457 5200
Head: Mrs Dawn Moore MA(London)
Age range: 4–18
No. of pupils: 615 VIth70
Fees: Day £11,310–£13,635

The Mount School
Milespit Hill, Mill Hill, London NW7 2RX
Tel: 020 8959 3403
Head: Ms Catherine Cozens
Age range: 4–18
No. of pupils: 307 G307 VIth24
Fees: Day £2912–£3510

The Mulberry House School
7 Minster Road, West Hampstead,
London NW2 3SD
Tel: 020 8452 7340
Headteacher: Ms Julie Kirwan
Age range: 2–8
No. of pupils: 184 B109 G75
Fees: Day £8460–£15,698

The Phoenix School
36 College Crescent, London NW3 5LF
Tel: 020 7722 4433
Headmistress: Mrs Lisa Mason-Jones
Age range: 3–7
No. of pupils: 130 B70 G60
Fees: Day £2585–£3795

The Royal School, Hampstead
65 Rosslyn Hill, Hampstead,
London NW3 5UD
Tel: 020 7794 7708
Headmistress: Ms J Ebner
BEd(Hons)(Cantab), MA(London),
PGDipCouns, Cert FT, NPQH
Age range: 3–16
No. of pupils: 210
Fees: Day £9645–£11,340 WB £18,630
FB £22,350

**The School of the Islamic Republic of
Iran**
100 Carlton Vale, London NW6 5HE
Tel: 020 7372 8051
Headteacher: Mr Farzad Farzan
Age range: 6–16
No. of pupils: 53 B22 G31

The Village School
2 Parkhill Road, Belsize Park,
London NW3 2YN
Tel: 020 7485 4673
Headmistress: Miss C E F Gay
BSc(Hons), PGCE
Age range: 3–11
No. of pupils: 130
Fees: Day £12,600

**The Welsh School (Ysgol Gymraeg
Llundain)**
c/o The Stonebridge School,
Shakespeare Avenue,
London NW10 5200
Tel: 020 8965 3585
Headteacher: Mrs Menna George
Age range: 2½–11
No. of pupils: 30
Fees: Day £1950

Torah Vodaas
41 Dunstan Road, London NW11 8AE
Tel: 020 8458 4003
Headteacher: Mr Stanley Klor
Age range: 2–10
No. of pupils: 130

Trevor Roberts School
55-57 Eton Avenue, London NW3 3ET
Tel: 020 7586 1444
Headmaster: Simon Trevor-Roberts BA
Age range: 5–13
No. of pupils: 176 B116 G60
Fees: Day £10,026–£12,240

University College School
Frognal, Hampstead, London NW3 6XH
Tel: 020 7435 2215
Headmaster: Kenneth J Durham MA
Age range: 11–18
No. of pupils: 850 B780 G70 VIth300
Fees: Day £16,005

University College School (Junior)
11 Holly Hill, London NW3 6QN
Tel: 020 7435 3068
Headmaster: Mr K J Douglas BA, BSc
Age range: 7–11
No. of pupils: 245
Fees: Day £4930

Wentworth Tutorial College
6-10 Brentmead Place,
London NW11 9LH
Tel: 020 8458 8524/5
Principal: Alan Davies BSc, MSc
Age range: 14–19
No. of pupils: 115 B82 G33

SOUTH-EAST LONDON

Alleyn's School
Townley Road, Dulwich,
London SE22 8SU
Tel: 020 8557 1500
Headmaster: Dr G Savage MA, PhD,
FRSA
Age range: 4–18
No. of pupils: 1224 B580 G644 VIth296
Fees: Day £12,861–£15,255

Bellerbys College
Bounty House, Greenwich,
London SE8 3DE
Tel: 020 8694 7000
Head: Mr Andy Quin
Age range: 15–19
No. of pupils: B150 G150
Fees: Day £9600–£13,800
FB £16,730–£20,930

Blackheath High School GDST
Vanbrugh Park, Blackheath,
London SE3 7AG
Tel: 020 8853 2929
Head: Mrs Elizabeth Laws BA(Hons),
PGCE
Age range: 3–18
No. of pupils: 650
Fees: Day £7212–£12,006

Blackheath Nursery & Preparatory School
4 St Germans Place, Blackheath,
London SE3 0NJ
Tel: 020 8858 0692
Headmistress: Mrs P J Thompson
Age range: 3–11
No. of pupils: 366 B184 G182
Fees: Day £4560–£9315

Chrysolyte Independent Christian School
Bethel House, Lansdowne Place,
London SE1 4XH
Tel: 020 7407 9990/9996
Matron: Mrs R Ikiebe
Age range: 2–11
No. of pupils: B50 G53
Fees: Day £3750–£5100

Colfe's Preparatory School
Horn Park Lane, Lee, London SE12 8AW
Tel: 020 8463 8240
Headmaster: Mr John Gallagher
Age range: 3–11
No. of pupils: 355
Fees: Day £8730–£10,134

Colfe's School
Horn Park Lane, Lee, London SE12 8AW
Tel: 020 8852 2283
Head: Mr R F Russell MA(Cantab)
Age range: 3–18
No. of pupils: 1020

Dulwich College
London SE21 7LD
Tel: 020 8299 9263
Master: Dr J A F Spence
Age range: 7–18
No. of pupils: 1400 VIth420
Fees: Day £14,892 WB £29,010
FB £30,639

Dulwich College Kindergarten & Infants School
Eller Bank, 87 College Road,
London SE21 7HH
Tel: 020 8693 1538
Head: Mrs H M Friell
Age range: 3 months–7 years
No. of pupils: 251

Dulwich College Preparatory School
42 Alleyn Park, Dulwich,
London SE21 7AA
Tel: 020 8670 3217
Headmaster: Mr M W Roulston
Age range: B3–13 G3–5
No. of pupils: 817 B793 G24
Fees: Day £4350–£13,542
WB £18,213–£19,662

Eltham College
Grove Park Road, Mottingham,
London SE9 4QF
Tel: 020 8857 1455
Headmaster: Mr P J Henderson BA, FRSA
Age range: B7–18 G16–18
No. of pupils: 830 B770 G60 VIth220
Fees: Day £10,800–£12,525

Greenwich Steiner School
Woodlands, 90 Mycenae Road,
Blackheath, London SE3 7SE
Tel: 020 8858 4404
Age range: 3–14
No. of pupils: 90 B50 G40
Fees: Day £4000–£5600

Heath House Preparatory School
37 Wemyss Road, Blackheath,
London SE3 0TG
Tel: 020 8297 1900
Headmaster: Mr Ian Laslett MA, FRGS
Age range: 4–11
No. of pupils: 95 B47 G48
Fees: Day £9600–£10,200

Herne Hill School
The Old Vicarage, 127 Herne Hill,
London SE24 9LY
Tel: 020 7274 6336
Head: Mrs Jane Beales
Age range: 3–7
No. of pupils: 250
Fees: Day £4230–£10,530

James Allen's Girls' School
East Dulwich Grove, Dulwich,
London SE22 8TE
Tel: 020 8693 1181
Headmistress: Mrs Marion Gibbs
BA(Hons), PGCE, MLitt, FRSA
Age range: 4–18
No. of pupils: 1100
Fees: Day £12,057–£13,560

Kings Kids Christian School
New Testament Church of God, Bawtree
Road, New Cross, London SE14 6ET
Tel: 020 8691 5813
Headteacher: Mrs M Okenwa
Age range: 5–11
No. of pupils: 36 B22 G14

London Christian School
40 Tabard Street, London SE1 4JU
Tel: 020 3130 6430
Headmistress: Georgina Hale
Age range: 3–11
No. of pupils: 65 B32 G33
Fees: Day £7200

London City College
Royal Waterloo House, 51-55 Waterloo
Road, London SE1 8TX
Tel: 020 7928 0029
Principal: Dr N Kyritsis MA, DMS, MCIM

Marathon Science School
1-9 Evelyn Street, Surrey Quays,
London SE8 5RQ
Tel: 020 7231 3232
Headteacher: Mr Uzeyir Onur
Age range: 11–16
No. of pupils: 67

Oakfield Preparatory School
125-128 Thurlow Park Road, Dulwich,
London SE21 8HP
Tel: 020 8670 4206
Principal: Mr John Gibson BEd(Hons)
Age range: 2–11
No. of pupils: 450 B235 G215
Fees: Day £4600–£7335

Riverston School
63-69 Eltham Road, Lee Green,
London SE12 8UF
Tel: 020 8318 4327
Headmistress: Mrs S E Salathiel
Age range: 1–18
No. of pupils: 245 B150 G95

Rosemead Preparatory School and Pre Prep
70 Thurlow Park Road, London SE21 8HZ
Tel: 020 8670 5865
Headmaster: Arthur Bray CertEd
Age range: 3–11
No. of pupils: 337 B156 G181
Fees: Day £8310–£8820

Springfield Christian School
145 Perry Hill, Catford, London SE6 4LP
Tel: 020 8291 4433
Principal: Mr B Oludimu BSc
Age range: 2¹⁄₂–11
No. of pupils: 85
Fees: Day £2550–£4710

St Dunstan's College
Stanstead Road, London SE6 4TY
Tel: 020 8516 7200
Headmistress: Mrs J D Davies BSc
Age range: 3–18
No. of pupils: 870
Fees: Day £6918–£12,174

St Olave's Preparatory School
106 Southwood Road, New Eltham,
London SE9 3QS
Tel: 020 8294 8930
Head: Mr J Tilly
Age range: 3–11
No. of pupils: 220 B130 G90
Fees: Day £5414–£8700

Sydenham High School GDST
19 Westwood Hill, London SE26 6BL
Tel: 020 8768 8000
Headteacher: Mrs K Pullen MA
Age range: 4–18
No. of pupils: 649 VIth70
Fees: Day £4764–£6132

The Pointer School
19 Stratheden Road, Blackheath,
London SE3 7TH
Tel: 020 8293 1331
Headmaster: Mr R J S Higgins MA, BEd,
CertEd, FCollP
Age range: 3–11
No. of pupils: 300 B150 G150
Fees: Day £6912–£13,782

THE VILLA PRE-PREPARATORY SCHOOL & NURSERY
For further details see p. 109
54 Lyndhurst Grove, Peckham,
London SE15 5AH
Tel: 020 7703 6216
Email: enquiries@thevillaschoolandnursery.com
Website: www.thevillaschoolandnursery.com
Head Teacher: Lisa Mason-Jones MA,
BA(Hons), Dip TTC
Age range: 2–7
No. of pupils: 210

Virgo Fidelis Preparatory School
Central Hill, Upper Norwood,
London SE19 1RS
Tel: 020 8653 2169
Head Teacher: Mrs Meg Baines
Age range: 3–11
No. of pupils: B125 G119
Fees: Day £2520–£6930

SOUTH-WEST LONDON

Abbey College - London
22 Grosvenor Gardens, Belgravia,
London SW1W 0DH
Tel: 020 7824 7300
Principal: Mr Mark Love BEd
Age range: 14–19
No. of pupils: 150 B70 G80 VIth150
Fees: Day £5950–£16,400 FB £30,200

Al-Muntada Islamic School
7 Bridges Place, Parsons Green,
London SW6 4HW
Tel: 020 7471 8283
Headmaster: Mr Z Chehimi
Age range: 4–11
No. of pupils: 165
Fees: Day £2500

Balham Preparatory School
145 Upper Tooting Road,
London SW17 7TJ
Tel: 020 8767 6057
Headmaster: Mr K Bahauddin
Age range: 3–16
No. of pupils: 250 B110 G140

Beechwood School
55 Leigham Court Road, Streatham,
London SW16 2NJ
Tel: 020 8677 8778
Headmistress: Mrs M Marshall
Age range: 0–11
No. of pupils: 100
Fees: Day £6726–£7875

Bertrum House School
290 Balham High Road,
London SW17 7AL
Tel: 020 8767 4051
Principal: Mrs Jane Fletcher
Age range: 2¹⁄₂–7
No. of pupils: B74 G58
Fees: Day £900–£9450

Broomwood Hall School
68-74 Nightingale Lane,
London SW12 8NR
Tel: 020 8682 8810
Principal: Lady Colquhoun BEd, DipT
Age range: B4–8 G4–13
No. of pupils: 605 B186 G419
Fees: Day £11,940–£14,640

CAMERON HOUSE
For further details see p. 90
4 The Vale, Chelsea, London SW3 6AH
Tel: 020 7352 4040
Email: info@cameronhouseschool.org
Website: www.cameronhouseschool.org
Headmistress: Mrs Lucie Moore
BEd(Hons)
Age range: 4–11
No. of pupils: 116 B53 G63
Fees: Day £15,285

Centre Academy London
92 St John's Hill, Battersea,
London SW11 1SH
Tel: 020 7738 2344
Principal: Duncan Rollo BA, MA, PhD
Age range: 8–19
No. of pupils: 60 B45 G15 VIth13
Fees: Day £25,000–£37,500

Colet Court (St Paul's Preparatory School)
Colet Court, Lonsdale Road,
London SW13 9JT
Tel: 020 8748 3461
Headmaster: Mr T A Meunier
MA(Cantab)
Age range: 7–13
No. of pupils: 434
Fees: Day £14,334

Collingham
23 Collingham Gardens,
London SW5 oHL
Tel: 020 7244 7414
Principal: Mr G Hattee MA(Oxon), DipEd
Age range: 14–19
No. of pupils: B130 G110 VIth200
Fees: Day £4140–£11,850

Dolphin School
106 Northcote Road, London SW11 6QW
Tel: 020 7924 3472
Principal: Mrs Jo Glen BA(Hons)
Age range: 2½–11
No. of pupils: 253
Fees: Day £8400–£9075

Donhead
33 Edge Hill, London SW19 4NP
Tel: 020 8946 7000
Headmaster: Mr G C McGrath BA(Hons),
PGCE, MBA(Ed)
Age range: 4–11
No. of pupils: 280
Fees: Day £7800–£8325

Duff Miller College
59 Queen's Gate, South Kensington,
London SW7 5JP
Tel: 020 7225 0577
Principals: C Denning BSc, PGCE & C
Kraft BSc, BPS
Age range: 14–19
No. of pupils: 260
Fees: Day £10,000–£16,000

Eaton House Belgravia
3-5 Eaton Gate, London SW1W 9BA
Tel: 020 7730 9343
Headmistress: Miss Lucy Watts
Age range: 4–8
No. of pupils: B220
Fees: Day £11,925

Eaton House The Manor Girls School
58 Clapham Common Northside,
London SW4 9RU
Tel: 020 7924 6000
Head: Mrs S Segrave
Age range: 4–11
No. of pupils: G104
Fees: Day £12,405

Eaton House The Manor Prep School
58 Clapham Common Northside,
London SW4 9RU
Tel: 020 7924 6000
Head: Mr Jeremy Edwards
Age range: B8–13
No. of pupils: 350 B140
Fees: Day £15,330

Eaton House The Vale
2 Elvaston Place, London SW7 5QH
Tel: 020 7924 6000
Head: Mr Robin Greenwood
Age range: 3–11
No. of pupils: B40 G40
Fees: Day £11,925

Eaton Square School
79 Eccleston Square, London SW1V 1PP
Tel: 020 7931 9469
Headmaster: Mr Sebastian Hepher
BEd(Hons)
Age range: 2½–13
No. of pupils: 529 B280 G249
Fees: Day £2880–£15,360

Emanuel School
Battersea Rise, London SW11 1HS
Tel: 020 8870 4171
Headmaster: Mr Mark Hanley-Browne
Age range: 10–18
No. of pupils: 740 B464 G276 VIth190
Fees: Day £14,583

Eridge House Preparatory School
1 Fulham Park Road, Fulham,
London SW6 4LJ
Tel: 020 7471 4816
Headteacher: Mrs Janie Richardson
Age range: 3–11
No. of pupils: 180 B90 G90
Fees: Day £3962–£4212

Eveline Day & Nursery Schools
14 Trinity Crescent, Upper Tooting,
London SW17 7AE
Tel: 020 8672 4673
Headmistress: Ms Eveline Drut
Age range: 3 months–11 years
No. of pupils: 80
Fees: Day £11,059

Falkner House
19 Brechin Place, South Kensington,
London SW7 4QB
Tel: 020 7373 4501
Headteacher: Mrs Anita Griggs
BA(Hons), PGCE
Age range: B3–4 G3–11
No. of pupils: 200 B10 G190
Fees: Day £14,100

Finton House School
171 Trinity Road, London SW17 7HL
Tel: 020 8682 0921
Headmaster: Adrian Floyd BSc, PGCE
Age range: 4–11
No. of pupils: 305 B109 G196
Fees: Day £11,880–£12,885

FRANCIS HOLLAND SCHOOL, SLOANE SQUARE, SW1
For further details see p. 97
39 Graham Terrace, London SW1W 8JF
Tel: 020 7730 2971
Email: registrar@fhs-sw1.org.uk
Website: www.francisholland.org.uk
Head: Mrs Lucy Elphinstone MA(Cantab)
Age range: 4–18
No. of pupils: 450 VIth60
Fees: Day £13,350–£15,300

Garden House School
Boys' School & Girls' School, Turk's Row,
London SW3 4TW
Tel: 020 7730 1652
Headmistresses: Mrs J Webb CertEd,
Southampton (Girls' Upper School)
Age range: B3–8 G3–11
No. of pupils: 449
Fees: Day £9300–£15,885

GEMS HAMPSHIRE SCHOOL
For further details see p. 95
15 Manresa Road, Chelsea,
London SW3 6NB
Tel: 020 7352 7077
Email: info@ghs.gemsedu.co.uk
Website: www.ths.westminster.sch.uk
Principal: Mr Stephen J Chynoweth
Age range: 3–13
Fees: Day £10,305–£14,460

Glendower School
86/87 Queen's Gate, London SW7 5JX
Tel: 020 7370 1927
Headmistress: Mrs R E Bowman BA,
PGCE (retiring July 2012)
Age range: 4–11+
No. of pupils: 206
Fees: Day £14,280

Hall School, Wimbledon Junior School
Beavers Holt, Stroud Crescent, Putney
Vale, London SW15 3EQ
Tel: 020 8788 2370
Headmaster: Timothy J Hobbs MA
Age range: 4–11
No. of pupils: 520 B320 G200
Fees: Day £9072–£12,000

Hall School, Wimbledon Senior School
17 The Downs, Wimbledon,
London SW20 8HF
Tel: 020 8879 9200
Headmaster: Timothy J Hobbs MA
Age range: 11–16
No. of pupils: 520 B320 G200
Fees: Day £9072–£12,000

Hill House International Junior School

17 Hans Place, Chelsea,
London SW1X 0EP
Tel: 020 7589 1206
Headmaster: Richard Townend
FLSM(Chm)
Age range: 4–13
No. of pupils: 980 B560 G420
Fees: Day £9600–£12,600

Hornsby House School

Hearnville Road, Balham,
London SW12 8RS
Tel: 020 8673 7573
Headmaster from September 2012: Mr
Edward Rees
Age range: 4–11
No. of pupils: B195 G197
Fees: Day £11,670–£12,525

Hurlingham School

122 Putney Bridge Road, Putney,
London SW15 2NQ
Tel: 020 8874 7186
Headteacher: Mr Jonathan Brough
Age range: 4–11
No. of pupils: 320 B150 G170
Fees: Day £12,594–£13,320

Ibstock Place School

Clarence Lane, Roehampton,
London SW15 5PY
Tel: 020 8876 9991
Head: Mrs Anna Sylvester-Johnson
BA(Hons), PGCE
Age range: 3–18
No. of pupils: B450 G420
Fees: Day £5700–£14,500

Inchbald School of Design

Interior Design Faculty, 7 Eaton Gate,
London SW1W 9BA
Tel: 020 7730 5508
Principal: Mrs Jacqueline Duncan FIIDA,
FIDDA
Age range: 18–50
No. of pupils: 120 B20 G100

Kensington Prep School GDST

596 Fulham Road, London SW6 5PA
Tel: 020 7731 9300
Head: Mrs P Lynch MA(Hons)
Age range: 4–11
No. of pupils: 280
Fees: Day £11,103

King's College Junior School

Southside, Wimbledon Common,
London SW19 4TT
Tel: 020 8255 5335
Headmaster: Dr G A Silverlock
Age range: 7–13
No. of pupils: 460
Fees: Day £13,320–£15,030

King's College School

Southside, Wimbledon Common,
London SW19 4TT
Tel: 020 8255 5352
Head Master: A D Halls MA
Age range: 13–18
No. of pupils: 762 VIth295
Fees: Day £15,450

Knightsbridge School

67 Pont Street, Knightsbridge,
London SW1X 0BD
Tel: 020 7590 9000
Head: Mr Magoo Giles
Age range: 4–13
No. of pupils: 341 B177 G164
Fees: Day £12,285–£14,985

L'Ecole Bilingue

24 Collingham Road, St Jude's Church,
London SW5 0LX
Tel: 020 7835 1144
Headteacher: Ms Veronique Ferreira
Age range: 3–11
No. of pupils: 68 B42 G26
Fees: Day £6000–£6600

L'Ecole de Battersea

Trott Street, Battersea,
London SW11 3DS
Tel: 020 7371 8350
Head: Mrs F Brisset
Age range: 3–11
No. of pupils: 240
Fees: Day £9480–£9660

L'Ecole des Petits

2 Hazlebury Road, Fulham,
London SW6 2NB
Tel: 020 7371 8350
Head: Mrs F Brisset
Age range: 3–6
No. of pupils: 136 B70 G66
Fees: Day £9360–£9660

Lion House School

The Old Methodist Hall, Gwendolen
Avenue, London SW15 6EH
Tel: 020 8780 9446
Head: Miss H J Luard MontDip
Age range: 2½–7½
No. of pupils: 115

Lycee Francais Charles de Gaulle

35 Cromwell Road, London SW7 2DG
Tel: 020 7584 6322
Proviseur: Mr Bernard Vasseur
Age range: 3–18
No. of pupils: 3961 VIth467
Fees: Day £4311–£8472

Mander Portman Woodward - London

90-92 Queen's Gate, London SW7 5AB
Tel: 020 7835 1355
Principal: Matthew Judd BA, PGCE
Age range: 14–19
No. of pupils: 434 B256 G178 VIth384
Fees: Day £7218–£17,973

More House School

22-24 Pont Street, Knightsbridge,
London SW1X 0AA
Tel: 020 7235 2855
Headmaster: Mr R M Carlysle
Age range: 11–18
No. of pupils: 200 VIth45
Fees: Day £14,055

New Mind School

Suite 9 Warwick House, Overton Road,
Brixton, London SW9 7JP
Tel: 020 7978 9978
Headteacher: Odartei L Muhammad
BSc(Hons), PGCE
Age range: 2½–11
No. of pupils: 18 B10 G8

Newton Prep

149 Battersea Park Road,
London SW8 4BX
Tel: 020 7720 4091
Headmaster: Mr Nicholas M Allen BA,
PGCE
Age range: 3–13
No. of pupils: 549 B313 G236
Fees: Day £7380–£15,570

Northcote Lodge School

26 Bolingbroke Grove, London SW11 6EL
Tel: 020 8682 8888
Headmaster: Mr John Hansford
Age range: 8–13
No. of pupils: 200
Fees: Day £13,485

Oliver House Preparatory School

7 Nightingale Lane, London SW4 9AH
Tel: 020 8772 1911
Headteacher: Mr Robert Teague
BSc(Hons)
Age range: 2½–13
No. of pupils: 144 B68 G76
Fees: Day £4200–£9300

PARKGATE HOUSE SCHOOL
For further details see p. 103

80 Clapham Common North Side,
London SW4 9SD
Tel: 020 7350 2461
Email: admissions@parkgate-school.co.uk
Website: www.parkgate-school.co.uk
Principal: Miss C M Shanley
Age range: 2–11 years
No. of pupils: 243
Fees: Day £4200–£11,550

PROSPECT HOUSE SCHOOL
For further details see p. 100

75 Putney Hill, London SW15 3NT
Tel: 020 8780 0456
Headmistress: Mrs D Barratt
Age range: 3–11
No. of pupils: 174 B83 G91
Fees: Day £1600–£3470

Putney High School GDST
35 Putney Hill, London SW15 6BH
Tel: 020 8788 4886
Headmistress: Dr Denise Lodge BSc,
MSc, PhD
Age range: 4–18
No. of pupils: 875 VIth150

Putney Park School
Woodborough Road, London SW15 6PY
Tel: 020 8788 8316
Headmistress: Mrs Ruth Mann
BSc(Hons), PGCE, DPSE(School
Management)
Age range: B4–8 G4–16
No. of pupils: 220 B40 G180
Fees: Day £10,281–£11,745

Queen's Gate School
133 Queen's Gate, London SW7 5LE
Tel: 020 7589 3587
Principal: Mrs R M Kamaryc BA, MSc,
PGCE
Age range: 4–18
No. of pupils: 460 VIth66
Fees: Day £12,750–£15,300

Quest Business Training
5 Grosvenor Gardens, Belgravia,
London SW1W 0BD
Tel: 020 7233 5957
Age range: 16–45

**Ravenstone Preparatory School and
Nursery**
24 Elvaston Place, South Kensington,
London SW7 5NL
Tel: 020 7225 3131
Headmistress: Mrs Elizabeth Heath BA,
PGCE
Age range: 2¾–11
No. of pupils: 110 B62 G48
Fees: Day £11,800–£12,020

Redcliffe School Trust Ltd
47 Redcliffe Gardens, Chelsea,
London SW10 9JH
Tel: 020 7352 9247
Head: Mrs Susan Bourne BSc, PGCE
Age range: B2½–8 G2½–11
No. of pupils: B62 G103
Fees: Day £12,030

SINCLAIR HOUSE SCHOOL
For further details see p. 104
159 Munster Road, Fulham,
London SW6 6DA
Tel: 020 7736 9182
Email: info@sinclairhouseschool.co.uk
Website: www.sinclairhouseschool.co.uk
Headmistress: Mrs Carlotta T M
O'Sullivan
Age range: 2–11
No. of pupils: B50 G50
Fees: Day £3405–£9105

St Mary's Summerstown Montessori
46 Wimbledon Road, Tooting,
London SW17 0UQ
Tel: 020 8947 7359
Head: Liz Maitland NNEB, RSH, MontDip
Age range: 18 months–5 years
No. of pupils: 30
Fees: Day £1300

St Nicholas Preparatory School
23 Princes Gate, Kensington,
London SW7 1PT
Tel: 020 7225 1277
Head: Mrs Jill Aisher BA, MCIL, PGCE
Age range: 2 years 9 months–11+ years
No. of pupils: 280
Fees: Day £11,475–£13,110

St Paul's School
Lonsdale Road, Barnes,
London SW13 9JT
Tel: 020 8748 9162
High Master: Prof Mark Bailey
Age range: 13–18
No. of pupils: 815 VIth320
Fees: Day £11,085 FB £16,485

St Philip's School
6 Wetherby Place, London SW7 4NE
Tel: 020 7373 3944
Headmaster: H J Biggs-Davison
MA(Cantab)
Age range: 7–13
No. of pupils: 106
Fees: Day £12,375

**Streatham & Clapham High School
GDST**
42 Abbotswood Road,
London SW16 1AW
Tel: 020 8677 8400
Head: Mrs S Mitchell MA(St Hugh's
College)Oxford, PGCE(Leeds)
Age range: B3–5 G3–18
No. of pupils: 603 B3 G600 VIth70
Fees: Day £5886–£9810

Sussex House School
68 Cadogan Square, Knightsbridge,
London SW1X 0EA
Tel: 020 7584 1741
Headmaster: Mr N P Kaye MA(Cantab),
ACP, FRSA
Age range: 8–13
No. of pupils: 182
Fees: Day £12,855

Swedish School
82 Lonsdale Road, London SW13 9JS
Tel: 020 8741 1751
Headmaster: Mr Jan Dackenberg
Age range: 3–18
No. of pupils: 242 B104 G138
Fees: Day £6600

Thames Christian College
Wye Street, Battersea,
London SW11 2HB
Tel: 020 7228 3933
Executive Head: Stephen Holsgrove PhD
Age range: 11–16
No. of pupils: 120 B70 G50
Fees: Day £9660

The Harrodian School
Lonsdale Road, London SW13 9QN
Tel: 020 8748 6117
Headmaster: James R Hooke
Age range: 5–18
No. of pupils: 890 B460 G430 VIth95
Fees: Day £10,407–£15,219

The Merlin School
4 Carlton Drive, Putney Hill,
London SW15 2BZ
Tel: 020 8788 2769
Principal: Mrs K Prest
Age range: 4–8
No. of pupils: 170

The Moat School
Bishops Avenue, Fulham,
London SW6 6ED
Tel: 020 7610 9018
Head: Abigail Gray
Age range: 11–16
No. of pupils: B69 G18
Fees: Day £24,150

**The Montessori Pavilion - The
Kindergarten School**
Vine Road, Barnes, London SW13 0NE
Tel: 020 8878 9695
Age range: 3–8
No. of pupils: 50
Fees: Day £1950–£3600

The Norwegian School
28 Arterberry Road, Wimbledon,
London SW20 8AH
Tel: 020 8947 6617
Head: Ms Kirsti H Jacobsen
Age range: 3–16
No. of pupils: B52 G52

The Roche School
11 Frogmore, London SW18 1HW
Tel: 020 8877 0823
Principal: J A Roche BSc, PhD
Age range: 2–11
No. of pupils: 239 B129 G110
Fees: Day £8850–£10,800

The Rowans School
19 Drax Avenue, Wimbledon,
London SW20 0EG
Tel: 020 8946 8220
Head Teacher: Mrs S Wingrove
Age range: 3–8
No. of pupils: B82 G49
Fees: Day £4920–£9660

The Study Preparatory School
Wilberforce House, Camp Road,
Wimbledon Common, London SW19 4UN
Tel: 020 8947 6969
Headmistress: Mrs Susan Pepper, MA
Oxon, PGCE
Age range: 4–11
No. of pupils: 315
Fees: Day £3395–£3530

The Vale School
2 Elvaston Place, London SW7 5QH
Tel: 020 7924 6000
Headmaster: Mr R Greenwood
Age range: B3–8 G3–11
No. of pupils: 70 B35 G35
Fees: Day £11,385

The Waldorf School of South West London
Streatham Methodist Church, Riggindale
Road, London SW16 1QH
Tel: 020 8671 6846
Age range: 3½–14
No. of pupils: 80
Fees: Day £4515–£6217

THE WHITE HOUSE PREPARATORY SCHOOL & WOODENTOPS KINDERGARTEN
For further details see p. 110
24 Thornton Road, London SW12 0LF
Tel: 020 8674 9514
Email:
schooloffice@WhiteHouseSchool.com
Website: www.whitehouseschool.com
Head: Ms Mary McCahery
Age range: 2–11
No. of pupils: B65 G65
Fees: Day £9800–£10,500

Thomas's Preparatory School - Battersea
28-40 Battersea High Street,
London SW11 3JB
Tel: 020 7978 0900
Head: Ben V R Thomas MA
Age range: 4–13
No. of pupils: 474 B254 G220
Fees: Day £8292–£11,715

Thomas's Preparatory School - Clapham
Broomwood Road, London SW11 6JZ
Tel: 020 7326 9300
Headmistress: Mrs Carol Evelegh DipCE,
DipSpLD
Age range: 4–13
No. of pupils: B264 G275
Fees: Day £10,365–£11,730

Thomas's Preparatory School - Fulham
Hugon Road, London SW6 3ES
Tel: 020 7751 8200
Head: Miss Annette Dobson BEd(Hons),
PGCertDys
Age range: 4–11

Tower House School
188 Sheen Lane, London SW14 8LF
Tel: 020 8876 3323
Head: Mr Gregory Evans
Age range: 4–13
No. of pupils: 180
Fees: Day £10,035–£11,385

Ursuline Preparatory School
18 The Downs, London SW20 8HR
Tel: 020 8947 0859
Headmistress: Mrs Anne Farnish, BA
(Hons) Ldn, PGCE
Age range: B3–4½ G3–11
No. of pupils: B30 G170
Fees: Day £3660–£6210

Westminster Abbey Choir School
Dean's Yard, London SW1P 3NY
Tel: 020 7222 6151
Headmaster: Jonathan Milton BEd
Age range: 8–13
No. of pupils: 34
Fees: FB £5607

Westminster Cathedral Choir School
Ambrosden Avenue, London SW1P 1QH
Tel: 020 7798 9081
Headmaster: Mr Neil McLaughlan
Age range: 8–13
No. of pupils: 150
Fees: Day £13,656 FB £6945

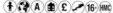

WESTMINSTER SCHOOL
For further details see p. 111
17 Dean's Yard, Westminster,
London SW1P 3PF
Tel: 020 7963 1003
Email: registrar@westminster.org.uk
Website: www.westminster.org.uk
Headmaster: Dr Stephen Spurr
Age range: B13–18 G16–18
No. of pupils: 750 B615 G135
Fees: Day £21,078–£22,854 FB £30,438

WESTMINSTER TUTORS
For further details see p. 112
86 Old Brompton Road, South
Kensington, London SW7 3LQ
Tel: 020 7584 1288
Email: info@westminstertutors.co.uk
Website: www.westminstertutors.co.uk
Principal: Virginia Maguire BA, MLitt
Age range: 14–mature
No. of pupils: B25 G25 VIth40
Fees: Day £6300–£20,400

Westminster Under School
Adrian House, 27 Vincent Square,
London SW1P 2NN
Tel: 020 7821 5788
Headteacher: Mrs E A Hill MA
Age range: 7–13
No. of pupils: 265 B265
Fees: Day £14,676

Willington School
Worcester Road, Wimbledon,
London SW19 7QQ
Tel: 020 8944 7020
Head: Graham Hill MA(Oxon)
Age range: 4–13
No. of pupils: 240
Fees: Day £7950–£9450

Wimbledon Common Preparatory
113 Ridgway, Wimbledon,
London SW19 4TA
Tel: 020 8946 1001
Head Teacher: Mrs Tracey Buck
Age range: 4–8
No. of pupils: 160
Fees: Day £7275–£8115

Wimbledon High School GDST
Mansel Road, Wimbledon,
London SW19 4AB
Tel: 020 8971 0900
Headmistress: Mrs H Hanbury
Age range: 4–18
No. of pupils: 900 VIth155
Fees: Day £10,902–£14,004

WEST LONDON

Albemarle Independent College
18 Dunraven Street, London W1K 7FE
Tel: 020 7409 7273
Co-Principals: Beverley Mellon & James
Eytle
Age range: 16–19
No. of pupils: 160 B85 G75
Fees: Day £15,000–£18,000

American InterContinental University (AIU) - London
110 Marylebone High Street,
London W1U 4RY
Tel: 020 7467 5600
Dean: Dr Allan Plath
Age range: 16+

Arts Educational Schools London Sixth Form
Cone Ripman House, 14 Bath Road,
Chiswick, London W4 1LY
Tel: 020 8987 6666
Head Teacher: Mr Greg Beavis
Age range: 16–18
No. of pupils: 68 B14 G54
Fees: Day £12,050

Arts Educational Schools London Years 7-11
Cone Ripman House, 14 Bath Road,
Chiswick, London W4 1LY
Tel: 020 8987 6666
Head Teacher: Mr Greg Beavis
Age range: 11–16
Fees: Day £12,050

Ashbourne Independent Sixth Form College
17 Old Court Place, Kensington,
London W8 4PL
Tel: 020 7937 3858
Principal: M J Kirby MSc, BApSc
Age range: 16–19
No. of pupils: 170 B80 G90
Fees: Day £19,725 FB £21,500

Ashbourne Middle School
17 Old Court Place, Kensington,
London W8 4PL
Tel: 020 7937 3858
Principal: M J Kirby MSc, BApSc
Age range: 13–16
No. of pupils: B80 G90 VIth150
Fees: Day £14,725 FB £21,500

Aston House School
1 Aston Road, Ealing, London W5 2RL
Tel: 020 8566 7300
Headmistress: Mrs P Seabrook
BA(Hons), MA
Age range: 2–11
No. of pupils: 120 B60 G60
Fees: Day £7860–£9825

Avenue House School
70 The Avenue, Ealing, London W13 8LS
Tel: 020 8998 9981
Headteacher: Mrs Carolyn Self CertEd
Age range: 3–11
No. of pupils: 113
Fees: Day £5070–£8670

(IAPS)

Bales College
742 Harrow Road, Kensal Town,
London W10 4AA
Tel: 020 8960 5899
Principal: William Moore
Age range: 11–19
No. of pupils: 90 B60 G30
Fees: Day £7950–£8550 FB £16,050

Barbara Speake Stage School
East Acton Lane, East Acton,
London W3 7EG
Tel: 020 8743 1306
Principal: Miss B M Speake MBE, ARAD,
MISTD, MIDTA
Age range: 3–16
No. of pupils: B40 G72
Fees: Day £5700–£6000

BASSETT HOUSE SCHOOL
For further details see p. 100
60 Bassett Road, London W10 6JP
Tel: 020 8969 0313
Headmistress: Mrs Andrea Harris
BEd(Lond), MontCert, CEPLF(CAEN)
Age range: 3–11
No. of pupils: 161 B65 G96
Fees: Day £6006–£12,390

Bute House Preparatory School for Girls
Bute House, Luxemburg Gardens,
London W6 7EA
Tel: 020 7603 7381
Head: Mrs Helen Lowe
Age range: 4–11
No. of pupils: 314
Fees: Day £12,324

(IAPS)

Chiswick & Bedford Park Prep School
Priory House, Priory Avenue,
London W4 1TX
Tel: 020 8994 1804
Headmistress: Mrs C A Sunderland
Age range: B4–7+ G4–11
No. of pupils: 180
Fees: Day £8850

Clifton Lodge
8 Mattock Lane, Ealing, London W5 5BG
Tel: 020 8579 3662
Head: Mr David Baldwin
Age range: 4–13
No. of pupils: 105
Fees: Day £9930–£10,755

Colegio Espanol Vicente Canada Blanch
317 Portobello Road, London W10 5SZ
Tel: 020 8969 2664
Principal: Mr A Vitria
Age range: 4–19
No. of pupils: 405

Connaught House School
47 Connaught Square, London W2 2HL
Tel: 020 7262 8830
Principals: Mrs J Hampton & Mr F
Hampton MA, RCA
Age range: B4–8 G4–11
No. of pupils: 75 B28 G47
Fees: Day £12,300–£13,800

David Game College
David Game House, 69 Notting Hill
Gate, London W11 3JS
Tel: 020 7221 6665
Principal: D T P Game MA, MPhil
Age range: 14–19
No. of pupils: 200 B100 G100 VIth150
Fees: Day £12,000–£13,000

Davies, Laing & Dick Independent College
100 Marylebone Lane, London W1U 2QB
Tel: 020 7935 8411
Principal: Mr David Lowe MA(Cantab),
FRSA
Age range: 15+
No. of pupils: 320 B170 G150 VIth280
Fees: Day £15,000–£17,300 FB £30,000

DURSTON HOUSE
For further details see p. 93
12-14 Castlebar Road, Ealing,
London W5 2DR
Tel: 020 8991 6532
Email: info@durstonhouse.org
Website: www.durstonhouse.org
Headmaster: Mr Ian Kendrick MA,
BEd(Hons)
Age range: 4–13
No. of pupils: 415
Fees: Day £9810–£12,570

Ealing College Upper School
83 The Avenue, Ealing, London W13 8JS
Tel: 020 8248 2312
Headmaster: Mr Christopher Morris
Age range: 11–18
No. of pupils: 82 B70 G12 VIth28
Fees: Day £8200

Ealing Independent College
83 New Broadway, Ealing,
London W5 5AL
Tel: 020 8579 6668
Principal: Dr Ian Moores
Age range: 13–22
No. of pupils: 100 B60 G40 VIth70
Fees: Day £3865–£12,600

Ecole Francaise Jacques Prevert
59 Brook Green, London W6 7BE
Tel: 020 7602 6871
Principal: P Possenti
Age range: 4–11
No. of pupils: B139 G124

Fulham Prep School
200 Greyhound Road, London W14 9SD
Tel: 020 7386 2448
Head: Mrs J Emmett
Age range: 4½–13
No. of pupils: 579 B345 G234
Fees: Day £12,825–£14,250

Great Beginnings Montessori School
The Welsh Church Hall, 82a Chiltern
Street, Marylebone, London W1M 1PS
Tel: 020 7486 2276
Age range: 2–6
No. of pupils: B35 G35
Fees: Day £1095–£1650

Greek Primary School of London
3 Pierrepoint Road, Acton,
London W3 9JR
Tel: 020 8992 6156
Age range: 1–11

Harvington School
20 Castlebar Road, Ealing,
London W5 2DS
Tel: 020 8997 1583
Headmistress: Mrs Anna Evans
Age range: B3–4 G3–16
No. of pupils: 210 B10 G200
Fees: Day £7560–£9840

HAWKESDOWN HOUSE SCHOOL KENSINGTON
For further details see p. 98
27 Edge Street, Kensington,
London W8 7PN
Tel: 020 7727 9090
Email: admin@hawkesdown.co.uk
Website: www.hawkesdown.co.uk
Head: Mrs C Bourne MA(Cantab)
Age range: 3–8
No. of pupils: 140
Fees: Day £12,825–£14,685

Heathfield House School
Turnham Green Church Hall, Heathfield
Gardens, Chiswick, London W4 4JU
Tel: 020 8994 3385
Headteacher: Mrs Goodsman
Age range: 4–11
No. of pupils: B50 G50
Fees: Day £6300–£6900

Holland Park Pre Prep School and Day Nursery
5 & 9 Holland Road, Kensington,
London W14 8HJ
Tel: 020 7602 9066/020 7602 9266
Principal: Mrs Kitty Mason
Age range: 3 months–8 years
No. of pupils: 128 B68 G60
Fees: Day £4650–£10,935

HOUSE SCHOOLS GROUP
For further details see p. 100
42 Hartington Road, London W4 3TX
Tel: 020 8580 9626
Website: www.houseschools.com

International School of London
139 Gunnersbury Avenue, Acton,
London W3 8LG
Tel: +44 (0)20 8992 5823
Head of School: Huw Davies
Age range: 3–18
No. of pupils: 350
Fees: Day £16,000–£21,500

King Fahad Academy
Bromyard Avenue, Acton, London W3 7HD
Tel: 020 8743 0131
Director: Dr Sumaya Alyusuf
Age range: 3–18
No. of pupils: 446
Fees: Day £3000

La Petite Ecole Francais
90 Oxford Gardens, London W10 5UW
Tel: 020 8960 1278
Principal: Ms A Stones
Age range: 2–6

Lansdowne College
40-44 Bark Place, London W2 4AT
Tel: 02076164400
Principal: John Southworth
Age range: 14–19
No. of pupils: 265 B140 G125 VIth230
Fees: Day £16,475

Latymer Prep School
36 Upper Mall, Hammersmith,
London W6 9TA
Tel: 0845 638 5700
Principal: Mr Stuart Dorrian BA(Hons),
PGCE
Age range: 7–11
No. of pupils: 163 B110 G53
Fees: Day £13,800

Latymer Upper School
King Street, Hammersmith,
London W6 9LR
Tel: 0845 638 5800
Head: Mr D Goodhew MA(Oxon)
Age range: 11–18
No. of pupils: 1123 VIth354
Fees: Day £14,995

Le Herisson
River Court Methodist Church, Rover
Court Road, Hammersmith,
London W6 9JT
Tel: 020 8563 7664
Head: B Rios
Age range: 2–6
No. of pupils: 64
Fees: Day £3060–£4260

LEITHS SCHOOL OF FOOD & WINE
For further details see p. 101
16-20 Wendell Road, Shepherd's Bush,
London W12 9RT
Tel: 020 8749 6400
Email: info@leiths.com
Website: www.leiths.com
Managing Director: Camilla Schneideman
Age range: 17–99
No. of pupils: 96

Norland Place School
162-166 Holland Park Avenue,
London W11 4UH
Tel: 020 7603 9103
Headmaster: Mr Patrick Mattar MA
Age range: B4–8 G4–11
No. of pupils: 240
Fees: Day £10,578–£13,068

Notting Hill & Ealing High School GDST
2 Cleveland Road, West Ealing,
London W13 8AX
Tel: 020 8991 2165
Headmistress: Ms Lucinda Hunt
Age range: 4–18
No. of pupils: 870 VIth130
Fees: Day £9387–£12,063

Notting Hill Preparatory School
95 Lancaster Road, London W11 1QQ
Tel: 020 7221 0727
Headmistress: Mrs Jane Cameron
Age range: 4–13
No. of pupils: 285 B156 G129
Fees: Day £4890

One World Montessori Nursery & Pre-Prep
69-71 Brock Green, Hammersmith,
London W6 7BE
Tel: 020 7603 6065
Headteacher: Ms N Greer
Age range: 2–8
No. of pupils: 21 B14 G7

One World Preparatory School
10 Stanley Gardens, Acton,
London W3 7SZ
Tel: 020 87433300
Head: Mrs F Aspill
Age range: 3–11
No. of pupils: 52 B28 G24
Fees: Day £3000

ORCHARD HOUSE SCHOOL
For further details see p. 100
16 Newton Grove, Bedford Park,
London W4 1LB
Tel: 020 8742 8544
Headmistress: Mrs S A B Hobbs
BA(Hons)(Exon), PGCE, AMBDA, MontDip
Age range: 3–11
No. of pupils: 234 B90 G144
Fees: Day £6006–£12,390

Pembridge Hall School for Girls
18 Pembridge Square, London W2 4EH
Tel: 020 7229 0121
Headteacher: Mrs Elizabeth Marsden
Age range: 4–11
No. of pupils: 385
Fees: Day £13,905

Portland Place School
56-58 Portland Place, London W1N 1NJ
Tel: 020 7307 8700
Head: Tim Cook
Age range: 11–18
No. of pupils: 300 B200 G100 VIth50
Fees: Day £12,522–£16,425

Queen's College
43-49 Harley Street, London W1G 8BT
Tel: 020 7291 7000
Head: Dr F M R Ramsey MA, DPhil(Oxon)
Age range: 11–18
No. of pupils: 360 VIth90

Ravenscourt Park Preparatory School
16 Ravenscourt Avenue, London W6 0SL
Tel: 020 8846 9153
Headmaster: Mr Robert Relton
Age range: 4–11
No. of pupils: 340
Fees: Day £13,305

Ravenscourt Theatre School
8-30 Galena Road, Hammersmith,
London W6 0LT
Tel: 020 8741 0707
Head: Judy Swinney
Age range: 7–16
No. of pupils: B45 G48
Fees: Day £4350

Ravenstone Day Nursery & Nursery School
The Long Garden, St George's Fields,
Albion Street, London W2 2AX
Tel: 020 7262 1190
Head of Early Years: Miss Vanessa
Dowman BEd
Age range: 2–7
No. of pupils: 74 B39 G35
Fees: Day £11,800–£12,020

Ray Cochrane Beauty School
118 Baker Street, London W1U 6TT
Tel: 020 7486 6291
Principal: Miss Baljeet Suri CIDESCO,
CIBTAC, FETC, IFA
Age range: 16–50
No. of pupils: 40
Fees: Day £2195–£8995

Southbank International School - Kensington
36-38 Kensington Park Road,
London W11 3BU
Tel: 020 7243 3803
Principal: Mark Case
Age range: 3–11
No. of pupils: 220 B115 G105
Fees: Day £13,200–£20,550

Southbank International School - Westminster
63-65 Portland Place, London W1B 1QR
Tel: 020 7243 3803
Principal: Terry Hedger
Age range: 11–18
No. of pupils: 348 B178 G170 VIth104
Fees: Day £22,140–£24,150

ST AUGUSTINE'S PRIORY
For further details see p. 105
Hillcrest Road, Ealing, London W5 2JL
Tel: 020 8997 2022
Email: registrar@staugustinespriory.org.uk
Website: www.saintaugustinespriory.org.uk
Headteacher: Mrs Sarah Raffray MA
Age range: 3–18
No. of pupils: 494
Fees: Day £8250–£11,760

St Benedict's School
54 Eaton Rise, Ealing, London W5 2ES
Tel: 020 8862 2254
Headmaster: Mr C J Cleugh BSc, MSc
Age range: 3–18
No. of pupils: 1079 B790 G289 VIth213
Fees: Day £10,560–£12,360

St James Junior School
Earsby Street, London W14 8SH
Tel: 020 7348 1777
Headmistress: Mrs Catherine
Thomlinson
Age range: B4–11 G4–10
No. of pupils: B113 G146
Fees: Day £10,650

St James Senior Girls' School
Earsby Street, London W14 8SH
Tel: 020 7348 1777
Headmistress: Mrs Laura Hyde CertEd,
MEd
Age range: 10–18
No. of pupils: 318 VIth61
Fees: Day £13,080

St Paul's Girls' School
Brook Green, London W6 7BS
Tel: 020 7603 2288
High Mistress: Ms Clarissa Farr BA, MA,
PGCE
Age range: 11–18
No. of pupils: 710 G710 VIth200
Fees: Day £13,623

Stephenson School
175 Kensal Road, London W10 5BJ
Tel: 020 8965 7374
Head: Mrs Yvonne Didushko
Age range: 4–11
Fees: Day £5760

Tabernacle School
32 St Anns Villas, Holland Park,
London W11 4RS
Tel: 020 7602 6232
Headteacher: Mrs P Wilson
Age range: 3–16
Fees: Day £4500

The Falcons School for Boys
2 Burnaby Gardens, Chiswick,
London W4 3DT
Tel: 020 8747 8393
Acting Head: Mr Henk Weyers
Age range: 3–7
No. of pupils: 225
Fees: Day £3875–£11,625

The Falcons School for Girls
15 Gunnersbury Avenue, Ealing,
London W5 3XD
Tel: 020 8992 5189
Headteacher: Miss Joan McGillewie
Age range: 4–11
No. of pupils: 102
Fees: Day £3625

The Godolphin and Latymer School
Iffley Road, Hammersmith,
London W6 0PG
Tel: +44 (0)20 8741 1936
Head Mistress: Mrs R Mercer BA
Age range: 11–18
No. of pupils: 700
Fees: Day £15,525

The Japanese School
87 Creffield Road, Acton,
London W3 9PU
Tel: 020 8993 7145
Headteacher: Mrs Kiyoe Tsuruoka
Age range: 6–16
No. of pupils: 500 B257 G243

THE LLOYD WILLIAMSON SCHOOL
For further details see p. 108
12 Telford Road, London W10 5SH
Tel: 020 8962 0345
Email: admin@lws.org.uk
Website: www.lws.org.uk
Co-Principals: Lucy Meyer & Aaron
Williams
Age range: 6 months–14 years
Fees: Day £10,440

Thomas's Preparatory School - Kensington
17-19 Cottesmore Gardens,
London W8 5PR
Tel: 020 7361 6500
Headmistress: Mrs Diana Maine MA,
BEd(Hons), NPQH
Age range: 4–11
No. of pupils: B166 G185
Fees: Day £14,505–£15,795

Wetherby Preparatory School
48 Bryanston Square, London W1H 2EA
Tel: 020 7535 3520
Headteacher: Mr Nick Baker
Age range: 8–13
No. of pupils: 192
Fees: Day £4665

Wetherby Pre-Preparatory School
11 Pembridge Square, London W2 4ED
Tel: 020 7727 9581
Headmaster: Mr Mark Snell
Age range: 4–8
No. of pupils: 248
Fees: Day £16,470

Young Dancers Academy
25 Bulwer Street, London W12 8AR
Tel: 020 8743 3856
Head: Mrs K Williams
Age range: 11–16
Fees: Day £10,500–£11,100

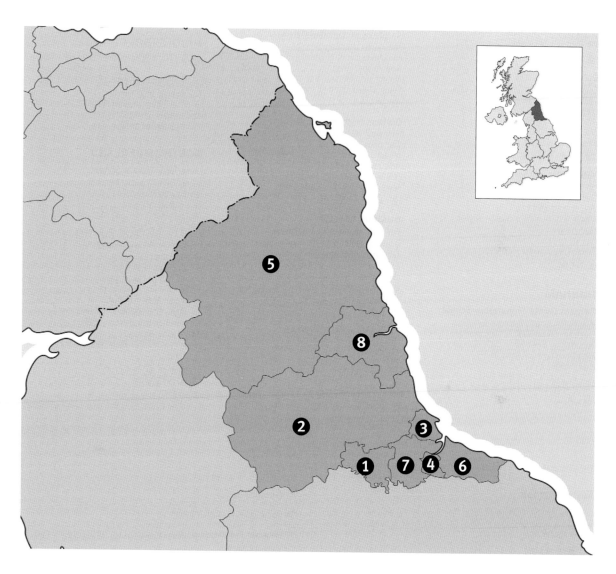

Key and page index:

1 Darlington: D302

2 Durham: D302

3 Hartlepool

4 Middlesborough: D302

5 Northumberland: D302

6 Redcar & Cleveland

7 Stockton-on-Tees: D303

8 Tyne & Wear: D303

DARLINGTON

Diamond Junior School
Grange Road, Darlington DL1 5PA
Tel: 01325 463383
Head: Mrs A P J Foster Dept of Ed,
TCert(Dunelm)
Age range: 2–11
No. of pupils: 182
Fees: Day £6150–£8550
WB £16,755–£16,755
FB £17,355–£17,355

(🏫)(£)(✏)

Polam Hall School
Grange Road, Darlington DL1 5PA
Tel: 01325 463383
Headmaster: Mr John Moreland
Age range: 11–18
No. of pupils: B40 G160
Fees: Day £11,670 FB £22,425

(🌍)(A)(🏫)(£)(✏)(16+)(GSA)(BSA)

Yarm At Raventhorpe
96 Carmel Road North,
Darlington DL3 8JB
Tel: 01325 463373
Head Teacher: Mrs Gillian Taylor
Age range: 3–11
No. of pupils: 70 B40 G30
Fees: Day £4050–£4950

(£)(✏)(HMC)(S)

DURHAM

Barnard Castle Preparatory School
Westwick Road, Barnard Castle,
Durham DL12 8UW
Tel: 01833 696032
Headmaster: C F Rycroft
Age range: 4–11
No. of pupils: 180 B96 G84
Fees: Day £7671 FB £14,832

(🏫)(✏)(IAPS)

Barnard Castle Senior School
Barnard Castle, Durham DL12 8UN
Tel: 01833 690222
Headmaster: Alan D Stevens BA, MA
Age range: 11–18
No. of pupils: 570 B370 G200 VIth160
Fees: Day £10,980 FB £19,716

(🌍)(A)(🏫)(£)(✏)(16+)(HMC)(BSA)

Bow, Durham School
South Road, Durham DH1 3LS
Tel: 0191 384 8233
Headmaster: R N Baird BA(Hons), PGCE
Age range: 3–11
No. of pupils: 150 B125 G25
Fees: Day £5370–£7938

(£)(✏)(IAPS)

Durham High School for Girls
Farewell Hall, Durham DH1 3TB
Tel: 0191 384 3226
Headmistress: Mrs Lynne Renwick
Age range: 3–18
No. of pupils: 555 VIth99
Fees: Day £6270–£9945

(👧)(A)(£)(✏)(16+)(GSA)

DURHAM SCHOOL
For further details see p. 114
Durham DH1 4SZ
Tel: 0191 386 4783
Email:
d.woodlands@durhamschool.co.uk
Website: www.durhamschool.co.uk
Headmaster: Mr Martin George
Age range: 3–18
No. of pupils: 590 B416 G174 VIth143
Fees: Day £6225–£15,225
WB £17,175–£20,985
FB £19,497–£23,097

(🌍)(A)(🏫)(£)(✏)(16+)(HMC)(BSA)

The Chorister School
The College, Durham DH1 3EL
Tel: 0191 384 2935
Headmistress: Mrs Y F S Day
Age range: 3–13
No. of pupils: 214 B130 G84
Fees: Day £7500–£10,125 WB £17,460
FB £9120–£17,460

(🏫)(£)(✏)(IAPS)(BSA)

MIDDLESBOROUGH

Moordale Academy
Sotherbury Road,
Middlesborough TS3 8BS
Tel: 01642 224960
Headteacher: Steven Waugh Mytton
Age range: 11–16
No. of pupils: 26 B12 G14

NORTHUMBERLAND

Longridge Towers School
Longridge Towers, Berwick-upon-Tweed,
Northumberland TD15 2XH
Tel: 01289 307584
Headmaster: Mr T M Manning BSc
Age range: 3–18
No. of pupils: B155 G160 VIth45
Fees: Day £5235–£8385
WB £14,625–£15,855
FB £16,320–£17,550

(🌍)(A)(🏫)(£)(✏)(16+)(BSA)(S)

Mowden Hall School
Newton, Stocksfield,
Northumberland NE43 7TP
Tel: 01661 842147
Headmaster: Mr Ben Beardmore-Gray
Age range: 3–13
Fees: Day £7920–£13,770 FB £17,790

(🏫)(£)(✏)(IAPS)(BSA)

Key to symbols

(♂) Boys' school

(♀) Girls' school

(🌍) International school

(16+) Tutorial or sixth form college

(A) A levels

(🏫) Boarding accommodation

(£) Bursaries

(IB) International Baccalaureate

(✏) Learning support

(16+) Entrance at 16+

(🌀) Vocational qualifications

(IAPS) Member of Independent Association of Preparatory Schools

(HMC) The Headmasters' & Headmistresses' Conference

(ISA) Independent Schools Association

(GSA) Girls' School Association

(BSA) Boarding Schools' Association

(S) SHMIS

Unless otherwise indicated, all schools are coeducational
day schools. Single-sex and boarding schools will be
indicated by the relevant icon.

Rock Hall School
Rock Moor, Alnwick,
Northumberland NE66 2TQ
Tel: 01665 579224
Headmistress: Lalage Ann Bosanquet
Age range: 3–13
No. of pupils: B31 G29

STOCKTON-ON-TEES

Red House School
36 The Green, Norton, Stockton-on-
Tees TS20 1DX
Tel: 01642 553370
Headmaster: Mr A R W Taylor BSc, MSc,
PGCE, CBiol, MSB
Age range: 2–16
No. of pupils: 438 B237 G201
Fees: Day £6150–£8220

Teesside High School
The Avenue, Eaglescliffe, Stockton-on-
Tees TS16 9AT
Tel: 01642 782095
Headmaster: Mr Thomas Packer BSc,
MSc, FInstP
Age range: 3–18
No. of pupils: 390 B70 G320 VIth70

Yarm Preparatory School
Grammar School Lane, Yarm, Stockton-
on-Tees TS15 9ES
Tel: 01642 781447
Headteacher: Mr Bill Toleman
Age range: 3–11
No. of pupils: 339 B168 G171
Fees: Day £4308–£8859

Yarm School
The Friarage, Yarm, Stockton-on-
Tees TS15 9EJ
Tel: 01642 786023
Headmaster: Mr D M Dunn BA
Age range: 3–18
No. of pupils: B600 G800 VIth200
Fees: Day £5600–£9500

TYNE & WEAR

Argyle House School
19/20 Thornhill Park, Tunstall Road,
Sunderland, Tyne & Wear SR2 7LA
Tel: 0191 510 0726
Headmaster: Mr C Johnson
Age range: 2½–16
No. of pupils: 195 B116 G79
Fees: Day £5550–£6720

Central Newcastle High School GDST
Eskdale Terrace, Jesmond, Newcastle
upon Tyne, Tyne & Wear NE2 4DS
Tel: 0191 281 1768
Head: Mrs H J French MA, MEd, NPQH
Age range: 3–18
No. of pupils: 850 VIth155
Fees: Day £5328–£8898

Dame Allan's Boys' School
Fowberry Crescent, Fenham, Newcastle
upon Tyne, Tyne & Wear NE4 9YJ
Tel: 0191 275 0608
Principal: Dr John R Hind
Age range: 8–18
No. of pupils: 518 VIth200
Fees: Day £7758–£9873

Dame Allan's Girls' School
Fowberry Crescent, Fenham, Newcastle
upon Tyne, Tyne & Wear NE4 9YJ
Tel: 0191 275 0708
Principal: Dr John R Hind
Age range: 8–18
No. of pupils: 413 VIth200
Fees: Day £6456–£8205

Dame Allan's Sixth Form
Fowberry Crescent, Fenham, Newcastle
upon Tyne, Tyne & Wear NE4 9YJ
Tel: 0191 275 0608
Principal: J R Hind MA, MEd, PhD
Age range: 8–18
No. of pupils: 200 B100 G100 VIth200
Fees: Day £7758–£9873

Gateshead Jewish Boarding School
10 Rydal Street, Gateshead,
Tyne & Wear NE8 1HG
Tel: 0191 477 1431
Principal: Rabbi M Kupetz
Age range: 10–16
No. of pupils: 105

Gateshead Jewish High School for Girls
6 Gladstone Terrace, Gateshead,
Tyne & Wear NE8 4DY
Tel: 0191 4773471
Headteacher: Rabbi D Bowden
Age range: 11–16
No. of pupils: 132

Gateshead Jewish Primary School
18-20 Gladstone Terrace, Gateshead,
Tyne & Wear NE8 4EA
Tel: 0191 477 2154 / 0191 478 5841
Headmasters: A Hammond & Y Spitzer
Age range: 5–11
No. of pupils: 446
Fees: Day £2392–£3016

Linden School (Dame Allan Junior School)
72-74 Station Road, Forest Hall,
Newcastle upon Tyne,
Tyne & Wear NE12 9BQ
Tel: 0191 266 2943
Acting Head: Mr Brian Metcalf MEd,
PGCE, BSc(Hons), PGCE, AMinstP
Age range: 3–11
No. of pupils: 140 B72 G68
Fees: Day £3150

Newcastle Preparatory School
6 Eslington Road, Jesmond, Newcastle
upon Tyne, Tyne & Wear NE2 4RH
Tel: 0191 281 1769
Head Teacher: Mrs Margaret Coates
Age range: 3–11
No. of pupils: 273 B184 G89
Fees: Day £7779–£8742

Newcastle School for Boys
30 West Avenue, Gosforth, Newcastle
upon Tyne, Tyne & Wear NE3 4ES
Tel: 0191 255 9300
Headmaster: Mr L Francis
Age range: 3–18
No. of pupils: 400
Fees: Day £6900–£9270

Royal Grammar School
Eskdale Terrace, Newcastle upon Tyne,
Tyne & Wear NE2 4DX
Tel: 0191 281 5711
Headmaster: Dr Bernard St J Trafford
Age range: 7–18
No. of pupils: 1254 B1045 G209 VIth360
Fees: Day £6600–£7830

Sunderland High School
Mowbray Road, Sunderland,
Tyne & Wear SR2 8HY
Tel: 0191 567 4984
Head: Dr Angela J Slater BA, PhD
Age range: 2–18
No. of pupils: B309 G259 VIth75
Fees: Day £5022–£7194

The King's School (HMC)
Huntington Place, Tynemouth, North
Shields, Tyne & Wear NE30 4RF
Tel: 0191 258 5995
Headmaster: Edward Wesson
Age range: 4–18
No. of pupils: 665 B403 G262 VIth162
Fees: Day £7026–£8853

The Newcastle Upon Tyne Church High School
Tankerville Terrace, Jesmond, Newcastle
upon Tyne, Tyne & Wear NE2 3BA
Tel: 0191 281 4306
Headmistress: Mrs J Gatenby
Age range: 3–18
No. of pupils: 450 VIth70
Fees: Day £8631–£11,397

Westfield School
Oakfield Road, Gosforth, Newcastle
upon Tyne, Tyne & Wear NE3 4HS
Tel: 0191 255 3980
Headmistress: Mrs M Farndale
BA(Hons)(Lon), PGCE(Oxon), FRSA
Age range: 3–18
No. of pupils: 315 VIth50
Fees: Day £1398–£4140

(♣)(A)(16+)(GSA)

WEST YORKSHIRE

Eternal Light Secondary School
Christopher Street, Off Little Horton
Lane, Bradford, West Yorkshire BD5 9DH
Tel: 01274 501597
Headteacher: Mr Yusuf Collector
Age range: 11–15
No. of pupils: 91

(♣)

Key and page index:

1. Cheshire: D306

2. Cumbria: D307

3. Lancashire: D311

4. Greater Manchester: D308

5. Merseyside: D312

6. Isle of Man: D311

7. Blackpool: D306

8. Blackburn with Darwen: D306

BLACKBURN WITH DARWEN

Al-Asr Primary School
58-60 St Silas Road, Blackburn,
Blackburn with Darwen BB2 6JX
Tel: 01254 696933
Headteacher: Mrs Hameed
Age range: 4–10
No. of pupils: B32 G56
Fees: Day £1200

Al-Islah Schools
108 Audley Range, Blackburn,
Blackburn with Darwen BB1 1TF
Tel: 01254 261573
Headteacher: Nizammuddin I Makda
Age range: 9–17
No. of pupils: 192 B11 G181

Islamiyah School
Willow Street, Blackburn,
Blackburn with Darwen BB1 5NH
Tel: 01254 661 259
Headteacher: Mrs Zarina Seedat
Age range: 11–16
No. of pupils: 178

Jamiatul-Ilm Wal-Huda UK School
15 Moss Street, Blackburn,
Blackburn with Darwen BB1 5HW
Tel: 01254 673105
Headteacher: Mr A Ahmed
Age range: 11–16
No. of pupils: 348

Markazul Uloom
Park Lee Road, Blackburn,
Blackburn with Darwen BB2 3NY
Tel: 01254 581569
Headteacher: Mr Nu'amaan Limbada
Age range: 11–19
Fees: Day £1200 FB £2700

Queen Elizabeth's Grammar School
West Park Road, Blackburn,
Blackburn with Darwen BB2 6DF
Tel: 01254 686300
Headmaster: S A Corns MA
Age range: 3–18
No. of pupils: B550 G110 VIth140
Fees: Day £5355–£9459

Tauheedul Islam Girls High School
31 Bicknell Street, Blackburn,
Blackburn with Darwen BB1 7EY
Tel: 01254 54021
Headmaster: Mr I M Patel BA, BEd
Age range: 11–16
No. of pupils: 200
Fees: Day £500

Westholme School
Meins Road, Blackburn,
Blackburn with Darwen BB2 6QU
Tel: 01254 506070
Principal: Mrs Lillian Croston
BSc(Hons)(Dunelm), PGCE(Cantab),
ALCM
Age range: B2–13 G2–18
No. of pupils: 1070 B140 G930 VIth140
Fees: Day £5571–£8850

BLACKPOOL

Arnold School
488 Lytham Road, Blackpool FY4 1JG
Tel: 01253 346391
Headmaster: Jim E Keefe
Age range: 2–18
No. of pupils: 800 B409 G391 VIth165
Fees: Day £6537–£8541

Langdale Preparatory School
95 Warbreck Drive, Blackpool FY2 9RZ
Tel: 01253 354812
Head Teacher: Miss Melanie Hayes
Age range: 3–11
No. of pupils: 86 B42 G44
Fees: Day £2600–£3050

CHESHIRE

ABBEY GATE COLLEGE
For further details see p. 116
Saighton Grange, Saighton, Chester,
Cheshire CH3 6EN
Tel: 01244 332077
Email: admin@abbeygatecollege.co.uk
Website: www.abbeygatecollege.co.uk
Head: Mrs Lynne M Horner
Age range: 4–18
No. of pupils: 513 VIth75
Fees: Day £7116–£10,404

Abbey Gate School
Clare Avenue, Hoole, Chester,
Cheshire CH2 3HR
Tel: 01244 319649
Headmistress: Mrs S M Fisher
Age range: 3–11
No. of pupils: 54 B37 G17
Fees: Day £6150–£6615

Alderley Edge School for Girls
Wilmslow Road, Alderley Edge,
Cheshire SK9 7QE
Tel: 01625 583028
Headmistress: Mrs Susan Goff
Age range: 2–18
No. of pupils: 500 VIth60
Fees: Day £5070–£9201

Key to symbols

(†) Boys' school

(‡) Girls' school

(🌐) International school

(16) Tutorial or sixth form college

(A) A levels

(⊞) Boarding accommodation

(£) Bursaries

(IB) International Baccalaureate

(✐) Learning support

(16·) Entrance at 16+

(⚙) Vocational qualifications

(IAPS) Member of Independent Association of Preparatory Schools

(HMC) The Headmasters' & Headmistresses' Conference

(ISA) Independent Schools Association

(GSA) Girls' School Association

(BSA) Boarding Schools' Association

(S) SHMIS

Unless otherwise indicated, all schools are coeducational
day schools. Single-sex and boarding schools will be
indicated by the relevant icon.

Beech Hall School
Beech Hall Drive, Tytherington,
Macclesfield, Cheshire SK10 2EG
Tel: 01625 422192
Headmistress: Mrs G Yandell BA
Age range: 6 months–16 years
No. of pupils: 230 B130 G100
Fees: Day £6285–£8940

Cransley School
Belmont Hall, Great Budworth,
Northwich, Cheshire CW9 6HN
Tel: 01606 891747
Headmistress: Mrs G Gaunt
Age range: B3–11 G3–16
No. of pupils: B31 G162
Fees: Day £1173–£2673

Greater Grace School of Christian Education
Church Lane, Backford, Chester,
Cheshire CH2 4BE
Tel: 01244 851 797
Head Teacher: Mrs A Mulligan
Age range: 5–18
No. of pupils: B2 G9
Fees: Day £1900

Green Meadow Independent Primary School
Robson Way, Lowton, Warrington,
Cheshire WA3 2RD
Tel: 01942 671138
Head: Mrs S Green
Age range: 4–11
Fees: Day £6390

Hammond School
Hoole Bank, Mannings Lane, Chester,
Cheshire CH2 2PB
Tel: 01244 305350
Principal: Mrs M Evans
Age range: 4–19
No. of pupils: 248 B103 G145
Fees: Day £9858–£15,414
FB £16,857–£22,413

Pownall Hall School
Carrwood Road, Wilmslow,
Cheshire SK9 5DW
Tel: 01625 523141
Headmaster: Mr J J Meadmore RD, BSc,
CertEd
Age range: 2–11
No. of pupils: B116 G74
Fees: Day £2475–£5385

Staleydene Preparatory School
Dukinfield Methodist Church, Wellington
Parade, Dukinfield, Cheshire SK16 4LE
Head: Mr E Ogbogu
Age range: 3–11
No. of pupils: 23

Terra Nova School
Jodrell Bank, Holmes Chapel, Crewe,
Cheshire CW4 8BT
Tel: 01477 571251
Headmaster: Mr A Lewin
Age range: 3–13
No. of pupils: 304 B178 G126
Fees: Day £3750–£12,150

The Firs School
Newton Lane, Upton, Chester,
Cheshire CH2 2HJ
Tel: 01244 322443
Headmistress: Mrs M Denton CertEd
Age range: 3–11
No. of pupils: 226 B137 G89
Fees: Day £6720

The Grange School
Bradburns Lane, Hartford, Northwich,
Cheshire CW8 1LU
Tel: 01606 74007 or 77447
Headmaster: Mr C P Jeffery BA, FRSA
Age range: 4–18
No. of pupils: 1185 B636 G549 VIth193
Fees: Day £7080–£9480

The King's School
Wrexham Road, Chester,
Cheshire CH4 7QL
Tel: 01244 689500
Headmaster: C D Ramsey MA
Age range: 7–18
No. of pupils: 977 B658 G319 VIth217
Fees: Day £8148–£10,632

The King's School
Cumberland Street, Macclesfield,
Cheshire SK10 1DA
Tel: 01625 260000
Headmaster: Dr Simon Hyde
Age range: 3–18
No. of pupils: 1503 B848 G655 VIth284
Fees: Day £5790–£8355

The Queen's School
City Walls Road, Chester,
Cheshire CH1 2NN
Tel: 01244 312078
Headmistress: Mrs E S Clark
Age range: 4–18
No. of pupils: 610 VIth100
Fees: Day £7455–£10,650

THE RYLEYS SCHOOL
For further details see p. 120
Ryleys Lane, Alderley Edge,
Cheshire SK9 7UY
Tel: 01625 583241
Email: ryleysoffice@btconnect.com
Website: www.theryleys.com
Headmaster: Paul Berry BSc(Hons),
PGCE, NPQH
Age range: 3–13
No. of pupils: 261 B186 G75
Fees: Day £8400–£9750

Wilmslow Preparatory School
Grove Avenue, Wilmslow,
Cheshire SK9 5EG
Tel: 01625 524246
Head of School: Mr Paul Reynolds
Age range: 2–11
No. of pupils: 166
Fees: Day £1854–£6540

Yorston Lodge School
18 St John's Road, Knutsford,
Cheshire WA16 0DP
Tel: 01565 633177
Headmistress: Mrs J Dallimore
BEd(Hons)
Age range: 3–11
No. of pupils: B63 G64
Fees: Day £5160

CUMBRIA

Austin Friars School
Etterby Scaur, Carlisle, Cumbria CA3 9PB
Tel: 01228 528042
Headmaster: Mr Christopher Lumb BSc,
MEd
Age range: 3–18
No. of pupils: 507 B301 G206 VIth70
Fees: Day £4470–£9210

Casterton School
Kirkby Lonsdale, Cumbria LA6 2SG
Tel: 01524 279200
Headmistress: Mrs M Lucas MA
Age range: B3–11 G3–18
No. of pupils: 283 B17 G266 VIth60
Fees: Day £6570–£14,109
WB £17,478–£18,759
FB £17,949–£23,580

Chetwynde School
Croslands, Rating Lane, Barrow-in-
Furness, Cumbria LA13 0NY
Tel: 01229 824210
Head of School: Mr R Collier
Age range: 3–18
No. of pupils: 327 B164 G163 VIth38
Fees: Day £6900–£8100

Hunter Hall School
Frenchfield, Penrith, Cumbria CA11 8UA
Tel: 01768 891291
Headmaster: Dr F A Winzor
Age range: 3–11
No. of pupils: 133 B59 G74
Fees: Day £6534

Lime House School
Holm Hill, Dalston, Carlisle,
Cumbria CA5 7BX
Tel: 01228 710225
Headmaster: Mr N A Rice BA, CertEd,
MA(EdMem)
Age range: 3½–18+
No. of pupils: 211 B128 G83 VIth40
Fees: Day £3000–£7050
WB £7500–£15,000 FB £9000–£16,500

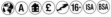

SEDBERGH SCHOOL
For further details see p. 118
Sedbergh, Cumbria LA10 5HG
Tel: 015396 20535
Email: admissions@sedberghschool.org
Website: www.sedberghschool.org
Headmaster: Mr A Fleck MA
Age range: 4–18
No. of pupils: 550 B387 G163 VIth209

St Bees School
St Bees, Cumbria CA27 0DS
Tel: 01946 828000
Head: Mr Philip Capes BSc
Age range: 11–18
No. of pupils: 300 B174 G126 VIth101
Fees: Day £10,743–£13,872
WB £13,776–£19,746
FB £16,785–£23,145

Windermere Preparatory School
Ambleside Road, Windermere,
Cumbria LA23 1AP
Tel: 015394 43308
Head: Mr Ben Freeman BEd(Hons), PG
Dip
Age range: 2–11
No. of pupils: 120 B59 G61
Fees: Day £6459–£13,617
WB £20,271–£23,166
FB £21,414–£24,378

Windermere School
Patterdale Road, Windermere,
Cumbria LA23 1NW
Tel: 015394 46164
Head of School: Ian Lavender
Age range: 2–18
No. of pupils: 403 B176 G227 VIth53
Fees: Day £8205–£12,510
WB £18,630–£21,294
FB £19,680–£23,598

GREATER MANCHESTER

Abbey College - Manchester
Cheapside, King Street, Manchester,
Greater Manchester M2 4WG
Tel: 0161 817 2700
Principal: MsLiz Elam
Age range: 15–19
No. of pupils: 215 B129 G86 VIth175
Fees: Day £10,800

Abbotsford Preparatory School
211 Flixton Road, Urmston, Manchester,
Greater Manchester M41 5PR
Tel: 0161 748 3261
Head Teacher: Mrs Pamela Shiels
Age range: 3–11
No. of pupils: 106 B55 G51
Fees: Day £5065–£5469

Al Jamiah Al Islamiyyah
Willows Lane, Bolton,
Greater Manchester BL3 4HF
Tel: 017792 334278
Headmaster: Mr S J Haneef
Age range: 12–18
No. of pupils: 140
Fees: Day £750 FB £1500

Altrincham Preparatory School
Marlborough Road, Bowdon, Altrincham,
Greater Manchester WA14 2RR
Tel: 0161 928 3366
Headmaster: Mr Andrew C Potts
Age range: 3–11
No. of pupils: 310
Fees: Day £6180–£6840

Beech House School
184 Manchester Road, Rochdale,
Greater Manchester OL11 4JQ
Tel: 01706 646309
Headmaster: K Sartain BSc(Hons), PGCE,
DipSp, CBiol, FIBiol
Age range: 2–16
No. of pupils: B130 G132
Fees: Day £3945–£4938

Beis Rochel School
1-7 Seymour Road, Crumpsall,
Manchester,
Greater Manchester M8 5BQ
Tel: 0161 795 1830
Headmistress: Mrs E Krausz
Age range: 3–16
No. of pupils: 200

Bnos Yisroel School
Foigel Esther Shine House, Leicester
Road, Manchester,
Greater Manchester M7 4DA
Tel: 0161 792 3896
Headmaster: Rabbi R Spitzer
Age range: 2–16
No. of pupils: 489 B16 G473

Bolton School (Boys' Division)
Chorley New Road, Bolton,
Greater Manchester BL1 4PA
Tel: 01204 840201
Headmaster: Philip J Britton MBE
Age range: 7–18
No. of pupils: 1106 VIth205
Fees: Day £7140–£9357

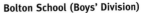

Bolton School (Girls' Division)
Chorley New Road, Bolton,
Greater Manchester BL1 4PB
Tel: 01204 840201
Headmistress: Miss Sue Hincks
MA(Oxon)
Age range: B0–7 G0–18
No. of pupils: 1191 B112 G1079 VIth202
Fees: Day £7140–£9357

Bowdon Preparatory School for Girls
48 Stamford Road, Bowdon, Altrincham,
Greater Manchester WA14 2JP
Tel: 0161 928 0678
Headmistress: Mrs J H Tan BA, DipEd
Age range: 3–11
No. of pupils: 200
Fees: Day £4986

Brabyns School
34-36 Arkwright Road, Marple,
Stockport, Greater Manchester SK6 7DB
Tel: 0161 427 2395
Headteacher: Mr Lee Sanders
Age range: 2½–11
No. of pupils: 134 B67 G67
Fees: Day £1313–£1779

Branwood Preparatory School
Stafford Road, Monton, Eccles,
Manchester,
Greater Manchester M30 9HN
Tel: 0161 789 1054
Head: Mrs K Higginbottom LWCMD,
PGCE
Age range: 3–11
No. of pupils: 156 B78 G78
Fees: Day £4839–£5667

BRIDGEWATER SCHOOL
For further details see p. 117
Drywood Hall, Worsley Road, Worsley,
Manchester,
Greater Manchester M28 2WQ
Tel: 0161 794 1463
Email: admin@bwslive.co.uk
Website: www.bridgewater-school.co.uk
Head Teacher: Mrs J A T Nairn
CertEd(Distinction)
Age range: 3–18
No. of pupils: 467 B237 G230
Fees: Day £6750–£9000

Bury Catholic Preparatory School
Arden House, Manchester Road, Bury,
Greater Manchester BL9 9BH
Tel: 0161 764 2346
Headteacher: Mrs A C Dean
Age range: 3–11
No. of pupils: B70 G54
Fees: Day £4500

Bury Grammar School Boys
Tenterden Street, Bury,
Greater Manchester BL9 0HN
Tel: 0161 797 2700
Headmaster: Revd S C Harvey MA
Age range: 7–18
No. of pupils: 597 B402 VIth95
Fees: Day £6492–£8736

Bury Grammar School for Girls
Bridge Road, Bury,
Greater Manchester BL9 0HH
Tel: 0161 797 2808
Headmistress: Mrs R S Georghiou
Age range: B4–7 G4–18
No. of pupils: 936 B102 G834 VIth134
Fees: Day £6492–£8736

Cheadle Hulme School
Claremont Road, Cheadle Hulme,
Cheadle, Greater Manchester SK8 6EF
Tel: 0161 488 3330
Head: Miss Lucy Pearson
Age range: 4–18
No. of pupils: 1391 B750 G641 VIth277
Fees: Day £6612–£9156

Chetham's School of Music
Long Millgate, Manchester,
Greater Manchester M3 1SB
Tel: 0161 834 9644
Head: Mrs C J Hickman MA
Age range: 8–18
No. of pupils: 296 B141 G155 VIth137
Fees: Day £23,988 WB £30,987
FB £30,987

Clarendon Cottage School
Ivy Bank House, Half Edge Lane, Eccles,
Manchester,
Greater Manchester M30 9BJ
Tel: 0161 950 7868
Headteacher: Mrs E L Howard
Age range: 3–11
No. of pupils: 81 B49 G32
Fees: Day £3210–£3840

Clevelands Preparatory School
425 Chorley New Road, Bolton,
Greater Manchester BL1 5DH
Tel: 01204 843898
Headteacher: Mrs Lesley Parlane
Age range: 2¾–11
No. of pupils: 141 B75 G106
Fees: Day £6240

Covenant Christian School
The Hawthorns, 48 Heaton Moor Road,
Stockport, Greater Manchester SK4 4NX
Tel: 0161 432 3782
Head: Dr Roger Slack
Age range: 5–16
No. of pupils: 32 B18 G14

Culcheth Hall
Ashley Road, Altrincham,
Greater Manchester WA14 2LT
Tel: 0161 928 1862
Headteacher: Alistair Todd
Age range: B2½–4 G2–16
No. of pupils: 247 B25 G222
Fees: Day £1710–£7620

Darul Uloom Al Arabiya Al Islamiya
Holcombe Hall, Holcombe, Bury,
Greater Manchester BL8 4NG
Tel: 01706 826106
Head: R Abdulla
Age range: 12–16
No. of pupils: 326

Etz Chaim School at The Belmont
89 Middleton Road, Crumpsall,
Manchester, Greater Manchester M8 4JY
Tel: 0161 740 6800
Headteacher: Rabbi Eli Cohen
Age range: 11–16
No. of pupils: 98

Farrowdale House Preparatory School
Farrow Street, Shaw, Oldham,
Greater Manchester OL2 7AD
Tel: 01706 844533
Headteacher: Miss K Brook
BSc(Mathematics), QTS
Age range: 3–11
No. of pupils: 140 B70 G70
Fees: Day £4995

Firwood Manor Preparatory School
Broadway, Chadderton, Oldham,
Greater Manchester OL9 0AD
Tel: 0161 6206570
Headteacher: Mrs P M Wild
Age range: 2¾–11
No. of pupils: B85 G65
Fees: Day £5400

Forest Park School
Lauriston House, 27 Oakfield, Sale,
Greater Manchester M33 6NB
Tel: 0161 973 4835
Headteacher: Mrs Helen Gee BEd(Hons)
Age range: 3–11
No. of pupils: 145 B85 G60
Fees: Day £4515–£4950

Forest School
Moss Lane, Timperley, Altrincham,
Greater Manchester WA15 6LJ
Tel: 0161 980 4075
Headmaster: Rick Hyde
Age range: 2–11
No. of pupils: 193 B94 G99
Fees: Day £5337–£5994

Grafton House Preparatory School
1 Warrington Street, Ashton-under-Lyne,
Greater Manchester OL6 6XB
Tel: 0161 343 3015
Head: Mrs Pamela Oaks
Age range: 2–11
No. of pupils: 110

Grasscroft Independent School
Lydgate Parish Hall, Stockport Road,
Lydgate, Oldham,
Greater Manchester OL4 4JJ
Tel: 01457 820485
Head: Mrs Jennifer O'Hara
Age range: 2½–7
No. of pupils: 75
Fees: Day £3300

Greenbank School
Heathbank Road, Cheadle Hulme,
Cheadle, Greater Manchester SK8 6HU
Tel: 0161 485 3724
Headmistress: Mrs J L Lowe
Age range: 3–11
No. of pupils: B84 G57
Fees: Day £6120

Hale Preparatory School
Broomfield Lane, Hale, Altrincham,
Greater Manchester WA15 9AS
Tel: 0161 928 2386
Headmaster: John Connor
Age range: 4–11
No. of pupils: B99 G87
Fees: Day £5625

Hillcrest Grammar School
Beech Avenue, Stockport,
Greater Manchester SK3 8HB
Tel: 0161 480 0329
Headmaster: Mr J D Williams
Age range: 3–16
No. of pupils: 260 B130 G130
Fees: Day £6120–£7710

Hulme Hall Grammar School
75 Hulme Hall Road, Cheadle Hulme,
Cheadle, Greater Manchester SK8 6LA
Tel: 0161 485 4638
Headmaster: Mr Philip Marland
BSc(Hons), MA, PGCE
Age range: 11–16
No. of pupils: 224 B138 G86
Fees: Day £7008

Hulme Hall Grammar School (Junior School)
75 Hulme Hall Road, Cheadle Hulme, Cheadle, Greater Manchester SK8 6LA
Tel: 0161 486 9970
Headmaster: Mr Philip Marland BSc(Hons), MA, PGCE
Age range: 2–11
No. of pupils: 122 B69 G53
Fees: Day £4143–£5482

Jewish Senior Boys School
Hubert House, 4 Newhall Road, Salford, Greater Manchester M7 4EL
Tel: 0161 708 9175
Headmaster: Rabbi Joshua Michael Israel
Age range: 10–16

Kassim Darwish Grammar School for Boys
Hartley Hall, Alexandra Road South, Manchester,
Greater Manchester M16 8NH
Tel: 0161 8607676
Headteacher: Mr Wahid Anwar
Age range: 11–16
No. of pupils: 170
Fees: Day £5644

King of Kings School
142 Dantzic Street, Manchester, Greater Manchester M4 4DN
Tel: 0161 834 4214
Head Teacher: Mrs B Lewis
Age range: 3–18
No. of pupils: 29

Lady Barn House School
Langlands, Schools Hill, Cheadle, Greater Manchester SK8 1JE
Tel: 0161 428 2912
Headmistress: Mrs S Marsh
Age range: 3–11
No. of pupils: 463 B262 G201
Fees: Day £5469–£6246

Lighthouse Christian School
193 Ashley Lane, Moston, Manchester, Greater Manchester M9 4NQ
Tel: 0161 205 0957
Head: Mr A I Akinyele
Age range: 3–11
No. of pupils: 18 B12 G6
Fees: Day £2880

Lord's Independent School
53 Manchester Road, Bolton, Greater Manchester BL2 1ES
Tel: 01204 523731
Headteacher: Mrs Anne Ainsworth
Age range: 11–16
No. of pupils: 83 B47 G36

Loreto Preparatory School
Dunham Road, Altrincham, Greater Manchester WA14 4GZ
Tel: 0161 928 8310
Headteacher: Mrs R A Hedger
Age range: B3–7 G3–11
No. of pupils: 163
Fees: Day £4650

Madrasatul Imam Muhammad Zakariya
Keswick Street, Bolton, Greater Manchester BL1 8LX
Tel: 01204 384434
Headteacher: Mrs Amena Sader
Age range: 11–19
No. of pupils: 110

Manchester High School for Girls
Grangethorpe Road, Manchester, Greater Manchester M14 6HS
Tel: 0161 224 0447
Head Mistress: Mrs A C Hewitt
Age range: 4–18
No. of pupils: 938 VIth192
Fees: Day £7053–£9900

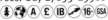

Manchester Islamic High School for Girls
55 High Lane, Chorlton Cum Hardy, Manchester,
Greater Manchester M21 9FA
Tel: 0161 881 2127
Headmistress: Mrs Mona Mohamed
Age range: 11–16
No. of pupils: 235
Fees: Day £3980

Manchester Junior Girls School
64 Upper Park Road, Salford, Greater Manchester M7 4JA
Tel: 0161 740 0566
Headmistress: Mrs Lieberman
Age range: 3–11
No. of pupils: 200

Manchester Muslim Preparatory School
551 Wilmslow Road, Withington, Manchester,
Greater Manchester M20 4BA
Tel: 0161 445 5452
Head Teacher: Mrs A Ali
Age range: 3–11
No. of pupils: 186
Fees: Day £3810–£4065

Mechinoh L'Yeshivah
Shenstone House, 13 Upper Park Road, Salford, Greater Manchester M7 4HY
Tel: 0161 795 9275
Headmaster: The Head
Age range: 11–15
No. of pupils: 49

Monton Village School
Francis Street, Monton, Eccles, Manchester,
Greater Manchester M30 9PR
Tel: 0161 789 0472
Head: Mrs K S McWilliams
Age range: 1–7
No. of pupils: 109

Moor Allerton School
131 Barlow Moor Road, West Didsbury, Manchester,
Greater Manchester M20 2PW
Tel: 0161 445 4521
Headmaster: P S Millard BA, MSc, NPQH
Age range: 3–11
No. of pupils: B120 G107
Fees: Day £6660–£7185

North Cestrian Grammar School
Dunham Road, Altrincham, Greater Manchester WA14 4AJ
Tel: 0161 928 1856
Headmaster: D G Vanstone MA
Age range: 11–18
No. of pupils: 322 B290 G32 VIth69
Fees: Day £7980

Oholei Yosef Yitzchok School
Kinderton Mansions, Upper Park Road, Salford, Greater Manchester M7 0HL
Tel: 0161 740 3752
Head: Rabbi M Wechter
Age range: 4–11
No. of pupils: 100
Fees: Day £2000

Oldham Hulme Grammar School
Chamber Road, Oldham, Greater Manchester OL8 4BX
Tel: 0161 624 4497
Principal: Dr Paul G Neeson
Age range: 3–18
No. of pupils: 1073 B597 G476 VIth207
Fees: Day £4509–£7071

OYY Lubavitch Girls School
Beis Menachem, Park Lane, Salford, Greater Manchester M7 4JD
Tel: 0161 795 0002
Headmistress: Mrs J Hanson
Age range: 2–16
No. of pupils: 82 B21 G61

Prestwich Preparatory School
St Margaret's Building, 400 Bury Old Road, Prestwich, Manchester,
Greater Manchester M25 1PZ
Tel: 0161 773 1223
Headmistress: Miss P Shiels
Age range: 2–11
No. of pupils: 122 B60 G62
Fees: Day £3336

Ramillies Hall School
Cheadle Hulme, Cheadle,
Greater Manchester SK8 7AJ
Tel: 0161 485 3804
Principal: Miss D M Patterson BA, PGCE
& Mrs A L Poole
Age range: 0–16
No. of pupils: 166 B105 G61
Fees: Day £6000–£8550

Rivington Park Independent School and Nursery
Knowle House, Rivington Lane, Horwich,
Bolton, Greater Manchester BL6 7RX
Tel: 01204 669332
Head: Mr Michael Ruaux
Age range: 3 months–11 years
No. of pupils: 60
Fees: Day £4410

Rochdale Girls School
36 Taylor Street, Rochdale,
Greater Manchester OL12 0HX
Tel: 01706 646642
Headteacher: Mr A Razzak
Age range: 11–16
No. of pupils: 76

Saddleworth Preparatory School
1195 Huddersfield Road, Scouthead,
Oldham, Greater Manchester OL4 4AG
Tel: 01457 877442
Headmistress: Mrs L K Hirst
Age range: 3–7

St Ambrose Preparatory School
Hale Barns, Altrincham,
Greater Manchester WA15 0HE
Tel: 0161 903 9193
Headmaster: F J Driscoll
Age range: B3–11 G3–4
No. of pupils: 150
Fees: Day £6195

St Bede's College
Alexandra Park Road, Manchester,
Greater Manchester M16 8HX
Tel: 0161 226 3323
Headmaster: Daniel Kearney
Age range: 11–19
No. of pupils: B515 G417
Fees: Day £7170

Stella Maris Junior School
St Johns Road, Heaton Mersey,
Stockport, Greater Manchester SK4 3BR
Tel: 0161 432 0532
Headmaster: Mr A Whittell
Age range: 3–11
No. of pupils: 63 B27 G36
Fees: Day £4890

Stockport Grammar School
Buxton Road, Stockport,
Greater Manchester SK2 7AF
Tel: 0161 456 9000
Head: Mr A H Chicken BA, MEd, FRSA
Age range: 3–18
No. of pupils: 1393 B763 G630 VIth268
Fees: Day £7146–£9270

Tashbar School
20 Upper Park Road, Salford,
Greater Manchester M7 4HL
Tel: 0161 7208254
Headteacher: Mr Pinczewski
Age range: 5–11
No. of pupils: 325

The Manchester Grammar School
Old Hall Lane, Fallowfield, Manchester,
Greater Manchester M13 0XT
Tel: 0161 224 7201
High Master: Dr Christopher Ray
Age range: 7–18
No. of pupils: B1500
Fees: Day £9996

The Potters House School
6 Arley Avenue, Bury,
Greater Manchester BL9 5HD
Tel: 0161 7051885
Headteacher: Mrs C M Mitchell
Age range: 4–10
No. of pupils: 12 B7 G5

Trinity Christian School
Birbeck Street, Stalybridge,
Greater Manchester SK15 1SH
Tel: 0161 303 0674
Headteacher: Mr W Ross Evans
Age range: 3–16
No. of pupils: B52 G58
Fees: Day £2964–£4146

Withington Girls' School
Wellington Road, Fallowfield,
Manchester,
Greater Manchester M14 6BL
Tel: 0161 224 1077
Headmistress: Mrs S E Marks MA
Age range: 7–18
No. of pupils: 650 VIth167
Fees: Day £9300

Yeshivah Ohr Torah School
28 Broom Lane, Salford,
Greater Manchester M7 4FX
Tel: 0161 7921230
Headteacher: Rabbi Y Wind
Age range: 11–16
No. of pupils: 40

ISLE OF MAN

King William's College
Castletown, Isle of Man IM9 1TP
Tel: +44 (0)1624 820400
Principal: Mr Martin A C Humphreys MA
Age range: 11–18
No. of pupils: 388
Fees: Day £12,876–£18,309
FB £21,231–£26,664

The Buchan School
West Hill, Castletown,
Isle of Man IM9 1RD
Tel: 01624 820481
Headteacher: Mrs Alison Hope Hedley
Age range: 4–11
No. of pupils: 195 B96 G99
Fees: Day £2645–£3449

LANCASHIRE

Abrar Academy
56 Garstang Road, Preston,
Lancashire PR1 1NA
Tel: 01772 82 87 32
Head: Mr A Esmail
Age range: 11–16

Ashbridge Independent School
Lindle Lane, Hutton, Preston,
Lancashire PR4 4AQ
Tel: 01772 619900
Headteacher: Mrs H Sharples
Age range: 0–11
No. of pupils: 315
Fees: Day £6318

Clifton Tutorial Centre
293 Clifton Drive South, St Annes-on-Sea, Lytham St Annes,
Lancashire FY8 1HN
Tel: 01253 725815
Headteacher: Mrs S M Welsby
Age range: 14–19

Emmanuel Christian School
Fylde Community, Normoss Road,
Poulton-le-Fylde, Lancashire FY3 0BE
Tel: 01253 882873
Head Teacher: Mrs Susan Perry
Age range: 3½–16
No. of pupils: 37
Fees: Day £4620

Ghausia Girls' High School
1-3 Cross Street, Nelson,
Lancashire BB9 7EN
Tel: 01282 699214
Principal: Jamil Mohammed
Age range: 11–16
No. of pupils: 35
Fees: Day £1000

Heathland School
Broadoak, Sandy Lane, Accrington,
Lancashire BB5 2AN
Tel: 01254 234284
Principal: Mrs J Harrison BA(Hons),
CertEd, FRSA
Age range: 4–16
No. of pupils: B45 G37
Fees: Day £4515

Highfield Priory School
Fulwood Row, Fulwood, Preston,
Lancashire PR2 5RW
Tel: 01772 709624
Headmaster: Mr Jeremy Duke BEd(Hons)
Age range: 6 months–11
No. of pupils: B129 G225
Fees: Day £6210

Jamea Al Kauthar
Ashton Road, Lancaster,
Lancashire LA1 5AJ
Tel: 01524 389898
Headteacher: Miss Ayesha Uddin
Age range: 11–16
No. of pupils: 392

King Edward VII & Queen Mary School
Clifton Drive, Lytham St Annes,
Lancashire FY8 1DT
Tel: 01253 784100
Principal: Mr R J Karling MA, MBA
Age range: 2–18
No. of pupils: 653 B356 G297 Vlth110
Fees: Day £5400–£7800

Kingsfold Christian School
Moss Lane, Hesketh Bank, Preston,
Lancashire PR4 6AA
Tel: 01772 813824
Age range: 4–16

Kingswood College at Scarisbrick School
Southport Road, Scarisbrisk, Ormskirk,
Lancashire L40 9RQ
Tel: 01704 880200
Principal: E J Borowski
Age range: 2¹⁄₂–16
No. of pupils: B175 G193
Fees: Day £3000–£6225

Kirkham Grammar School
Ribby Road, Kirkham, Preston,
Lancashire PR4 2BH
Tel: 01772 671079
Headmaster: Mr D R Walker MA(Cantab)
Age range: 3–18
No. of pupils: 950 B493 G457 Vlth150
Fees: Day £6795–£9060 WB £16,772
FB £17,178

Lancaster Steiner School
Lune Road, Lancaster,
Lancashire LA1 5QU
Tel: 01524 841351
Headteacher: Mrs Denise Randal
Age range: 0–14

Moorland School
Ribblesdale Avenue, Clitheroe,
Lancashire BB7 2JA
Tel: 01200 423833
Principal: Mr T Smith BSc(Hons), PGCE
Age range: 3 months–16 years
No. of pupils: B75 G61
Fees: Day £4650–£5190
WB £10,800–£12,750
FB £11,250–£13,500

Mount Carmel School
1 Aughton Park Drive, Aughton Park,
Ormskirk, Lancashire L39 5BU
Tel: 01695 573254
Headteacher: Mrs Anne Eckersley CertEd
Age range: 4–11
No. of pupils: 75 B30 G45
Fees: Day £4485–£4920

Oakhill College
Wiswell Lane, Whalley, Clitheroe,
Lancashire BB7 9AF
Tel: 01254 823546
Principal: Michael A Kennedy BSc, MA
Age range: 2–16
No. of pupils: 268 B133 G135
Fees: Day £4767–£7389

Preston Muslim Girls High School
36 Deepdale Mill Street, Preston,
Lancashire PR1 6QL
Tel: 01772 651906
Head Teacher & Proprietor: Mr Y Seedat
Age range: 11–16
No. of pupils: 120
Fees: Day £650

Rossall School
Broadway, Fleetwood,
Lancashire FY7 8JW
Tel: +44 (0)1253 774260
Headmaster: Dr Stephen Winkley
Age range: 2–18
No. of pupils: 696 B390 G306 Vlth216
Fees: Day £7260–£11,700
WB £11,880–£19,350
FB £17,700–£29,220

St Anne's College Grammar School
293 Clifton Drive South, Lytham St
Annes, Lancashire FY8 1HN
Tel: 01253 725815
Joint Principals: Mr & Mrs S Welsby
Age range: 3–18
No. of pupils: B90 G95 Vlth15
Fees: Day £4500–£6300 WB £5000
FB £7000

St Joseph's Convent School
Park Hill, Padiham Road, Burnley,
Lancashire BB12 6TG
Tel: 01282 455622
Headmistress: Mrs Annette Robinson
Age range: 3–11
No. of pupils: B60 G65
Fees: Day £4650

St Mary's Hall
Stonyhurst, Lancashire BB7 9PU
Tel: 01254 827016
Headmaster: Mr L A Crouch BA, MA,
PGCE
Age range: 3–13
No. of pupils: 270 B124 G93
Fees: Day £6141–£12,246 WB £15,522
FB £17,646

St Pius X Preparatory School
Oak House, 200 Garstang Road,
Fulwood, Preston, Lancashire PR2 8RD
Tel: 01772 719937
Headmistress: Miss B M Banks MA
Age range: 2–11
No. of pupils: 260 B138 G122
Fees: Day £5300–£6150

STONYHURST COLLEGE
For further details see p. 119
Stonyhurst, Clitheroe,
Lancashire BB7 9PZ
Tel: 01254 826345
Email: admissions@stonyhurst.ac.uk
Website: www.stonyhurst.ac.uk
Headmaster: A Johnson BA
Age range: 13–18
No. of pupils: 470 Vlth221
Fees: Day £6681–£15,915
WB £17,289–£23,703
FB £20,406–£28,443

The Alternative School
The Old Library, Fern Lea Avenue,
Barnoldswick, Lancashire BB18 5DW
Tel: 01282 851800
Age range: 13–16
No. of pupils: B21 G7

The Bennett House School
332 Eaves Lane, Chorley,
Lancashire PR6 0DX
Tel: 01257 267393
Headmistress: Mrs C A Mills MA
Age range: 0–5
No. of pupils: B12 G12

MERSEYSIDE

Auckland College
65-67 Parkfield Road, Wavertree,
Liverpool, Merseyside L17 4LE
Tel: 0151 727 0083
Headmaster: Simon Parris
Age range: 0–18
No. of pupils: 172 B98 G74 Vlth15
Fees: Day £5656

Avalon Preparatory School
Caldy Road, West Kirby, Wirral,
Merseyside CH48 2HE
Tel: 0151 625 6993
Headmaster: Mr M Lloyd
Age range: 2–11
No. of pupils: 178 B88 G90
Fees: Day £1860–£5205

Belvedere Preparatory School
23 Belvidere Road, Princes Park,
Aigburth, Liverpool, Merseyside L8 3TF
Tel: 0151 471 1137
Head: Mrs J Humble
Age range: 3–11
No. of pupils: 180

Birkenhead School
The Lodge, 58 Beresford Road,
Birkenhead, Merseyside CH43 2JD
Tel: 0151 652 4014
Headmaster: Mr David John Clark MA
Age range: 3 months–18 years
No. of pupils: B562 G245 VIth103
Fees: Day £6645–£9606

Carleton House Preparatory School
145 Menlove Avenue, Liverpool,
Merseyside L18 3EE
Tel: 0151 722 0756
Head: Mr Peter Andrew
Age range: 4–11
No. of pupils: 145
Fees: Day £5928

Christian Fellowship School
Overbury Street, Edge Hill, Liverpool,
Merseyside L7 3HL
Tel: 0151 709 1642
Headteacher: Miss Barbara Lord
Age range: 4–16
No. of pupils: 191
Fees: Day £1752–£3528

Clarendon College School
Garston Old Road, Garston, Liverpool,
Merseyside L19 9AF
Tel: 0151 494 2094
Head: Mr D Thomas
Age range: 3–16
No. of pupils: 25

Kingsmead School
Bertram Drive, Hoylake, Wirral,
Merseyside CH47 0LL
Tel: 0151 632 3156
Headmaster: Mr M G Gibbons BComm,
MSc, QTS
Age range: 3–16
No. of pupils: B135 G81
Fees: Day £2625–£9105
WB £13,050–£15,345
FB £13,755–£16,050

Liverpool College
Queen's Drive, Mossley Hill, Liverpool,
Merseyside L18 8BG
Tel: 0151 724 4000
Principal: Hans van Mourik Broekman
Age range: 3–18
No. of pupils: 806
Fees: Day £5415–£8595

Merchant Taylors' Boys' School
Liverpool Road, Crosby, Liverpool,
Merseyside L23 0QP
Tel: 0151 928 3308
Headmaster: Mr D Cook MA
Age range: 7–18
No. of pupils: 760 VIth165
Fees: Day £6201–£8424

Merchant Taylors' Girls' School
Liverpool Road, Crosby, Liverpool,
Merseyside L23 5SP
Tel: 0151 924 3140
Headmistress: Mrs L A Robinson MEd,
BA(Hons), NPQH
Age range: B4–7 G4–18
No. of pupils: 880 B80 G800 VIth130
Fees: Day £6936–£9375

Newton Bank Preparatory School
34 High Street, Newton-le-Willows,
Merseyside WA12 9SN
Tel: 01925 225979
Headmistress: Mrs J Butler
Age range: 3–11
No. of pupils: 60 B30 G30
Fees: Day £1350

Prenton Preparatory School
Mount Pleasant, Oxton, Wirral,
Merseyside CH43 5SY
Tel: 0151 652 3182
Headmistress: Mrs N M Aloe
Age range: 2½–11
Fees: Day £4650

Redcourt St Anselm's
Redcourt, Devonshire Place, Birkenhead,
Merseyside L43 1TX
Tel: 0151 652 5228
Headmaster: Mr K S Davey
Age range: 3–11
No. of pupils: 320 B160 G160
Fees: Day £2500–£3000

Riverside Study Centre
Stretton Way, Huyton, Liverpool,
Merseyside L36 6JF
Tel: 0151 4804000
Headteacher: Mr H T Davies
Age range: 5–18
No. of pupils: 78 B29 G49 VIth12

Runnymede St Edward's School
North Drive, Sandfield Park, Liverpool,
Merseyside L12 1LE
Tel: 0151 281 2300
Headmaster: Mr Bradley Slater
Age range: 3–11
No. of pupils: 270 B180 G90
Fees: Day £6276–£6617

St Mary's College
Crosby, Liverpool, Merseyside L23 3AB
Tel: 0151 924 3926
Principal: Mr Michael Kennedy
Age range: 0–18
No. of pupils: 880 B459 G421 VIth132
Fees: Day £4815–£7533

Streatham House School
Victoria Road West, Blundellsands,
Liverpool, Merseyside L23 8UQ
Tel: 0151 924 1514
Executive Headteacher: Mrs Debby
Rigby BA(Hons), PGCE, CertEd(Man)
Age range: B3 months–11 G3 months–17
No. of pupils: B25 G90
Fees: Day £4680–£7352

TOWER COLLEGE
For further details see p. 121
Mill Lane, Rainhill, Prescot,
Merseyside L35 6NE
Tel: 0151 426 4333
Email: missoxley@towercollege.com
Website: www.towercollege.com
Principal: Miss R J Oxley NNEB, RSH
Age range: 3–16
No. of pupils: 486 B234 G252
Fees: Day £5013–£5895

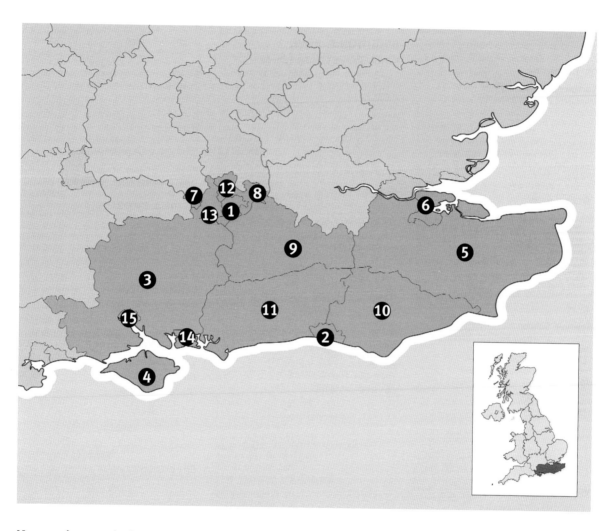

Key and page index:

BRACKNELL FOREST

EAGLE HOUSE SCHOOL
For further details see p. 128
Sandhurst, Bracknell Forest GU47 8PH
Tel: 01344 772134
Email: info@eaglehouseschool.com
Website: www.eaglehouseschool.com
Headmaster: Mr A P N Barnard
BA(Hons), PGCE
Age range: 3–13
No. of pupils: 360 B220 G140
Fees: Day £9300–£14,850 FB £19,950

Lambrook School
Winkfield Row, Bracknell,
Bracknell Forest RG42 6LU
Tel: 01344 882717
Headmaster: Mr Jonathan Perry
Age range: 3–13
No. of pupils: 440 B273 G167
Fees: Day £9078–£15,180
WB £16,803–£18,009
FB £17,433–£18,639

Meadowbrook Montessori School
Malt Hill Road, Warfield, Bracknell,
Bracknell Forest RG12 6JQ
Tel: 01344 890869
Head of School: Mrs S Gunn
Age range: 2½–12
No. of pupils: B60 G60
Fees: Day £670–£2215

Newbold School
Popeswood Road, Binfield, Bracknell,
Bracknell Forest RG42 4AH
Tel: 01344 421088
Headteacher: Mrs P Eastwood
Age range: 3–11
No. of pupils: B40 G55
Fees: Day £3000–£4000

Wellington College
Duke's Ride, Crowthorne,
Bracknell Forest RG45 7PU
Tel: +44 (0)1344 444 000
Master: Dr Anthony Seldon
Age range: 13–18
No. of pupils: 1050 B646 G404 VIth484
Fees: Day £23,610–£26,760 FB £31,500

BRIGHTON & HOVE

Bartholomews Tutorial College
22-23 Prince Albert Street, Brighton,
Brighton & Hove BN1 1HF
Tel: 01273 205965/205141
Governor: W A Duncombe BSc
Age range: 14+
No. of pupils: 40 B20 G20 VIth30
Fees: Day £16,300–£19,300
WB £20,000–£23,000
FB £20,000–£23,000

Bellerbys College
44 Cromwell Road, Hove,
Brighton & Hove BN3 3EU
Tel: 01273 339373
Principal: N Addison
Age range: 14–20
No. of pupils: 700 VIth610
Fees: FB £17,500–£21,000

Brighton & Hove High School GDST
Montpelier Road, Brighton,
Brighton & Hove BN1 3AT
Tel: 01273 280280
Head: Mrs Lorna Duggleby
Age range: 3–18
No. of pupils: 680 VIth70
Fees: Day £5028–£8898

Brighton & Hove Montessori School
67 Stanford Avenue, Brighton,
Brighton & Hove BN1 6FB
Tel: 01273 702485
Headteacher: Mrs Daisy Cockburn AMI,
MontDip
Age range: 2–11
No. of pupils: B33 G27
Fees: Day £1400–£5900

Brighton College
Eastern Road, Brighton,
Brighton & Hove BN2 0AL
Tel: 01273 704200
Head Master: Richard Cairns MA
Age range: 3–18
No. of pupils: 945 B497 G448 VIth340
Fees: Day £4890–£18,675
WB £24,729–£25,884
FB £28,575–£30,141

Brighton Steiner School
John Howard House, Roedean Road,
Brighton, Brighton & Hove BN2 5RA
Tel: 01273 386300
Chair of the College of Teachers: Carrie
Rawle
Age range: 3–16
No. of pupils: B94 G98
Fees: Day £6540

Deepdene School
195 New Church Road, Hove,
Brighton & Hove BN3 4ED
Tel: 01273 418984
Heads: Mrs L V Clark-Darby BEd(Hons),
CertFS & Mrs N K Gane NNEB
Age range: 1–11
No. of pupils: B114 G106
Fees: Day £1800–£5760

Key to symbols

(†) Boys' school

(♦) Girls' school

(🌐) International school

(16) Tutorial or sixth form college

(A) A levels

(⌂) Boarding accommodation

(£) Bursaries

(IB) International Baccalaureate

(✎) Learning support

(16) Entrance at 16+

(❀) Vocational qualifications

(IAPS) Member of Independent Association of Preparatory Schools

(HMC) The Headmasters' & Headmistresses' Conference

(ISA) Independent Schools Association

(GSA) Girls' School Association

(BSA) Boarding Schools' Association

(S) SHMIS

Unless otherwise indicated, all schools are coeducational
day schools. Single-sex and boarding schools will be
indicated by the relevant icon.

Dharma School
The White House, Ladies Mile Road,
Patcham, Brighton,
Brighton & Hove BN1 8TB
Tel: 01273 502055
Headmaster: Kevin Fossey BEd
Age range: 3–11
No. of pupils: B33 G31
Fees: Day £3000

K-BIS Theatre School
Clermont Hall, Cumberland Road,
Brighton, Brighton & Hove BN1 6SL
Tel: 01273 566739
Principal: Mrs Marcia King LGSM
Age range: 5–18
No. of pupils: B11 G33 VIth7
Fees: Day £5980

Lancing College Preparatory School at Mowden
The Droveway, Hove,
Brighton & Hove BN3 6LU
Tel: 01273 503452
Headmaster: A P Laurent
Age range: 3–13
No. of pupils: 181 B136 G45
Fees: Day £2550–£10,155

Roedean School
Roedean Way, Brighton,
Brighton & Hove BN2 5RQ
Tel: 01273 667500
Headmistress: Mrs Frances King
MA(Oxon), MA(London), MBA(Hull)
Age range: 11–18
No. of pupils: 400 VIth177
Fees: Day £15,750–£18,150
WB £24,450–£27,300
FB £28,200–£31,350

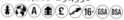

St Aubyns
76 High Street, Rottingdean, Brighton,
Brighton & Hove BN2 7JN
Tel: 01273 302170
Headmaster: Mr Simon Hitchings
Age range: 3–13
No. of pupils: B117 G67
Fees: Day £4992–£13,350
WB £12,000–£15,900

St Christopher's School
33 New Church Road, Hove,
Brighton & Hove BN3 4AD
Tel: 01273 735404
Headmaster: Mr I McIntyre
Age range: 4–13
No. of pupils: B177 G65
Fees: Day £6570–£8688

The Drive Prep School
101 The Drive, Hove,
Brighton & Hove BN3 3JE
Tel: 01273 738444
Head Teacher: Mrs S Parkinson CertEd,
CertPerfArts
Age range: 7–16
No. of pupils: B42 G30
Fees: Day £3885–£7500

Torah Academy
31 New Church Road, Hove,
Brighton & Hove BN3 4AD
Tel: 01273 683 390
Principal: P Efune
Age range: 4–11
No. of pupils: B24 G28

Windlesham School
190 Dyke Road, Brighton,
Brighton & Hove BN1 5AA
Tel: 01273 553645
Headmistress: Mrs Aoife Bennett-Odlum
Age range: 3–11
No. of pupils: 233 B118 G115
Fees: Day £5100–£7200

EAST SUSSEX

Ashdown House School
Forest Row, East Sussex RH18 5JY
Tel: 01342 822574
Headmaster: Dominic Floyd
Age range: 7–13
No. of pupils: 141 B71 G70
Fees: FB £20,640

Battle Abbey School
Battle, East Sussex TN33 0AD
Tel: 01424 772385
Headmaster: Mr R C Clark BA(Hons),
MA(Ed)
Age range: 2–18
No. of pupils: 286 B140 G146 VIth48
Fees: Day £6630–£13,390 FB £23,190

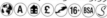

Bricklehurst Manor Preparatory
Bardown Road, Stonegate, Wadhurst,
East Sussex TN5 7EL
Tel: 01580 200448
Headteacher: Mrs C Flowers
Age range: 3–11
No. of pupils: 127 B48 G79
Fees: Day £980–£8925

Buckswood School
Broomham Hall, Rye Road, Guestling,
Hastings, East Sussex TN35 4LT
Tel: 01424 813813
Headmaster: Mr Tim Fish BA
Age range: 10–19
No. of pupils: 280
Fees: Day £9270 WB £14,970
FB £15,660–£19,800

Buckswood St George's
Broomham Hall, Rye Road, Guestling, Nr
Hastings, East Sussex TN35 4LT
Tel: 01424 813696
Age range: 16
Fees: FB £17,250–£21,000

Charters Ancaster College
Woodsgate Place, Gunters Lane, Bexhill-
on-Sea, East Sussex TN39 4EB
Tel: 01424 216670
Headmistress: Mrs Miriam Black
Age range: 2½–13
No. of pupils: 125 B62 G63
Fees: Day £5325–£6750

Claremont Preparatory & Nursery School
Ebdens Hill, Baldslow, St Leonards-on-
Sea, East Sussex TN37 7PW
Tel: 01424 751555
Headmaster: Mr R Keeble
Age range: 1–14
No. of pupils: B200 G200
Fees: Day £5025–£8550

Darvell School
Darvell Bruderhof, Robertsbridge,
East Sussex TN32 5DR
Tel: 01580 883300
Headteacher: Mr Arnold Meier
Age range: 4–16
No. of pupils: 121 B56 G65

EASTBOURNE COLLEGE
For further details see p. 129
Old Wish Road, Eastbourne,
East Sussex BN21 4JX
Tel: 01323 452323
Email: admissions@eastbourne-
college.co.uk
Website: www.eastbourne-college.co.uk
Headmaster: Mr S P Davies MA
Age range: 13–19
No. of pupils: 621 B355 G266 VIth273
Fees: Day £17,985 FB £27,315

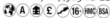

Greenfields School
Priory Road, Forest Row,
East Sussex RH18 5JD
Tel: 01342 822189
Headteacher: Mr G Hudson
Age range: 3–19
No. of pupils: 112 B74 G38 VIth5
Fees: Day £2100–£7500
WB £17,100–£19,000
FB £17,100–£19,000

Lewes New School
Talbot Terrace, Lewes,
East Sussex BN7 2DS
Tel: 01273 477074
Head Teacher: Lizzie Overton
Age range: 3–11
No. of pupils: 76
Fees: Day £3300–£3600

Lewes Old Grammar School
High Street, Lewes,
East Sussex BN7 1XS
Tel: 01273 472634
Headmaster: Mr Robert Blewitt
Age range: 3–18
No. of pupils: 463 B284 G179 VIth50
Fees: Day £5550–£10,815

Michael Hall School
Kidbrooke Park, Forest Row,
East Sussex RH18 5JB
Tel: 01342 822275
Age range: 3–19
No. of pupils: B233 G281 VIth35
Fees: Day £7900–£11,250
WB £170–£200 FB £5400–£7800

Moira House Girls School
Upper Carlisle Road, Eastbourne,
East Sussex BN20 7TE
Tel: 01323 644144
Principal: Mrs L A Watson MA(Ed),
MInstD
Age range: 2–18
No. of pupils: 360 VIth105
Fees: Day £6150–£14,295
WB £18,510–£23,130
FB £19,920–£25,530

Newlands School
Eastbourne Road, Seaford,
East Sussex BN25 4NP
Tel: 01323 490000
Headmaster: Mr C Bridgman BEd(Hons)
Age range: 2–18
Fees: Day £5400–£10,800
WB £12,450–£17,850
FB £12,600–£18,000

Sacred Heart School
Mayfield Lane, Durgates, Wadhurst,
East Sussex TN5 6DQ
Tel: 01892 783414
Headteacher: Mrs H Blake BA(Hons),
PGCE
Age range: 3–11
No. of pupils: B63 G43
Fees: Day £2175–£6030

Skippers Hill Manor Prep School
Five Ashes, Mayfield,
East Sussex TN20 6HR
Tel: 01825 830234
Headmaster: T W Lewis BA(Exon),
PGCE(London)
Age range: 4–13
No. of pupils: 101 B60 G41
Fees: Day £5021–£12,189

St Andrew's Preparatory School
Meads, Eastbourne,
East Sussex BN20 7RP
Tel: 01323 733203
Headmaster: Jeremy Griffith BA, PGCE
Age range: 2–13
No. of pupils: B252 G143
Fees: Day £7842–£13,020 WB £16,431
FB £18,495

St Bede's Preparatory School
Duke's Drive, Eastbourne,
East Sussex BN20 7XL
Tel: 01323 734222
Head: Mr Nicholas Bevington
Age range: 3 months–13 years
No. of pupils: 395 B235 G160

St Bede's School
The Dicker, Hailsham,
East Sussex BN27 3QH
Tel: 01323 843252
Head: Dr Richard Maloney
Age range: 12½–18+
No. of pupils: 800 B485 G315 VIth295
Fees: Day £15,450 FB £25,725

St Leonards-Mayfield School
The Old Palace, Mayfield,
East Sussex TN20 6PH
Tel: 01435 874600
Head: Miss Antonia Beary MA,
Mphil(Cantab), PGCE
Age range: 11–18
No. of pupils: 420 G420 VIth100
Fees: Day £15,285 WB £23,010
FB £23,010

VINEHALL SCHOOL
For further details see p. 142
Robertsbridge, East Sussex TN32 5JL
Tel: 01580 880413
Email: registrar@vinehallschool.com
Website: www.vinehallschool.com
Headmaster: Richard Follett
Age range: 2–13
No. of pupils: 270 B146 G124
Fees: Day £1035–£15,180
FB £19,440–£26,400

Walsh Manor School
Walshes Road, Crowborough,
East Sussex TN6 3RB
Tel: 01892 610823
Headteacher: Mrs Angela Paris
Age range: 10–16
No. of pupils: 22 B8 G14

HAMPSHIRE

Allbrook School
The Old School, Pitmore Road, Allbrook,
Eastleigh, Hampshire SO50 4LW
Tel: 023 8061 6316
Head of Studies: Mrs Hilary Laider
Age range: 11–16
No. of pupils: 79 B51 G28

Alton Convent School
Anstey Lane, Alton,
Hampshire GU34 2NG
Tel: 01420 82070
Headmistress: Mrs S Kirkham BA(Hons),
MA
Age range: B0–11 G0–18
No. of pupils: 504 B80 G424 VIth35
Fees: Day £8580–£10,290

Ballard School
Fernhill Lane, New Milton,
Hampshire BH25 5SU
Tel: 01425 611153
Headmaster: Mr Alastair Reid
Age range: 1–16
No. of pupils: 500 B275 G225
Fees: Day £2193–£3933

Bedales School
Church Road, Steep, Petersfield,
Hampshire GU32 2DG
Tel: 01730 711569
Head: Keith Budge MA
Age range: 13–18
No. of pupils: 444 B209 G235 VIth166
Fees: Day £22,550 FB £29,955

Boundary Oak School
Roche Court, Fareham,
Hampshire PO17 5BL
Tel: 01329 280955/820373
Headmaster: Mr Stephen Symonds
BAEd(Hons)
Age range: 2¾–13
No. of pupils: 140
Fees: Day £3240–£10,800
WB £11,310–£15,390
FB £14,970–£17,295

Brockwood Park & Inwoods School
Bramdean, Hampshire SO24 0LQ
Tel: 01962 771 744
Principals: Bill Taylor & Adrian
Sydenham
Age range: 4–19
No. of pupils: 92 B46 G46
Fees: Day £3150 FB £17,270

Brookham School
Highfield Lane, Liphook,
Hampshire GU30 7LQ
Tel: 01428 722005
Headmistress: Mrs D Gardiner
Age range: 3–8
No. of pupils: 141 B76 G65
Fees: Day £2190–£7875

CHURCHER'S COLLEGE
For further details see p. 127
Petersfield, Hampshire GU31 4AS
Tel: 01730 263033
Email: enquiries@churcherscollege.com
Website: www.churcherscollege.com
Headmaster: Mr Simon Williams MA, BSc
Age range: 4–18
No. of pupils: 1055 B606 G449 VIth216
Fees: Day £7350–£11,550

Daneshill School
Stratfield Turgis, Basingstoke,
Hampshire RG27 0AR
Tel: 01256 882707
Headmaster: S V Spencer CertEd,
DipPhysEd
Age range: 3–13
No. of pupils: B147 G150
Fees: Day £3900–£9150

Ditcham Park School
Ditcham Park, Petersfield,
Hampshire GU31 5RN
Tel: 01730 825659
Headteacher: A P N Rowley BSc (Hons),
PGCE
Age range: 4–16
No. of pupils: 366 B186 G180
Fees: Day £6786–£11,328

Dunhurst (Bedales Junior School)
Petersfield, Hampshire GU32 2DP
Tel: 01730 300200
Head: Jane Grubb
Age range: 8–13
No. of pupils: 199 B87 G112
Fees: Day £16,635 FB £21,255

Durlston Court
Becton Lane, Barton-on-Sea, New
Milton, Hampshire BH25 7AQ
Tel: 01425 610010
Headmaster: David Wansey
Age range: 2–13
No. of pupils: 304 B170 G134
Fees: Day £3540–£12,255

Farleigh School
Red Rice, Andover, Hampshire SP11 7PW
Tel: 01264 710766
Headmaster: Father Simon Everson
Age range: 3–13
No. of pupils: B230 G188
Fees: Day £3870–£14,085
FB £16,515–£18,345

Farnborough Hill
Farnborough Road, Farnborough,
Hampshire GU14 8AT
Tel: 01252 545197
Headmistress: Mrs S Buckle BSc, MA,
PGCE, NPQH
Age range: 11–18
No. of pupils: 528 VIth70
Fees: Day £10,320

Forres Sandle Manor
Fordingbridge, Hampshire SP6 1NS
Tel: 01425 653181
Headmaster: Mr M N Hartley BSc(Hons)
Age range: 3–13
No. of pupils: 264 B146 G118
Fees: Day £3150–£14,205 WB £19,380
FB £19,380

GEMS Sherfield School
Sherfield-on-Loddon, Hook,
Hampshire RG27 0HU
Tel: +44 (0)1256 884 800
Headmaster: Mr Dick Jaine
Age range: 3 months–18 years
No. of pupils: 445 B253 G192 VIth16
Fees: Day £7350–£13,890 FB £20,946

Glenhurst School
16 Beechworth Road, Havant,
Hampshire PO9 1AX
Tel: 023 9248 4054
Principal: Mrs E M Haines
Age range: 3 months–8 years
No. of pupils: B50 G50
Fees: Day £4500

Hampshire Collegiate School
Embley Park, Romsey,
Hampshire SO51 6ZE
Tel: 01794 512206
Principal: Hector McDonald
Age range: 2–18
No. of pupils: 691 B386 G305 VIth100

Highfield School
Liphook, Hampshire GU30 7LQ
Tel: 01428 728000
Headmaster: Mr Philip Evitt MA
Age range: 8–13
No. of pupils: B114 G105
Fees: Day £10,800–£14,100
FB £14,100–£16,050

Hill Head Preparatory School
51 Crofton Lane, Hill Head, Fareham,
Hampshire PO14 3LW
Tel: 01329 662666
Headmistress: Mrs B M A Barber
BEd(Hons), CertEd
Age range: 2–8
No. of pupils: 55 B24 G31
Fees: Day £2400–£2700

Hordle Walhampton School
Walhampton, Lymington,
Hampshire SO41 5ZG
Tel: 01590 672013
Headmaster: R H C Phillips BA(Hons),
CertEd, LGSM
Age range: 2–13
No. of pupils: B177 G159
Fees: Day £5970–£11,940 FB £15,720

Kingscourt School
Catherington Lane, Catherington,
Hampshire PO8 9NJ
Tel: 023 9259 3251
Headmistress: Mrs J L Easton
Age range: 2¾–11
No. of pupils: B80 G80
Fees: Day £5430

Lord Wandsworth College
Long Sutton, Hook,
Hampshire RG29 1TB
Tel: 01256 862201
Headmaster: Mr Fergus Livingstone
MA(Cantab)
Age range: 11–18
No. of pupils: 530 B360 G170 VIth160
Fees: Day £17,718–£18,660
WB £23,730–£25,044
FB £23,730–£26,310

Meoncross School
Burnt House Lane, Stubbington,
Fareham, Hampshire PO14 2EF
Tel: 01329 662182
Headmaster: Mr Adrian Steele
Age range: 2¾–16
No. of pupils: 405
Fees: Day £5940–£8835

Moyles Court School
Moyles Court, Ringwood,
Hampshire BH24 3NF
Tel: 01425 472856
Headmaster: Mr Dean
Age range: 3–16
No. of pupils: B83 G63
Fees: Day £3285–£4650
FB £6690–£7740

New Forest Small School
1 Southampton Road, Lyndhurst,
Hampshire SO43 7BU
Tel: 07720722100
Headteacher: Mr Nicholas Alp
Age range: 3–16
No. of pupils: B11 G8

Prince's Mead School
Worthy Park House, Kings Worthy,
Winchester, Hampshire SO21 1AN
Tel: 01962 888000
Headmistress: Miss P S Kirk
Age range: 3–11
No. of pupils: 266 B97 G169
Fees: Day £9000–£12,630

Ringwood Waldorf School
Folly Farm Lane, Ashley, Ringwood,
Hampshire BH24 2NN
Tel: 01425 472664
Age range: 3–16
No. of pupils: B144 G116
Fees: Day £1500–£6000

Rookesbury Park School
Wickham, Hampshire PO17 6HT
Tel: 01329 833108
Head: Mr Erawin Olie
Age range: 3–13
No. of pupils: 90 B45 G45
Fees: Day £3384–£12,378
FB £14,034–£18,372

Rookwood School
Weyhill Road, Andover,
Hampshire SP10 3AL
Tel: 01264 325900
Headmistress: Mrs L Whetstone MA
Age range: 3–16
No. of pupils: B120 G189
Fees: Day £6885–£11,340
FB £17,340–£20,295

Salesian College
Reading Road, Farnborough,
Hampshire GU14 6PA
Tel: 01252 893000
Headmaster: Mr P A Wilson BA(Hons),
MA, CertEd
Age range: B11–18 G16–18
No. of pupils: 650 B620 G30 VIth140
Fees: Day £9000

Sherborne House School
Lakewood Road, Chandlers Ford,
Eastleigh, Hampshire SO53 1EU
Tel: 023 8025 2440
Headmistress: Mrs Heather Hopson-Hill
Age range: 2 3/4–11
No. of pupils: 250 B125 G125
Fees: Day £1761–£8100

St Neot's School
St Neot's Road, Eversley, Hook,
Hampshire RG27 0PN
Tel: 0118 973 2118
Headmaster: Mr R J Thorp BA(Dunelm),
PGCE(Cantab)
Age range: 3–13
No. of pupils: 326 B184 G142
Fees: Day £7965–£13,095 WB £16,230

St Nicholas School
Redfields House, Redfields Lane, Church
Crookham, Fleet, Hampshire GU13 0RE
Tel: 01252 850121
Headmistress: Mrs A V Whatmough BA,
CertEd
Age range: B3–7 G3–16
No. of pupils: 372 B10 G362
Fees: Day £3843–£10,440

St Swithun's Junior School
Alresford Road, Winchester,
Hampshire SO21 1HA
Tel: 01962 835750
Headmistress: Mrs P Grimes BA(Hons)
Age range: B3–7 G3–11
No. of pupils: 183 B7 G176
Fees: Day £1415–£3650

St Swithun's School
Alresford Road, Winchester,
Hampshire SO21 1HA
Tel: 01962 835700
Headmistress: Jane Gandee MA Cantab
Age range: 11–18
No. of pupils: 482 VIth120
Fees: Day £16,815 FB £27,210

Stanbridge Earls School
Stanbridge Lane, Romsey,
Hampshire SO51 0ZS
Tel: 01794 529400
Headmaster: Mr P Trythall BA
Age range: 10–19
No. of pupils: 197 B159 G38 VIth60
Fees: Day £14,232–£15,489
FB £19,095–£20,895

Stockton House School
Stockton Avenue, Fleet,
Hampshire GU13 8NS
Tel: 01252 616323
Early Years Manager: Mrs Sally Forrest
Age range: 2–5
No. of pupils: B60 G60

The Children's House and Grantham Farm Montessori School
Grantham Farm, Baughurst, Tadley,
Hampshire RG26 5JT
Tel: 0118 981 5821
Head: Mrs S De Boinville
Age range: 3–8

The Grey House School
Mount Pleasant, Hartley Wintney,
Hampshire RG27 8PW
Tel: 01252 842353
Head: Mrs C E Allen BEd(Cantab)
Age range: 4–11+
No. of pupils: B93 G50
Fees: Day £6708–£8418

The King's School
Basingstoke Community Church, Sarum
Hill, Basingstoke, Hampshire RG21 8SR
Tel: 01256 467092
Headteacher: Mr David Robotham
Age range: 7–16
No. of pupils: 172 B99 G73

The Pilgrims' School
3 The Close, Winchester,
Hampshire SO23 9LT
Tel: 01962 854189
Headmaster: Mr Paddy Watson
Age range: 4–13
No. of pupils: 250 B250
Fees: Day £15,440 FB £19,440

The Stroud School
Highwood House, Highwood Lane,
Romsey, Hampshire SO51 9ZH
Tel: 01794 513231
Headmaster: Mr Alastair J L Dodds
MA(Cantab)
Age range: 3–13
No. of pupils: B180 G128
Fees: Day £3420–£12,345

The Westgate School
Cheriton Road, Winchester,
Hampshire SO22 5AZ
Tel: 01962 854757
Headteacher: Mr P Nicholson
Age range: 11–16
No. of pupils: B545 G591
Fees: WB £7380 FB £7865

Twyford School
Twyford, Winchester,
Hampshire SO21 1NW
Tel: 01962 712269
Headmaster: Dr S J Bailey, Bed, PhD,
FRSA
Age range: 3–13
Fees: Day £7185–£16,780 WB £19,875

WEST HILL PARK PREPARATORY SCHOOL
For further details see p. 143
Titchfield, Fareham,
Hampshire PO14 4BS
Tel: 01329 842356
Email: admissions@westhillpark.com
Website: www.westhillpark.com
Headmaster: A P Ramsay BEd(Hons),
MSc
Age range: 2–13
No. of pupils: 288 B180 G108
Fees: Day £8985–£14,985
FB £13,785–£19,785

WINCHESTER COLLEGE
For further details see p. 144
College Street, Winchester,
Hampshire SO23 9NA
Tel: 01962 621247
Email: admissions@wincoll.ac.uk
Website: www.winchestercollege.org
Headmaster: R D Townsend MA, DPhil
Age range: 13–18
No. of pupils: 690 VIth280
Fees: FB £31,350

Woodhill School, Chandlers Ford
61 Brownhill Road, Chandlers Ford,
Hampshire SO53 2EH
Tel: 023 8026 8012
Head Teacher: Mr K Verdon
Age range: 3–11
No. of pupils: 100
Fees: Day £2199–£4965

Wykeham House School
East Street, Fareham,
Hampshire PO16 0BW
Tel: 01329 280178
Headmistress: Mrs L Clarke BSc(Hons),
PGCE, PGDip
Age range: 2¾–16
No. of pupils: 250
Fees: Day £9000

Yateley Manor School
51 Reading Road, Yateley,
Hampshire GU46 7UQ
Tel: 01252 405500
Headmaster: Mr R J Williams
MA(Hons)Edinburgh, PGCE Bedford
Age range: 3–13
No. of pupils: 453 B287 G166
Fees: Day £4500–£12,150

ISLE OF WIGHT

Priory School
Alverstone Manor, Luccombe Road,
Shanklin, Isle of Wight PO37 6RR
Tel: 01983 861222
Principal: Mr E Matyjaszek
Age range: 5–18
No. of pupils: B55 G45
Fees: Day £3360–£7200

Ryde School with Upper Chine
Queens Road, Ryde,
Isle of Wight PO33 3BE
Tel: 01983 562229
Headmaster: Dr Nicholas J England
Age range: 3–18
No. of pupils: 800 B395 G405 VIth136
Fees: Day £4290–£9045
WB £16,455–£17,325
FB £17,625–£18,495

KENT

Ashford School
East Hill, Ashford, Kent TN24 8PB
Tel: 01233 739030
Head: Mr M R Buchanan BSc(Hons),
CertEd, NPQH, CPhys
Age range: 3 months–18 years
No. of pupils: 813 B394 G419 VIth151
Fees: Day £6384–£14,763 WB £23,709
FB £27,225–£28,581

Beech Grove School
Beech Grove Bruderhof, Sandwich Road,
Nonington, Dover, Kent CT15 4HH
Tel: 01304 842980
Head: Mr Benjamin Shirky
Age range: 4–14
No. of pupils: 63 B33 G30

Beechwood Sacred Heart
12 Pembury Road, Tunbridge Wells,
Kent TN2 3QD
Tel: 01892 532747
Headmaster: Mr Nicholas Beesley
MA(Oxon)
Age range: 3–18
No. of pupils: 437 B185 G252 VIth70
Fees: Day £8505–£14,505
WB £21,330–£21,330
FB £24,060–£24,060

Benenden School
Cranbrook, Kent TN17 4AA
Tel: 01580 240592
Headmistress: Mrs C M Oulton
MA(Oxon)
Age range: 11–18
No. of pupils: 539 VIth186
Fees: FB £29,940

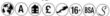

Bethany School
Goudhurst, Cranbrook, Kent TN17 1LB
Tel: 01580 211273
Headmaster: Mr N D B Dorey
MA(Cantab)
Age range: 11–18
No. of pupils: B293 G136 VIth128
Fees: Day £14,184 WB £21,504
FB £22,143

Bronte School
Mayfield, 7 Pelham Road, Gravesend,
Kent DA11 0HN
Tel: 01474 533805
Headmaster: Mr R Dyson
Age range: 4–11
No. of pupils: 120 B70 G50
Fees: Day £7500

Bryony School
Marshall Road, Rainham, Gillingham,
Kent ME8 0AJ
Tel: 01634 231511
Joint Heads: D E and Mrs M P Edmunds
Age range: 2–11
No. of pupils: 174 B89 G85
Fees: Day £4457–£4954

Canterbury Steiner School
Garlinge Green, Chartham, Canterbury,
Kent CT4 5RU
Tel: 01227 738285
Age range: 3–18
No. of pupils: B112 G121
Fees: Day £3246–£4406

CATS College Canterbury
68 New Dover Road, Canterbury,
Kent CT1 3LQ
Tel: +44 (0)1223 345698
Principal: Jonathan Ullmer MA, LRAM,
FCollP, ACP, Dip Arts, NPQH
Age range: 15–22
No. of pupils: 275

Chartfield School
45 Minster Road, Westgate on Sea,
Kent CT8 8DA
Tel: 01843 831716
Head & Proprietor: Miss L P Shipley
Age range: 4–11
No. of pupils: 50 B25 G25
Fees: Day £2580–£3000

Cobham Hall School
Cobham, Gravesend, Kent DA12 3BL
Tel: 01474 823371
Headmaster: Mr Paul Mitchell BSc
Age range: 11–18
No. of pupils: G200 VIth60
Fees: Day £13,500–£16,950
FB £20,250–£25,500

Combe Bank School
Sundridge, Sevenoaks, Kent TN14 6AE
Tel: 01959 563720
Head: Mrs J Abbotts MEd, NPQH
Age range: B3–5 G3–18
No. of pupils: 418 B18 G400 VIth50
Fees: Day £7830–£14,040

Cranbrook School
Waterloo Road, Cranbrook,
Kent TN17 3JD
Tel: 01580 711800
Head: Mrs Angela Daly BA(Hons)
Age range: 13–18
No. of pupils: 770 B405 G365 VIth340
Fees: FB £9300–£10,005

Derwent Lodge School for Girls
Somerhill, Tonbridge, Kent TN11 0NJ
Tel: 01732 352124
Headmistress: Mrs S Michau MA(Oxon),
PGCE
Age range: 7–11
No. of pupils: 144
Fees: Day £12,675

Dover College
Effingham Crescent, Dover,
Kent CT17 9RH
Tel: 01304 205969 Ext 201
Headmaster: Gary Holden
Age range: 3–18
No. of pupils: 340 B170 G170 VIth100
Fees: Day £6120–£12,990
WB £17,400–£20,780
FB £19,050–£25,950

Dulwich Preparatory School
Coursehorn, Cranbrook, Kent TN17 3NP
Tel: 01580 712179
Headmaster: Mr Paul David BEd(Hons)
Age range: 3–13
No. of pupils: 535 B295 G240
Fees: Day £4890–£14,400

Elliott Park School
18-20 Marina Drive, Minster, Sheerness,
Kent ME12 2DP
Tel: 01795 873372
Head: Mr R Barson
Age range: 4–11
No. of pupils: 60
Fees: Day £3897

Fosse Bank School
Mountains, Noble Tree Road,
Hildenborough, Tonbridge,
Kent TN11 8ND
Tel: 01732 834212
Headmistress: Mrs Lovatt-Young
Age range: 3–11
No. of pupils: 124 B74 G50
Fees: Day £1380–£9435

Haddon Dene School
57 Gladstone Road, Broadstairs,
Kent CT10 2HY
Tel: 01843 861176
Head: Mrs E Rowe
Age range: 3–11
No. of pupils: 200 B105 G95
Fees: Day £4950–£6135

Hilden Grange School
62 Dry Hill Park Road, Tonbridge,
Kent TN10 3BX
Tel: 01732 351169
Headmaster: Mr J Withers BA(Hons)
Age range: 3–13
No. of pupils: 300 B200 G100
Fees: Day £8844–£11,154

Hilden Oaks School
38 Dry Hill Park Road, Tonbridge,
Kent TN10 3BU
Tel: 01732 353941
Headmistress: Mrs S A Sunderland
Age range: 0–11
No. of pupils: B24 G156
Fees: Day £6450–£8805

Holmewood House School
Langton Green, Tunbridge Wells,
Kent TN3 0EB
Tel: 01892 860000
Headmaster: Mr A S R Corbett MA
Age range: 3–13
No. of pupils: 440 B260 G180
Fees: Day £5165–£15,165

Kent College
Whitstable Road, Canterbury,
Kent CT2 9DT
Tel: 01227 763231
Head Master: Dr D J Lamper
Age range: 11–18
No. of pupils: 457 VIth156
Fees: Day £8805–£14,028
WB £23,000–£23,340
FB £18,390–£24,690

Kent College Nursery, Infant & Junior School
Vernon Holme, Harbledown, Canterbury,
Kent CT2 9AQ
Tel: 01227 762436
Headmaster: Mr A J Carter
Age range: 3–11
No. of pupils: 190 B101 G89
Fees: Day £8805–£9615 WB £14,196
FB £18,400

KENT COLLEGE PEMBURY
For further details see p. 134
Old Church Road, Pembury, Tunbridge
Wells, Kent TN2 4AX
Tel: 01892 822006
Email:
admissions@kentcollege.kent.sch.uk
Website: www.kent-college.co.uk
Headmistress: Mrs Sally-Anne Huang
MA(Oxon), MSc, PGCE
Age range: 3–18
No. of pupils: 600 VIth102
Fees: Day £7584–£18,156
FB £20,646–£26,850

Linton Park School
3 Eccleston Road, Tovil, Maidstone,
Kent ME17 4HT
Tel: 01622 740820
Headteacher: Mr C Allen
Age range: 7–18
No. of pupils: 134 B80 G54

Lorenden Preparatory School
Painter's Forstal, Faversham,
Kent ME13 0EN
Tel: 01795 590030
Headmistress: Mrs P Tebbit CertEd,
DipPrimEng(Adu)
Age range: 3–11
No. of pupils: 100 B50 G50
Fees: Day £3180–£8520

Marlborough House School
High Street, Hawkhurst, Kent TN18 4PY
Tel: 01580 753555
Headmaster: Mr David N Hopkins
MA(Oxon), PGCE
Age range: 3–13
No. of pupils: 334 B184 G150
Fees: Day £2550–£14,295

Meredale Independent Primary School
Solomon Road, Rainham, Gillingham,
Kent ME8 8EB
Tel: 01634 231405
Headteacher: Miss Michelle Ingledew
Age range: 3–11
No. of pupils: 53 B29 G24
Fees: Day £5100

Northbourne Park School
Betteshanger, Deal, Kent CT14 0NW
Tel: 01304 611215/218
Headmaster: Mr Edward Balfour
Age range: 3–13
No. of pupils: 185 B95 G90
Fees: Day £11,400–£13,740
WB £16,140–£16,140
FB £119,200–£19,200

Rose Hill School
Coniston Avenue, Tunbridge Wells,
Kent TN4 9SY
Tel: 01892 525591
Headmaster: Mr D Westcombe BA, PGCE
Age range: 3–13
No. of pupils: 314 B177 G137
Fees: Day £2775–£3880

Russell House School
Station Road, Otford, Sevenoaks,
Kent TN14 5QU
Tel: 01959 522352
Headmistress: Mrs Alison Cooke
Age range: 2–11
No. of pupils: B96 G97
Fees: Day £4650–£9840

Sackville School
Tonbridge Rd, Hildenborough,
Tonbridge, Kent TN11 9HN
Tel: 01732 838888
Headteacher: Mr Peter S Lane BSc
Age range: 11–18
No. of pupils: 184 B143 G41 VIth35
Fees: Day £12,195

Saint Ronan's School
Water Lane, Hawkhurst, Kent TN18 5DJ
Tel: 01580 752271
Headmaster: William Trelawny-Vernon
BSc(Hons)
Age range: 3–13
No. of pupils: 300 B170 G130
Fees: Day £6951–£11,892

Sevenoaks Preparatory School
Fawke Cottage, Godden Green,
Sevenoaks, Kent TN15 0JU
Tel: 01732 762336
Headmaster: Mr P J Oldroyd
Age range: 2–13
No. of pupils: 388 B224 G164
Fees: Day £2320–£3280

Sevenoaks School
High Street, Sevenoaks, Kent TN13 1HU
Tel: +44 (0)1732 455133
Head: Mrs Katy Ricks MA
Age range: 11–18
No. of pupils: 1020 B496 G524 Vlth421
Fees: Day £17,838–£20,265
FB £28,611–£31,038

Shernold School
Hill Place, Queens Avenue, Maidstone,
Kent ME16 0ER
Tel: 01622 752868
Headmistress: Mrs L Dack
Age range: 3–11
No. of pupils: 142 B50 G92
Fees: Day £3525–£4200

Solefield School
Solefield Road, Sevenoaks,
Kent TN13 1PH
Tel: 01732 452142
Headmaster: Mr D A Philps BSc(Hons)
Age range: 4–13
No. of pupils: 160
Fees: Day £2730–£3360

Somerhill Pre-Prep
Somerhill, Five Oak Green Road,
Tonbridge, Kent TN11 0NJ
Tel: 01732 352124
Headmistress: Mrs J Ruth Sorensen
BEd(Hons), CertEd
Age range: 3–7
No. of pupils: 245 B141 G104
Fees: Day £8400–£9735

Spring Grove School
Harville Road, Wye, Ashford,
Kent TN25 5EZ
Tel: 01233 812337
Headmaster: Mr Bill Jones
Age range: 2–13
No. of pupils: 194
Fees: Day £2050–£3125

St Christopher's School
New Dover Road, Canterbury,
Kent CT1 3DT
Tel: 01227 462960
The Master: Mr D Evans
Age range: 3–11
No. of pupils: B70 G70
Fees: Day £7600

St Edmund's Junior School
St Thomas Hill, Canterbury,
Kent CT2 8HU
Tel: 01227 475600
Master: R G Bacon BA(Hons)(Durham)
Age range: 3–13
No. of pupils: 230 B140 G90
Fees: Day £5100–£14,724 WB £14,526
FB £15,942–£22,803

St Edmund's School
St Thomas' Hill, Canterbury,
Kent CT2 8HU
Tel: 01227 475600
Head Mistress: Louise Moelwyn-Hughes
Age range: 13–18
No. of pupils: 310 B170 G140 Vlth120
Fees: Day £15,999 FB £24,900

St Faith's at Ash School
5 The Street, Ash, Canterbury,
Kent CT3 2HH
Tel: 01304 813409
Headmaster: Mr S G I Kerruish
MA(Cantab), CertEd(London)
Age range: 3–11
No. of pupils: 206 B105 G101
Fees: Day £3075–£6681

St Joseph's Convent Prep School
46 Old Road East, Gravesend,
Kent DA12 1NR
Tel: 01474 533012
Head Teacher: Mrs Carola Timney
Age range: 3–11
No. of pupils: 146 B66 G80
Fees: Day £6655

St Lawrence College
Ramsgate, Kent CT11 7AE
Tel: 01843 572931
Headmaster: Reverend Mark Aitken
Age range: 3–18
No. of pupils: 528 B314 G214 Vlth117
Fees: Day £5820–£14,682
FB £19,152–£25,485

St Michael's Preparatory School
Otford Court, Otford, Sevenoaks,
Kent TN14 5SA
Tel: 01959 522137
Headmaster: Mr K Crombie
Age range: 2–13
No. of pupils: 454 B278 G176
Fees: Day £1932–£11,997

Steephill School
Off Castle Hill, Fawkham, Longfield,
Kent DA3 7BG
Tel: 01474 702107
Head: Mrs C Birtwell BSc, MBA, PGCE
Age range: 3–11
No. of pupils: 131 B66 G65
Fees: Day £6860

Sutton Valence Preparatory School
Underhill, Chart Sutton, Maidstone,
Kent ME17 3RF
Tel: 01622 842117
Head: Mr C Gibbs BA(Hons), HDE(1st
Class)
Age range: 3–11
No. of pupils: 375 B200 G175
Fees: Day £1630–£9135

Sutton Valence School
North Street, Sutton Valence,
Kent ME17 3HL
Tel: 01622 845200
Headmaster: Mr B C W Grindlay
MA(Cantab), MusB, FRCO, CHM
Age range: 11–18
No. of pupils: 520 B358 G162 Vlth165
Fees: Day £4590–£6005
WB £7210–£9450 FB £7210–£9450

The Cedars School
70 Maidstone Road, Rochester,
Kent ME1 3DE
Tel: 01634 828030
Joint Headteachers: Miss C M G
Pakington & Miss S P Bolton
Age range: 3–16
No. of pupils: 15 B7 G8

The Granville School
2 Bradbourne Park Road, Sevenoaks,
Kent TN13 3LJ
Tel: 01732 453039
Headmistress: Mrs J Scott BEd(Cantab)
Age range: B3–4 G3–11
No. of pupils: 190

The Junior King's School, Canterbury
Milner Court, Sturry, Canterbury,
Kent CT2 0AY
Tel: 01227 714000
Headmaster: Mr Peter Wells BEd(Hons)
Age range: 3–13
No. of pupils: B208 G176
Fees: Day £8610–£14,610 FB £19,830

The King's School, Canterbury
The Precincts, Canterbury, Kent CT1 2ES
Tel: 01227 595501
Head: Mr P Roberts
Age range: 13–18
No. of pupils: 790 B438 G352 Vlth359
Fees: Day £18,330 FB £24,690

The Mead School
16 Frant Road, Tunbridge Wells,
Kent TN2 5SN
Tel: 01892 525837
Headmistress: Mrs A Culley
CertEd(Oxon)
Age range: 3–11
No. of pupils: 188 B97 G91
Fees: Day £3597–£9168

The New Beacon School
Brittains Lane, Sevenoaks,
Kent TN13 2PB
Tel: 01732 452131
Headmaster: Mr M Piercy BA(Hons)
Age range: 4–13
No. of pupils: 400
Fees: Day £8685–£11,205

Tonbridge School
Tonbridge, Kent TN9 1JP
Tel: 01732 365555
Headmaster: T H P Haynes
Age range: 13–18
No. of pupils: 780 VIth325
Fees: Day £23,340 FB £31,263

Walthamstow Hall Pre-Prep and Junior School
Sevenoaks, Kent TN13 3LD
Tel: 01732 451334
Headmistress: Mrs Jill Milner MA(Oxford)
Age range: 2½–11
No. of pupils: 218
Fees: Day £1230–£9990

Walthamstow Hall School
Sevenoaks, Kent TN13 3UL
Tel: 01732 451334
Headmistress: Mrs J Milner MA(Oxford)
Age range: 2½–18
No. of pupils: 500 VIth80
Fees: Day £8070–£13,710

Wellesley House
114 Ramsgate Road, Broadstairs,
Kent CT10 2DG
Tel: 01843 862991
Headmaster: Mr S T P O'Malley
MA(Hons), PGCE
Age range: 7–13
No. of pupils: 140 B81 G59
Fees: Day £14,100–£15,900 FB £20,850

Yardley Court
Somerhill, Five Oak Green Road,
Tonbridge, Kent TN11 0NJ
Tel: 01732 352124
Headmaster: J T Coakley MA, BA(Hons),
PGCE
Age range: 7–13
No. of pupils: 236
Fees: Day £12,900

MEDWAY

Gad's Hill School
Higham, Rochester, Medway ME3 7PA
Tel: 01474 822366
Headmaster: Mr D G Craggs BSc, MA,
NPQH, FCollP, FRSA
Age range: 3–16
No. of pupils: 370 B185 G185
Fees: Day £6000–£7600

King's Preparatory School, Rochester
King Edward Road, Rochester,
Medway ME1 1UB
Tel: 01634 888577
Headmaster: Mr R Overend
Age range: 4–13
No. of pupils: 228 B168 G60
Fees: Day £7125–£10,380 FB £16,005

King's School, Rochester
Satis House, Boley Hill, Rochester,
Medway ME1 1TE
Tel: 01634 888555
Headmaster: Dr I R Walker BA, PhD, LTh,
ABIA, FCollP, FRSA
Age range: 13–18
No. of pupils: 688 B482 G206 VIth113
Fees: Day £7655–£14,400
FB £17,145–£24,210

Rochester Independent College
Star Hill, Rochester, Medway ME1 1XF
Tel: 01634 828115
Principals: Alistair Brownlow, Brian Pain,
Pauline Bailey
Age range: 11–19
No. of pupils: 240 B140 G100 VIth150
Fees: Day £9990–£13,500
WB £21,000–£21,000
FB £23,718–£24,426

St Andrew's School
24-28 Watts Avenue, Rochester,
Medway ME1 1SA
Tel: 01634 843479
Principal: Mrs J Jabbour BSc
Age range: 3–11
No. of pupils: 367 B185 G182
Fees: Day £5568–£5892

PORTSMOUTH

Mayville High School
35/37 St Simon's Road, Southsea,
Portsmouth PO5 2PE
Tel: 023 9273 4847
Headteacher: Mr M Castle BA, PGCE
Age range: 6 months–16 years
No. of pupils: 479 B254 G225
Fees: Day £5481–£8040

Portsmouth High School GDST
Kent Road, Southsea,
Portsmouth PO5 3EQ
Tel: 023 9282 6714
Headmistress: Mrs Jenny Clough
Age range: 3–18
No. of pupils: 600 VIth59
Fees: Day £5820–£9720

St John's College
Grove Road South, Southsea,
Portsmouth PO5 3QW
Tel: 023 9281 5118
Headmaster: Mr G J Best
Age range: 2–18
No. of pupils: 650 B435 G215 VIth105
Fees: Day £7155–£9300
FB £20,100–£21,450

The Portsmouth Grammar School
High Street, Portsmouth PO1 2LN
Tel: +44 (0)23 9236 0036
Headmaster: J E Priory MA
Age range: 2½–18
No. of pupils: 1645 VIth298
Fees: Day £8057–£12,558

READING

Alder Bridge School
Bridge House, Mill Lane, Padworth,
Reading RG7 4JU
Tel: 0118 971 4471
Age range: 1–11
No. of pupils: 58 B33 G25
Fees: Day £3420–£4470

BRADFIELD COLLEGE
For further details see p. 126
Bradfield, Reading RG7 6AU
Tel: 0118 964 4500
Email:
admissions@bradfieldcollege.org.uk
Website: www.bradfieldcollege.org.uk
Headmaster: Mr Simon Henderson
Age range: 13–18
No. of pupils: 734 B483 G251 VIth299
Fees: Day £24,708 FB £30,885

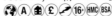

Caversham School
16 Peppard Road, Caversham,
Reading RG4 8JZ
Tel: 01189 478 684
Head: Mrs Jacqueline Lawson
Age range: 4–11
No. of pupils: 60
Fees: Day £6750

Crosfields School
Shinfield, Reading RG2 9BL
Tel: 0118 987 1810
Headmaster: Mr J P Wansey
Age range: 3–13
No. of pupils: 510 B408 G102
Fees: Day £6600–£10,710

Dolphin School
Waltham Road, Hurst, Reading RG10 0FR
Tel: 0118 934 1277
Head: Veronica Gibbs BSc, PGCE
Age range: 3–13
No. of pupils: B119 G93
Fees: Day £8340–£11,190

Elstree School
Woolhampton, Reading RG7 5TD
Tel: 0118 971 3302
Headmaster: Mr M J Sayer
Age range: B3–13 G3–7
No. of pupils: 248 B229 G19
Fees: Day £8700–£15,300 FB £19,200

Hemdean House School
Hemdean Road, Caversham,
Reading RG4 7SD
Tel: 0118 947 2590
Headmistress: Mrs J Harris BSc
Age range: B3–11 G3–16
No. of pupils: B40 G125
Fees: Day £5280–£7200

Leighton Park School
Shinfield Road, Reading RG2 7ED
Tel: 0118 987 9608
Head: Alex McGrath MA(Dist), BA, PGCE
Age range: 11–18
No. of pupils: 500 B313 G187 VIth152
Fees: Day £15,759–£18,552
WB £21,168–£24,870
FB £24,072–£28,314

Padworth College
Padworth, Reading RG7 4NR
Tel: 0118 983 2644
Principal: Mrs Linde Melhuish
Age range: 13–19
No. of pupils: 116 B65 G51 VIth50
Fees: Day £12,525 WB £23,850
FB £26,100

Pangbourne College
Pangbourne, Reading RG8 8LA
Tel: 0118 984 2101
Headmaster: Thomas J C Garnier
Age range: 11–18
No. of pupils: 387 B301 G86 VIth117
Fees: Day £7500–£10,335
FB £10,710–£14,745

Queen Anne's School
6 Henley Road, Caversham,
Reading RG4 6DX
Tel: 0118 918 7300
Headmistress: Mrs Julia Harrington
BA(Hons), PGCE, NPQH
Age range: 11–18
No. of pupils: 336 VIth100
Fees: Day £5695 WB £7545–£7975
FB £8395

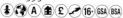

Reading Blue Coat School
Holme Park, Sonning Lane, Sonning,
Reading RG4 6SU
Tel: 0118 944 1005
Headmaster: M J Windsor
Age range: B11–18 G16–18
No. of pupils: 710 B635 G75 VIth230
Fees: Day £13,470

St Andrew's School
Buckhold, Pangbourne,
Reading RG8 8QA
Tel: 0118 974 4276
Headmaster: Dr D Livingstone BSc, PhD,
NPQH
Age range: 3–13
No. of pupils: B153 G112
Fees: Day £3705–£13,380 WB £15,960

St Edward's School
64 Tilehurst Road, Reading RG30 2JH
Tel: 0118 957 4342
Principal: G W Mottram
Age range: 4–13
No. of pupils: 170
Fees: Day £6660–£8550

St Joseph's College
Upper Redlands Road, Reading RG1 5JT
Tel: 0118 966 1000
Headmistress: Mrs Maureen Sheridan
BA(Hons), CertEd, MA(Ed), NPQH
Age range: 3–18
No. of pupils: B11 G320 VIth40
Fees: Day £5370–£9180

The Abbey School
Kendrick Road, Reading RG1 5DZ
Tel: 0118 987 2256
Headmistress: Mrs Barbara Stanley
BA(Hons), PGCE, FRGS
Age range: 3–18
No. of pupils: 1040 VIth163
Fees: Day £2650–£4200

The Deenway Montessori School
3-5 Sidmouth Street, Reading RG1 4QX
Tel: 0118 9574737
Headteacher: Mr M Karim
Age range: 3–11
No. of pupils: B19 G25

The Oratory Preparatory School
Great Oaks, Goring Heath,
Reading RG8 7SF
Tel: 0118 984 4511
Headmaster: Mr J J Smith BA, PGCE
Age range: 3–13
No. of pupils: 400 B250 G150
Fees: Day £3425–£11,475 WB £14,565
FB £15,825

THE ORATORY SCHOOL
For further details see p. 141
Woodcote, Reading RG8 0PJ
Tel: 01491 683500
Email: enquiries@oratory.co.uk
Website: www.oratory.co.uk
Head Master: Mr C I Dytor MC, KHS,
MA(Cantab), MA(Oxon)
Age range: 11–18
No. of pupils: 420 VIth120
Fees: Day £14,835–£20,565
FB £19,920–£28,395

The Vine Christian School
SORCF Christian Centre, Basingstoke
Road, Three Mile Cross,
Reading RG7 1AT
Tel: 01189 886464
Head: Mrs Joan Muirhead
Age range: 5–13
No. of pupils: 9

SLOUGH

Eton End PNEU School
35 Eton Road, Datchet, Slough SL3 9AX
Tel: 01753 541075
Headmistress: Mrs V M Pilgerstorfer
BA(Hons), PGCE
Age range: B3–7 G3–11
No. of pupils: 245 B72 G173
Fees: Day £5850–£6900

Langley Manor School
St Mary's Road, Langley,
Slough SL3 6BZ
Tel: 01753 825368
Head: Mr N Owlett
Age range: 2–11
No. of pupils: 284 B164 G120
Fees: Day £5355–£5595

Long Close School
Upton Court Road, Upton,
Slough SL3 7LU
Tel: 01753 520095
Head: Mr David Brazier
Age range: 2–16
No. of pupils: 283
Fees: Day £5715–£10,080

St Bernard's Preparatory School
Hawtrey Close, Slough SL1 1TB
Tel: 01753 521821
Head Teacher: Mrs M B Smith CertEd,
NPQH
Age range: 2½–11
No. of pupils: B149 G97

Teikyo School UK
Framewood Road, Wexham,
Slough SL2 4QS
Tel: 01753 663711
Headmaster: A Watanabe BA
Age range: 16–18
No. of pupils: B58 G42

SOUTHAMPTON

King Edward VI School
Wilton Road, Southampton SO15 5UQ
Tel: 023 8070 4561
Head Master: Mr A J Thould MA(Oxon)
Age range: 11–18
No. of pupils: 960 B590 G370 VIth240
Fees: Day £11,610

St Mary's College
57 Midanbury Lane, Bitterne Park,
Southampton SO18 4DJ
Tel: 023 8067 1267
Headmaster: J Davis
Age range: 3–16
No. of pupils: 470 B350 G120
Fees: Day £1750–£2350

St Winifred's School
17-19 Winn Road, Southampton SO17 1EJ
Tel: 023 8055 7352
Head: Mrs Carole A Pearcey BEd
Age range: 2–11
No. of pupils: B63 G53
Fees: Day £6330

The Gregg School
Townhill Park House, Cutbush Lane,
Southampton SO18 2GF
Tel: 023 8047 2133
Headteacher: Mrs S Sellers PGDip, MSc,
BSc(Hons), NPQH, PGCE
Age range: 11–16
No. of pupils: 302
Fees: Day £10,320

The King's School
Lakesmere House, Allington Lane, Fair
Oak, Eastleigh, Southampton SO50 7DB
Tel: 023 8060 0986
Headmaster: Mr Paul Johnson
Age range: 3–16
No. of pupils: 256 B126 G130
Fees: Day £3095–£5495

Wessex Tutors
44 Shirley Road,
Southampton SO15 3EU
Tel: 023 8033 4719
Principal: Mrs J E White BA(London)
Age range: 14–21
No. of pupils: B20 G20
Fees: Day £800–£7000

Woodhill School, Botley
Brook Lane, Botley,
Southampton SO30 2ER
Tel: 01489 781112
Head Teacher: Mrs M Dacombe
Age range: 3–11
No. of pupils: 100
Fees: Day £2199–£4965

SURREY

Aberdour School
Brighton Road, Burgh Heath, Tadworth,
Surrey KT20 6AJ
Tel: 01737 354119
Headmaster: Mr Simon Collins
Age range: 2–13
No. of pupils: 255 B150 G105
Fees: Day £3990–£10,605

ACS Cobham International School
Heywood, Portsmouth Road, Cobham,
Surrey KT11 1BL
Tel: +44 (0) 1932 867251
Head of School: Mr A Eysele
Age range: 2–18
No. of pupils: 1360 VIth471
Fees: Day £9240–£20,820
FB £30,380–£36,440

ACS Egham International School
Woodlee, London Road, Egham,
Surrey TW20 0HS
Tel: +44 (0) 1784 430 800
Head of School: Jeremy Lewis
Age range: 2–18
No. of pupils: 632
Fees: Day £6260–£19,990

Aldro School
Shackleford, Godalming,
Surrey GU8 6AS
Tel: 01483 409020
Headmaster: Mr D W N Aston BA(Hons),
PGCE
Age range: 7–13
No. of pupils: 220
Fees: Day £14,610 FB £18,795

Amesbury
Hazel Grove, Hindhead,
Surrey GU26 6BL
Tel: 01428 604322
Headmaster: Mr Nigel Taylor MA
Age range: 2–13
No. of pupils: 325 B211 G114
Fees: Day £7890–£12,105

Barfield School
Runfold, Farnham, Surrey GU10 1PB
Tel: 01252 782271
Head: Robin Davies
Age range: 2–13
No. of pupils: 200 B120 G80
Fees: Day £2718–£11,670

Barrow Hills School
Roke Lane, Witley, Godalming,
Surrey GU8 5NY
Tel: 01428 683639/682634
Headmaster: Mr M Unsworth BEng,
PGCE
Age range: 3–13
No. of pupils: 258 B172 G86
Fees: Day £7725–£12,285

Belmont Preparatory School
Feldemore, Holmbury St Mary, Dorking,
Surrey RH5 6LQ
Tel: 01306 730852
Headmistress: Mrs Helen Skrine BA,
PGCE, NPQH, FRSA
Age range: 2–13
No. of pupils: 227 B159 G68
Fees: Day £6120–£10,428 WB £15,345

Bishopsgate School
Bishopsgate Road, Englefield Green,
Egham, Surrey TW20 0YJ
Tel: 01784 432109
Headmaster: Mr Andrew Cowell BEd,
CPSE
Age range: 2½–13
No. of pupils: 336 B200 G136
Fees: Day £3795–£11,400

Bloo House
The Lodge (Moore Place), Portsmouth
Road, Esher, Surrey KT10 9LN
Tel: 01372 477113
Principal: Melissa Carter
Age range: 5–11
Fees: Day £10,500

Box Hill School
Old London Road, Mickleham, Dorking,
Surrey RH5 6EA
Tel: 01372 373382
Headmaster: Mr Mark Eagers
MA(Cantab), MA(Bath)
Age range: 11–18
No. of pupils: 425 B280 G145 VIth96
Fees: Day £14,100–£15,600
WB £21,465–£22,500
FB £25,500–£26,250

Bramley School
Chequers Lane, Walton-on-the-Hill,
Tadworth, Surrey KT20 7ST
Tel: 01737 812004
Headmistress: Mrs P Burgess
Age range: 3–11
No. of pupils: 110
Fees: Day £3858–£8418

Caterham School
Harestone Valley, Caterham,
Surrey CR3 6YA
Tel: 01883 343028
Head: Mr J P Thomas BSc(Hons), MBA,
FRSA
Age range: 3–18
No. of pupils: 1063 B631 G432 VIth273
Fees: Day £7566–£14,451
FB £25,578–£26,964

Charterhouse
Godalming, Surrey GU7 2DX
Tel: 01483 291500
Headmaster: Rev John Witheridge MA
Age range: B13–18 G16–18
No. of pupils: 803 B672 G131 VIth422
Fees: Day £21,681 FB £30,534

Chinthurst School
Tadworth Street, Tadworth,
Surrey KT20 5QZ
Tel: 01737 812011
Headmaster: I D Thorpe MA(Ed), BA(Ed)
Age range: 3–13
No. of pupils: 120 B110 G10
Fees: Day £3800–£10,650

City of London Freemen's School
Ashtead Park, Ashtead, Surrey KT21 1ET
Tel: 01372 277933
Headmaster: Mr Philip MacDonald
MA(Oxon)
Age range: 7–18
No. of pupils: 877 VIth213
Fees: Day £10,872–£14,598 FB £23,238

Claremont Fan Court School
Claremont Drive, Esher, Surrey KT10 9LY
Tel: 01372 467841
Head of Senior School: Mr Jonathan
Insall-Reid
Age range: 2½–18
No. of pupils: 684 B384 G300 VIth60
Fees: Day £4245–£14,190

Cornerstone School
22 West Hill, Epsom, Surrey KT19 8JD
Tel: 01372 742940
Headmaster: Mr G R Davies BEd
Age range: 5–16
No. of pupils: B25 G27

Coworth-Flexlands School
Valley End, Chobham, Woking,
Surrey GU24 8TE
Tel: 01276 855707
Headmistress: Mrs Anne Sweeney
Age range: B3–7 G3–11
No. of pupils: 145 B12 G133
Fees: Day £3885–£10,185

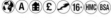

Cranleigh Preparatory School
Horseshoe Lane, Cranleigh,
Surrey GU6 8QH
Tel: 01483 274199
Headmaster: Mr M T Wilson BSc
Age range: 7–13
No. of pupils: 290
Fees: Day £11,385 FB £14,025

Cranleigh School
Horseshoe Lane, Cranleigh,
Surrey GU6 8QQ
Tel: 01483 273666
Head: Mr G de W Waller MA, MSc,
FRSA(Worcester College, Oxford)
Age range: 13–18
No. of pupils: 606 B401 G205 VIth237
Fees: Day £21,225 FB £26,040

Cranmore School
Epsom Road, West Horsley,
Leatherhead, Surrey KT24 6AT
Tel: 01483 280340
Headmaster: Mr M Connolly BSc, BA,
MA, MEd
Age range: 2–13
No. of pupils: 470 B460 G10
Fees: Day £5250–£11,550

Danes Hill School
Leatherhead Road, Oxshott,
Surrey KT22 0JG
Tel: 01372 842509
Headmaster: Mr W Murdock BA
Age range: 3–13
No. of pupils: 872 B476 G396
Fees: Day £1682–£4662

Danesfield Manor School
Rydens Avenue, Walton-on-Thames,
Surrey KT12 3JB
Tel: 01932 220930
Head: Mrs Helen Chalmers
Age range: 2 years–11 years
No. of pupils: 175
Fees: Day £6000–£6500

Date Valley School
9 Commonside East, Mitcham,
Surrey CR4 2QA
Tel: 020 8648 4647
Headteacher: Mrs Razina Karim
Age range: 3–11
No. of pupils: 110 B48 G62
Fees: Day £1869–£3150

Downsend School
Ashtead Lodge, 22 Oakfield Road,
Ashtead, Surrey KT21 2RE
Tel: 01372 385439
Head Teacher: Mrs K Barrett
Age range: 2–6
No. of pupils: 66 B35 G31
Fees: Day £2190–£8250

Downsend School
1 Leatherhead Road, Leatherhead,
Surrey KT22 8TJ
Tel: 01372 372197
Headmaster: Floyd Steadman
Age range: 6–13
No. of pupils: 580 B320 G260
Fees: Day £11,640

Downsend School
Leatherhead Lodge, Epsom Road,
Leatherhead, Surrey KT22 8ST
Tel: 01372 372123
Headteacher: Mrs Gill Brooks
Age range: 2½–6
No. of pupils: B65 G73
Fees: Day £6780–£8250

Downsend School
Epsom Lodge, 6 Norman Avenue,
Epsom, Surrey KT17 3AB
Tel: 01372 385438
Head Teacher: Miss J Birchall
Age range: 2–6
No. of pupils: 110 B58 G52
Fees: Day £2325–£11,640

Drayton House School
35 Austen Road, Guildford,
Surrey GU1 3NP
Tel: 01483 504707
Headmistress: Mrs J Tyson-Jones
FroibelCertEd(LondonUni)
Age range: 3 months–7 years
No. of pupils: B45 G45
Fees: Day £4420–£12,500

Duke of Kent School
Peaslake Road, Ewhurst,
Surrey GU6 7NS
Tel: 01483 277313
Head: Mrs Judith Fremont-Barnes
Age range: 3–16
No. of pupils: 234 B168 G66
Fees: Day £4860–£14,130
WB £13,350–£16,770
FB £15,735–£18,855

Dunottar School
High Trees Road, Reigate,
Surrey RH2 7EL
Tel: 01737 761945
Headmistress: Mrs Nicola Matthews
BSc(Hons), PGCE
Age range: 3–18
No. of pupils: 320 VIth50
Fees: Day £1345–£12,075

Edgeborough
Frensham, Farnham, Surrey GU10 3AH
Tel: 01252 792495
Headmaster: Mr C J Davies BA
Age range: 2–13
No. of pupils: 285 B185 G100
Fees: Day £9105–£14,850
WB £16,752–£18,282

Emberhurst School
94 Ember Lane, Esher, Surrey KT10 8EN
Tel: 020 8398 2933
Headmistress: Mrs P Chadwick BEd
Age range: 2½–7+
No. of pupils: 70 B40 G30
Fees: Day £2265–£6495

Epsom College
Epsom, Surrey KT17 4JQ
Tel: 01372 821234
Headmaster: Jay Piggot MA
Age range: 13–18
No. of pupils: 720 B474 G246 VIth324
Fees: Day £20,655 WB £27,582
FB £30,222

Essendene Lodge School
Essendene Road, Caterham,
Surrey CR3 5PB
Tel: 01883 348349
Head Teacher: Mrs J Wermig
Age range: 2–11
No. of pupils: 153 B66 G87
Fees: Day £2775–£5550

Ewell Castle School
Church Street, Ewell, Epsom,
Surrey KT17 2AW
Tel: 020 8393 1413
Principal: Andrew Tibble
Age range: B3–18 G3–11
No. of pupils: 545 B474 G71 VIth60
Fees: Day £6360–£12,450

(A) (£) (🖊) (16+) (IAPS) (S)

Feltonfleet School
Cobham, Surrey KT11 1DR
Tel: 01932 862264
Headmaster: P C Ward
Age range: 3–13
No. of pupils: 356 B236 G120
Fees: Day £7680–£11,250 WB £15,750

(🏫) (£) (🖊) (IAPS) (BSA)

Frensham Heights
Rowledge, Farnham, Surrey GU10 4EA
Tel: 01252 792561
Headmaster: Mr Andrew Fisher BA, MEd,
FRSA
Age range: 3–18
No. of pupils: 497 B267 G230 VIth105
Fees: Day £5205–£15,300
FB £19,485–£22,680

(🌐) (A) (🏫) (£) (🖊) (16+) (HMC) (BSA)

Glenesk School
Ockham Road North, East Horsley,
Surrey KT24 6NS
Tel: 01483 282329
Headmistress: Mrs S Christie-Hall
Age range: 2–7
No. of pupils: B77 G73
Fees: Day £1350–£8112

 (£) (🖊)

GORDON'S SCHOOL
For further details see p. 130
West End, Woking, Surrey GU24 9PT
Tel: 01276 858084
Email: registrar@gordons.surrey.sch.uk
Website: www.gordons.surrey.sch.uk
Head Teacher: Andrew Moss MEd
Age range: 11–18
No. of pupils: B379 G348 VIth160
Fees: FB £13,083–£14,181

(A) (🏫) (£) (🖊) (16+) (BSA)

Greenacre School for Girls
Sutton Lane, Banstead, Surrey SM7 3RA
Tel: 01737 352114
Headmistress: Mrs L E Redding
Age range: 3–18
No. of pupils: 350 VIth40
Fees: Day £7200–£12,300

(👤) (A) (£) (🖊) (16+) (GSA)

Greenfield
Brooklyn Road, Woking,
Surrey GU22 7TP
Tel: 01483 772525
Headmistress: Mrs Tania Botting BEd
Age range: 3–11
No. of pupils: 179 B92 G87
Fees: Day £4284–£9450

(£) (🖊) (IAPS)

Guildford High School
London Road, Guildford, Surrey GU1 1SJ
Tel: 01483 561440
Headmistress: Mrs F J Boulton BSc, MA
Age range: 4–18
No. of pupils: 950 VIth160
Fees: Day £8043–£13,302

 (A) (£) (16+) (IAPS) (HMC)

Hall Grove School
London Road, Bagshot,
Surrey GU19 5HZ
Tel: 01276 473059
Headmaster: Mr A R Graham BSc, PGCE
Age range: 4–13
No. of pupils: 310
Fees: Day £7110–£9825

(🏫) (IAPS)

Halstead Preparatory School
Woodham Rise, Woking,
Surrey GU21 4EE
Tel: 01483 772682
Headmistress: Mrs S G Fellows
BA(Hons)
Age range: 3–11
No. of pupils: 200
Fees: Day £2358–£10,827

(👤) (£) (🖊) (IAPS)

Hampton Court House
Hampton Court Road, East Molesey,
Surrey KT8 9BS
Tel: 020 8943 0889
Headmistress: Lady Houstoun-Boswall
Age range: 3–16
No. of pupils: B74 G74 VIth8
Fees: Day £7842–£10,017

(£)

Haslemere Preparatory School
The Heights, Hill Road, Haslemere,
Surrey GU27 2JP
Tel: 01428 642350
Head: Mr K J Merrick BA(Hons), PGCE
Age range: 2–13
No. of pupils: 191
Fees: Day £2199–£3145

(👤) (£) (🖊) (IAPS)

Hawley Place School
Fernhill Road, Blackwater, Camberley,
Surrey GU17 9HU
Tel: 01276 32028
Co-Principals: Mr T G Pipe
BA(CombHons), MA & Mrs M L Pipe LÈs
Lettres
Age range: B2–11 G2–16
No. of pupils: 370 B105 G265
Fees: Day £7560–£9450

(£) (🖊) (ISA)

Hazelwood School
Wolf's Hill, Limpsfield, Oxted,
Surrey RH8 0QU
Tel: 01883 712194
Head: Mrs Maxine Shaw
Age range: 2½–13
No. of pupils: 399 B246 G153
Fees: Day £3585–£11,100

(£) (🖊) (IAPS)

Highcombe Edge School
Highcombe Edge, Hindhead,
Surrey GU26 6SJ
Tel: 01428 2860 1800
Head: Mr S Hardy
Age range: 8–18
No. of pupils: 90

HOE BRIDGE SCHOOL
For further details see p. 132
Hoe Place, Old Woking Road, Woking,
Surrey GU22 8JE
Tel: 01483 760018 & 01483 772194
Email:
enquiriesprep@hoebridgeschool.co.uk
Website: www.hoebridgeschool.co.uk
Head: Mr N Arkell BSc
Age range: 2½–14
No. of pupils: B339 G130
Fees: Day £1800–£12,840

(£) (🖊) (IAPS)

Hurtwood House
Holmbury St Mary, Dorking,
Surrey RH5 6NU
Tel: 01483 279000
Principal: Mr Cosmo Jackson
Age range: 16–18
No. of pupils: 300 B150 G150
Fees: FB £30,600–£35,100

(16+) (A) (🏫) (ISA) (BSA)

International School of London (ISL) in Surrey
Old Woking Road, Woking,
Surrey GU22 8HY
Tel: 01483 750 409
Head of School: Dr James A Doran
Age range: 2–14
No. of pupils: 140 B73 G67
Fees: Day £9000–£15,800

(🌐) (£) (🖊)

King Edward's School Witley
Petworth Road, Wormley, Godalming,
Surrey GU8 5SG
Tel: +44 (0)1428 686700
Head: John F Attwater MA
Age range: 11–18
No. of pupils: 400 B240 G160 VIth145
Fees: Day £14,985–£18,990
FB £20,880–£27,150

(🌐) (🏫) (£) (IB) (🖊) (16+) (HMC) (BSA)

Kingswood House School
56 West Hill, Epsom, Surrey KT19 8LG
Tel: 01372 723590
Headmaster: Mr Peter R Brooks MA,
BEd(Hons)
Age range: B3–13 G3–7
No. of pupils: 210
Fees: Day £7440–£9825

(👤) (£) (🖊) (IAPS)

Lanesborough
Maori Road, Guildford, Surrey GU1 2EL
Tel: 01483 880650
Head: Mrs Clare Turnbull BA(Hons)
Age range: 3–13
No. of pupils: 350
Fees: Day £7437–£10,026

(👤) (£) (🖊) (IAPS)

Lingfield Notre Dame School
Lingfield, Surrey RH7 6PH
Tel: 01342 833176
Headmaster: Mr R Bool
Age range: 2½–18
No. of pupils: 837 B318 G419 Vlth111
Fees: Day £3510–£9935

Longacre School
Shamley Green, Guildford,
Surrey GU5 0NQ
Tel: 01483 893225
Headmaster: Mr Mark Beach BA(Hons),
AdDipAd, MAAd
Age range: 2–11
No. of pupils: 237 B117 G120
Fees: Day £4635–£6540

Lyndhurst School
36 The Avenue, Camberley,
Surrey GU15 3NE
Tel: 01276 22895
Headmaster: Mr S G Yeo BMus, LTCL
(MusEd), NPQH
Age range: 2–11
No. of pupils: 157 B89 G68
Fees: Day £7275–£8790

Manor House School
Manor House Lane, Little Bookham,
Leatherhead, Surrey KT23 4EN
Tel: 01372 458538
Headmistress: Miss Zara Axton
Age range: 2–16
No. of pupils: 360
Fees: Day £750–£4070

Maple House School
23 Parchmore Road, Thornton Heath,
Surrey CR7 8LY
Tel: 020 8653 1827
Headteacher: Mrs Pauline Khoo
Age range: 5–10
No. of pupils: 97

Micklefield School
10/12 Somers Road, Reigate,
Surrey RH2 9DU
Tel: 01737 242615
Headmistress: Mrs L Rose BEd(Hons),
CertEd, Dip PC
Age range: 3–11
No. of pupils: 272 B130 G142
Fees: Day £2565–£9030

Milbourne Lodge School
Arbrook Lane, Esher, Surrey KT10 9EG
Tel: 01372 462737
Head: Mrs Wendy Holland
Age range: 8–13
No. of pupils: 200 B168 G32
Fees: Day £7450–£8100

Notre Dame Preparatory School
Burwood House, Convent Lane,
Cobham, Surrey KT11 1HA
Tel: 01932 869991
Headmaster: Mr D S Plummer
BEd(Hons), DipHE, FRSA
Age range: B2¾–5 G2¾–11
No. of pupils: 335 B5 G330
Fees: Day £1150–£3595

Notre Dame Senior School
Burwood House, Cobham,
Surrey KT11 1HA
Tel: 01932 869990
Headmistress: Mrs Bridget Williams MA,
NPQH, BEd(Oxon)
Age range: 11–18
No. of pupils: 382 Vlth57
Fees: Day £11,130

Oakfield School
Coldharbour Road, Pyrford, Woking,
Surrey GU22 8SJ
Tel: 01932 342465
Principal: Mrs S H Goddard BA(Joint
Hons)
Age range: B3–7 G3–16
No. of pupils: 170 B20 G150
Fees: Day £7500–£12,600

Oakhyrst Grange School
160 Stanstead Road, Caterham,
Surrey CR3 6AF
Tel: 01883 343344
Headmaster: Mr A Gear
Age range: 4–11
No. of pupils: 128 B72 G57
Fees: Day £1059–£2343

(ISA)

Parkside School
The Manor, Stoke d'Abernon, Cobham,
Surrey KT11 3PX
Tel: 01932 862749
Headmaster: Mr David Aylward
BEd(Hons), MA
Age range: B2½–13 G2½–4
No. of pupils: 382 B353 G29

(IAPS)

Peaslake School
Colmans Hill, Peaslake, Guildford,
Surrey GU5 9ST
Tel: 01306 730411
Headteacher: Mrs S Dangerfield
Age range: 3–7
No. of pupils: 44 B19 G25

Prior's Field School
Priorsfield Road, Godalming,
Surrey GU7 2RH
Tel: 01483 810551
Head: Mrs J Roseblade MA
Age range: 11–18
No. of pupils: 380 Vlth63
Fees: Day £4555 WB £7365 FB £7365

Priory Preparatory School
Bolters Lane, Banstead, Surrey SM7 2AJ
Tel: 01737 366920
Headmaster: Graham D Malcom MA,
BEd, FRSA
Age range: 2–13
No. of pupils: 200
Fees: Day £4650–£10,350

Redehall Preparatory School
Redehall Road, Smallfield, Horley,
Surrey RH6 9QL
Tel: 01342 842987
Headmistress: Mrs M Bateup
Age range: 3–11
No. of pupils: B26 G35
Fees: Day £1620

Reed's School
Sandy Lane, Cobham, Surrey KT11 2ES
Tel: 01932 869001
Headmaster: Mr D W Jarrett MA
Age range: B11–18 G16–18
No. of pupils: 625 B550 G60 Vlth210
Fees: Day £15,585–£19,494
FB £20,778–£25,785

Reigate Grammar School
Reigate Road, Reigate, Surrey RH2 0QS
Tel: 01737 222231
Headmaster: Mr D Thomas MA
Age range: 11–18
No. of pupils: 862 B538 G324 Vlth217
Fees: Day £12,072

Reigate St Mary's Prep & Choir School
Chart Lane, Reigate, Surrey RH2 7RN
Tel: 01737 244880
Headmaster: Marcus Culverwell MA
Age range: 3–11
No. of pupils: 277 B198 G79

Ripley Court School
Rose Lane, Ripley, Surrey GU23 6NE
Tel: 01483 225217
Headmaster: Mr A J Gough
Age range: 3–13
No. of pupils: 252 B169 G83
Fees: Day £7755–£11,640

Rowan Preparatory School
6 Fitzalan Road, Claygate, Esher,
Surrey KT10 0LX
Tel: 01372 462627
Headteacher: Mrs Kathy Kershaw CertEd
Age range: 2–11
No. of pupils: 280
Fees: Day £9063–£11,616

ROYAL ALEXANDRA AND ALBERT SCHOOL

For further details see p. 136
Gatton Park, Reigate, Surrey RH2 oTD
Tel: 01737 649 000
Email: admissions@gatton-park.org.uk
Website: www.raa-school.co.uk
Headmaster: P Spencer Ellis BA, MPhil, NPQH
Age range: 7–18
No. of pupils: 1000 B510 G490 Vlth200
Fees: Day £4695 WB £12,630
FB £12,630

ROYAL GRAMMAR SCHOOL, GUILDFORD

For further details see p. 135
High Street, Guildford, Surrey GU1 3BB
Tel: 01483 880600
Email: admissions@rgs-guildford.co.uk
Website: www.rgs-guildford.co.uk
Headmaster: Dr J M Cox BSc, PhD
Age range: 11–18
No. of pupils: 900
Fees: Day £14,070–£14,325

Royal School Haslemere

Farnham Lane, Haslemere,
Surrey GU27 1HQ
Tel: 01428 603052
Headmistress: Mrs Lynne Taylor-Gooby BEd, MA
Age range: 0–18
No. of pupils: 370 Vlth50

Rydes Hill Preparatory School

Rydes Hill House, Aldershot Road,
Guildford, Surrey GU2 6BP
Tel: 01483 563160
Headmistress: Mrs Stephanie Bell MA(Oxon)
Age range: B3–7 G3–11
No. of pupils: 160 B20 G140
Fees: Day £870–£2960

Shrewsbury Lodge School

22 Milbourne Lane, Esher,
Surrey KT10 9EA
Tel: 01372 462781
Head: Mrs Gill Hope
Age range: 3–7
No. of pupils: B100 G25
Fees: Day £2254–£3571

Sir William Perkins's School

Guildford Road, Chertsey,
Surrey KT16 9BN
Tel: 01932 574900
Head: Mrs S D Cooke
Age range: 11–18
No. of pupils: 556 G556 Vlth130
Fees: Day £12,846

ST ANDREW'S SCHOOL

For further details see p. 140
Church Hill House, Horsell, Woking,
Surrey GU21 4QW
Tel: 01483 760943
Email: admin@st-andrews.woking.sch.uk
Website: www.st-andrews.woking.sch.uk
Headmaster: Mr A Perks
Age range: 3–13
No. of pupils: 300 B217 G83
Fees: Day £3222–£12,930

St Catherine's School

Bramley, Guildford, Surrey GU5 oDF
Tel: 01483 893363
Headmistress: Mrs A M Phillips MA(Cantab)
Age range: 4–18
No. of pupils: 780 Vlth140
Fees: Day £5790–£11,760 WB £18,315
FB £18,315

St Christopher's School

6 Downs Road, Epsom, Surrey KT18 5HE
Tel: 01372 721807
Headteacher: Mrs A C Thackray MA, BA(Hons)
Age range: 3–7
No. of pupils: 137 B69 G68
Fees: Day £1250–£2450

St Edmund's School

Portsmouth Road, Hindhead,
Surrey GU26 6BH
Tel: 01428 604808
Headmaster: Mr A J Walliker MA(Cantab), MBA, PGCE
Age range: 2–13
No. of pupils: B195 G35
Fees: Day £2160–£13,842

St George's College

Weybridge Road, Addlestone,
Weybridge, Surrey KT15 2QS
Tel: 01932 839300
Headmaster: Mr Joseph A Peake MA(Oxon), PGCE
Age range: 11–18
No. of pupils: 898 B561 G337 Vlth239
Fees: Day £10,470–£12,045

St George's College Junior School

Thames Street, Weybridge,
Surrey KT13 8NL
Tel: 01932 839400
Head Master: Mr Antony Hudson
Age range: 3–11
No. of pupils: 611 B306 G305

St Hilary's School

Holloway Hill, Godalming,
Surrey GU7 1RZ
Tel: 01483 416551
Headmistress: Mrs S Bailes BA(Hons), MA, PGCE
Age range: B2–7 G2–11
No. of pupils: 252 B74 G178
Fees: Day £7950–£11,550

St Ives School

Three Gates Lane, Haslemere,
Surrey GU27 2ES
Tel: 01428 643734
Headteacher: Mrs S E Cattaneo CertEd
Age range: B3–4 G3–11
No. of pupils: 149
Fees: Day £6600–£9225

St John's School

Epsom Road, Leatherhead,
Surrey KT22 8SP
Tel: 01372 373000
Headmaster: Martin A R Collier
Age range: 13–18
No. of pupils: 499 B429 G70 Vlth236
Fees: Day £19,395 WB £24,252
FB £26,595

St Teresa's Effingham (Preparatory School)

St Teresa's, Effingham, Surrey RH5 6ST
Tel: 01372 453456
Headmistress: Mrs Mary Arnal
Age range: 2–11
No. of pupils: 100
Fees: Day £735–£11,235
WB £19,845
FB £21,780

St Teresa's Effingham (Senior School)

St Teresa's, Effingham, Surrey RH5 6ST
Tel: 01372 452037
Head: Michael Farmer
Age range: 2–18
No. of pupils: 300
Fees: Day £14,190–£14,730
WB £22,800–£23,340
FB £24,735–£25,275

Surbiton Preparatory School

3 Avenue Elmers, Surbiton,
Surrey KT6 4SP
Tel: 020 8390 6640
Head of Surbiton High, Junior Girls' & Bo: Ms C Bufton BA(Hons)
Age range: 4–11
No. of pupils: 135
Fees: Day £6783–£9246

TASIS The American School in England
Coldharbour Lane, Thorpe,
Surrey TW20 8TE
Tel: +44 (0)1932 582316
Head: Mr Michael V McBrien
Age range: 3–18
No. of pupils: 750 B375 G375
Fees: Day £6105–£19,810 FB £33,760

The Hawthorns School
Pendell Court, Bletchingley, Redhill,
Surrey RH1 4QJ
Tel: 01883 743048
Headmaster: Mr T R Johns BA, PGCE,
FRGS
Age range: 2–13
No. of pupils: B290 G250

Tormead School
27 Cranley Road, Guildford,
Surrey GU1 2JD
Tel: 01483 575101
Headmistress: Mrs Christina Foord
Age range: 4–18
No. of pupils: 760 VIth120
Fees: Day £5520–£11,565

Warlingham Park School
Chelsham Common, Warlingham,
Surrey CR6 9PB
Tel: 01883 626844
Headmaster: Mr M R Donald BSc
Age range: 3–11
No. of pupils: 110 B52 G58
Fees: Day £3660–£7410

Weston Green School
Weston Green Road, Thames Ditton,
Surrey KT7 0JN
Tel: 020 8398 2778
Head: Mrs Lucia Harvey CertEd
Age range: 4–8
No. of pupils: B70 G70
Fees: Day £4574–£7800

Westward Preparatory School
47 Hersham Road, Walton-on-Thames,
Surrey KT12 1LE
Tel: 01932 220911
Headmistress: Mrs P Robertson CertEd
Age range: 3–12
No. of pupils: 140 B80 G60
Fees: Day £4560–£5655

Woldingham School
Marden Park, Woldingham,
Surrey CR3 7YA
Tel: 01883 349431
Headmistress: Mrs Jayne Triffitt
MA(Oxon)
Age range: 11–18
No. of pupils: 530 VIth150
Fees: Day £23,700 FB £28,410

Woodcote House School
Snows Ride, Windlesham,
Surrey GU20 6PF
Tel: 01276 472115
Headmaster: Mr Henry Knight
Age range: 7–13
No. of pupils: 100
Fees: Day £14,025 FB £18,900

Yehudi Menuhin School
Stoke Road, Stoke d'Abernon, Cobham,
Surrey KT11 3QQ
Tel: 01932 864739
Headmaster: Dr Richard J Hillier MA
(Cantab), PhD
Age range: 8–19
No. of pupils: B31 G42 VIth21
Fees: Day £40,044 FB £41,106

WEST SUSSEX

Arabesque School of Performing Arts
Quarry Lane, Chichester,
West Sussex PO19 8NY
Tel: 01243 531144
Principal: Cynthia J Ryder
Age range: 11–18
No. of pupils: 20
Fees: Day £6930

Ardingly College
College Road, Ardingly, Haywards Heath,
West Sussex RH17 6SQ
Tel: +44 (0)1444 893000
Headmaster: Mr Peter Green
Age range: 13–18
No. of pupils: 521 B322 G199 VIth218
Fees: Day £19,590–£20,640
FB £26,130–£27,315

Ardingly College Preparatory School
Haywards Heath,
West Sussex RH17 6SQ
Tel: 01444 893200
Headmaster: Mr Chris Calvey BEd
Age range: 2½–13
No. of pupils: B146 G91
Fees: Day £4050–£12,300

Ashton Park School
Brinsbury Campus East, Stane Street,
North Heath, Pulborough,
West Sussex RH20 1DJ
Tel: 01798 875836
Head: Mr G Holding
Age range: 11–16
No. of pupils: 66

Brambletye
Brambletye, East Grinstead,
West Sussex RH19 3PD
Tel: 01342 321004
Headmaster: N T Westlake
Age range: 3–13
No. of pupils: 292 B150 G140
Fees: Day £15,600 FB £20,550

Broadwater Manor School
Broadwater Road, Worthing,
West Sussex BN14 8HU
Tel: 01903 201123
Headteacher: Mrs E K Woodley
BA(Hons), CertEd
Age range: 2–13
No. of pupils: 177 B98 G79
Fees: Day £540–£8400

BURGESS HILL SCHOOL FOR GIRLS
For further details see p. 124
Keymer Road, Burgess Hill,
West Sussex RH15 0EG
Tel: 01444 241050
Email: registrar@burgesshill-school.com
Website: www.burgesshill-school.com
Headmistress: Mrs Ann Aughwane BSc,
CertEd, NPQH
Age range: B2½–4 G2½–18
No. of pupils: 640 VIth65
Fees: Day £6750–£14,250 FB £25,200

Christ's Hospital
Horsham, West Sussex RH13 0YP
Tel: 01403 211293
Head Master: John R Franklin BA,
MEd(Admin)
Age range: 11–18
No. of pupils: 816 B415 G415 VIth260
Fees: Day £14,010–£17,505 FB £27,000

Conifers School
Easebourne, Midhurst,
West Sussex GU29 9BG
Tel: 01730 813243
Headmistress: Mrs Jennie Peel
Age range: 2–11
No. of pupils: 107 B33 G74
Fees: Day £6030–£8400

Copthorne Prep School
Effingham Lane, Copthorne, Crawley,
West Sussex RH10 3HR
Tel: 01342 712311
Headmaster: Mr C Jones
Age range: 3–13
No. of pupils: 245 B140 G105
Fees: Day £5220–£9390 WB £10,800

Cottesmore School
Buchan Hill, Pease Pottage,
West Sussex RH11 9AU
Tel: 01293 520648
Head: T F Rogerson
Age range: 4–13
No. of pupils: 150 B100 G50
Fees: Day £4800–£12,600 WB £16,875
FB £18,750

Cumnor House School
Danehill, Haywards Heath,
West Sussex RH17 7HT
Tel: 01825 790347
Headmaster: C St J Heinrich BA
Age range: 4–13
No. of pupils: 368 B186 G182
Fees: Day £8100–£18,210 FB £18,210

Dorset House School
The Manor, Church Lane, Bury,
Pulborough, West Sussex RH20 1PB
Tel: 01798 831456
Headmaster: R C M Brown MA, PGCE
Age range: 3–13
No. of pupils: 135
Fees: Day £7290–£14,595
WB £15,810–£17,685

Farlington School
Strood Park, Horsham,
West Sussex RH12 3PN
Tel: 01403 254967
Headmistress: Mrs Jonnie Goyer MA
Age range: 3–18
No. of pupils: 320 VIth40
Fees: Day £6975–£15,390
WB £21,270–£24,255
FB £22,260–£25,245

Great Ballard School
Eartham, Chichester,
West Sussex PO18 0LR
Tel: 01243 814236
Head: Mr Richard E T Jennings CertEd
Age range: 2½–13
No. of pupils: 192 B103 G89
Fees: Day £3000–£10,800 WB £12,975

GREAT WALSTEAD SCHOOL
For further details see p. 131
East Mascalls Lane, Lindfield, Haywards
Heath, West Sussex RH16 2QL
Tel: 01444 483528
Email: admin@greatwalstead.co.uk
Website: www.greatwalstead.co.uk
Headmaster: Mr C Baty NPQH,
BEd(Waikato NZ)
Age range: 2½–13
No. of pupils: 400 B235 G165
Fees: Day £6780–£13,200

Handcross Park School
Handcross, Haywards Heath,
West Sussex RH17 6HF
Tel: 01444 400526
Headmaster: Mr Graeme Owton
BEd(Hons)
Age range: 2–13
No. of pupils: 235 B125 G110
Fees: Day £1632–£14,307 WB £16,764

HURSTPIERPOINT COLLEGE
For further details see p. 133
Hassocks, West Sussex BN6 9JS
Tel: 01273 833636
Website: www.hppc.co.uk
Headmaster: Mr T J Manly BA, MSc
Age range: 4–18
No. of pupils: 1030
Fees: Day £19,785 WB £24,945
FB £27,885–£29,430

Lancing College
Lancing, West Sussex BN15 0RW
Tel: 01273 452213
Head Master: Mr Jonathan W J Gillespie
MA
Age range: 13–18
No. of pupils: 546 B348 G198 VIth234
Fees: Day £20,160 FB £28,845

Lavant House
West Lavant, Chichester,
West Sussex PO18 9AB
Tel: 01243 527211
Headmistress: Mrs K Bartholomew
MA(London)
Age range: 7–18
No. of pupils: 150 VIth20
Fees: Day £8250–£13,545
WB £17,775–£21,315
FB £17,775–£21,315

Oakwood School
Chichester, West Sussex PO18 9AN
Tel: 01243 575209
Headteacher: Mrs Gill Proctor
Age range: 3–11
No. of pupils: 247 B121 G126
Fees: Day £2760–£8880

Our Lady of Sion School
Gratwicke Road, Worthing,
West Sussex BN11 4BL
Tel: 01903 204063
Headmaster: Mr M Scullion MA, BEd
Age range: 2½–18
No. of pupils: 528 B255 G273 VIth55
Fees: Day £5715–£9150

Pennthorpe School
Church Street, Horsham,
West Sussex RH12 3HJ
Tel: 01403 822391
Headmaster: Mr Matthew King BA(Hons)
Age range: 2–13
No. of pupils: 362 B234 G128
Fees: Day £1392–£12,690

Rikkyo School in England
Guildford Road, Rudgwick, Horsham,
West Sussex RH12 3BE
Tel: 01403 822107
Headmaster: Mr Roger Munechika
Age range: 10–18
No. of pupils: 116 B65 G51
Fees: FB £15,000–£20,400

SEAFORD COLLEGE
For further details see p. 138
Lavington Park, Petworth,
West Sussex GU28 0NB
Tel: 01798 867392
Email: admissions@seaford.org
Website: www.seaford.org
Headmaster: T J Mullins MBA, BA
Age range: 7–18
No. of pupils: 621 B436 G185 VIth143
Fees: Day £8100–£16,890
WB £17,400–£22,500
FB £16,440–£26,700

Shoreham College
St Julians Lane, Shoreham-by-Sea,
West Sussex BN43 6YW
Tel: 01273 592681
Headmaster: Mr J S Stearns MA, BSc,
PGCE, NPQH
Age range: 3–16
No. of pupils: 418 B308 G110
Fees: Day £7350–£11,850

Slindon College
Slindon House, Slindon, Arundel,
West Sussex BN18 0RH
Tel: 01243 814320
Headmaster: Mr I P Graham BEd, MA
Age range: 9–16
No. of pupils: 80
Fees: Day £5135 FB £8220

**Sompting Abbotts Preparatory School
for Boys and Girls**
Church Lane, Sompting,
West Sussex BN15 0AZ
Tel: 01903 235960
Principal: Mrs P M Sinclair
Age range: 2½–13
No. of pupils: 185 B135 G50
Fees: Day £7560–£9690

Steyning Grammar School
Church Street, Steyning,
West Sussex BN44 3LB
Tel: +44 (0)1903 814786
Headteacher: C D Taylor
Age range: 11–18
No. of pupils: 1986
Fees: WB £8250 FB £9750

Tavistock & Summerhill School
Summerhill Lane, Haywards Heath,
West Sussex RH16 1RP
Tel: 01444 450256
Headmaster: Mr M Barber BEd, FRGS
Age range: 3–13
No. of pupils: 170 B100 G70
Fees: Day £3000–£5400

(£)

The Prebendal School
54 West Street, Chichester,
West Sussex PO19 1RT
Tel: 01243 772220
Head Master: Mr T R Cannell
Age range: 3–13
No. of pupils: 210 B116 G94
Fees: Day £6300–£12,335 WB £15,981
FB £16,680

(☝)(£)(✎)(IAPS)

The Towers Convent School
Convent of the Blessed Sacrement,
Henfield Road, Upper Beeding, Steyning,
West Sussex BN44 3TF
Tel: 01903 812185
Headmistress: Mrs Carole A Baker MA,
BEd
Age range: B3–8 G3–16
No. of pupils: 313 B6 G307
Fees: Day £5760–£7740
WB £11,070–£12,000
FB £11,910–£13,020

(☝)(🌐)(☝)(£)(✎)(ISA)(BSA)

Westbourne House School
Shopwyke, Chichester,
West Sussex PO20 2BH
Tel: 01243 782739
Headmaster: Mr Martin Barker
Age range: 3–13
No. of pupils: 468 B253 G215
Fees: Day £8670–£14,625 FB £17,910

(☝)(£)(✎)(IAPS)(BSA)

Willow Tree Montessori School
Charlwood House, Charlwood Road,
Lowfield Heath, Crawley,
West Sussex RH11 0QA
Tel: 01293 820721
Headmistress: Mrs G Kerfante MontDip
Age range: 1–8
No. of pupils: B50 G50
Fees: Day £2310–£2700

Windlesham House School
Washington, Pulborough,
West Sussex RH20 4AY
Tel: 01903 874700
Headmaster: Mr Richard Foster
BEd(Hons)
Age range: 4–13
No. of pupils: 366 B212 G154
Fees: Day £7635–£18,075
FB £20,730–£21,075

(☝)(£)(✎)(IAPS)(BSA)

Worth School
Paddockhurst Road, Turners Hill,
Crawley, West Sussex RH10 4SD
Tel: +44 (0)1342 710200
Head Master: Gino Carminati MA, FRSA
Age range: 11–18
No. of pupils: 570 VIth222
Fees: Day £19,551 FB £26,649

(🌐)(A)(☝)(£)(IB)(✎)(16+)(HMC)

WINDSOR & MAIDENHEAD

Brigidine School Windsor
Queensmead, King's Road, Windsor,
Windsor & Maidenhead SL4 2AX
Tel: 01753 863779
Headmistress: Mrs Elizabeth Robinson
Age range: B2–7 G3–18
No. of pupils: 300
Fees: Day £3945–£11,865

(☝)(A)(£)(✎)(16+)(GSA)

Claires Court School
Ray Mill Road East, Maidenhead,
Windsor & Maidenhead SL6 8TE
Tel: 01628 411470
Headmaster: Mr J M Rayer BSc, PGCE
Age range: 11–16
No. of pupils: 300 VIth112
Fees: Day £11,835

(☝)(A)(£)(✎)(16+)(ISA)

Claires Court Schools, Ridgeway
Maidenhead Thicket, Maidenhead,
Windsor & Maidenhead SL6 3QE
Tel: 01628 411490
Head: Mr J Watkins BEd, CertEd
Age range: 4–11
No. of pupils: 226
Fees: Day £6615–£9855

(☝)(£)(✎)(ISA)

Claires Court Schools, The College
1 College Avenue, Maidenhead,
Windsor & Maidenhead SL6 6AW
Tel: 01628 411480
Head: Mrs L Green CPhys, MInstP, BSc,
PGCE
Age range: B16–18 G3–18
No. of pupils: 3308 B47 G3261 VIth112
Fees: Day £6615–£11,520

(☝)(A)(£)(✎)(16+)(ISA)

Eton College
Windsor,
Windsor & Maidenhead SL4 6DW
Tel: 01753 671249
Head Master: A R M Little MA
Age range: 13–18
No. of pupils: 1300
Fees: FB £30,981

(☝)(🌐)(A)(☝)(£)(✎)(16+)(HMC)(BSA)

Heathfield School
London Road, Ascot,
Windsor & Maidenhead SL5 8BQ
Tel: 01344 898342
Head: Mrs Jo Heywood BSc(Hons), PGCE
Age range: 11–18
No. of pupils: 200 G200 VIth80
Fees: FB £28,950

(☝)(🌐)(A)(☝)(£)(✎)(16+)(GSA)(BSA)

Herries Preparatory School
Dean Lane, Cookham Dean,
Windsor & Maidenhead SL6 9BD
Tel: 01628 483350
Headmistress: Sophie Green
Age range: 3–11
No. of pupils: 90 B28 G62
Fees: Day £6258–£8472

(£)(✎)(IAPS)

Highfield Preparatory School
2 West Road, Maidenhead,
Windsor & Maidenhead SL6 1PD
Tel: 01628 624918
Headteacher: Ms A Lee
Age range: B3–5 G3–11
No. of pupils: B3 G148
Fees: Day £1164–£8250

(☝)(☝)(£)(✎)(IAPS)

Hurst Lodge
Bagshot Road, Ascot,
Windsor & Maidenhead SL5 9JU
Tel: 01344 622154
Headmistress: Kate Leiper
Age range: 3–18
No. of pupils: 182 B21 G161 VIth18
Fees: Day £4020–£12,930 WB £21,045

(🌐)(A)(☝)(£)(✎)(16+)(🎭)(ISA)(BSA)

LVS Ascot (Licensed Victuallers' School)
London Road, Ascot,
Windsor & Maidenhead SL5 8DR
Tel: 01344 882770
Headmistress: Mrs Christine Cunniffe
BA(Hons), MMus
Age range: 4–18
No. of pupils: 901 B542 G359 VIth150
Fees: Day £8220–£15,435
FB £21,015–£24,900

(🌐)(A)(☝)(£)(✎)(16+)(ISA)(BSA)(S)

Papplewick School
Windsor Road, Ascot,
Windsor & Maidenhead SL5 7LH
Tel: 01344 621488
Head: Mr T W Bunbury BA, PGCE
Age range: 6–13
No. of pupils: 195

(☝)(☝)(£)(IAPS)(BSA)

Redroofs
Littlewick Green, Maidenhead,
Windsor & Maidenhead SL6 3QY
Tel: 01628 822982
Principal: June Rose
Age range: 8–18
No. of pupils: B32 G50
Fees: Day £3401–£3850

(16+)(£)(16+)(🎭)

St George's School
Windsor Castle, Windsor,
Windsor & Maidenhead SL4 1QF
Tel: 01753 865553
Headmaster: Mr A Salmond Smith
Age range: 3–13
No. of pupils: B245 G162
Fees: Day £7656–£12,699 WB £16,866
FB £17,316

St George's School
Wells Lane, Ascot,
Windsor & Maidenhead SL5 7DZ
Tel: 01344 629900
Headmistress: Mrs Caroline Jordan
MA(Oxon), PGCE
Age range: 11–18
No. of pupils: 280 VIth85
Fees: Day £16,440 FB £25,350

St John's Beaumont Preparatory School
Old Windsor,
Windsor & Maidenhead SL4 2JN
Tel: 01784 432428
Headmaster: Mr G E F Delaney
BA(Hons), PGCE
Age range: 3½–13
No. of pupils: 310
Fees: Day £7140–£13,320 WB £17,520
FB £20,250

St Mary's School Ascot
St Mary's Road, Ascot,
Windsor & Maidenhead SL5 9JF
Tel: 01344 293614
Headmistress: Mrs Mary Breen BSc, MSc
Age range: 11–18
No. of pupils: 380 G380 VIth120
Fees: Day £20,100 FB £28,230

St Piran's Preparatory School
Gringer Hill, Maidenhead,
Windsor & Maidenhead SL6 7LZ
Tel: 01628 594302
Headmaster: Mr J A Carroll BA(Hons),
BPhilEd, PGCE, NPQH
Age range: 3–11
No. of pupils: B192 G180
Fees: Day £2469–£11,940

Sunningdale School
Dry Arch Road, Sunningdale,
Windsor & Maidenhead SL5 9PY
Tel: 01344 620159
Headmaster: T A C N Dawson MA, PGCE
Age range: 7–13
No. of pupils: 90
Fees: Day £13,950 FB £17,985

The Marist Preparatory School
King's Road, Sunninghill, Ascot,
Windsor & Maidenhead SL5 7PS
Tel: 01344 624137
Headteacher: J Finlayson
Age range: 2½–11
No. of pupils: 238
Fees: Day £7845–£8325

The Marist Schools
King's Road, Sunninghill, Ascot,
Windsor & Maidenhead SL5 7PS
Tel: 01344 624291
Headteacher: Mr K McCloskey (Senior
School)
Age range: 2½–18
No. of pupils: 550 VIth60
Fees: Day £7845–£10,695

Upton House School
115 St Leonard's Road, Windsor,
Windsor & Maidenhead SL4 3DF
Tel: 01753 862610
Headmistress: Mrs Madeleine Collins
BA(Hons), PGCE(Oxford)
Age range: B2–7 G2–11
No. of pupils: 240
Fees: Day £4605–£11,985

WOKINGHAM

Bearwood College
Bearwood, Wokingham RG41 5BG
Tel: 0118 974 8300
Headmaster: Mr S G G Aiano
MA(Cantab)
Age range: 0–18
No. of pupils: 487 B338 G149 VIth80
Fees: Day £13,890–£16,365
FB £24,360–£28,080

Holme Grange School
Heathlands Road, Wokingham RG40 3AL
Tel: 0118 978 1566
Headteacher: Mrs C Robinson
Age range: 3–13
No. of pupils: 257 B153 G104
Fees: Day £4350–£10,980

Luckley-Oakfield School
Luckley Road, Wokingham RG40 3EU
Tel: 0118 978 4175
Headmistress: Miss V A Davis
BSc(London), ARCS
Age range: 11–18
No. of pupils: 300 VIth50
Fees: Day £13,476 WB £21,858
FB £23,586

Ludgrove
Wokingham RG40 3AB
Tel: 0118 978 9881
Joint Headmasters: S W T Barber & A C
T Inglis
Age range: 8–13
No. of pupils: 180
Fees: FB £185

Our Lady's Preparatory School
The Avenue, Crowthorne,
Wokingham RG45 6PB
Tel: 01344 773394
Headmistress: Mrs Helene Robinson
Age range: 3 months–11 years
No. of pupils: 100 B50 G50
Fees: Day £5328–£10,464

Waverley School
Waverley Way, Finchampstead,
Wokingham RG40 4YD
Tel: 0118 973 1121
Principal: Mrs Jane Sculpher
Age range: 3–11
No. of pupils: B78 G60
Fees: Day £3300–£7362

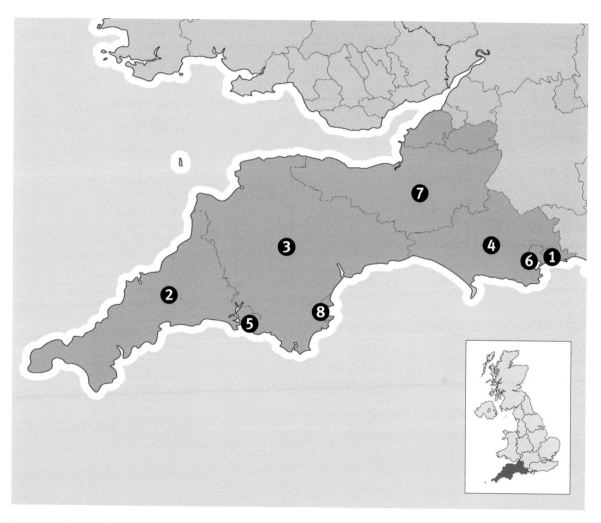

Key and page index:

1 Bournemouth: D336   **2** Cornwall: D336   **3** Devon: D337

4 Dorset: D338   **5** Plymouth: D339   **6** Poole: D340

7 Somerset: D340   **8** Torbay: D341

BOURNEMOUTH

St Martin's School
15 Stokewood Road,
Bournemouth BH3 7NA
Tel: 01202 760744
Headmaster: T Shenton MA
Age range: 4–11
No. of pupils: 100 B50 G50
Fees: Day £3000–£4500

St Thomas Garnet's School
Parkwood Road, Boscombe,
Bournemouth BH5 2BH
Tel: 01202 420172
Headteacher: Julie-Ann Cutler
Age range: 0–11
No. of pupils: B80 G66
Fees: Day £5250–£7350

Talbot Heath
Rothesay Road, Bournemouth BH4 9NJ
Tel: 01202 761881
Head: Mrs A Holloway MA, PGCE
Age range: 3–18
No. of pupils: 535 VIth80
Fees: Day £4890–£10,665 WB £17,286
FB £17,763

Talbot House Preparatory School
8 Firs Glen Road, Bournemouth BH9 2LR
Tel: 01202 510348
Headteacher: Mrs C N Oosthuizen
Age range: 3½–12
No. of pupils: 130 B65 G65
Fees: Day £750–£1429

The Park School
45-49 Queens Park, South Drive,
Bournemouth BH8 9BJ
Tel: 01202 396640
Headmaster: Mr C G Cole BA
Age range: 4–11
No. of pupils: 273 B161 G112
Fees: Day £5100–£7140

CORNWALL

GEMS Bolitho School
Polwithen Road, Penzance,
Cornwall TR18 4JR
Tel: +44 (0)1736 363271
Headmaster: Mr Clive Keevil
Age range: 1–19
No. of pupils: 214 B115 G99
Fees: Day £6435–£13,860
WB £5576–£22,176 FB £18,996–£24,474

Highfields Private School
Lower Cardrew Lane, Redruth,
Cornwall TR15 1SY
Tel: 01209 210665
Head: Mrs Mary Haddy
Age range: 4½–16
No. of pupils: 56 B38 G18
Fees: Day £5400

Polwhele House School
Truro, Cornwall TR4 9AE
Tel: 01872 273011
Headmaster: Mr Alex McCullough
Age range: 3–13
No. of pupils: 100
Fees: Day £1350–£10,845
WB £10,929–£14,865

Roselyon School
St Blazey Road, Par, Cornwall PL24 2HZ
Tel: 01726 812110
Head Teacher: Hilary Mann
Age range: 3–11
No. of pupils: 103 B54 G49
Fees: Day £837–£7680

St Ia School
St Ives Road, Carbis Bay, St Ives,
Cornwall TR26 2SF
Tel: 01736 796963
Headmistress: Miss Betsan Hill BEd
Age range: 4–11
No. of pupils: 22 B10 G12
Fees: Day £1500–£1620

St Joseph's School
15 St Stephen's Hill, Launceston,
Cornwall PL15 8HN
Tel: 01566 772580
Headmaster: Mrs Sue Rowe
Age range: B3–11 G3–16
No. of pupils: 190 B31 G159
Fees: Day £4566–£8475

St Michael's Catholic Small School
The Old St George's Chapel, St George's
Road, Truro, Cornwall TR1 3JD
Tel: 01872 242123
Head: Mr Neil Anderson
Age range: 5–16
No. of pupils: 46

St Petroc's School
Ocean View Road, Bude,
Cornwall EX23 8NJ
Tel: 01288 352876
Headmaster: Matthew Way
Age range: 0–11
No. of pupils: B52 G48
Fees: Day £4950–£7335

St Piran's School
Trelissick Road, Hayle,
Cornwall TR27 4HY
Tel: 01736 752612
Headteacher: Mrs Carol de Labat
BEd(Hons), CertEd
Age range: 3–16
No. of pupils: B50 G50
Fees: Day £4380–£5475

Truro High School for Girls
Falmouth Road, Truro, Cornwall TR1 2HU
Tel: 01872 272830
Head: Michael McDowell
Age range: B3–5 G3–18
No. of pupils: 432 B3 G429 VIth60
Fees: Day £5100–£8184
WB £14,706–£15,234
FB £14,901–£15,429

Key to symbols

(†) Boys' school

(‡) Girls' school

(🌐) International school

(16·) Tutorial or sixth form college

(A) A levels

(🏠) Boarding accommodation

(£) Bursaries

(IB) International Baccalaureate

(✎) Learning support

(16·) Entrance at 16+

(🎓) Vocational qualifications

(IAPS) Member of Independent Association of Preparatory Schools

(HMC) The Headmasters' & Headmistresses' Conference

(ISA) Independent Schools Association

(GSA) Girls' School Association

(BSA) Boarding Schools' Association

(S) SHMIS

Unless otherwise indicated, all schools are coeducational
day schools. Single-sex and boarding schools will be
indicated by the relevant icon.

Truro School

Trennick Lane, Truro, Cornwall TR1 1TH
Tel: 01872 272763
Headmaster: Mr P K Smith MA, MEd
Age range: 3–18
No. of pupils: 1081 B678 G403 VIth210

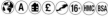

Wheelgate House School

Trevowah Road, Crantock, Newquay,
Cornwall TR8 5RU
Tel: 01637 830680
Principal: Mrs Gail P Wilson
Age range: 3 months–12 years
No. of pupils: B22 G24
Fees: Day £1098–£2700

DEVON

Bendarroch School

Aylesbeare, Exeter, Devon EX5 2BY
Tel: 01395 233553
Headmaster: Mr Nigel Home
Age range: 4–14
No. of pupils: B25 G20
Fees: Day £4900–£5800

Blundell's Preparatory School

Milestones House, Blundell's Road,
Tiverton, Devon EX16 4NA
Tel: 01884 252393
Head Master: Mr Nicholas A Folland
BSC, PGCE
Age range: 3–11
No. of pupils: 267 B147 G120
Fees: Day £1638–£8325

Blundell's School

Tiverton, Devon EX16 4DN
Tel: 01884 252543
Head Master: Mr I R Davenport BA
Age range: 11–18
No. of pupils: 570 B340 G230 VIth185
Fees: Day £9750–£15,645
WB £14,790–£21,345
FB £16,365–£24,255

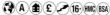

Bramdean School

Richmond Lodge, Homefield Road,
Heavitree, Exeter, Devon EX1 2QR
Tel: 01392 273387
Head: D Stoneman NAHT
Age range: 3–18
No. of pupils: 180 B97 G83 VIth12
Fees: Day £4740–£7875

Buckeridge International College

Trinity School, Buckeridge Road,
Teignmouth, Devon TQ14 8LY
Tel: 01626 774138
Headmaster: Mr Tim Waters
Age range: 7–19
No. of pupils: 43 B29 G14 VIth16
Fees: Day £6945–£9435
WB £17,010–£19,500
FB £17,310–£19,800

Emmanuel School

36-38 Blackboy Road, Exeter,
Devon EX4 6SZ
Tel: 01392 258150
Principal: Mr John Parker
Age range: 3–16
No. of pupils: 26 B16 G10
Fees: Day £2988

Exeter Cathedral School

The Chantry, Palace Gate, Exeter,
Devon EX1 1HX
Tel: 01392 255298
Headmaster: Brian McDowell
Age range: 3–13
No. of pupils: 197 B108 G89
Fees: Day £1314–£8730
WB £13,314–£13,659
FB £13,956–£14,274

Exeter School

Victoria Park Road, Exeter,
Devon EX2 4NS
Tel: 01392 273679
Headmaster: Mr R Griffin
Age range: 7–18
No. of pupils: 870 B530 G340 VIth203
Fees: Day £9150–£10,140

Exeter Tutorial College

44/46 Magdalen Road, Exeter,
Devon EX2 4TE
Tel: 01392 278101
Principal: K D Jack BA, DipEd
Age range: 16+
No. of pupils: 75 B33 G42
Fees: Day £1500–£8500

Kelly College

Tavistock, Devon PL19 0HZ
Tel: 01822 813100
Headmaster: G W R Hawley
Age range: 11–18
No. of pupils: 353 B205 G148 VIth107
Fees: Day £3950–£4875
WB £6450–£7900 FB £7175–£8500

Kelly College Preparatory School

Hazeldon House, Parkwood Road,
Tavistock, Devon PL19 0JS
Tel: 01822 612919
Headmaster: Mr M Foale BEd(Hons), MSc
Age range: 3–11
No. of pupils: 160 B85 G75
Fees: Day £5880–£8100 WB £15,300

KINGSLEY SCHOOL

For further details see p. 147
Northdown Road, Bideford,
Devon EX39 3LY
Tel: 01237 426200
Email:
admissions@kingsleyschoolbideford.co.uk
Website:
www.kingsleyschoolbideford.co.uk
Headmaster: Mr Andy Waters BEd, MA
Age range: 3 months–18 years
No. of pupils: 400 VIth80
Fees: Day £5010–£11,640
FB £14,430–£22,200

Magdalen Court School

Mulberry House, Victoria Park Road,
Exeter, Devon EX2 4NU
Tel: 01392 494919
Head: Mr Jeremy Bushrod
Age range: 0–18+
No. of pupils: 150 B75 G75 VIth20
Fees: Day £1800–£8250

Maria Montessori School

3 St Leonards Place, Exeter,
Devon EX2 4LZ
Tel: 01392 201303
Principal: Ruth Bloomfield AIL, MontDip
Age range: 2+–8
No. of pupils: 62 B30 G32
Fees: Day £1100–£3600

Moor View School

Staplehill Road, Liverton, Newton Abbot,
Devon TQ12 6JD
Tel: 01626 821686
Headteacher: Mr Powell
Age range: 11–16
No. of pupils: 57 B31 G26

Mount House Preparatory School

Tavistock, Devon PL19 9JL
Tel: 01822 612244
Headmaster: Mr J R O Massey BSc
Age range: 3–13
No. of pupils: 205 B99 G87 VIth18
Fees: Day £6510–£13,629
FB £16,065–£18,171

Park School

Park Road, Dartington, Totnes,
Devon TQ9 6EQ
Tel: 01803 864588
Teacher-in-charge: Amanda Bellamy
Age range: 3–12
No. of pupils: 54 B37 G17

Plymouth College
Ford Park, Plymouth, Devon PL4 6RN
Tel: +44 (0)1752 203300
Headmaster: Dr S J Wormleighton
Age range: 11–18
No. of pupils: 513 B298 G215 VIth170
Fees: Day £11,475–£12,855
FB £15,995–£25,155

Rudolf Steiner School
Hood Manor, Buckfastleigh Road,
Dartington, Totnes, Devon TQ9 6AB
Tel: 01803 762528
Education Manager: Ms Gillian Mills
Age range: 3–16
No. of pupils: 307 B150 G157
Fees: Day £2397–£3978

Sands School
Greylands, 48 East Street, Ashburton,
Devon TQ13 7AX
Tel: 01364 653666
Administrator: Sean Bellamy
MA(Cantab), PGCE
Age range: 11–17
No. of pupils: B33 G23
Fees: Day £5850

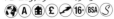

Shebbear College
Shebbear, Beaworthy, Devon EX21 5HJ
Tel: 01409 282000
Headmaster: Mr R S Barnes BA
Age range: 3–18
No. of pupils: 350 B210 G140 VIth54
Fees: Day £6870–£10,950
WB £12,390–£17,190
FB £15,090–£20,985

Small School
Fore Street, Hartland, Bideford,
Devon EX39 6AB
Tel: 01237 441672
Headteacher: Ms Maya Buckley
Age range: 11–16
No. of pupils: 25 B15 G10

St Christopher's Preparatory School
Mount Barton, Staverton,
Devon TQ9 6PF
Tel: 01803 762202
Headmistress: Mrs J E Kenyon
Age range: 3–11
No. of pupils: 100 B55 G45
Fees: Day £3600–£5565

St John's School
Broadway, Sidmouth, Devon EX10 8RG
Tel: 01395 513984
Headmistress: Mrs Angela Parry-Davies
Age range: 2–13
No. of pupils: B90 G80
Fees: Day £5130–£7164 WB £12,141
FB £12,141–£13,779

St Margaret's School, Exeter
147 Magdalen Road, Exeter,
Devon EX2 4TS
Tel: 01392 273197
Headmistress: Miss R Edbrooke
BEd(Hons)
Age range: 7–18
No. of pupils: 321 VIth67
Fees: Day £6768–£8172

St Michael's School
Tawstock Court, Barnstaple,
Devon EX31 3HY
Tel: 01271 343242
Headmaster: Mr J P Foley BA
Age range: 3 months–13+ years
No. of pupils: 250

St Peter's School
Harefield, Lympstone, Exmouth,
Devon EX8 5AU
Tel: 01395 272148
Headmaster: N Neeson NPQH,
BEd(Hons)
Age range: 3–13
No. of pupils: 275 B167 G108
Fees: Day £6042–£10,350 WB £15,580

St Wilfrid's School
25 St David's Hill, Exeter,
Devon EX4 4DA
Tel: 01392 276171
Headmistress: Mrs Alexandra E M
MacDonald-Dent DPhyEd
Age range: 5–16
No. of pupils: B90 G55
Fees: Day £2085–£3060

Stover School
Newton Abbot, Devon TQ12 6QG
Tel: 01626 354505
Principal: Mrs Sue Bradley BSc, CBiol,
MSB
Age range: 3–18
No. of pupils: 423 B189 G234 VIth67
Fees: Day £6879–£10,695
WB £15,183–£21,894
FB £16,575–£20,850

The Dolphin Pre School & Nursery
Raddenstile Lane, Exmouth,
Devon EX8 2JH
Tel: 01395 272418
Headmaster: Mr Bill Gott BSc,
PGCE(Oxon), CPhys, MInstP
Age range: 0–5
Fees: Day £3600–£3900

The Maynard School
Denmark Road, Exeter, Devon EX1 1SJ
Tel: 01392 273417
Headmistress: Ms B Hughes
Age range: 7–18
No. of pupils: 420 G420 VIth100
Fees: Day £7566–£9465

The New School
The Avenue, Exminster, Exeter,
Devon EX6 8AT
Tel: 01392 496122
Headmistress: Miss M Taylor BA(Hons),
PGCE
Age range: 3–7
No. of pupils: 61 B30 G31
Fees: Day £690–£5430

Trinity School
Buckeridge Road, Teignmouth,
Devon TQ14 8LY
Tel: 01626 774138
Headmaster: Mr Tim Waters
Age range: 3–19
No. of pupils: 495 B270 G225 VIth115
Fees: Day £6585–£8940
WB £16,080–£18,435
FB £16,380–£18,735

West Buckland School
Barnstaple, Devon EX32 0SX
Tel: 01598 760281
Headmaster: J Vick MA(Cantab)
Age range: 3–18
No. of pupils: B378 G351 VIth135
Fees: Day £2130–£3975
WB £6400–£7510 FB £6400–£7510

DORSET

Bryanston School
Blandford Forum, Dorset DT11 0PX
Tel: 01258 452411
Head: Ms S J Thomas
Age range: 13–18
No. of pupils: 667 B384 G283 VIth270
Fees: Day £22,404 FB £27,660

Canford School
Canford Magna, Wimborne,
Dorset BH21 3AD
Tel: 01202 841254
Headmaster: J D Lever MA
Age range: 13–18
No. of pupils: 629 B372 G257 VIth263
Fees: Day £21,735 FB £27,915

Castle Court School
Knoll Lane, Corfe Mullen, Wimborne,
Dorset BH21 3RF
Tel: 01202 694438
Headmaster: Mr Richard Stevenson
Age range: 2–13
No. of pupils: 307 B175 G132
Fees: Day £1350–£12,945

Claytesmore Preparatory School
Iwerne Minster, Blandford Forum,
Dorset DT11 8PH
Tel: 01747 811707
Head of Prep: Mr R Geffen
Age range: 2–13
No. of pupils: 263 B160 G103
Fees: Day £6741–£13,710
FB £16,845–£18,462

Clayesmore School
Iwerne Minster, Blandford Forum,
Dorset DT11 8LL
Tel: 01747 812122
Headmaster: Mr M G Cooke
Age range: 13–18
No. of pupils: 421 B273 G148 VIth146
Fees: Day £18,579 FB £25,392

Dumpton School
Deans Grove House, Wimborne,
Dorset BH21 7AF
Tel: 01202 883818
Headmaster: A W Browning BSc(Hons),
MA(Ed), PGCE
Age range: 2–13
No. of pupils: B211 G133
Fees: Day £1850–£13,179

Hanford School
Child Okeford, Blandford Forum,
Dorset DT11 8HL
Tel: 01258 860219
Headmaster: Mr N S Mackay
Age range: 7–13
No. of pupils: 100
Fees: Day £16,500 FB £19,950

Knighton House School
Durweston, Blandford Forum,
Dorset DT11 0PY
Tel: 01258 452065
Head: Mrs Claire Renton Bourne MA, Dip
RS
Age range: B2–7 G2–13
No. of pupils: 128 B2 G126
Fees: Day £6786–£13,410 WB £17,850
FB £17,850

Leweston Preparatory School
Leweston, Sherborne, Dorset DT9 6EN
Tel: 01963 210790
Headteacher: Mrs M Allen
Age range: 2–11
No. of pupils: 84 B18 G66
Fees: Day £7485–£10,695 WB £13,695
FB £15,855

Leweston School
Senior School, Sherborne,
Dorset DT9 6EN
Tel: 01963 210691
Head: Mr A Aylward MA(Oxon), PGCE
Age range: 11–18
No. of pupils: 240 VIth70
Fees: Day £15,270 WB £20,055
FB £23,625

MILTON ABBEY SCHOOL
For further details see p. 148
For further details see p. 148
Blandford Forum, Dorset DT11 0BZ
Tel: 01258 880484
Email: admissions@miltonabbey.co.uk
Website: www.miltonabbey.co.uk
Headmaster: G E Doodes MA
Age range: 13–18
No. of pupils: 228 B201 G27 VIth106
Fees: Day £21,300 FB £28,350

Port Regis
Motcombe Park, Shaftesbury,
Dorset SP7 9QA
Tel: 01747 857800
Headmaster: B H Dunhill
BA(Hons)(London), PGCE(Sussex)
Age range: 3–13
No. of pupils: 324 B180 G144
Fees: Day £6300–£15,105 WB £19,395
FB £19,395

Sherborne Girls
Bradford Road, Sherborne,
Dorset DT9 3QN
Tel: +44 (0)1935 818224
Headmistress: Mrs J Dwyer BEd(Hons)
Age range: 11–18
No. of pupils: 410 VIth144
Fees: Day £5750–£6865
FB £7850–£9450

Sherborne Preparatory School
Acreman Street, Sherborne,
Dorset DT9 3NY
Tel: 01935 812097
Headmaster: Mr P S Tait MA(Massey)
Age range: 2–13
No. of pupils: 258 B174 G84
Fees: Day £7305–£13,515
WB £18,495–£19,350
FB £18,495–£19,350

Sherborne School
Abbey Road, Sherborne, Dorset DT9 3AP
Tel: +44 (0)1935 810512
Headmaster: Mr C Davis MA
Age range: 13–18
No. of pupils: 596 VIth210
Fees: Day £23,625 FB £29,175

Sherborne School International College
Newell Grange, Newell, Sherborne,
Dorset DT9 4EZ
Tel: 01935 814743
Principal: Dr Christopher Greenfield MA,
MEd
Age range: 11–16
No. of pupils: 160 B82 G78
Fees: FB £34,500

St Mary's School
Shaftesbury, Dorset SP7 9LP
Tel: 01747 854005
Headmaster: Mr Richard James
BMus(Hons)(London), ARCM
Age range: 11–18
No. of pupils: 325 G325 VIth86
Fees: Day £14,820–£15,570
FB £21,570–£22,650

Sunninghill Preparatory School
South Court, South Walks, Dorchester,
Dorset DT1 1EB
Tel: 01305 262306
Headmaster: Mr Andrew Roberts-Wray
BA(Hons) Dunelm, PGCE
Age range: 3–13
No. of pupils: B62 G68

Thornlow Preparatory School
Connaught Road, Weymouth,
Dorset DT4 0SA
Tel: 01305 785703
Headmaster: Mr R A Fowke BEd(Hons)
Age range: 3–13
No. of pupils: B40 G36
Fees: Day £6510

PLYMOUTH

Fletewood School
88 North Road East, Plymouth PL4 6AN
Tel: 01752 663782
Headmaster: J Martin
Age range: 3–11
No. of pupils: B35 G35
Fees: Day £3540

King's School
Hartley Road, Mannamead,
Plymouth PL3 5LW
Tel: 01752 771789
Headteacher: Mrs Jane Lee
Age range: 3–11
No. of pupils: 142 B75 G67
Fees: Day £4980–£5730

Plantings School
33 Old Park Road, Peverell,
Plymouth PL3 4PY
Tel: 01752 265171
Headmistress: Miss D J Webber CertEd
Age range: 3–16
No. of pupils: 12 B7 G5
Fees: Day £1080–£1320

Plymouth College Preparatory School
St Dunstan's Abbey, The Millfields,
Plymouth PL1 3JL
Tel: 01752 201352
Headmaster: Chris Gatherer
Age range: 3–11
No. of pupils: 310 B156 G154
Fees: Day £1867–£6000

POOLE

Bournemouth Collegiate School
St Osmunds Road, Parkstone,
Poole BH14 9JY
Tel: 01202 742626
Head Teacher: Mrs Mercer
Age range: 2½–16
No. of pupils: 301 B184 G117
Fees: Day £2925–£9225

Buckholme Towers School
18 Commercial Road, Lower Parkstone,
Poole BH14 0JW
Tel: 01202 742871
Headteacher: Mr I Robertson
Age range: 3–12½
No. of pupils: 104 B50 G54
Fees: Day £863–£1819

Yarrells Preparatory School
Yarrells House, Upton, Poole BH16 5EU
Tel: 01202 622229
Headmistress: Mrs Natalie A Covell BA,
MSc
Age range: 2–13
No. of pupils: 212 B100 G112
Fees: Day £1642–£3365

SOMERSET

All Hallows School
Cranmore Hall, Shepton Mallet,
Somerset BA4 4SF
Tel: 01749 881600
Headmaster: Mr Ian Murphy BA(Hons),
PGCE(Durham)
Age range: 4–13
No. of pupils: 289 B164 G125
Fees: Day £5850–£11,400 WB £17,100
FB £17,100

Bruton School for Girls
Sunny Hill, Bruton, Somerset BA10 0NT
Tel: 01749 814400
Headmaster: Mr John Burrough
Age range: 2–18
No. of pupils: 304 VIth61
Fees: Day £12,510 WB £15,120–£19,215
FB £21,015

Chard School
Fore Street, Chard, Somerset TA20 1QA
Tel: 01460 63234
Headmaster: J G Stotesbury MEd
Age range: 2–11
No. of pupils: 100 B50 G50
Fees: Day £4545–£5400

Chilton Cantelo School
Chilton Cantelo, Yeovil,
Somerset BA22 8BG
Tel: 01935 850555
Headmaster: Dr John Price BSc, PhD
Age range: 4–18
No. of pupils: 316 B197 G119
Fees: Day £5787–£11,496
WB £16,125–£21,495
FB £16,125–£21,495

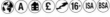

Hazlegrove
Hazlegrove, Sparkford, Yeovil,
Somerset BA22 7JA
Tel: 01963 442606/440314
Headmaster: Mr Richard Fenwick MA
Age range: 2–13
No. of pupils: 381 B201 G180
Fees: Day £7041–£14,271
WB £15,930–£20,325
FB £15,930–£20,325

King's Bruton
Bruton, Somerset BA10 0ED
Tel: 01749 814200
Headmaster: Mr I S Wilmshurst MA
Age range: 13–18
No. of pupils: 306 B221 G85 VIth145
Fees: Day £18,486 FB £25,455

King's College
Taunton, Somerset TA1 3DX
Tel: 01823 328204
Headmaster: R R Biggs
Age range: 13–18
No. of pupils: 440 B285 G155 VIth180
Fees: Day £13,650 FB £19,980

King's Hall School
Kingston Road, Taunton,
Somerset TA2 8AA
Tel: 01823 285920
Headmaster: Mr James Macpherson
Age range: 3–13
No. of pupils: B215 G160
Fees: Day £4350–£11,520
FB £13,110–£17,040

Millfield Preparatory School
Edgarley Hall, Glastonbury,
Somerset BA6 8LD
Tel: 01458 832446
Headmistress: Mrs S I Shayler
Age range: 2–13
No. of pupils: 453 B237 G216
Fees: Day £4330–£5300 FB £7770

Millfield School
Street, Somerset BA16 0YD
Tel: 01458 442 291/296
Headmaster: Craig A Considine
Age range: 13–18
No. of pupils: 1218 B756 G462 VIth566
Fees: Day £21,075 FB £31,260

Perrott Hill
North Perrott, Crewkerne,
Somerset TA18 7SL
Tel: 01460 72051
Headteacher: Mr R Morse BEd
Age range: 3–13
No. of pupils: 204
Fees: Day £5265–£13,755 WB £14,835
FB £18,345

Queen's College
Trull Road, Taunton, Somerset TA1 4QS
Tel: 01823 272559
Headmaster: Mr Christopher J Alcock
BSc, FRSG, FRSA
Age range: 3–18
No. of pupils: 784 B404 G380 VIth150
Fees: Day £5250–£14,700
FB £10,605–£23,400

**Springmead Preparatory School &
Nursery**
Castle Corner, Beckington, Frome,
Somerset BA11 6TA
Tel: 01373 831555
Co-principals: Mr Stephen Taylor & Mrs
Madeleine Taylor
Age range: 2–11
No. of pupils: 105 B56 G49
Fees: Day £5445–£6051

Sunny Hill Prep School
Sunny Hill, Bruton, Somerset BA10 0NT
Tel: 01749 814 427
Head: Mrs Helen Snow BEd
Age range: B2–7 G2–11
No. of pupils: 68 B8 G60
Fees: Day £4650–£9600
WB £15,750–£16,050
FB £16,905–£17,205

Taunton Preparatory School
Staplegrove Road, Taunton,
Somerset TA2 6AE
Tel: 01823 703305
Headmaster: Jimmy Beale
Age range: 2–13
No. of pupils: 436 B236 G200
Fees: Day £5775–£12,555
FB £11,115–£20,145

Taunton School
Staplegrove Road, Taunton,
Somerset TA2 6AD
Tel: 01823 703200
Headmaster: Dr John Newton MA
Age range: 2–18
No. of pupils: 589 B321 G268 VIth273
Fees: Day £2225–£5150
FB £3705–£8535

The Meadow Steiner School
18-20 High Street, Bruton,
Somerset BA10 0AA
Tel: 01749 813176
Age range: 3–11
No. of pupils: B38 G29
Fees: Day £2400

The Park School
The Park, Yeovil, Somerset BA20 1DH
Tel: 01935 423514
Head: Mrs J Huntington ARAM GRSM
LRAM CPSEd
Age range: 3–18+
No. of pupils: B111 G108 VIth30
Fees: Day £4350–£8640
WB £14,385–£15,405
FB £15,750–£17,550

Wellington Junior School
South Street, Wellington,
Somerset TA21 8NT
Tel: 01823 668700
Headmaster: Adam Gibson
Age range: 3–11
No. of pupils: 246 B127 G119
Fees: Day £4470–£8490 WB £13,332
FB £16,665

Wellington School
South Street, Wellington,
Somerset TA21 8NT
Tel: 01823 668800
Headmaster: M S Reader
Age range: 10–18
No. of pupils: 833 B464 G369 VIth173
Fees: Day £10,974–£12,030
FB £21,860–£23,115

Wells Cathedral Junior School
8 New Street, Wells, Somerset BA5 2LQ
Tel: 01749 834400
Headteacher: Mr N M Wilson BA, PGCE
Age range: 3–11
No. of pupils: 150 B78 G72
Fees: Day £6054–£11,265 WB £15,951
FB £19,545

Wells Cathedral School
Wells, Somerset BA5 2ST
Tel: 01749 834200
Head: Mrs Elizabeth Cairncross BA,
PGCE(UnivCollLondon)
Age range: 11–18
No. of pupils: 737 B369 G368 VIth197
Fees: Day £6054–£14,250
FB £19,545–£23,820

TORBAY

Abbey School
Hampton Court, St Marychurch, Torquay,
Torbay TQ1 4PR
Tel: 01803 327868
Principal: Mrs S J Greinig
Age range: 0–11
No. of pupils: B80 G80
Fees: Day £673–£7200

EF INTERNATIONAL ACADEMY TORBAY
For further details see p. 146
EF House, Castle Road, Torquay,
Torbay TQ1 3BG
Tel: +41 41 41 74 525
Head of School: David Davies
Age range: 14–18
No. of pupils: 150
Fees: FB £19,950

Stoodley Knowle School
Ansteys Cove Road, Torquay,
Torbay TQ1 2JB
Tel: 01803 293160
Headteacher: Jane White
Age range: 2–18
No. of pupils: 305 VIth20
Fees: Day £4944

Tower House School
Fisher Street, Paignton, Torbay TQ4 5EW
Tel: 01803 557077
Headmaster: Mr W J Miller BEd
Age range: 2–16
No. of pupils: B137 G96
Fees: Day £4188–£6396

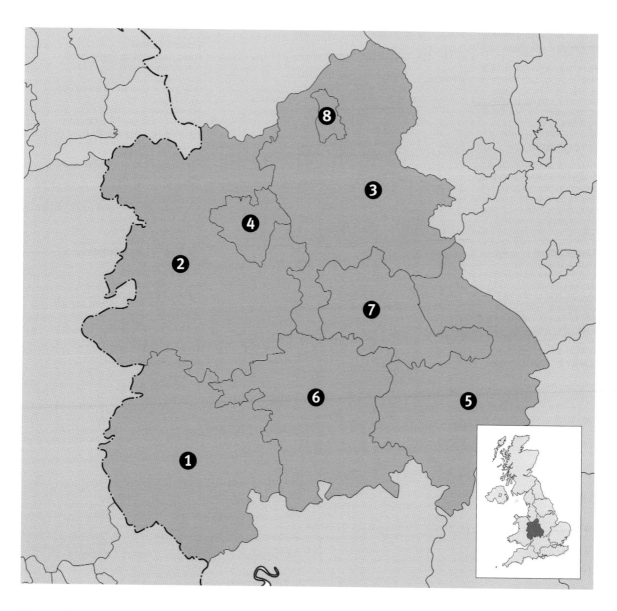

Key and page index:

1 Herefordshire: D344

2 Shropshire: D344

3 Staffordshire: D345

4 Telford & Wrekin: D346

5 Warwickshire: D346

6 Worcestershire: D350

7 West Midlands: D347

8 Stoke on Trent: D346

HEREFORDSHIRE

Hereford Cathedral Junior School
28 Castle Street, Hereford,
Herefordshire HR1 2NW
Tel: 01432 363511
Headmaster: Mr T C Wheeler MA, BA,
PGCE
Age range: 3–11
No. of pupils: 258 B118 G140
Fees: Day £6960–£8640

 (£) (✎) (IAPS)

Hereford Cathedral School
Old Deanery, Cathedral Close, Hereford,
Herefordshire HR1 2NG
Tel: 01432 363521
Headmaster: Mr Paul Smith
Age range: 11–18
No. of pupils: 535 VIth130

(A) (£) (✎) (16+) (HMC)

Hereford Waldorf School
Much Dewchurch, Hereford,
Herefordshire HR2 8DL
Tel: 01981 540221
Age range: 3–16
No. of pupils: B96 G110

(✎)

Lucton School
Lucton, Leominster,
Herefordshire HR6 9PN
Tel: 01568 782000
Headmistress: Mrs Gill Thorne MA
Age range: 1–19
No. of pupils: B180 G133 VIth57
Fees: Day £5697–£11,115
WB £18,568–£21,870
FB £18,568–£25,110

(🌍) (A) (🏫) (£) (✎) (16+) (ISA) (BSA)

St Richard's School
Bredenbury Court, Bromyard,
Herefordshire HR7 4TD
Tel: 01885 482491
Head: Mr N S Cheesman BEd(Hons)
Age range: 3–13
No. of pupils: 142 B71 G71
Fees: Day £3699–£10,665 WB £14,640
FB £15,420

(🏫) (£) (✎) (BSA)

SHROPSHIRE

Adcote School for Girls
Little Ness, Shrewsbury,
Shropshire SY4 2JY
Tel: 01939 260202
Head: Mr Gary Wright
Age range: 4–18
No. of pupils: 120
Fees: Day £3960–£11,400
WB £12,885–£18,480
FB £14,640–£20,235

(👧) (🌍) (A) (🏫) (£) (✎) (16+) (ISA) (BSA)

Bedstone College
Bedstone, Bucknell, Shropshire SY7 0BG
Tel: 01547 530303
Headmaster: Mr M S Symonds BSc,
PGCE
Age range: 3–18
No. of pupils: B150 G120 VIth34
Fees: Day £3960–£11,550
FB £13,800–£20,955

(🌍) (A) (🏫) (£) (✎) (16+) (ISA) (BSA) (S)

Birchfield School
Albrighton, Wolverhampton,
Shropshire WV7 3AF
Tel: 01902 372534
Headmaster: Mr H Myott
Age range: B4–13 G4–10
No. of pupils: 145 B105 G40
Fees: Day £5685–£11,775 WB £16,650

(🏫) (£) (✎) (IAPS) (BSA)

Castle House School
Chetwynd End, Newport,
Shropshire TF10 7JE
Tel: 01952 811035
Headmaster: Mr R M Walden
MA(Cantab), CEd, MEd, FCollP
Age range: 2–11
No. of pupils: 100 B48 G52
Fees: Day £5838–£6699

(£) (✎) (ISA)

Concord College
Acton Burnell Hall, Shrewsbury,
Shropshire SY5 7PF
Tel: 01694 731631
Principal: N G Hawkins MA, PGCE
Age range: 12–19
No. of pupils: 402 B202 G200 VIth298
Fees: Day £11,500 FB £24,900

(🌍) (A) (🏫) (£) (✎) (16+) (BSA) (S)

Ellesmere College
Ellesmere, Shropshire SY12 9AB
Tel: 01691 622321
Head: Mr B J Wignall MA, FRSA, MCMI
Age range: 7–18
No. of pupils: 586 B386 G200 VIth172
Fees: Day £9423–£15,435
WB £19,404–£20,044
FB £20,835–£26,037

(🌍) (A) (🏫) (£) (IB) (✎) (16+) (HMC) (BSA)

Moor Park School
Ludlow, Shropshire SY8 4DZ
Tel: 01584 876061
Headmaster: Mr Jonathan Bartlett
Age range: 3–13
No. of pupils: 248 B137 G111
Fees: Day £5550–£11,985
FB £13,470–£16,380

(🏫) (£) (✎) (IAPS) (BSA)

Key to symbols

(👦) Boys' school

(👧) Girls' school

(🌍) International school

(16+) Tutorial or sixth form college

(A) A levels

(🏫) Boarding accommodation

(£) Bursaries

(IB) International Baccalaureate

(✎) Learning support

(16+) Entrance at 16+

(🎓) Vocational qualifications

(IAPS) Member of Independent Association of Preparatory Schools

(HMC) The Headmasters' & Headmistresses' Conference

(ISA) Independent Schools Association

(GSA) Girls' School Association

(BSA) Boarding Schools' Association

(S) SHMIS

Unless otherwise indicated, all schools are coeducational
day schools. Single-sex and boarding schools will be
indicated by the relevant icon.

Moreton Hall
Weston Rhyn, Oswestry,
Shropshire SY11 3EN
Tel: 01691 773671
Head: Jonathan Forster BA, PGCE, FRSA
Age range: B3–11 G3–18
No. of pupils: 386 B25 G361 VIth100
Fees: Day £7710–£22,395
FB £17,730–£27,345

Oswestry School
Upper Brook Street, Oswestry,
Shropshire SY11 2TL
Tel: 01691 655711
Headmaster: Mr Douglas Robb MA, MEd
Age range: 4–18
No. of pupils: 443 B240 G203 VIth92
Fees: Day £7305–£12,720 WB £17,835
FB £18,735–£22,140

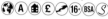

PACKWOOD HAUGH SCHOOL
For further details see p. 152
Ruyton XI Towns, Shrewsbury,
Shropshire SY4 1HX
Tel: 01939 260217
Email: enquiries@packwood-
haugh.co.uk
Website: www.packwood-haugh.co.uk
Headmaster: Clive Smith-Langridge BA
(Hons), PGCE
Age range: 4–13
No. of pupils: 240 B160 G80
Fees: Day £6669–£14,919 FB £18,645

Prestfelde Preparatory School
London Road, Shrewsbury,
Shropshire SY2 6NZ
Tel: 01743 245400
Headmaster: Mr M C Groome
Age range: 3–13
No. of pupils: 275 B191 G84
Fees: Day £4020–£12,825 WB £16,500

Shrewsbury High School GDST
32 Town Walls, Shrewsbury,
Shropshire SY1 1TN
Tel: 01743 494000
Headmistress: Mrs M L R Cass
BA(Hons)Exeter, MA(EdMgmt)Bath
Age range: B2–13 G2–18
No. of pupils: 776 B95 G681 VIth129
Fees: Day £6978–£9627

Shrewsbury School
The Schools, Shrewsbury,
Shropshire SY3 7BA
Tel: 01743 280500
Headmaster: Mr Mark Turner MA
Age range: B13–18 G16–18
No. of pupils: 714 B679 G35 VIth290
Fees: Day £19,785 FB £28,260

St Winefride's Convent School
Belmont, Shrewsbury,
Shropshire SY1 1TE
Tel: 01743 369883
Headmistress: Sister M Felicity CertEd,
BA(Hons)
Age range: 3–11
No. of pupils: 174 B66 G108
Fees: Day £3345–£3495

White House School
Heath Road, Whitchurch,
Shropshire SY13 2AA
Tel: 01948 662730
Headmistress: Mrs H M Clarke
Age range: 3–11
No. of pupils: B76 G100
Fees: Day £3750

STAFFORDSHIRE

ABBOTS BROMLEY SCHOOL
For further details see p. 150
High Street, Abbots Bromley, Rugeley,
Staffordshire WS15 3BW
Tel: 01283 840232
Email: enquiries@abbotsbromley.net
Website: www.abbotsbromley.net
Headmistress: Mrs J Dowling
MA(Cantab), PGCE, NPQH
Age range: B3–11 G3–18
No. of pupils: 251 B4 G247 VIth54
Fees: Day £4386–£14,910
WB £16,545–£20,925
FB £20,295–£24,975

Abbotsholme School
Rocester, Uttoxeter,
Staffordshire ST14 5BS
Tel: 01889 590217
Headmaster: Steve Fairclough
Age range: 5–18
No. of pupils: 318 B199 G119 VIth68
Fees: Day £8100–£15,000
WB £14,400–£18,300
FB £18,900–£21,900

Brooklands School
167 Eccleshall Road, Stafford,
Staffordshire ST16 1PD
Tel: 01785 251399
Headmaster: D R Williams BA, PGCE
(Cantab)
Age range: 3 months–11 years
No. of pupils: 180 B90 G90
Fees: Day £999–£8395

Chase Academy
Lyncroft House, St John's Road,
Cannock, Staffordshire WS11 0UR
Tel: 01543 501800
Principal: Mr Mark Ellse
Age range: 3–18
No. of pupils: 218 B107 G111 VIth16
Fees: Day £2352–£8100
FB £11,610–£18,150

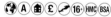

**Chase Academy International Study
Centre**
Lyncroft House, St John's Road,
Cannock, Staffordshire WS11 0UR
Tel: 01543 501800
Principal: Mr M D Ellse MA, CPhys,
MInstP
Age range: 11–18
No. of pupils: 93 B45 G48
Fees: FB £11,610–£18,150

Copsewood Primary School
Verulam Road, Stafford,
Staffordshire ST16 3EA
Tel: 01785 258482
Head: Mr J Spicer
Age range: 7–11
No. of pupils: 20

Denstone College
Uttoxeter, Staffordshire ST14 5HN
Tel: 01889 590484
Headmaster: Mr David Derbyshire MSc,
BA
Age range: 11–18
No. of pupils: 591 B377 G214 VIth177
Fees: Day £10,083–£12,183
FB £14,601–£21,216

Edenhurst School
Westlands Avenue, Newcastle-under-
Lyme, Staffordshire ST5 2PU
Tel: 01782 619348
Headmaster: N H F Copestick BSc,
CertEd
Age range: 3 months–13 years
No. of pupils: 210 B110 G100
Fees: Day £7100–£9150

Howitt House School
New Lodge, Hanbury, Burton upon Trent,
Staffordshire DE13 8TG
Tel: 01283 820236
Headmistress: Mrs S Hall
Age range: 2½–11
No. of pupils: 75 B39 G36
Fees: Day £4200

Lichfield Cathedral School
The Palace, Lichfield,
Staffordshire WS13 7LH
Tel: 01543 306170
Headmaster: Mr M Chanter BSc(Hons),
MA
Age range: 3–18
No. of pupils: 449 B242 G207
Fees: Day £6258–£9783
WB £12,111–£14,196 FB £13,875–£15,057

Maple Hayes Dyslexia School
Abnalls Lane, Lichfield,
Staffordshire WS13 8BL
Tel: 01543 264387
Principal: Dr E N Brown MSc, BA, MINS,
MSCMe, AFBPsS, CPsychol
Age range: 7–17
No. of pupils: 118 B97 G23
Fees: Day £13,020–£17,670

£ ISA

Newcastle-under-Lyme School
Mount Pleasant, Newcastle-under-Lyme,
Staffordshire ST5 1DB
Tel: 01782 631197
Headmaster: N A Rugg
Age range: 3–18
No. of pupils: 953 B502 G451 VIth200
Fees: Day £6684–£9183

A £ 16+ HMC

Smallwood Manor Preparatory School
Smallwood Manor, Uttoxeter,
Staffordshire ST14 8NS
Tel: 01889 562083
Headmaster: Mr M Harrison
Age range: 2–11
No. of pupils: 146 B74 G72
Fees: Day £2346–£10,125

£ IAPS

St Bede's School
Bishton Hall, Wolseley Bridge, Stafford,
Staffordshire ST17 0XN
Tel: 01889 881277
Headmaster: Mr C Stafford BA(Hons)
Age range: 3–13
No. of pupils: 75 B55 G20
Fees: Day £6000–£9900 WB £12,000
FB £12,000

St Dominic's High School for Girls
32 Bargate Street, Brewood,
Staffordshire ST19 9BA
Tel: 01902 850248
Headteacher: Mr Harevy R J Trump MA,
NPQH
Age range: B3–7 G3–18
No. of pupils: 300
Fees: Day £1955–£3780

A £ 16+ ISA GSA

St Dominic's Priory School Stone
21 Station Road, Stone,
Staffordshire ST15 8EN
Tel: 01785 814181
Headteacher: Mrs Patricia Adamson
Age range: B18 months–11 G18
months–18
No. of pupils: 320 B20 G300 VIth40
Fees: Day £6650–£9768

A £ 16+ ISA GSA

Stafford Grammar School
Burton Manor, Stafford,
Staffordshire ST18 9AT
Tel: 01785 249752
Headmaster: Mr M R Darley BA
Age range: 11–18
No. of pupils: 413 B214 G199 VIth120
Fees: Day £10,131

Vernon Lodge Preparatory School
School Lane, Stretton, Brewood,
Staffordshire ST19 9LJ
Tel: 01902 850568
Headteacher: Mrs P Sills BEd, CertEd,
RSA, CertSpLd
Age range: 2–11
No. of pupils: 78 B44 G34
Fees: Day £5685–£6720

£ ISA

Yarlet School
Yarlet, Stafford, Staffordshire ST18 9SU
Tel: 01785 286568
Headmaster: Mr I Raybould BEd(Hons)
Age range: 2–13
No. of pupils: 169 B110 G59
Fees: Day £2075–£3460

STOKE-ON-TRENT

St Joseph's Preparatory School
London Road, Trent Vale, Stoke-on-
Trent ST4 5NT
Tel: 01782 417533
Head: Mrs S D Hutchinson
Age range: 3–11
No. of pupils: B75 G58
Fees: Day £1460–£1930

£ ISA

TELFORD & WREKIN

The Old Hall School
Stanley Road, Wellington, Telford,
Telford & Wrekin TF1 3LB
Tel: 01952 223117
Headmaster: Mr M Stott
Age range: 4–11
No. of pupils: 239 B136 G103
Fees: Day £6060–£9402

£ IAPS

Wrekin College
Wellington, Telford,
Telford & Wrekin TF1 3BG
Tel: 01952 265600
Headmaster: Mr R T F Fleming
Age range: 11–18
No. of pupils: 415 B240 G175 VIth140
Fees: Day £12,525–£15,132
FB £21,570–£24,975

WARWICKSHIRE

Abbotsford School
Bridge Street, Kenilworth,
Warwickshire CV8 1BP
Tel: 01926 852826
Headmaster: Dominic Cook
Age range: 2 years 9 months–11 years
No. of pupils: 105
Fees: Day £4845–£6060

£

Arnold Lodge School
15-17 Kenilworth Road, Leamington Spa,
Warwickshire CV32 5TW
Tel: 01926 778050
Headmaster: David Williams
Age range: 3–16
No. of pupils: 252 B162 G90
Fees: Day £6960–£9540

£

Bilton Grange
Dunchurch, Rugby,
Warwickshire CV22 6QU
Tel: 01788 810217
Headmaster: Mr Peter Kirk BSc
Age range: 4–13
No. of pupils: 304 B194 G110
Fees: Day £8190–£15,675 WB £19,245
FB £19,245

£ IAPS BSA

Crackley Hall School
St Joseph's Park, Kenilworth,
Warwickshire CV8 2FT
Tel: 01926 514444
Headmaster: Mr P Ryan
Age range: 2–11
No. of pupils: 159 B82 G77
Fees: Day £6345–£6900

£ ISA

Emscote House School
46 Warwick Place, Leamington Spa,
Warwickshire CV32 5DE
Tel: 01926 425067
Headmistress: Mrs G J Andrews CertEd,
BEd
Age range: 2½–8
No. of pupils: 47 B29 G18
Fees: Day £6450

Jamia Islamia Islamic Studies Centre
Watling Street, Nuneaton,
Warwickshire CV11 6BE
Tel: 024 7664 1333
Headteacher: Mr Tauqir Ishaq
Age range: 11–21
No. of pupils: 61
Fees: FB £4550–£5400

King's High School for Girls
Smith Street, Warwick,
Warwickshire CV34 4HJ
Tel: 01926 494485
Headmistress: Mrs E Surber BA(Hons),
MA
Age range: 11–18
No. of pupils: 650 VIth155
Fees: Day £9519

Milverton House School
Holman Way, Park Street, Attleborough,
Warwickshire CV11 4EL
Tel: 024 7664 1722
Head Teacher: Mr O Pipe
Age range: 0–11
No. of pupils: 275 B140 G135
Fees: Day £3400–£3800

Princethorpe College
Leamington Road, Princethorpe, Rugby,
Warwickshire CV23 9PX
Tel: 01926 634200
Headmaster: Mr E D Hester
Age range: 11–18
No. of pupils: B410 G350 VIth160
Fees: Day £9000

RUGBY SCHOOL
For further details see p. 153
Rugby, Warwickshire CV22 5EH
Tel: 01788 556274
Email: admissions@rugbyschool.net
Website: www.rugbyschool.net
Headmaster: P S J Derham
Age range: 11–18
No. of pupils: 792 B442 G350 VIth344
Fees: Day £15,165 WB £17,700
FB £27,225

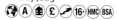

Stratford Preparatory School
Church House, Old Town, Stratford-
upon-Avon, Warwickshire CV37 6BG
Tel: 01789 297993
Principal: Mrs C A Quinn BEd(Hons),
MBA, Dip RE
Age range: 2–11
No. of pupils: B77 G79
Fees: Day £1300–£8625

The Crescent School
Bawnmore Road, Bilton, Rugby,
Warwickshire CV22 7QH
Tel: 01788 521595
Headteacher: Mr Marshall
Age range: 3–11
No. of pupils: 158 B75 G83
Fees: Day £6735–£7440

The Croft Preparatory School
Alveston Hill, Loxley Road, Stratford-
upon-Avon, Warwickshire CV37 7RL
Tel: 01789 293795
Headmistress: Dr Patricia Thompson
Age range: 2–11
No. of pupils: 475 B257 G218
Fees: Day £1410–£9795

(IAPS)

The Kingsley School
Beauchamp Avenue, Leamington Spa,
Warwickshire CV32 5RD
Tel: 01926 425127
Headteacher: Ms Heather Owens
Age range: B3–7 G3–18
No. of pupils: B2 G342 VIth53
Fees: Day £3444–£10,797

Twycross House Pre-Preparatory School
The Hollies, The Green, Atherstone,
Warwickshire CV9 3PQ
Tel: 01827 880725
Joint Heads: Mr S D Assinder BA & Mrs
R T Assinder BEd
Age range: 4–8
No. of pupils: B93 G59
Fees: Day £6000

Twycross House School
Main Road, Twycross, Atherstone,
Warwickshire CV9 3QA
Tel: 01827 880651
Headmaster: Mr S D Assinder
Age range: 8–18
No. of pupils: B155 G157
Fees: Day £5775–£6750

(A) (16+) (ISA)

Warwick Preparatory School
Bridge Field, Banbury Road, Warwick,
Warwickshire CV34 6PL
Tel: 01926 491545
Headmaster: Mr M Turner BA(Hons),
PCGE, NPQH
Age range: B3–7 G3–11
No. of pupils: 438 B104 G334
Fees: Day £3393–£8670

(IAPS)

Warwick School
Myton Road, Warwick,
Warwickshire CV34 6PP
Tel: 01926 776400
Head Master: Mr E B Halse BSc(Econ)
Age range: 7–18
No. of pupils: 1187 VIth249
Fees: Day £8058–£10,359 WB £20,718
FB £22,107

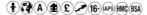

WEST MIDLANDS

Abbey College - Birmingham
10 St Paul's Square, Birmingham,
West Midlands B3 1QU
Tel: 0121 236 7474
Principal: Andrew Jedras
Age range: 14–19
No. of pupils: B87 G66
Fees: Day £7200–£9150

Abu Bakr Girls School
154-160 Wednesbury Road, Palfrey,
Walsall, West Midlands WS1 4JJ
Tel: 01922 620618
Head: Mr Mohammad Luqman
Age range: 11–15

Al Huda Girls School
74-76 Washwood Heath Road, Saltley,
Birmingham, West Midlands B8 1RD
Tel: 0121 328 8999
Headmistress: Mrs Y Jawaid
Age range: 11–17
No. of pupils: 87

Al-Ameen Primary School
Stanfield House, 447 Warwick Way,
Birmingham, West Midlands B11 2JR
Tel: 0121 706 3322
Officer in Charge: Mrs Shefa Malik
Age range: 3–11
No. of pupils: 22 B12 G10

Al-Burhan Grammar School
28A George Street, Balsall Heath,
Birmingham, West Midlands B12 9RG
Tel: 0121 4405454
Head: Dr Mohammad Nasrullah
Age range: 11–16
No. of pupils: 80
Fees: Day £3000

Al-Furqan Community College
Reddings Lane, Tyseley, Birmingham,
West Midlands B11 3EY
Tel: 0121 777 8666
Principal: Mr Amjad Ahmed BSc, PGCE
Age range: 11–16
Fees: Day £3600

Al-Hijrah School
Cherrywood Centre, Burbidge Road,
Bordesley Green, Birmingham,
West Midlands B9 4US
Tel: 0121 7737979
Headteacher: Mohammad Abdul Karim
Saqib
Age range: 5–10
No. of pupils: 306 B144 G162

Al-Hira School
99-103 Clifton Road, Balsall Heath,
Birmingham, West Midlands B12 8SR
Tel: 0121 4426775
Headteacher: S N Ul Hussan
Age range: 10–16
No. of pupils: 72

Archway Academy
86 Watery Lane Middleway, Bordesley,
Birmingham, West Midlands B9 4HN
Tel: 0121 772 7772
Executive Managing Director: Jim Ryan
Age range: 14–19
No. of pupils: B27 G1

Bablake Junior School
Coundon Road, Coventry,
West Midlands CV1 4AU
Tel: 024 7627 1260
Head: Neil Price
Age range: 3–11
No. of pupils: B150 G150
Fees: Day £5538–£6939

Bablake School
Coundon Road, Coventry,
West Midlands CV1 4AU
Tel: 024 7627 1200
Headmaster: Mr J W Watson MA
Age range: 11–18
No. of pupils: 850 B454 G396 VIth259
Fees: Day £9441

Birchfield Independent Girls' School
Beacon House, 30 Beacon Hill, Aston,
Birmingham, West Midlands B6 6JU
Tel: 0121 327 7707
Head: Mr Anwar Teladia
Age range: 11–17
No. of pupils: 150 VIth100
Fees: Day £1050

Birmingham Muslim School
Bisley Works, Golden Hillock Road,
Sparkbrook, Birmingham,
West Midlands B11 2PZ
Tel: 0121 7668129
Principal: Ms A Abdrabba
Age range: 4–10
No. of pupils: 90

Cheshunt Pre-Preparatory School
8 Park Road, Coventry,
West Midlands CV1 2LH
Tel: 024 7622 1677
Headmistress: Mrs F P Ward CertEd
Age range: 3–8
No. of pupils: B66 G59
Fees: Day £2070–£2220

Copsewood School
168-170 Roland Avenue, Holbrooks,
Coventry, West Midlands CV6 4LX
Tel: 024 7668 0680
Headteacher: Mr A R G Shedden
Age range: 11–16
No. of pupils: 77 B36 G41

Coventry Muslim School
643 Foleshill Road, Coventry,
West Midlands CV6 5JQ
Tel: 024 7626 1803
Head: Mrs Ashique
Age range: 5–16
No. of pupils: 97 B19 G78
Fees: Day £1300

Darul Uloom Islamic High School
521 Coventry Road, Small Heath,
Birmingham, West Midlands B10 0LL
Tel: 0121 772 6408
Principal: Dr Asm Abdur Rahim
Age range: 11–16
No. of pupils: 70

Edgbaston High School for Girls
Westbourne Road, Edgbaston,
Birmingham, West Midlands B15 3TS
Tel: 0121 454 5831
Head: Dr Ruth A Weeks BSc, PhD
Age range: 2½–18
No. of pupils: 950 VIth104
Fees: Day £3880–£8725

Elmfield Rudolf Steiner School
14 Love Lane, Stourbridge,
West Midlands DY8 2EA
Tel: 01384 394633
Age range: 3–17
No. of pupils: B134 G129 VIth100
Fees: Day £3240–£6290

Elmhurst School for Dance
249 Bristol Road, Edgbaston,
Birmingham, West Midlands B5 7UH
Tel: 0121 472 6655
Principal: Jessica Ward BA(Hons), NPQH
Age range: 11–19
No. of pupils: B68 G118 VIth59
Fees: Day £18,015–£18,672
FB £23,091–£24,894

Emmanuel School
Bath Street, Walsall,
West Midlands WS1 3DB
Tel: 01922 635810
Head: J Swain
Age range: 3–16
No. of pupils: 82 B42 G40
Fees: Day £558–£7200

Enta Independent School
Mill Wharf, 10 Mill Street, Birmingham,
West Midlands B6 4BS
Tel: 0121 3804800
Head: Mr K Hayes
Age range: 14–16

Eversfield Preparatory School
Warwick Road, Solihull,
West Midlands B91 1AT
Tel: 0121 705 0354
Headmaster: Mr R A Yates BA, PGCE,
LPSH
Age range: 2–11
No. of pupils: B199 G96
Fees: Day £4265–£8910

Hallfield School
48 Church Road, Edgbaston,
Birmingham, West Midlands B15 3SJ
Tel: 0121 454 1496
Headmaster: Mr J A Shackleton MA
Age range: 3 months–11 years
No. of pupils: B367 G188
Fees: Day £7050–£9882

Hamd House Preparatory School
11-27 St Oswald's Road, Small Heath,
Birmingham, West Midlands B10 9RB
Tel: 0121 7727608
Headteacher: Mr I Khan
Age range: 5–10
No. of pupils: 206 B106 G100

Highclare School
10 Sutton Road, Erdington, Birmingham,
West Midlands B23 6QL
Tel: 0121 373 7400
Headmistress: Mrs M Viles BA(Hons),
MEd, PGCE
Age range: B1–12 G1–18
No. of pupils: 638 B212 G426 VIth28
Fees: Day £3990–£9330

Honeybourne School
621 Fox Hollies Road, Hall Green,
Birmingham, West Midlands B28 9DW
Tel: 0121 777 3778
Head Teacher: Mr A Azfar
Age range: 2½–11
No. of pupils: 65
Fees: Day £3000–£3500

Hydesville Tower School
25 Broadway North, Walsall,
West Midlands WS1 2QG
Tel: 01922 624374
Headteacher: Mrs Fiona Hims BSc, PGCE
Age range: 2–16
No. of pupils: 338
Fees: Day £5445–£9480

Jamia Islamia Birmingham Islamic College
Fallows Road, Sparkbrook, Birmingham,
West Midlands B11 1PL
Tel: 0121 7726400
Headteacher: Mohammed Govalia
Age range: 11–16
No. of pupils: 111

King Edward VI High School for Girls
Edgbaston Park Road, Birmingham,
West Midlands B15 2UB
Tel: 0121 472 1834
Headmistress: Sarah H Evans BA, MA
Age range: 11–18
No. of pupils: 550 VIth161
Fees: Day £9735

King Edward's School
Edgbaston Park Road, Birmingham,
West Midlands B15 2UA
Tel: 0121 472 1672
Chief Master: Mr J A Claughton MA
Age range: 11–18
No. of pupils: 840 VIth250
Fees: Day £10,395

King Henry VIII Preparatory School
Kenilworth Road, Coventry,
West Midlands CV3 6PT
Tel: 024 7627 1307
Headmaster: Mr Nicholas Lovell
Age range: 3–11
No. of pupils: 490 B290 G200
Fees: Day £7131–£7605

King Henry VIII School
Warwick Road, Coventry,
West Midlands CV3 6AQ
Tel: 024 7627 1111
Headmaster: Mr J Slack MA Ed
Age range: 11–18
No. of pupils: 862 B475 G387 VIth230
Fees: Day £8922

Kingswood School
St James Place, Shirley, Solihull,
West Midlands B90 2BA
Tel: 0121 744 7883
Headmaster: Mr Rob Luckham
BSc(Hons), PGCE
Age range: 2–11
No. of pupils: 66 B35 G31
Fees: Day £5586–£6264

Lambs Christian School
113 Soho Hill, Hockley, Birmingham,
West Midlands B19 1AY
Tel: 0121 5543790
Headteacher: Mrs Patricia Ekhuenelo
Age range: 3–11
No. of pupils: 43

**Mander Portman Woodward -
Birmingham**
17-18 Greenfield Crescent, Edgbaston,
Birmingham, West Midlands B15 3AU
Tel: 0121 454 9637
Principal: Dominica Jewell BA, MA
Age range: 14–19
No. of pupils: 160
Fees: Day £6585–£8250

Mayfield Preparatory School
Sutton Road, Walsall,
West Midlands WS1 2PD
Tel: 01922 624107
Headmaster: Mr Matthew Draper
Age range: 2–11
No. of pupils: 205 B114 G91
Fees: Day £7125

Newbridge Preparatory School
51 Newbridge Crescent, Tettenhall,
Wolverhampton,
West Midlands WV6 0LH
Tel: 01902 751088
Headmistress: Mrs Barbara Pring
Age range: B3–4 G3–11
No. of pupils: 148 B4 G144
Fees: Day £4215–£6408

Norfolk House School
4 Norfolk Road, Edgbaston, Birmingham,
West Midlands B15 3PS
Tel: 0121 454 7021
Headmistress: Mrs H Maresca BEd
Age range: 3–11
No. of pupils: 142 B70 G72
Fees: Day £5556–£7260

Palfrey Girls School
72 Queen Mary Street, Palfrey, Walsall,
West Midlands WS1 4AB
Tel: 01922 625510
Head: Mrs Hasina Varachia BA, MA
Age range: 11–16
No. of pupils: 169
Fees: Day £1100

Pattison College
86-90 Binley Road, Coventry,
West Midlands CV3 1FQ
Tel: 024 7645 5031
Joint Principals: Miss B Pattison MA,
ARAD, LISTD, LRAM & Mrs E A P
McConnell BEd(Hons)
Age range: 3–16
No. of pupils: B29 G124 VIth16
Fees: Day £4050–£5160

Priory School
39 Sir Harry's Road, Edgbaston,
Birmingham, West Midlands B15 2UR
Tel: 0121 440 4103
Headmistress: Mrs E Brook
Age range: 6 months–18 years
No. of pupils: 320 B70 G250 VIth38
Fees: Day £5094–£8571

Rathvilly School
119 Bunbury Road, Birmingham,
West Midlands B31 2NB
Tel: 0121 475 1509
Headteacher: Mrs D P Edwards
Age range: 2–11
No. of pupils: B60 G60
Fees: Day £1655–£3270

Rosslyn School
1597 Stratford Road, Hall Green,
Birmingham, West Midlands B28 9JB
Tel: 0121 744 2743
Principal: Mrs Jane Scott
Age range: 2–11
No. of pupils: B53 G53
Fees: Day £2000–£3900

Ruckleigh School
17 Lode Lane, Solihull,
West Midlands B91 2AB
Tel: 0121 705 2773
Headmistress: Mrs Barbara Forster
Age range: 3–11
No. of pupils: B136 G110
Fees: Day £2549–£7404

Saint Martin's School
Malvern Hall, Brueton Avenue, Solihull,
West Midlands B91 3EN
Tel: 0121 705 1265
Headmistress: Mrs J Carwithen BSc, MA,
PGCE
Age range: 3–18
No. of pupils: 430 VIth40
Fees: Day £7335–£10,095

Salafi Independent School
472 Coventry Road, Birmingham,
West Midlands B10 9SN
Tel: 0121 7724567
Headteacher: Abdul Moxin
Age range: 5–11
No. of pupils: 159 B86 G73

Solihull School
Warwick Road, Solihull,
West Midlands B91 3DJ
Tel: 0121 705 0958
Headmaster: Mr P J Griffiths MA
Age range: 7–18
No. of pupils: 995 B652 G343 VIth295
Fees: Day £7704–£9480

Sporting Edge Independent School
St George's Church Centre, Bridge Street
West, Newtown, Birmingham,
West Midlands B19 2YX
Tel: 0121 333 7325
Head: Mr S C McCullough
Age range: 14–16
No. of pupils: 19

St George's School, Edgbaston
31 Calthorpe Road, Birmingham,
West Midlands B15 1RX
Tel: 0121 625 0398
Headmaster: Sir Robert Dowling Kt
Age range: 2–18
No. of pupils: 368 B200 G168 VIth48
Fees: Day £4965–£9765

Tettenhall College
Wood Road, Tettenhall, Wolverhampton,
West Midlands WV6 8QX
Tel: 01902 751119
Headmaster: M C Long BSc
Age range: 2–18
No. of pupils: 363
Fees: Day £5778–£13,182
FB £14,214–£21,735

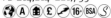

The Alyssa School
69 Whitmore Road, Small Heath,
Birmingham, West Midlands B10 0NR
Tel: 0121 773 4332
Head: Mrs B Graham
Age range: 14–16
No. of pupils: 40

The Birmingham Theatre School
The Old Rep Theatre, Station Street,
Birmingham, West Midlands B5 4DY
Tel: 0121 440 1665
Principal: C Rozanski BA(Hons)
Age range: 5–65
No. of pupils: B50 G75
Fees: Day £4100

The Blue Coat School
Somerset Road, Edgbaston,
Birmingham, West Midlands B17 0HR
Tel: 0121 410 6800
Headmaster: Mr A D J Browning
MA(Cantab)
Age range: 2–11
No. of pupils: 554 B297 G257
Fees: Day £6840–£10,530

The Davenport Lodge School
21 Davenport Road, Coventry,
West Midlands CV5 6QA
Tel: 024 7667 5051
Headteacher: Mrs M D Martin BPhilEd
Age range: 6weeks–8 years
No. of pupils: 97 B48 G49
Fees: Day £5910

The Royal Wolverhampton School
Penn Road, Wolverhampton,
West Midlands WV3 0EG
Tel: 01902 341230
Headmaster: Mr T J Brooker BSc, PGCE
Age range: 2–18
No. of pupils: 547 B340 G207 VIth116
Fees: Day £3345–£6975 WB £12,660
FB £14,310

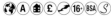

The Shrubbery School
Walmley Ash Road, Walmley, Sutton
Coldfield, West Midlands B76 1HY
Tel: 0121 351 1582
Head Teacher: Mrs Hilary Cook BA,
PGCE, MA
Age range: 3–11
No. of pupils: B159 G117
Fees: Day £1542–£3093

West House School
24 St James's Road, Edgbaston,
Birmingham, West Midlands B15 2NX
Tel: 0121 440 4097
Headmaster: Mr A M J Lyttle BA(Hons),
PGCE
Age range: B1–11 G1–4
No. of pupils: 255 B220 G35
Fees: Day £3948–£9990

Wolverhampton Grammar School
Compton Road, Wolverhampton,
West Midlands WV3 9RB
Tel: 01902 421326
Head: Mr Vincent Darby BA, NPQH
Age range: 10–18
No. of pupils: 666 B395 G271 VIth175
Fees: Day £8208–£10,995

Woodstock Girls' School
11-15 Moseley Road, Woodstock,
Birmingham, West Midlands B13 9BB
Tel: 0121 4496690
Headteacher: Mrs T Anees
Age range: 11–16
No. of pupils: 123

WORCESTERSHIRE

Abberley Hall
Abberley Hall, Worcester,
Worcestershire WR6 6DD
Tel: 01299 896275
Headmaster: J G W Walker BSc
Age range: 2–13
No. of pupils: B192 G103
Fees: Day £13,710 FB £17,220

Bowbrook House School
Peopleton, Pershore,
Worcestershire WR10 2EE
Tel: 01905 841242
Headteacher: Mr C D Allen BSc(Hons)
Age range: 3–16
No. of pupils: B118 G53
Fees: Day £3480–£6450

Bromsgrove Preparatory School
Old Station Road, Bromsgrove,
Worcestershire B60 2BU
Tel: 01527 579600
Headmaster: P Lee-Smith
Age range: 7–13
No. of pupils: B260 G191
Fees: Day £7860–£10,245
WB £10,260–£13,245
FB £15,600–£19,350

Bromsgrove Pre-preparatory & Nursery School
Avoncroft House, Hanbury Road,
Bromsgrove, Worcestershire B60 4JS
Tel: 01527 873007
Headmistress: Mrs Susan Pickering
BPhil(Ed), CertEd
Age range: 2–7
No. of pupils: B132 G101
Fees: Day £2490–£4800

Bromsgrove School
Worcester Road, Bromsgrove,
Worcestershire B61 7DU
Tel: +44 (0)1527 579679
Headmaster: Chris Edwards MA(Oxon)
Age range: 7–18
No. of pupils: 1300 VIth374
Fees: Day £12,855 FB £25,185–£28,155

Heathfield School
Wolverley, Kidderminster,
Worcestershire DY10 3QE
Tel: 01562 850 204
Head: Roger Brierly BEd
Age range: 3–16
No. of pupils: 263 B153 G110
Fees: Day £5523–£9153

Holy Trinity International School
Birmingham Road, Kidderminster,
Worcestershire DY10 2BY
Tel: 01562 822929
Headteacher: Mrs Pamela Leek-Wright
Age range: 0–18
No. of pupils: 282 B74 G208 VIth19
Fees: Day £1990–£3380

King's Hawford
Worcester, Worcestershire WR3 7SE
Tel: 01905 451292
Headmaster: Mr J Turner
Age range: 2½–11
No. of pupils: 357 B197 G160
Fees: Day £5150–£9585

King's St Alban's School
Mill Street, Worcester,
Worcestershire WR1 2NJ
Tel: 01905 354906
Headmaster: Mr R T Bellfield BEd
Age range: 4–11
No. of pupils: 216 B114 G102
Fees: Day £5874–£9381

Madinatul Uloom Islamic College
Butts Lane, Stone, Kidderminster,
Worcestershire DY10 4BH
Tel: 01562 66894
Head: The Head
Age range: 11–24
No. of pupils: 200

Madresfield Early Years Centre
Hayswood Farm, Madresfield, Malvern,
Worcestershire WR13 5AA
Tel: 01684 574378
Head: Mrs A Bennett
Age range: 1–8
No. of pupils: 218 B110 G108
Fees: Day £5434–£6080

Malvern College
College Road, Malvern,
Worcestershire WR14 3DF
Tel: 01684 581500
Headmaster: Antony R Clark
Age range: 13–18
No. of pupils: 675 B371 G304 VIth49
Fees: Day £20,313 FB £30,645–£31,716

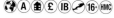

MALVERN ST JAMES
For further details see p. 151
Avenue Road, Great Malvern,
Worcestershire WR14 3BA
Tel: 01684 584624
Email: registrar@malvernstjames.co.uk
Website: www.malvernstjames.co.uk
Head Teacher: Mrs Patricia Woodhouse
BMus(Hons)
Age range: 4–18
No. of pupils: 400
Fees: Day £7095–£15,645
WB £15,240–£27,030
FB £16,935–£29,955

Moffats School
Kinlet Hall, Kinlet, Bewdley,
Worcestershire DY12 3AY
Tel: 01299 841230
Headmaster: M H Daborn MA(Cantab)
Age range: 4–13+
No. of pupils: 87 B49 G38
Fees: Day £2775–£6660 FB £10,050

New Elizabethan School
Quarry Bank, Hartlebury, Kidderminster,
Worcestershire DY11 7TE
Tel: 01299 250258
Principal: Annabel Goodman
Age range: 4–16
No. of pupils: 21
Fees: Day £3000–£7500

RGS Springfield
Springfield, Britannia Square, Worcester,
Worcestershire WR1 3DL
Tel: 01905 24999
Headmistress: Marion Lloyd
Age range: 2½–11
Fees: Day £1780–£3144

RGS The Grange
The Grange, Grange Lane, Claines
Worcester, Worcestershire WR3 7NN
Tel: 01905 451 205
Headmaster: Gareth Hughes
Age range: 2–11
No. of pupils: B245 G130
Fees: Day £1896–£3012

RGS Worcester
Upper Tything, Worcester,
Worcestershire WR1 1HP
Tel: 01905 613391
Headmaster: Mr A Rattue
Age range: 12–18
No. of pupils: B501 G375 VIth271
Fees: Day £3150

River School
Oakfield House, Droitwich Road,
Worcester, Worcestershire WR3 7ST
Tel: 01905 457047
Principal: Timothy Crow
Age range: 5–16
No. of pupils: B74 G77
Fees: Day £4140

Saint Michael's College
Oldwood Road, Tenbury Wells,
Worcestershire WR15 8PH
Tel: 01584 811300
Principal: Stuart Higgins BA, MEd, FRSA
Age range: 14–18
No. of pupils: 110 B60 G50 VIth55
Fees: FB £21,768–£23,422

St Mary's Worcester
Mount Battenhall, Worcester,
Worcestershire WR5 2HP
Tel: 01905 357786
Headmistress: Mrs Catherine Jawaheer
BA(Hons), PGCE, DASE, NPQH
Age range: B0–4 G0–18
No. of pupils: 360
Fees: Day £295–£3105

Sunnyside School
Barbourne Terrace, Worcester,
Worcestershire WR1 3JR
Tel: 01905 23973
Headmistress: Mrs Mitzi Edwards CertEd
Age range: 2–9
No. of pupils: B72 G57
Fees: Day £860–£2985

The Downs Malvern
Colwall, Malvern,
Worcestershire WR13 6EY
Tel: 01684 544100
Headmaster: Mr Alastair Cook
Age range: 3–13
No. of pupils: B129 G83

Fees: Day £5793–£13,908
FB £13,968–£18,408

The Elms
Colwall, Malvern,
Worcestershire WR13 6EF
Tel: 01684 540344
Headmaster: Mr A J L Thomas
Age range: 3–13
No. of pupils: 200 B107 G93
Fees: Day £6720–£17,052
FB £17,880–£18,870

The King's School
5 College Green, Worcester,
Worcestershire WR1 2LL
Tel: 01905 721700
Headmaster: Mr T H Keyes MA
Age range: 11–18
No. of pupils: 935 B510 G425 VIth270
Fees: Day £10,506

The Knoll School
33 Manor Avenue, Kidderminster,
Worcestershire DY11 6EA
Tel: 01562 822622
Headmaster: N J Humphreys BEd(Hons)
Age range: 3 months–11 years
No. of pupils: 116 B78 G38
Fees: Day £1404–£6105

Whitford Hall & Dodderhill School
Crutch Lane, Droitwich,
Worcestershire WR9 0BE
Tel: 01905 778290
Headmistress: Mrs J M Mumby
BA(Hons), DipEd
Age range: B3–9 G3–16
No. of pupils: 220 B10 G210
Fees: Day £5850–£8700

Winterfold House
Chaddesley Corbett, Kidderminster,
Worcestershire DY10 4PL
Tel: 01562 777234
Headmaster: Mr W Ibbetson-Price BA,
MA, NPQH
Age range: 6 weeks–13 years
No. of pupils: B165 G157
Fees: Day £6360–£10,680

Yorkshire & Humberside

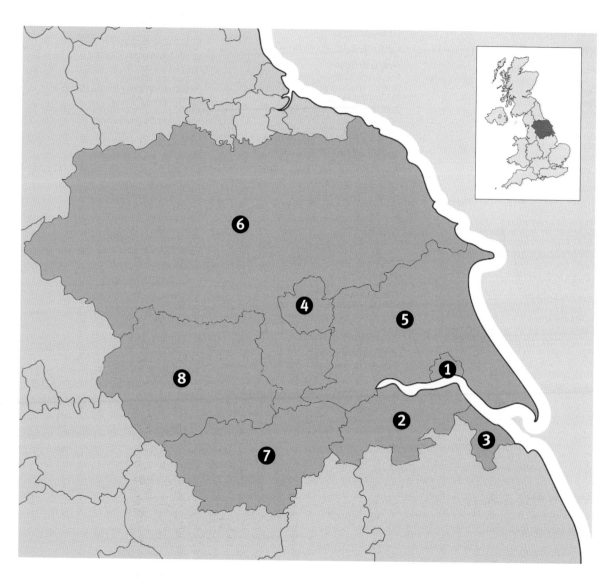

Key and page index:

1 Kingston upon Hull: D354

2 North Lincolnshire:

3 North-east Lincolnshire: D355

4 York: D359

5 Yorkshire, East: D354

6 Yorkshire, North: D354

7 Yorkshire, South: D355

8 Yorkshire, West: D356

EAST RIDING OF YORKSHIRE

Hessle Mount School
Jenny Brough Lane, Hessle,
East Riding of Yorkshire HU13 0JZ
Tel: 01482 643371
Headmistress: Mrs C Cutting
Age range: 3–8
No. of pupils: 155 B84 G71
Fees: Day £3300–£3525

KINGSTON UPON HULL

Froebel House School
5 Marlborough Avenue, Kingston upon
Hull HU5 3JP
Tel: 01482 342272
Headmistress: Mrs L A Roberts CertEd,
BA(Ed)
Age range: 4–11
No. of pupils: 116
Fees: Day £3558

Hull Collegiate School
Tranby Croft, Anlaby, Kingston upon
Hull HU10 7EH
Tel: 01482 657016
principle: Mr Rob Haworth
Age range: 2½–18
No. of pupils: B381 G448 VIth109
Fees: Day £5016–£5349

Hymers College
Hymers Avenue, Kingston upon
Hull HU3 1LW
Tel: 01482 343555
Headmaster: Mr D Elstone
Age range: 8–18
No. of pupils: 977 B537 G440 VIth215
Fees: Day £7443–£8946

NORTH YORKSHIRE

Ashville College
Green Lane, Harrogate,
North Yorkshire HG2 9JP
Tel: 01423 566358
Headmaster: D Mark Lauder
Age range: 4–18
No. of pupils: 802 B483 G319
Fees: Day £6660–£11,370
FB £6390–£10,890

Aysgarth School
Newton le Willows, Bedale,
North Yorkshire DL8 1TF
Tel: 01677 450240
Headmaster: Mr C A A Goddard
Age range: B3–13 G3–8
No. of pupils: 166 B155 G11
Fees: Day £5880–£14,610 FB £18,750

Belmont Grosvenor School
Swarcliffe Hall, Birstwith, Harrogate,
North Yorkshire HG3 2JG
Tel: 01423 771029
Headteacher: Mrs Jane Merriman BEd,
MA, NPQH
Age range: 3 months–11 years
No. of pupils: B120 G114
Fees: Day £6269–£7428

Botton Village School
Danby, Whitby, North Yorkshire YO21 2NJ
Tel: 01287 661 206
Age range: 4–14
No. of pupils: B54 G35

Brackenfield School
128 Duchy Road, Harrogate,
North Yorkshire HG1 2HE
Tel: 01423 508558
Headteacher: Mrs Judith Skillington
Age range: 2–11
No. of pupils: 179 B92 G87
Fees: Day £2065–£2230

Bramcote School
Filey Road, Scarborough,
North Yorkshire YO11 2TT
Tel: 01723 373086
Headmaster: Andrew Snow BSc, PGCE,
CM
Age range: 3–13
No. of pupils: 77 B39 G38
Fees: Day £9180–£9780 FB £16,830

Fyling Hall School
Robin Hood's Bay, Whitby,
North Yorkshire YO22 4QD
Tel: 01947 880353
Headmaster: Ken James LLB, PGCE
Age range: 4–18
No. of pupils: 200 B108 G92 VIth40
Fees: Day £5700–£7800
WB £14,100–£16,500
FB £14,700–£17,700

Giggleswick Junior School
Giggleswick, Settle,
North Yorkshire BD24 0DG
Tel: 01729 893100
Headmaster: Mr Mark Brotherton
Age range: 3–11
No. of pupils: 75 B50 G25
Fees: Day £1258–£11,184 FB £13,740

Giggleswick School
Giggleswick, Settle,
North Yorkshire BD24 0DE
Tel: 01729 893000
Head: Mr G P Boult
Age range: 13–18
No. of pupils: 320 B201 G119 VIth145
Fees: Day £14,730 FB £20,970

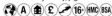

Key to symbols

(♂) Boys' school

(♀) Girls' school

(🌐) International school

(16) Tutorial or sixth form college

(A) A levels

(🏫) Boarding accommodation

(£) Bursaries

(IB) International Baccalaureate

(✎) Learning support

(16+) Entrance at 16+

(🎓) Vocational qualifications

(IAPS) Member of Independent Association of Preparatory Schools

(HMC) The Headmasters' & Headmistresses' Conference

(ISA) Independent Schools Association

(GSA) Girls' School Association

(BSA) Boarding Schools' Association

(𝒮) SHMIS

Unless otherwise indicated, all schools are coeducational
day schools. Single-sex and boarding schools will be
indicated by the relevant icon.

Harrogate Ladies' College
Clarence Drive, Harrogate,
North Yorkshire HG1 2QG
Tel: 01423 504543
Headmistress: Mrs R Wilkinson
Age range: 11–18
No. of pupils: 310 VIth120
Fees: Day £11,130 WB £18,765
FB £18,765

Harrogate Tutorial College
2 The Oval, Harrogate,
North Yorkshire HG2 9BA
Tel: 01423 501041
Principal: Keith W Pollard BSc(Hons),
DipEd, DipMaths
Age range: 15–25
No. of pupils: 60 B30 G30 VIth60
Fees: Day £8000–£13,500
WB £11,500–£16,000
FB £12,500–£18,500

Highfield Prep School
Clarence Drive, Harrogate,
North Yorkshire HG1 2QG
Tel: 01423 504 543
Headmistress: Rachel Colbourn
Age range: 4–10
No. of pupils: 216 B68 G148
Fees: Day £6090–£6600

Malsis School
Cross Hills, Skipton,
North Yorkshire BD20 8DT
Tel: 01535 633027
Headmaster: Mr M R Peel
Age range: 4–13
No. of pupils: 118 B79 G39
Fees: Day £7440–£13,380 FB £17,475

Queen Mary's School
Baldersby Park, Topcliffe, Thirsk,
North Yorkshire YO7 3BZ
Tel: 01845 575000
Headmaster: Mr R McKenzie Johnston
BA
Age range: B3–8 G3–16
No. of pupils: 235 B8 G227
Fees: Day £5445–£13,050
FB £14,400–£16,995

Read School
Drax, Selby, North Yorkshire YO8 8NL
Tel: 01757 618248
Headmaster: J A Sweetman BSc, PhD
Age range: 3–18
No. of pupils: B176 G112 VIth36
Fees: Day £6480–£9180
WB £15,447–£17,748
FB £17,295–£19,800

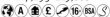

Ripon Cathedral Choir School
Whitcliffe Lane, Ripon,
North Yorkshire HG4 2LA
Tel: 01765 602134
Headmaster: Mr C McDade
Age range: 3–13
No. of pupils: B44 G23
Fees: Day £6195–£10,977 WB £13,869
FB £14,226

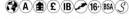

Scarborough College
Filey Road, Scarborough,
North Yorkshire YO11 3BA
Tel: +44 (0)1723 360620
Head of School: Isobel Nixon
Age range: 3–18
No. of pupils: 450
Fees: Day £5580–£9360
FB £16,140–£17,340

WHARFEDALE MONTESSORI SCHOOL
For further details see p. 157
Bolton Abbey, Skipton,
North Yorkshire BD23 6AN
Tel: 01756 710452
Email: secretary@wharfedalemontessori.co.uk
Website:
www.wharfedalemontessori.co.uk
Headmistress/Principal: Mrs J Lord
Age range: 2–12
No. of pupils: B17 G24
Fees: Day £6225

Woodleigh School Langton
Langton Hall, Malton,
North Yorkshire YO17 9QN
Tel: 01653 658215
Headmaster: Mr D M England BSc
Age range: 3–13
No. of pupils: B75 G50
Fees: Day £2700–£5820 WB £8110
FB £8110

NORTH-EAST LINCOLNSHIRE

Montessori School
Station Road, Stallingborough, North-
East Lincolnshire DN41 8AJ
Tel: 01472 886000
Headteacher: Ms Theresa Ellerby
Age range: 4–11
No. of pupils: 21 B10 G11

St James' School
22 Bargate, Grimsby, North-
East Lincolnshire DN34 4SY
Tel: 01472 503260
Headteacher: Mrs S M Isaac BA, PGCE
Age range: 2–18
No. of pupils: 238 B129 G109 VIth25
Fees: Day £3672–£8832
WB £10,056–£13,914
FB £10,761–£14,619

St Martin's Preparatory School
63 Bargate, Grimsby, North-
East Lincolnshire DN34 5AA
Tel: 01472 878907
Headmaster: Mr S Thompson BEd
Age range: 2–11
No. of pupils: 120 B58 G62
Fees: Day £2700–£4785

SOUTH YORKSHIRE

Al-Mahad-Al-Islam School
1 Industry Road, Sheffield,
South Yorkshire S9 5FP
Tel: 0114 242 3138
Headteacher: Mrs F Messoul
Age range: 11–17
No. of pupils: 70

Ashdell Preparatory School
266 Fulwood Road, Sheffield,
South Yorkshire S10 3BL
Tel: 0114 266 3835
Headteacher: Mrs Anne Camm
Age range: B3–4 G3–11
No. of pupils: 133 B23 G110
Fees: Day £8160–£8715

Barnsley Christian School
Hope House, Blucher Street, Barnsley,
South Yorkshire S70 1AP
Tel: 01226 211011
Headteacher: Mr G J Barnes
Age range: 4–16
No. of pupils: 73 B36 G37
Fees: Day £3900–£4500

Bethany School
Finlay Street, Sheffield,
South Yorkshire S3 7PS
Tel: 0114 272 6994
Headteacher: K Walze
Age range: 4–16
No. of pupils: 76 B45 G31

Birkdale School
Oakholme Road, Sheffield,
South Yorkshire S10 3DH
Tel: 0114 2668409
Head Master: Dr Paul Owen
Age range: B4–18 G16–18
No. of pupils: 802 B751 G51 VIth200
Fees: Day £7455–£10,677

Elsworth House School
Rother Way, Hellerby Estate, Rotherham,
South Yorkshire S66 8QN
Tel: 01709 533770
Headteacher: Mr F McCabe
Age range: 11–16
No. of pupils: 40 B18 G22

Handsworth Christian School

231 Handsworth Road, Handsworth,
Sheffield, South Yorkshire S13 9BJ
Tel: 0114 2430276
Headteacher: Mrs Pauline Elizabeth
Arnott
Age range: 4–16
No. of pupils: 148 B78 G70
Fees: Day £2340

Hill House St Mary's

Sixth Avenue, Auckley, Doncaster,
South Yorkshire DN9 3GG
Tel: 0845 302 1929
Principal: David Holland
Age range: 2¹/₂₃–16
No. of pupils: B221 G240
Fees: Day £6150–£879

Mylnhurst School & Nursery

Button Hill, Woodholm Road, Ecclesall,
Sheffield, South Yorkshire S11 9HJ
Tel: 0114 2361411
Headmaster: Christopher Emmott
BSc(Hons), PGCE
Age range: 3–11
No. of pupils: 185 B103 G82
Fees: Day £7575

Rudston Preparatory School

59-63 Broom Road, Rotherham,
South Yorkshire S60 2SW
Tel: 01709 837774
Principal: Mr Guy Willatt
Age range: 2–11
No. of pupils: 230 B117 G113
Fees: Day £6210

Sheffield High School GDST

10 Rutland Park, Sheffield,
South Yorkshire S10 2PE
Tel: 0114 266 0324
Headmistress: Mrs Dunsford BA
Age range: 4–18
No. of pupils: 1020
Fees: Day £6912–£9531

Sycamore Hall Preparatory School

1 Hall Flat Lane, Balby, Doncaster,
South Yorkshire DN4 8PT
Tel: 01302 856800
Headmistress: Miss J Spencer
Age range: 3–11
No. of pupils: B28 G28
Fees: Day £1650

Westbourne School

Westbourne Road, Sheffield,
South Yorkshire S10 2QT
Tel: 0114 2660374
Headmaster: Mr John B Hicks MEd
Age range: 4–16
No. of pupils: 338 B182 G156
Fees: Day £2550–£3590

WEST YORKSHIRE

Ackworth School

Barnsley Road, Ackworth, Pontefract,
West Yorkshire WF7 7LT
Tel: 01977 611401
Head: Kathryn Bell BSc(Hons)Exeter,
PGCE
Age range: 2–18
No. of pupils: 519 B246 G273 VIth112
Fees: Day £6759–£10,884 WB £17,817
FB £17,817

Al Mumin Primary School

15-17 Spring Gardens, Bradford,
West Yorkshire BD1 3EJ
Tel: 01274 733150
Headteacher: Mr M M Azam
Age range: 3–10
No. of pupils: 102 B49 G53

Al-Furqan Preparatory School

Ellahi Masjid Hunza Cour, off Hope
Street, Dewsbury,
West Yorkshire WF13 2BT
Tel: 01924 461 633
Headteacher: Mr Ahmad Farook Raja
Age range: 5–11
No. of pupils: 139 B63 G76

Bradford Christian School

Livingstone Road, Bolton Woods,
Bradford, West Yorkshire BD2 1BT
Tel: 01274 532649
Headmaster: P J Moon BEd(Hons)
Age range: 4–16
No. of pupils: B75 G65
Fees: Day £1236–£2532

Bradford Grammar School

Keighley Road, Bradford,
West Yorkshire BD9 4JP
Tel: 01274 553702
Headmaster: Stephen R Davidson DL,
BSc
Age range: 6–18
No. of pupils: B779 G334 VIth266
Fees: Day £7984–£10,204

Branch Christian School

17 Halifax Road, Dewsbury,
West Yorkshire WF13 2JH
Tel: 01924 465600
Headteacher: R Ward
Age range: 3–16
No. of pupils: 26 B13 G13

Bronte House School

Apperley Bridge, Bradford,
West Yorkshire BD10 0NR
Tel: 0113 2502811
Headmaster: Simon W Dunn
Age range: 2–11
No. of pupils: 300 B155 G145
Fees: Day £7500–£900 WB £17,000
FB £18,000

Brownberrie School

St Vincents House, 27 Church Street,
Boston Spa, Wetherby,
West Yorkshire LS23 6DW
Tel: 0113 3053350
Headteacher: Mr B G Davies
Age range: 11–17
No. of pupils: 44 B29 G15

Coral College for Girls

189 Manningham Lane, Bradford,
West Yorkshire BD8 7HP
Tel: 01274 370758
Head: Mr Metkin Askan
Age range: 5–16
No. of pupils: 87

Crystal Gardens

38-40 Greaves Street, Bradford,
West Yorkshire BD5 7PE
Tel: 01274 575400
Headteacher: Muhammad Abdur Raqeeb
Age range: 5–11
No. of pupils: 20 B11 G9

Dale House Independent School

Ruby Street, Carlinghow, Batley,
West Yorkshire WF17 8HL
Tel: 01924 422215
Headmistress: Mrs S M G Fletcher BA,
CertEd
Age range: 2–11
No. of pupils: 100 B50 G50

Darul Uloom Dawatul Imaan

Harry Street, Off Wakefield Road,
Bradford, West Yorkshire BD4 9PH
Tel: 01274 402233
Principal: Mr Mohamed Bilal Lorgat
Age range: 11–13
No. of pupils: 112

Feversham College

Cliffe Road, Undercliffe, Bradford,
West Yorkshire BD3 0LT
Tel: 01274 559500
Headteacher: Mrs Tracy McNally
Age range: 13–18
No. of pupils: 180 VIth40
Fees: Day £2100

FULNECK SCHOOL
For further details see p. 156

Fulneck, Pudsey, Leeds,
West Yorkshire LS28 8DS
Tel: 0113 2570235
Email: enquiries@fulneckschool.co.uk;
admissions@fulneckschool.co.uk
Website: www.fulneckschool.co.uk
Principal: Mrs Deborah Newman
Age range: 3–18
No. of pupils: 440 VIth67
Fees: Day £6210–£11,010
WB £15,390–£18,585
FB £16,725–£20,700

Gateways School
Harewood, Leeds,
West Yorkshire LS17 9LE
Tel: 0113 2886345
Headmistress: Mrs Y Wilkinson
Age range: B2–7 G2–18
No. of pupils: 508 B35 G473 VIth51
Fees: Day £5247–£9513

Ghyll Royd School
Greystone Manor, Ilkley Road, Burley in
Wharfedale, West Yorkshire LS29 7HW
Tel: 01943 865575
Headteacher: Mrs Irene Connor
Age range: 2–11
No. of pupils: 100
Fees: Day £1560–£5577

Glen House Montessori School
Cragg Vale, Hebden Bridge, Halifax,
West Yorkshire HX7 5SQ
Tel: 01422 884682
Headmistress: Mrs Margaret Scaife
MontDipAdv
Age range: 2–15
No. of pupils: 24 B16 G8
Fees: Day £827–£3405

Hearter Montessori West Cliffe School
206 Skipton Road, Keighley,
West Yorkshire BD21 2TA
Tel: 015435 609797
Principal: Mrs T Bisby
Age range: 0–8
No. of pupils: 42

Hipperholme Grammar Junior School
45 Wakefield Road, Lightcliffe, Halifax,
West Yorkshire HX3 8AQ
Tel: 01422 201330
Headteacher: Mrs Louise Reynolds
Age range: 3–11
No. of pupils: 131 B70 G61
Fees: Day £3250–£7845

Hipperholme Grammar School
Bramley Lane, Hipperholme, Halifax,
West Yorkshire HX3 8JE
Tel: 01422 202256
Headmaster: Mr Jack D Williams BSc
Age range: 3–18
No. of pupils: 250 B130 G120 VIth36
Fees: Day £10,650

Huddersfield Grammar School
Royds Mount, Luck Lane, Marsh,
Huddersfield, West Yorkshire HD1 4QX
Tel: 01484 424549/536409
Joint Heads: Mrs Joyce Jackson CertEd &
Mrs Janet Straughan BEd(Hons)
Age range: 3–16
No. of pupils: 428
Fees: Day £4755–£5895

Inglebrook Preparatory School
Northgate Close, Pontefract,
West Yorkshire WF8 1JL
Tel: 01977 700120
Head: Mrs J S Bellamy
Age range: 2–11
No. of pupils: 114 B56 G58
Fees: Day £1656–£3252

Institute of Islamic Education
South Street, Savile Town, Dewsbury,
West Yorkshire WF12 9NG
Tel: 01924 485712
Headteachers: Mr Seed Patel & Dr M M
Mulk
Age range: 12–16
No. of pupils: 184

Islamia Girls High School
2 Thornton Lodge Road, Thornton
Lodge, Huddersfield,
West Yorkshire HD1 3JQ
Tel: 01484 535674
Head: The Principal
Age range: 11–16
No. of pupils: 106
Fees: Day £5800

Islamic Tarbiyah Preparatory School
Ambler Street, Bradford,
West Yorkshire BD8 8AW
Tel: 01274 490462
Headteacher: Mr S A Nawaz
Age range: 5–10
No. of pupils: 123 B63 G60

**Jaamiatul Imaam Muhammad Zakaria
School**
Thornton View Road, Clayton, Bradford,
West Yorkshire BD14 6JX
Tel: 01274 882007
Headteacher: Mrs Z Hajee
Age range: 11–16
No. of pupils: 416

Lady Lane Park Preparatory School
Lady Lane, Bingley,
West Yorkshire BD16 4AP
Tel: 01274 551168
Headmistress: Mrs Gill Wilson
Age range: 2–11
No. of pupils: B83 G79
Fees: Day £6130

Leeds Menorah School
393 Street Lane, Leeds,
West Yorkshire LS17 6HQ
Tel: 0113 268 3390
Headteacher: Rabbi J Refson
Age range: 5–16
No. of pupils: 55 B25 G30

M A Institute
Lumb Lane, Bradford,
West Yorkshire BD8 7RZ
Tel: 01274 395454
Age range: 11–16
No. of pupils: 68

Madni Muslim Girls High School
Thornie Bank, Off Scarborough St,
Savile Town, Dewsbury,
West Yorkshire WF12 9AX
Tel: 01924 520720
Headmistress: Mrs S A Mirza
Age range: 3–18
No. of pupils: 250

Mill Cottage Montessori School
Wakefield Road, Brighouse,
West Yorkshire HD6 4HA
Tel: 01484 400500
Principal: Ailsa Nevile
Age range: 0–11

Moorfield School
Wharfedale Lodge, 11 Ben Rhydding
Road, Ilkley, West Yorkshire LS29 8RL
Tel: 01943 607285
Headmistress: Mrs Jessica Crossley
Age range: 2–11
No. of pupils: 100 G100
Fees: Day £6510

Moorlands School
Foxhill, Weetwood Lane, Leeds,
West Yorkshire LS16 5PF
Tel: 0113 2785286
Headmaster: Mr J Davies
Age range: 2.2–13
No. of pupils: 197 B124 G73
Fees: Day £7491–£8379

Mount School
3 Binham Road, Edgerton, Huddersfield,
West Yorkshire HD2 2AP
Tel: 01484 426432
Headteacher: Julie Goodchild
Age range: 3–11
No. of pupils: 130 B62 G68
Fees: Day £5610

Mountjoy House Preparatory School
63 New North Road, Huddersfield,
West Yorkshire HD1 5ND
Tel: 01484 429967
Headmistress: Mrs C Rogers
Age range: 3–11
No. of pupils: 91 B46 G45
Fees: Day £1500–£2640

Netherleigh & Rossefield School
Parsons Road, Heaton, Bradford,
West Yorkshire BD9 4AY
Tel: 01274 543162
Headteacher: Mrs R M Midgley
Age range: 3–11
No. of pupils: 110 B65 G45
Fees: Day £2880–£5115

New Horizon Community School
Newton Hill House, Newton Hill Road,
Leeds, West Yorkshire LS7 4JE
Tel: 0113 262 4001
Head: Hena Salim Hashmi
Age range: 11–16
No. of pupils: 87
Fees: Day £1500

Olive Secondary School
8 Cunliffe Villas, Bradford,
West Yorkshire BD8 7AN
Tel: 07909 541855
Headteacher: Mr Amjad Mohammed
Age range: 11–18
No. of pupils: 115 B75 G40
Fees: Day £1500

Paradise Primary School
1 Bretton Street, Dewsbury,
West Yorkshire WF12 9BB
Tel: 01924 439803
Headteacher: Mr Rashid Kola
Age range: 5–11
No. of pupils: 121 B62 G59

**Queen Elizabeth Grammar School
(Junior School)**
158 Northgate, Wakefield,
West Yorkshire WF1 3QY
Tel: 01924 373821
Head: Mrs L A Gray
Age range: 7–11
No. of pupils: 261
Fees: Day £6207–£6558

**Queen Elizabeth Grammar School
(Senior School)**
154 Northgate, Wakefield,
West Yorkshire WF1 3QY
Tel: 01924 373943
Headmaster: David Craig
Age range: 11–18
No. of pupils: 677
Fees: Day £7080

Queenswood School
Queen Street, Morley, Leeds,
West Yorkshire LS27 9EB
Tel: 0113 2534033
Headteacher: Mrs J A Tanner MMus, BA,
FTCL, ARCO
Age range: 4–11
No. of pupils: B25 G25
Fees: Day £3885–£4275

Rastrick Independent School
Ogden Lane, Rastrick, Brighouse,
West Yorkshire HD6 3HF
Tel: 01484 400344
Headmistress: Mrs S A Vaughey
Age range: 0–18+
No. of pupils: 200 B100 G100
Fees: Day £5985–£8760

Richmond House School
170 Otley Road, Leeds,
West Yorkshire LS16 5LG
Tel: 0113 2752670
Headmistress: Mrs J E Disley
Age range: 3–12
No. of pupils: 221 B123 G98
Fees: Day £4134–£6456

Rishworth School
Rishworth, Halifax,
West Yorkshire HX6 4QA
Tel: 01422 822217
Headmaster: Mr R A Baker MA(Cantab)
Age range: 3–18
No. of pupils: 600 B331 G269 VIth90
Fees: Day £4905–£9585
WB £15,285–£16,725
FB £16,830–£18,360

Silcoates School
Wrenthorpe, Wakefield,
West Yorkshire WF2 0PD
Tel: 01924 291614
Headmaster: Darryl S Wideman
Age range: 7–18
No. of pupils: 768 B413 G355
Fees: Day £6618–£11,181

St Hilda's School
Dovecote Lane, Horbury, Wakefield,
West Yorkshire WF4 6BB
Tel: 01924 260706
Headmistress: Mrs J L Sharpe
Age range: B0–7 G0–11
No. of pupils: 127 B43 G84
Fees: Day £4722–£4944

Sunny Hill House School
Wrenthorpe Lane, Wrenthorpe,
Wakefield, West Yorkshire WF2 0QB
Tel: 01924 291717
Headmistress: Mrs H K Cushing CertEd,
MA
Age range: 2–7
No. of pupils: 116 B64 G52
Fees: Day £5256

The Froebelian School
Clarence Road, Horsforth, Leeds,
West Yorkshire LS18 4LB
Tel: 0113 2583047
Headmaster: Mr J Tranmer MA, PGCE,
FCollP
Age range: 3–11
No. of pupils: 185 B92 G93
Fees: Day £4020–£6030

The Gleddings School
Birdcage Lane, Savile Park, Halifax,
West Yorkshire HX3 0JB
Tel: 01422 354605
School Director: Mrs P J Wilson CBE
Age range: 3–11
No. of pupils: 191 B83 G108
Fees: Day £3555–£5910

The Grammar School at Leeds
Alwoodley Gates, Harrogate Road,
Leeds, West Yorkshire LS17 8GS
Tel: 0113 2291552
Principal and CEO: Mr Michael Gibbons
Age range: 3–18
No. of pupils: 2167 B1206 G961 VIth442
Fees: Day £7362–£10,755

**Wakefield Girls' High School (Junior
School)**
2 St John's Square, Wakefield,
West Yorkshire WF1 2QX
Tel: 01924 374577
Headmistress: Daphne Cawthorne BEd
Age range: B3–7 G3–11
No. of pupils: 493 B79 G414
Fees: Day £6609–£7212

**Wakefield Girls' High School (Senior
School)**
Wentworth Street, Wakefield,
West Yorkshire WF1 2QS
Tel: 01924 372490
Headmistress: Gillian Wallwork
BA(Hons,) PGCE
Age range: 11–18
No. of pupils: 715
Fees: Day £9996

Wakefield Independent School
The Nostell Centre, Doncaster Road,
Nostell, Wakefield,
West Yorkshire WF4 1QG
Tel: 01924 865757
Headmistress: Mrs K E Caryl
Age range: 2½–16
No. of pupils: 190 B100 G90
Fees: Day £4143–£6183

Westville House Preparatory School
Carters Lane, Middleton, Ilkley,
West Yorkshire LS29 0DQ
Tel: 01943 608053
Headmaster: Mr C Holloway BA(Hons),
PGCE
Age range: 3–11
No. of pupils: B70 G55
Fees: Day £4395–£7620

WOODHOUSE GROVE SCHOOL
For further details see p. 158
Apperley Bridge, Bradford,
West Yorkshire BD10 0NR
Tel: 0113 250 2477
Email: gilks.tv@woodhousegrove.co.uk
Website: www.woodhousegrove.co.uk
Headmaster: David C Humphreys BA
Age range: 11–18
No. of pupils: 718 B437 G281 VIth176
Fees: Day £10,650–£10,920
WB £20,550–£20,850
FB £22,080–£22,200

YORK

Ampleforth College
York YO62 4ER
Tel: 01439 766000
Headmaster: Father Gabriel Everitt OSB,
MA, DPhil(Oxon)
Age range: 13–18
No. of pupils: B468 G175 VIth255
Fees: Day £17,265 FB £27,375

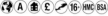

Bootham Junior School
Rawcliffe Lane, York YO30 6NP
Tel: 01904 655021
Head: Mrs Susan Ratcliffe
Age range: 3–11
No. of pupils: B70 G68
Fees: Day £2415–£7410

Bootham School
York YO30 7BU
Tel: 01904 623261
Headmaster: Jonathan Taylor MA, MEd
Age range: 11–18
No. of pupils: 484 B284 G200 VIth158
Fees: Day £14,310–£15,375
FB £15,540–£25,800

Chapter House Preparatory School
Thorpe Underwood Hall, Ouseburn,
York YO26 9SZ
Tel: 01423 333729
Head Teacher: Mrs Karen Kilkenny BSc
Age range: 3–10
No. of pupils: 122 B71 G51
Fees: Day £4518–£6144
FB £20,250–£20,904

Clifton Pre-Preparatory School
York YO30 6AB
Tel: 01904 527361
Head: Philip Hardy BA (Hons) PGCE
Age range: 3–8
No. of pupils: 175 B97 G78
Fees: Day £2268–£2355

Cundall Manor School
Helperby, York YO61 2RW
Tel: 01423 360200
Headmaster: Mr P Phillips BA(Hons),
MA(Ed), PGC(SPLD), NPQH
Age range: 2–16
No. of pupils: 368 B244 G124
Fees: Day £6909–£11,433 WB £15,030

Lyndhurst School
West Green, Pocklington,
York YO42 2NH
Tel: 01759 321228
Headmaster: Mr I D Wright BSc(Hons),
PGCE, NPQH
Age range: 4–11
No. of pupils: 181 B83 G98
Fees: Day £6180–£9696 FB £16,740

Pocklington Montessori School
Bielby Lane, Pocklington, York YO42 1NT
Tel: 01759 305436
Headmistress/Owner: Ms Rosie
Pressland DipComEd(Dist),
DipMontEd(Dist)
Age range: 0–8
No. of pupils: 300 B142 G158
Fees: Day £1550

Pocklington School
West Green, Pocklington, York YO42 2NJ
Tel: 01759 321200
Headmaster: Mr Mark Ronan
Age range: 11–18
No. of pupils: 659 B386 G273 VIth201
Fees: Day £11,223 WB £19,017
FB £20,091

Queen Ethelburga's Collegiate
Foundation
Thorpe Underwood Hall, Ouseburn,
York YO26 9SS
Tel: 01423 33 33 30
Principal: Steven Jandrell BA
Age range: 11–18
No. of pupils: 1091 B590 G501 VIth435
Fees: Day £9375–£10,575
FB £27,255–£36,690

Queen Margaret's School
Escrick Park, York YO19 6EU
Tel: 01904 728261
Headmaster: P R Silverwood
MA(Cantab), MSc, PhD(Manchester),
QTS, CChem, MRSC
Age range: 11–18
No. of pupils: 332 VIth115
Fees: Day £17,100 FB £26,988

St Martins Ampleforth
Gilling Castle, Gilling East,
York YO62 4HP
Tel: 01439 766600
Headmaster: Mr N J Higham
Age range: 3–13
No. of pupils: 164 B106 G58
Fees: Day £6678–£12,389 FB £19,266

St Olave's York, Preparatory School to
St Peter's
Clifton, York YO30 6AB
Tel: 01904 527416
The Master: Mr A Falconer
Age range: 8–13
No. of pupils: 318 B173 G145
Fees: Day £9768–£11,814
WB £16,230–£17,904
FB £18,033–£19,893

St Peter's School
Clifton, York YO30 6AB
Tel: 01904 527300
Head Master: Mr L Winkley MA(Oxon),
MEd(OU)
Age range: 13–18
No. of pupils: 540 B310 G230 VIth220
Fees: Day £14,517 FB £23,373

Terrington Hall
Terrington, York YO60 6PR
Tel: 01653 648227
Headmaster: M J Glen BA, PGCE
Age range: 3–13
No. of pupils: 150 B90 G60
Fees: Day £6414–£11,691 WB £16,629
FB £16,629

The Minster School
Deangate, York YO1 7JA
Tel: 01904 557230
Headmaster: Mr A Donaldson
Age range: 3–13
No. of pupils: B90 G77
Fees: Day £4674–£7188

The Mount School, York
Dalton Terrace, York YO24 4DD
Tel: 01904 667500
Headmistress: Diana Gant BD(Hons)
King's College London, PGCE
Age range: 11–18

Tregelles
Junior Department, The Mount School,
Dalton Terrace, York YO24 4DD
Tel: 01904 667513
Head: Mr Martyn Andrews BSc(Hons),
PGCE
Age range: 3–11
No. of pupils: B65 G146
Fees: Day £1710–£2280

York Steiner School
Danesmead, Fulford Cross,
York YO10 4PB
Tel: 01904 654983
Administrator: Maurice Dobie
Age range: 3½–14
No. of pupils: 197 B96 G101
Fees: Day £728–£4800

Northern Ireland

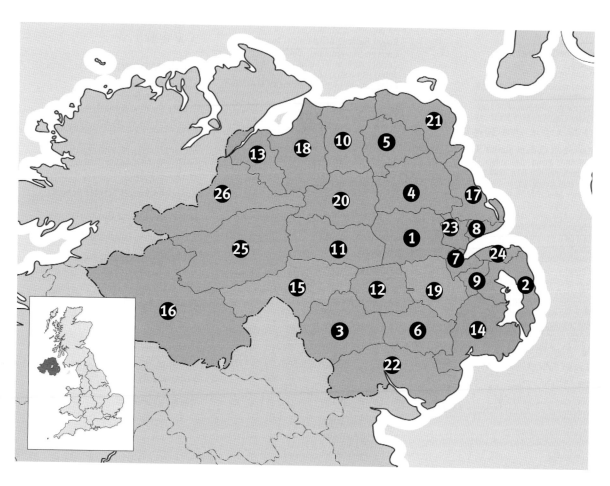

Key and page index:

1 Antrim: D362
2 Ards
3 Armagh: D362
4 Ballymena
5 Ballymoney
6 Banbridge
7 Belfast
8 Carrickfergus
9 Castlereagh
10 Coleraine
11 Cookstown
12 Craigavon
13 Londonderry: D363
14 Down: D362
15 Dungannon: D363
16 Fermanagh: D363
17 Larne
18 Limavady
19 Lisburn
20 Magherafelt
21 Moyle
22 Newry & Mourne
23 Newtownabbey
24 North Down
25 Omagh
26 Strabane

COUNTY ANTRIM

Belfast Royal Academy
7 Cliftonville Road, Belfast,
County Antrim BT14 6JL
Tel: 028 9074 0423
Headmaster: Mr J M G Dickson MA
Age range: 11–18
No. of pupils: B708 G708 VIth382
Fees: Day £140

(A) (16+) (HMC)

Campbell College
Belfast, County Antrim BT4 2ND
Tel: 028 9076 3076
Headmaster: J A Piggot MA
Age range: 11–18
No. of pupils: 896 VIth200
Fees: Day £2200 FB £10,951–£15,111

(♦) (♣) (A) (▩) (£) (✐) (16+) (✿) (HMC) (BSA)

Campbell College Junior School
Belmont Road, Belfast,
County Antrim BT4 2ND
Tel: 028 9076 3076
Head: Mrs H M Rowan
Age range: 3–11
No. of pupils: 216
Fees: Day £2750–£3000

(♦) (✐)

Hunterhouse College
Finaghy, Belfast,
County Antrim BT10 0LE
Tel: 028 9061 2293
Principal: Mr A Gibson MA, DipEd, PQH
Age range: 11–18
No. of pupils: 710 VIth180
Fees: Day £320

(♣) (A) (✐) (16+)

Lagan College
44 Manse Road, Lisnabreeny, Belfast,
County Antrim BT8 4SA
Tel: 028 9040 1810
Headmaster: Mrs H McHugh BA, MA,
PGCE, ATCL
Age range: 11–18
No. of pupils: 850 B464 G386 VIth105

(✐) (16+) (✿)

Methodist College
1 Malone Road, Belfast,
County Antrim BT9 6BY
Tel: 028 9020 5205
Principal: J Scott W Naismith
Age range: 4–19
No. of pupils: 2307 B1258 G1049
VIth548
Fees: Day £130–£3425

(🌐) (A) (✐) (16+) (HMC)

Royal Belfast Academical Institution
College Square East, Belfast,
County Antrim BT1 6DL
Tel: 028 9024 0461
Principal: Miss J A Williamson MA(Oxon),
NPQH
Age range: 4–18
No. of pupils: 1290 VIth275
Fees: Day £790–£2500

(♦) (A) (✐) (16+) (HMC)

St Mary's Christian Brothers Grammar School
Glen Road, Belfast,
County Antrim BT11 8NR
Tel: 028 9029 4000
Headmaster: Rev Br D Gleeson
Age range: 12–18
No. of pupils: 112

(♦) (A) (16+)

Victoria College Belfast
Cranmore Park, Belfast,
County Antrim BT9 6JA
Tel: 028 9066 1506
Principal: Ms Patricia Slevin
Age range: 5–18
No. of pupils: 1070 VIth224
Fees: Day £380 WB £7875
FB £7875–£13,125

(♣) (A) (▩) (✐) (16+)

COUNTY ARMAGH

The Royal School
College Hill, Armagh,
County Armagh BT61 9DH
Tel: 02837 522807
Headmaster: P Crute MA, BA, PGCE
Age range: 11–18
No. of pupils: 654 B325 G329 VIth157
Fees: Day £110–£163 WB £4165–£6365
FB £6365–£10,165

(A) (▩) (16+) (✿)

COUNTY DOWN

Bangor Grammar School
13 College Avenue, Bangor,
County Down BT20 5HJ
Tel: 028 9147 3734
Headmaster: Mr S D Connolly MA
Age range: 3–18
No. of pupils: 900 VIth220
Fees: Day £80–£450

(♦) (A) (✐) (16+) (HMC)

Holywood Rudolf Steiner School
Saralies House, 34 Croft Road,
Holywood, County Down BT18 0PR
Tel: 028 9042 8029
Administrator: Edward Galloway
Age range: 3–17
No. of pupils: 120 B65 G55
Fees: Day £3447

(£)

Rockport School
Craigavad, Holywood,
County Down BT18 0DD
Tel: 028 9042 8372
Principal: Mr George Vance
Age range: 3–16
No. of pupils: 200 B97 G103
Fees: Day £5370–£11,790
WB £8870–£13,040 FB £10,105–£14,275

(🌐) (▩) (£) (✐) (IAPS) (BSA)

Key to symbols

(♦) Boys' school

(♣) Girls' school

(🌐) International school

(16+) Tutorial or sixth form college

(A) A levels

(▩) Boarding accommodation

(£) Bursaries

(IB) International Baccalaureate

 Learning support

(16+) Entrance at 16+

(✿) Vocational qualifications

(IAPS) Member of Independent Association of Preparatory Schools

(HMC) The Headmasters' & Headmistresses' Conference

(ISA) Independent Schools Association

(GSA) Girls' School Association

(BSA) Boarding Schools' Association

(S) SHMIS

Unless otherwise indicated, all schools are coeducational day schools. Single-sex and boarding schools will be indicated by the relevant icon.

COUNTY FERMANAGH

Portora Royal School
Enniskillen,
County Fermanagh BT74 7HA
Tel: 028 6632 2658
Headmaster: Mr J N Morton MA(Ed), MA,
PQH(NI), BA, BSSc, DASE
Age range: 11–18
No. of pupils: 497 VIth134
Fees: Day £42

COUNTY LONDONDERRY

Coleraine Academical Institution
Castlerock Road, Coleraine,
County Londonderry BT51 3LA
Tel: 028 7034 4331
Headmaster: Dr D R J Carruthers
Age range: 11–18
No. of pupils: 711 VIth144
Fees: Day £140

COUNTY TYRONE

The Royal School Dungannon
2 Ranfurly Road, Dungannon,
County Tyrone BT71 6EG
Tel: 028 8772 2710
Headmaster: Dr David Burnett
Age range: 11–18
No. of pupils: 663 B214 G267 VIth182
Fees: Day £135 WB £6750 FB £13,635

Scotland

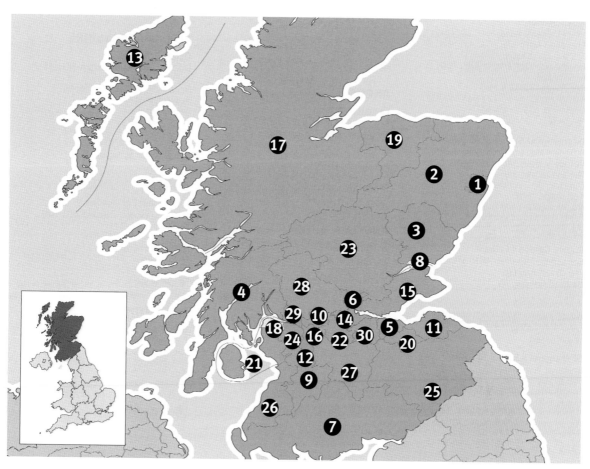

Key and page index:

ABERDEEN

Aberdeen Waldorf School
Craigton Road, Cults,
Aberdeen AB15 9QD
Tel: 01224 868366
Age range: 3–16
No. of pupils: 115

Albyn School
17-23 Queen's Road,
Aberdeen AB15 4PB
Tel: 01224 322408
Headmaster: Ian E Long AKC, PhD,
FRGS, FRSA
Age range: B2–14 G2–18
No. of pupils: 675 B223 G452 VIth57
Fees: Day £3500–£9785

International School of Aberdeen
Pitfodels House, North Deeside Road,
Pitfodels, Cults, Aberdeen AB15 9PN
Tel: 01224 730300
Director: Dr D A Hovde
Age range: 3–18
No. of pupils: B188 G197
Fees: Day £16,205–£18,145

Robert Gordon's College
Schoolhill, Aberdeen AB10 1FE
Tel: 01224 646346
Head of College: Mr Hugh Ouston MA,
DipEd
Age range: 4–18
No. of pupils: 1573 B963 G610 VIth350
Fees: Day £5949–£9264

St Margaret's School for Girls
17 Albyn Place, Aberdeen AB10 1RU
Tel: 01224 584466
Headmistress: Dr Julie Land BSc(Hons),
PGCE, EdD
Age range: B3–5 G3–18
No. of pupils: 406 B4 G402 VIth30
Fees: Day £5445–£9498

The Hamilton School
80-84 Queens Road, Aberdeen AB1 6YE
Tel: 01224 317295
Principal: Kathlyn A Taylor BEd
Age range: 0–13
No. of pupils: 340
Fees: Day £2352–£5760

Total Fina Elf French School
1-5 Whitehall Place, Aberdeen AB25 2RH
Tel: 01224 645545
Headmaster: Mr Jean Albert
Age range: 4–18
No. of pupils: 100

ANGUS

Lathallan School
Brotherton Castle, Johnshaven,
Montrose, Angus DD10 0HN
Tel: 01561 362220
Headmaster: Mr R Toley
Age range: 0–18
No. of pupils: 155 B95 G60
Fees: Day £9000–£14,500

ARGYLL & BUTE

Lomond School
10 Stafford Street, Helensburgh,
Argyll & Bute G84 9JX
Tel: 01436 672476
Headmaster: Mr Simon J Mills
Age range: 3–18
No. of pupils: B264 G256 VIth50
Fees: Day £4470–£9120 FB £20,030

BORDERS

St Mary's Prep School
Abbey Park, Melrose, Borders TD6 9LN
Tel: 01896 822517
Headmaster: Mr Liam Harvey
Age range: 2½–13
No. of pupils: B69 G93
Fees: Day £8700–£11,550 WB £14,250

CLACKMANNANSHIRE

Dollar Academy
Dollar, Clackmannanshire FK14 7DU
Tel: 01259 742511
Rector: Mr D Knapman Mphil
Age range: 5–18
No. of pupils: 1234 B632 G602 VIth142
Fees: Day £7335–£9810
WB £18,702–£21,177
FB £19,908–£22,383

DUNDEE

High School of Dundee
Euclid Crescent, Dundee DD1 1HU
Tel: 01382 202921
Rector: Dr John Halliday
Age range: 5–18
No. of pupils: 1019 B528 G491 VIth99
Fees: Day £6930–£9840

EAST LOTHIAN

Belhaven Hill
Dunbar, East Lothian EH42 1NN
Tel: 01368 862785
Headmaster: I K MacAskill BEd
Age range: 8–13
No. of pupils: B70 G55
Fees: Day £11,985 FB £17,280

Key to symbols

(†) Boys' school

(♣) Girls' school

(🌐) International school

(16⁺) Tutorial or sixth form college

(A) A levels

(≞) Boarding accommodation

(£) Bursaries

(IB) International Baccalaureate

(✎) Learning support

(16⁺) Entrance at 16+

(♣) Vocational qualifications

(IAPS) Member of Independent Association of Preparatory Schools

(HMC) The Headmasters' & Headmistresses' Conference

(ISA) Independent Schools Association

(GSA) Girls' School Association

(BSA) Boarding Schools' Association

(S) SHMIS

Unless otherwise indicated, all schools are coeducational day schools. Single-sex and boarding schools will be indicated by the relevant icon.

Loretto Junior School
North Esk Lodge, 1 North High Street,
Musselburgh, East Lothian EH21 6JA
Tel: 0131 653 4570
Headmaster: Richard Selley BEd
Age range: 3–12
No. of pupils: 200 B108 G92
Fees: Day £6210–£11,550
FB £13,500–£15,000

Loretto School
Musselburgh, East Lothian EH21 7RE
Tel: 0131 653 4455
Head: Mr Peter Hogan
Age range: 12–18
No. of pupils: 435 B225 G210 VIth161
Fees: Day £6255–£18,300
FB £17,595–£26,925

The Compass School
West Road, Haddington,
East Lothian EH41 3RD
Tel: 01620 822642
Headmaster: Mr Mark Becher MA(Hons),
PGCE
Age range: 4–12
No. of pupils: 120
Fees: Day £6685–£7755

EDINBURGH

Basil Paterson Tutorial College
66 Queen Street, Edinburgh EH2 4NA
Tel: 0131 225 3802
Principal: David Van Den Bergh
Age range: 16+
No. of pupils: 40 B20 G20 VIth35
Fees: Day £3440–£21,440 WB £140

Cargilfield
Barnton Avenue West,
Edinburgh EH4 6HU
Tel: 0131 336 2207
Headmaster: Mr John Elder
Age range: 3–13
No. of pupils: B165 G117
Fees: Day £4080–£11,850 WB £14,400
FB £15,000

Clifton Hall
Newbridge, Edinburgh EH28 8LQ
Tel: 0131 333 1359
Headmaster: Mr R Grant
Age range: 3–18
No. of pupils: 299 B150 G149 VIth8
Fees: Day £1500–£9500

Edinburgh Steiner School
60 Spylaw Road, Edinburgh EH10 5BR
Tel: 0131 337 3410
Age range: 3–18
No. of pupils: B136 G136
Fees: Day £3450–£7506

Fettes College
Carrington Road, Edinburgh EH4 1QX
Tel: 0131 332 2281
Headmaster: Mr M C B Spens MA
Age range: 7–18
No. of pupils: 676 B365 G311 VIth232
Fees: Day £11,331–£17,838
FB £17,739–£24,348

Fettes College Preparatory School
East Fettes Avenue, Edinburgh EH4 1QZ
Tel: 0131 332 2976
Headmaster: Mr A A Edwards
Age range: 7–13
No. of pupils: 169 B85 G84
Fees: Day £11,331 FB £17,739

George Heriot's School
Lauriston Place, Edinburgh EH3 9EQ
Tel: 0131 229 7263
Headmaster: Mr Alistair G Hector MA
Age range: 4–18
No. of pupils: 1617 B828 G789 VIth338
Fees: Day £6445–£9670

George Watson's College
Colinton Road, Edinburgh EH10 5EG
Tel: 0131 446 6000
Principal: Mr Gareth H Edwards
Age range: 3–18
No. of pupils: 2336 B1260 G1076
Fees: Day £6192–£9606

MERCHISTON CASTLE SCHOOL
For further details see p. 161
294 Colinton Road, Edinburgh EH13 0PU
Tel: 0131 312 2200
Email: admission@merchiston.co.uk
Website: www.merchiston.co.uk
Headmaster: Mr A R Hunter BA
Age range: 8–18
No. of pupils: 450 VIth157
Fees: Day £11,385–£17,940
FB £16,140–£24,780

St George's School for Girls
Garscube Terrace, Edinburgh EH12 6BG
Tel: 0131 311 8000
Head: Anne Everest BA(Hons)
Age range: B18 months–5 years G18
months–18 years
No. of pupils: 800 B10 VIth180
Fees: Day £1980–£8205
FB £14,730–£16,380

St Mary's Music School
Coates Hall, 25 Grosvenor Crescent,
Edinburgh EH12 5EL
Tel: 0131 538 7766
Headteacher: Mrs Jennifer Rimer
BMus(Hons), LRAM, DipEd, Hon ARAM
Age range: 9–19
No. of pupils: B27 G48 VIth17

Stewart's Melville College
Queensferry Road, Edinburgh EH4 3EZ
Tel: 0131 311 1000
Principal: Mr J N D Gray BA
Age range: B11–18 G16–18
No. of pupils: 864 B746 G118
Fees: Day £9096 FB £18,249

The Edinburgh Academy
42 Henderson Row, Edinburgh EH3 5BL
Tel: 0131 556 4603
Rector: Marco Longmore
Age range: 2–18
No. of pupils: 992 B660 G332 VIth93
Fees: Day £8860–£14,960

**The Mary Erskine & Stewart's Melville
Junior School**
Queensferry Road, Edinburgh EH4 3EZ
Tel: 0131 311 1111
Headmaster: Mr Bryan Lewis
Age range: 3–11
No. of pupils: 1218 B616 G602
Fees: Day £5574–£7218
WB £14,628–£14,814
FB £15,051–£15,237

The Mary Erskine School
Ravelston, Edinburgh EH4 3NT
Tel: 0131 347 5700
Headmaster: Mr J N D Gray BA
Age range: B16–18 G11–18
No. of pupils: B118 G751
Fees: Day £9096 FB £18,249

Wallace College
12 George IV Bridge, Edinburgh EH1 1EE
Tel: 0131 220 3634
Age range: 14–19
No. of pupils: B20 G20
Fees: Day £1410–£6900
FB £4070–£9590

FIFE

Osborne House School
Orchard Croft, West Port, Dysart,
Fife KY1 2TD
Tel: 01592 651461
Headteacher: Miss Eunice Cameron
Age range: 10–17
Fees: Day £7800

St Leonards School
St Andrews, Fife KY16 9QJ
Tel: 01334 472126
Headmaster: Dr Michael Carslaw
Age range: 4–19
No. of pupils: 520 B265 G255 VIth121
Fees: Day £7941–£10,950
FB £26,070–£26,070

GLASGOW

Belmont House School
Sandringham Avenue, Newton Mearns,
Glasgow G77 5DU
Tel: 0141 639 2922
Principal: Mr Melvyn D Shanks BSc,
DipEd, MInstP, CPhys, SQH
Age range: 3–18
No. of pupils: 300
Fees: Day £4932–£9339

Craigholme School
72 St Andrews Drive, Pollokshields,
Glasgow G41 4HS
Tel: 0141 427 0375
Principal: Ms Gillian C K Stobo BSc,
MSc, DipEd
Age range: B3–5 G3–18
No. of pupils: 442 B15 G427 VIth30
Fees: Day £4137–£9735

Fernhill School
Fernbrae Avenue, Burnside, Rutherglen,
Glasgow G73 4SG
Tel: 0141 634 2674
Headteacher: Mrs Jacqueline Sexton
BSc, PGCE
Age range: B4–11 G4–18
No. of pupils: 300 B50 G250 VIth16
Fees: Day £7470–£8976

Glasgow Steiner School
52 Lumsden Street, Yorkhill,
Glasgow G12 8HE
Tel: 0141 334 8855
Age range: 0–12
No. of pupils: 77
Fees: Day £780–£4380

Hutchesons' Grammar School
21 Beaton Road, Glasgow G41 4NW
Tel: 0141 423 2933
Rector: Dr Kenneth M Greig MA, PhD
Age range: 5–18
No. of pupils: 1650 B900 G750 VIth151
Fees: Day £7427–£9473

St Aloysius College
45 Hill Street, Glasgow G3 6RJ
Tel: 0141 332 3190
Headmaster: Mr J E Stoer BA
Age range: 3–18
No. of pupils: 1289 B661 G628 VIth81
Fees: Day £6804–£9009

The Glasgow Academy
Colebrooke Street, Kelvinbridge,
Glasgow G12 8HE
Tel: 0141 334 8558
Rector: Mr Peter Brodie MA, MA(Ed)
Age range: 3–18
Fees: Day £3255–£9645

The Glasgow Academy Dairsie
54 Newlands Road, Newlands,
Glasgow G43 2JG
Tel: 0141 632 0736
Headmistress: Mrs Shona McKnight
Age range: 3–9
No. of pupils: 74 B47 G27
Fees: Day £2730–£5505

The High School of Glasgow
637 Crow Road, Glasgow G13 1PL
Tel: 0141 954 9628
Rector: Colin D R Mair
Age range: 3–18
No. of pupils: 1037 B539 G498 VIth196
Fees: Day £3228–£9948

The Kelvinside Academy
33 Kirklee Road, Glasgow G12 0SW
Tel: 0141 357 3376
Rector: Mrs Lesley Douglas
Age range: 3–18
No. of pupils: 640 B378 G262 VIth73
Fees: Day £2313–£8895

INVERCLYDE

Cedars School of Excellence
31 Ardgowan Square, Greenock,
Inverclyde PA16 8NJ
Tel: 01475 723905
Headteacher: Mrs Alison Speirs
Age range: 5–16
No. of pupils: 95 B48 G47
Fees: Day £3400–£5000

St Columba's School
Duchal Road, Kilmacolm,
Inverclyde PA13 4AU
Tel: 01505 872238
Rector: Mr D Girdwood DL, BSc, MEd,
SQH
Age range: 3–18
No. of pupils: 731 B357 G374 VIth106
Fees: Day £2120–£8260

MORAY

Aberlour House
Aberlour, Moray AB38 9LJ
Tel: 01343 837829
Head of Junior School: Robert W
McVean
Age range: 8–13
No. of pupils: 66 B33 G33
Fees: Day £8169 WB £11,976 FB £14,643

Gordonstoun School
Elgin, Moray IV30 5RF
Tel: 01343 837829
Principal: Mr Simon Reid BA
Age range: 8–18
No. of pupils: 603 B356 G247 VIth261
Fees: Day £11,970–£21,600 WB £19,470
FB £19,470–£28,944

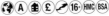

Moray Steiner School
Drumduan, Clovenside Road, Forres,
Moray IV36 0RD
Tel: 01309 676300
Age range: 3–16

PERTH & KINROSS

Ardvreck School
Gwydyr Road, Crieff,
Perth & Kinross PH7 4EX
Tel: 01764 653112
Headmaster: Peter Sutton
Age range: 4–13
No. of pupils: 167 B104 G63 VIth32
Fees: Day £975–£5865 FB £9045–£9465

Craigclowan Preparatory School
Edinburgh Road, Perth,
Perth & Kinross PH2 8PS
Tel: 01738 626310
Headmaster: Richard Evans
Age range: 3–13
No. of pupils: 267 B159 G108
Fees: Day £9975

Glenalmond College, Perth
Glenalmond, Perth,
Perth & Kinross PH1 3RY
Tel: 01738 842000
Warden: G C Woods
Age range: 12–18
No. of pupils: 410 B233 G177 VIth167
Fees: Day £13,890–£18,525
FB £20,364–£27,162

KILGRASTON SCHOOL
For further details see p. 160
Bridge of Earn, Perth,
Perth & Kinross PH2 9BQ
Tel: 01738 812257
Email: headoffice@kilgraston.com
Website: www.kilgraston.com
Principal: Mr Frank Thompson MA,
MPhil, PGCE
Age range: B2½–9 G2½–18
No. of pupils: 321 B4 G317 VIth91
Fees: Day £8265–£14,490
FB £19,620–£24,705

Morrison's Academy
Crieff, Perth & Kinross PH7 3AN
Tel: 01764 653885
Principal: Simon Pengelley BA(Hons)
Age range: 3–18
No. of pupils: 541 B286 G255 VIth47
Fees: Day £5931–£8973

QUEEN VICTORIA SCHOOL
For further details see p. 162
Dunblane, Perth & Kinross FK15 0JY
Tel: 0131 310 2927
Email: admissions@qvs.org.uk
Website: www.qvs.org.uk
Head: Mrs W Bellars MA(Hons), PGCE,
DipEd, MA(Ed Man)
Age range: 11–18
No. of pupils: 270 B141 G129 VIth28
Fees: FB £1179

STRATHALLAN SCHOOL
For further details see p. 164
Forgandenny, Perth,
Perth & Kinross PH2 9EG
Tel: 01738 812546
Email: admissions@strathallan.co.uk
Website: www.strathallan.co.uk
Headmaster: Mr B K Thompson
MA(Oxon)
Age range: 9–18
No. of pupils: 567 B318 G249 VIth200
Fees: Day £4044–£6163
FB £6479–£9083

SOUTH AYRSHIRE

Wellington School
Carleton Turrets, Ayr,
South Ayrshire KA7 2XH
Tel: 01292 269321
Head: Mr R M Parlour BSc(Hons), BA,
PGCE(Oxon), MMBA, FIAP, FRSA
Age range: 3–18
No. of pupils: B278 G309 VIth45
Fees: Day £4629–£9075

SOUTH LANARKSHIRE

Hamilton College
Bothwell Road, Hamilton,
South Lanarkshire ML3 0AY
Tel: 01698 282700
Principal: Ms Margaret Clarke
Age range: 3–18
No. of pupils: 673 B371 G302
Fees: Day £1810–£2410

STIRLING

Beaconhurst School
52 Kenilworth Road, Bridge of Allan,
Stirling FK9 4RR
Tel: 01786 832146
Headmaster: Mr Iain Kilpatrick BA, MEd,
FRSA
Age range: 3–18
No. of pupils: 403 B219 G184
Fees: Day £6474–£8706

Wales

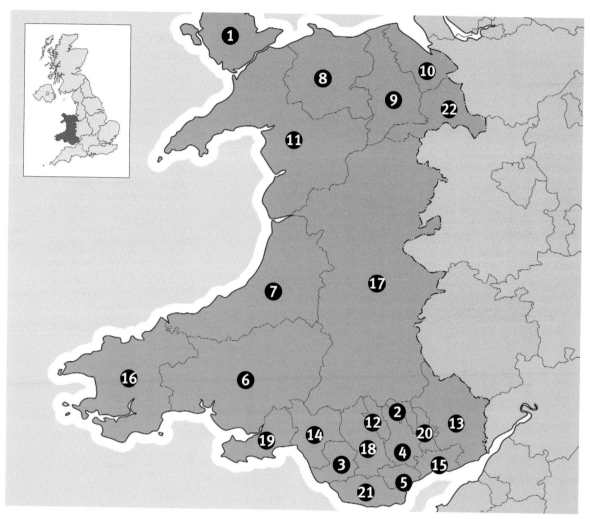

Key and page index:

1 Anglesey
2 Blaenau Gwent
3 Bridgend: D372
4 Caerphilly
5 Cardiff: D372
6 Carmarthenshire: D372
7 Ceredigion
8 Conwy: D372
9 Denbighshire: D373
10 Flintshire
11 Gwynedd: D373
12 Merthyr Tydfil
13 Monmouthshire: D373
14 Neath & Port Talbot
15 Newport: D373
16 Pembrokeshire: D373
17 Powys: D373
18 Rhondda, Cynon Taff
19 Swansea: D373
20 Torfaen
21 Vale of Glamorgan: D373
22 Wrexham

BRIDGEND

St Clare's School
Newton, Porthcawl, Bridgend CF36 5NR
Tel: 01656 782509
Headteacher: Mrs C M Barnard
Age range: 3–18
No. of pupils: 298 B128 G170 VIth45
Fees: Day £4080–£7665

Ⓐ 16·

St John's School
Newton, Porthcawl, Bridgend CF36 5NP
Tel: 01656 783404
Head: Mrs C Clint
Age range: 3–16
No. of pupils: 140 B87 G53
Fees: Day £3975–£9570

£ ✐

CARDIFF

Howell's School, Llandaff GDST
Cardiff Road, Llandaff, Cardiff CF5 2YD
Tel: 029 2056 2019
Principal: Mrs Sally Davis
Age range: B16–18 G3–18
No. of pupils: 778 B59 G719 VIth185
Fees: Day £6648–£11,346

👧 Ⓐ £ 16· GSA

Kings Monkton School
6 West Grove, Cardiff CF24 3XL
Tel: 029 2048 2854
Principal: Mr P Cox
Age range: 3–18
No. of pupils: 350 B200 G150 VIth35
Fees: Day £5460–£7164

Ⓐ ✐ 16· ISA

ST JOHN'S COLLEGE
For further details see p. 167
College Green, Cardiff CF3 5YX
Tel: 029 2077 8936
Email:
admin@stjohnscollegecardiff.co.uk
Website: www.stjohnscollegecardiff.com
Headmaster: Dr D J Neville MA(Cantab),
BSc, MusD, FRSA, AWACM, PGCE
Age range: 3–18
No. of pupils: 480 B260 G220
Fees: Day £6390–£12,072

Ⓐ £ ✐ 16· Ⓢ

The Cardiff Academy
40-41 The Parade, Cardiff CF24 3AB
Tel: 029 2040 9630
Principal: Dr S R Wilson
Age range: 14–18
No. of pupils: 51 B25 G26 VIth44
Fees: Day £7500

Ⓐ

The Cathedral School, Llandaff
Llandaff, Cardiff CF5 2YH
Tel: 029 2056 3179
Headmaster: Mr P L Gray MA(Cantab),
ARCO, PGCE
Age range: 3–16
No. of pupils: B430 G193
Fees: Day £5625–£8175

£ IAPS

CARMARTHENSHIRE

Llandovery College
Llandovery, Carmarthenshire SA20 0EE
Tel: 01550 723000
Warden: Mr I M Hunt
Age range: 3–18
No. of pupils: 295 B169 G126 VIth85
Fees: Day £5850–£12,810
FB £12,249–£20,754

🌐 Ⓐ ♨ £ 16· HMC BSA

St Michael's School
Bryn, Llanelli,
Carmarthenshire SA14 9TU
Tel: 01554 820325
Headmaster: Mr D T Sheehan
BSc(Hons), PGCE
Age range: 3–18
No. of pupils: 420 B222 G198 VIth80
Fees: Day £4179–£7968 FB £18,250

🌐 Ⓐ ♨ 16· ISA

CONWY

Rydal Penrhos Preparatory School
Pwllycrochan Avenue, Colwyn Bay,
Conwy LL29 7BP
Tel: 01492 530381
Headmaster: Mr Roger McDuff
Age range: 2½–11
No. of pupils: 200 B106 G94
Fees: Day £1990–£2770
WB £12,450–£14,415
FB £13,830–£16,005

♨ ✐ IAPS

RYDAL PENRHOS SCHOOL
For further details see p. 166
Pwllycrochan Avenue, Colwyn Bay,
Conwy LL29 7BT
Tel: +44 (0)1492 530155
Email: info@rydal-penrhos.com
Website: www.rydalpenrhos.com
Headmaster: Mr P A Lee-Browne MA
Age range: 2½–18
No. of pupils: 617 B355 G262
Fees: Day £5970–£14,055
WB £20,460–£25,245
FB £22,740–£28,020

🌐 Ⓐ ♨ £ IB ✐ 16· IAPS HMC Ⓢ

Key to symbols

🧑 Boys' school

👧 Girls' school

🌐 International school

16· Tutorial or sixth form college

Ⓐ A levels

♨ Boarding accommodation

£ Bursaries

IB International Baccalaureate

✐ Learning support

16· Entrance at 16+

🌐 Vocational qualifications

IAPS Member of Independent Association of Preparatory Schools

HMC The Headmasters' & Headmistresses' Conference

ISA Independent Schools Association

GSA Girls' School Association

BSA Boarding Schools' Association

Ⓢ SHMIS

Unless otherwise indicated, all schools are coeducational
day schools. Single-sex and boarding schools will be
indicated by the relevant icon.

St David's College
Gloddaeth Hall, Llandudno,
Conwy LL30 1RD
Tel: 01492 875974
Headmaster: Mr Chris Condrup MSc
Age range: 11–18
No. of pupils: 254 B188 G66 VIth77
Fees: Day £10,425–£15,210
FB £17,985–£22,665

DENBIGHSHIRE

Fairholme School
The Mount, Mount Road, St Asaph,
Denbighshire LL17 0DH
Tel: 01745 583505
Principal: Mrs E Perkins MA(Oxon)
Age range: 3–11
No. of pupils: 110 B60 G50
Fees: Day £6000–£6600

Howell's School
Denbigh, Denbighshire LL16 3EN
Tel: 01745 813631
Headmistress: Miss Emma Jones
Age range: B2–7 G2–18
No. of pupils: 235 B2 G233 VIth38
Fees: Day £6300–£11,700
WB £14,550–£20,700
FB £14,550–£20,700

Ruthin School
Ruthin, Denbighshire LL15 1EE
Tel: 01824 702543
Headmaster: Mr T J Belfield
Age range: 3–18
No. of pupils: 240 B171 G69 VIth41
Fees: Day £5550–£10,320 WB £13,965
FB £16,755

GWYNEDD

Hillgrove School
5 Ffriddoedd Road, Bangor,
Gwynedd LL57 2TW
Tel: 01248 353568
Headmaster: Mr & Mrs J G Porter
Age range: 3–16
No. of pupils: 155
Fees: Day £2475–£4200

St Gerard's School Trust
Ffriddoedd Road, Bangor,
Gwynedd LL57 2EL
Tel: 01248 351656
Headteacher: Miss Anne Parkinson
BA(Hons)
Age range: 3–18
No. of pupils: B110 G114 VIth40
Fees: Day £5250–£7950

MONMOUTHSHIRE

Haberdashers' Agincourt School
Dixton Lane, Monmouth,
Monmouthshire NP25 3SY
Tel: 01600 713970
Head: Mrs E Thomas
Age range: 3–7
No. of pupils: 124 B64 G60
Fees: Day £2574–£4134

Haberdashers' Monmouth School for Girls
Hereford Road, Monmouth,
Monmouthshire NP25 5XT
Tel: 01600 711104
Head: Mrs H Davy MA(Oxon)
Age range: 7–18
No. of pupils: 620 VIth173
Fees: Day £9426–£11,787
FB £19,779–£22,143

Monmouth School
Monmouth, Monmouthshire NP25 3XP
Tel: 01600 710433
Headmaster: Dr Steven G Connors BA
Age range: 7–18
No. of pupils: 693 VIth185
Fees: Day £8736–£12,345
FB £17,889–£21,498

ST JOHN'S-ON-THE-HILL
For further details see p. 168
Tutshill, Chepstow,
Monmouthshire NP16 7LE
Tel: 01291 622045
Email: registrar@stjohnsonthehill.co.uk
Website: www.stjohnsonthehill.co.uk
Headmaster: Mr N Folland BSc
Age range: 3 months–13 years
No. of pupils: 302
Fees: Day £6675–£11,025 WB £15,525
FB £15,525

NEWPORT

Rougemont School
Llantarnam Hall, Malpas Road,
Newport NP20 6QB
Tel: 01633 820800
Headmaster: Dr J N Tribbick
Age range: 3–18
No. of pupils: 700 B369 G331 VIth111
Fees: Day £5880–£9240

PEMBROKESHIRE

Nant-y-Cwm Steiner School
Llanycefn, Clunderwen,
Pembrokeshire SA66 7QJ
Tel: 01437 563 640
Age range: 0–14

Redhill Prep School
Merlin's Bridge, Haverfordwest,
Pembrokeshire SA62 4LA
Tel: 01437 762472
Principal: Mrs Lovegrove
Age range: 0–11
No. of pupils: B38 G30
Fees: Day £4950–£5100

POWYS

Christ College
Brecon, Powys LD3 8AF
Tel: 01874 615440
Head: Mrs E Taylor MA(Oxon)
Age range: 11–18
No. of pupils: 340 B195 G145 VIth120
Fees: Day £12,450–£14,175
FB £17,130–£21,900

SWANSEA

Craig-y-Nos School
Clyne Common, Bishopston,
Swansea SA3 3JB
Tel: 01792 234288
Headmaster: Mr G W Fursland CertEd
Age range: 2–11
No. of pupils: 110 B65 G45
Fees: Day £4080–£5400

Ffynone House School
36 St James's Crescent,
Swansea SA1 6DR
Tel: 01792 464967
Headteacher: Mrs Nicola Walker
BSc(Hons), PGCE, MBA, NPQH
Age range: 11–18
No. of pupils: B70 G70 VIth25
Fees: Day £8655

Oakleigh House School
38 Penlan Crescent, Uplands,
Swansea SA2 0RL
Tel: 01792 298537
Headmistress: Mrs R Ferriman
BA(Hons)Ed, MEd
Age range: 2–11
No. of pupils: 160 B80 G80
Fees: Day £4620–£6090

VALE OF GLAMORGAN

UWC Atlantic College
St Donat's Castle, St Donat's, Llantwit
Major, Vale of Glamorgan CF61 1WF
Tel: 01446 799002
Principal: John Walmsley
Age range: 16–20
No. of pupils: 340 B142 G198 VIth340
Fees: FB £23,500

Westbourne School
Hickman Road, Penarth,
Vale of Glamorgan CF64 2AJ
Tel: 029 2070 5705
Headmaster: Mr K W Underhill MA(Ed)
Age range: 3–18
No. of pupils: 169 B96 G73 VIth30
Fees: Day £5430–£9885
FB £24,850–£24,850

Examinations and qualifications

Qualifications

Common Entrance

The Common Entrance examinations are used in UK independent schools for transfer from junior to senior schools at the ages of 11+ and 13+. The papers are set centrally but the answers are marked by the senior school for which a candidate is entered. Candidates normally take the examination in their own junior or preparatory schools, either in the UK or overseas.

Common Entrance is not a public examination as, for example, GCSE, and candidates may normally be entered only in one of the following circumstances:

a) they have been offered a place at a senior school subject to their passing the examination, or

b) they are required to take the examination as a preliminary to sitting the scholarship examination, or

c) they are entered as a 'trial run', in which case the papers are corrected by the junior school concerned.

At 11+ the examination consists of English, mathematics and science. The 11+ examination is designed so that it can be taken by candidates either from independent preparatory schools or by candidates from schools in the maintained sector who have had no special preparation. At 13+ most candidates come from independent preparatory schools, and the compulsory subjects are English, mathematics and science. Papers in French, geography, German, Greek, history, Latin, Mandarin, religious studies and Spanish are also available and candidates offer as many subjects as they can.

Rapid changes in education nationally have resulted in regular reviews of the syllabuses for all the examinations. The introduction of GCSE and then the National Curriculum brought about a number of changes. Since preparation for GCSE starts at 11, and work for the National Curriculum Key Stage 3 starts at the same age, it is a guiding principle that Common Entrance should be part of the natural progression from 11-16, and not a diversion from it.

Details of the Common Entrance examinations are obtainable from the General Secretary at the address below. Copies of past papers and other publications are obtainable from Galore Park Publishing Ltd at www.galorepark.co.uk

Independent Schools Examinations Board, The Pump House, 16 Queen's Avenue, Christchurch, BH23 1BZ

Tel: +44 (0)1202 487538;   Fax: +44 (0)1202 473728

Email: enquiries@iseb.co.uk   Website: www.iseb.co.uk

General Certificate of Secondary Education (GCSE)

What are the GCSE qualifications?

GCSE qualifications were first introduced in 1986 and are the principal means of assessing Key Stage 4 and a range of other subjects. They command respect and have status not only in the UK but worldwide.

Main features of the GCSE

There are three unitary awarding organisations for GCSEs in England (see 'Awarding organisations and examination dates' section, p395). WJEC and CCEA also offer GCSE qualifications in Wales and Northern Ireland as well as England. Each examining group designs its own specifications but they are required to conform to set criteria. The award of a grade is intended to indicate that a candidate has met the required level of skills, knowledge and understanding.

A flexible approach to assessment is one of the main features of the GCSE. Candidates have the chance to demonstrate what they know and can do in a variety of ways. Many specifications give credit for assignments set and marked by the teacher, with some external moderation, and the marks awarded form a contribution towards the final grade achieved. This is in addition to more traditional examinations at the end of the course. The proportion of credit obtained from controlled assessment is subject to limits laid down by the regulatory authorities.

Grading

Candidate performance at GCSE is graded from A* to G.

There are 'differentiated' examination papers in many subjects. The scheme of GCSE assessment may involve two papers targeted at either grades A*-D or grades C-G. The higher tiered paper (graded A*-D) will also provide for an exceptional grade E on the higher tier, so that candidates who just miss a D grade are not disadvantaged. Mathematics uses three tiers; some subjects – such as history and art – use one.

Can anyone take GCSE qualifications?

GCSEs are intended mainly for 16-year-old pupils, but are open to anyone of any age, whether studying full-time or part-time at a school, college or privately. There are no formal entry requirements.

GCSEs are available in a wide range of subjects. Students normally study up to ten subjects over a two-year period. Short course GCSEs are available in some subjects (including ICT and religious studies) – these include half the content of a full GCSE, so two short course GCSEs are equivalent to one full GCSE.

General Qualifications at Advanced Level, General Certificate of Education (GCE), General Certificate of Education (GCE) in applied subjects, and Advanced Extension Award (AEA)

Typically, A level qualifications are studied over a two-year period. There are no lower or upper age limits. Schools and colleges usually expect students aged 16-18 to have obtained grades A*-C in five subjects at GCSE level before taking an advanced level course. This requirement may vary between centres and according to which specific subjects are to be studied. Mature students may be assessed on different criteria as to their suitability to embark on the course.

All these qualifications consist of a number of units. They can be assessed in stages, using opportunities in January and June, or at the end of the course.

GCE Qualifications

GCE qualifications are available at two levels. The Advanced Subsidiary (AS) is the two- or three-unit General Certificate of Education (GCE). It provides progression between GCSE at level 2 and the full A level. It is both the first half of an A level and a qualification in its own right. All A level specifications include an AS. There are currently five free-standing AS qualifications that do not lead to a full A level, namely critical thinking, European studies, science for public understanding, social science: citizenship, and world development.

The A level is the four- or six-unit GCE. It consists of the AS and a further three units called the A2, usually studied in the second year. Nearly 70 titles are available, covering a wide range of subject areas, including humanities, sciences, language, business, arts, mathematics and technology.

GCE AS and A levels normally contain a proportion of coursework up to 30% (though some practical or creative subjects have more). All GCE A levels contain in one or more of the A2 units an assessment that tests students' understanding of the whole specification (synoptic assessment). GCE AS are graded A-E and A levels are graded A*-E. Students generally take four or five subjects at AS level in the first year of advanced level study. In the second year, they generally study A2 units in two or three subjects, thereby completing A levels in those subjects.

Revised A level specifications were introduced in September 2008, with a new A* grade awarded from 2010 to those students who have achieved both of the following:

- Grade A overall (that is 90% of the maximum uniform marks for the whole A level qualification).

- 90% of the maximum uniform marks on the aggregate of the A2 unit scores.

The A* grade is awarded for the A level qualification only and not for the AS qualification or for individual units.

Over 30 A level subjects are available for study in the following fields: English, ICT, maths, science, business, arts, technology, physical education, languages and humanities.

GCEs in applied subjects

Formerly known as Vocational Certificates of Education (VCEs), GCE/A levels in applied subjects have an AS/A2 structure, comparable to existing GCEs.

Some applied A levels are being withdrawn by AQA in 2013: art and design, business, ICT, health and social care, leisure studies and travel and tourism.

Edexcel recently updated their applied GCEs, allowing the new grade of A* to be awarded where needed. These new qualifications allow for a nine-unit GCE for the double award qualifications. This is the advanced GCE with advanced subsidiary (additional), which will allow students to 'top up' from a six-unit award to achieve this. It also allows students unable to complete the full 12-unit award to go for the new nine-unit award. This qualification is the equivalent of one-and-a-half GCEs.

Advanced Extension Awards (AEA)

The AEA finished in 2009 with the exception of maths, which will end in 2015. This award is being replaced by the Extended Project Qualification (EPQ)

Cambridge International General Certificate of Secondary Education (IGCSE)

Cambridge IGCSE is an international qualification for 14 to 16-year-olds. It develops skills in creative thinking, enquiry and problem solving, in preparation for the next stage in a student's education. Cambridge IGCSE is taken in over 160 countries, and is widely recognised by employers and higher education institutions worldwide.

Cambridge IGCSE is graded from A*-G. In the UK, Cambridge IGCSE is accepted as equivalent to the GCSE. It can be used as preparation for Cambridge International A and AS levels, UK A and AS levels, IB or AP and in some instances entry into university. Cambridge IGCSE English as a Second Language (at grade C or above) is recognised by a number of UK universities as evidence of competence in the language for university entrance.

Available in over 70 subjects including: accounting, Afrikaans – first language, Afrikaans – second language, agriculture, Arabic – first language, Arabic – foreign language, art and design, Bangladesh studies, biology, business studies, chemistry, child development, Chinese – first language, Chinese (Mandarin) – foreign language, computer studies, Czech – first language, design and technology, development studies, drama, Dutch – first language, Dutch – foreign language, economics, English – first language, English – literature, English – second language, environmental management, food and nutrition, French – first language, French – foreign language, geography, German – first language, German – foreign language, global perspectives, Greek – foreign language, Hindi as a second language, history, Indonesian – foreign language, information and communication technology, information technology, IsiZulu as a second language, Japanese – first language, Japanese – foreign language, Kazakh as a second language, Korean – first language, Latin, Malay – foreign language, mathematics, mathematics – additional international mathematics, music, Pakistan studies, physical education, physical science, physics, Portuguese – first language, Portuguese – foreign language, religious studies, Russian – first language, science – combined, sciences – co-ordinated (double), sociology, Spanish – first language, Spanish – foreign language, Spanish – literature, Thai – first language, travel and tourism, Turkish – first language.

Website: www.cie.org.uk/igcse

Cambridge Pre-U

Cambridge Pre-U is a new post-16 qualification that equips students with the skills they need to succeed at university. Developed with universities, it was first introduced in UK schools in September 2008. It is now taught in 170 schools, including some schools outside the UK.

Cambridge Pre-U is a linear course, with exams taken at the end of two years. It encourages the development of well-informed, open and independent-minded individuals; promotes deep understanding through subject specialisation, with a depth and rigour appropriate to progression to higher education; and develops skills in independent research valued by universities.

Assessment

Cambridge Pre-U principal subjects are examined at the end of two years. Cambridge Pre-U short courses are typically examined at the end of one year. Students can study a combination of A levels and principal subjects. In order to gain the Cambridge Pre-U Diploma, students must study at least three Cambridge Pre-U principal subjects (up to two A levels can be substituted for principal subjects) and Cambridge Pre-U global perspectives and research (GPR). Cambridge Pre-U GPR includes an extended project in the second year, developing skills in research and critical thinking.

Subjects: available in 28 subjects including art and design, biology, business and management, chemistry, classical heritage, comparative government and politics, drama and theatre economics, literature in English, further mathematics, geography, global perspectives and research, classical Greek, history, art history, Latin, Mandarin Chinese, mathematics, modern foreign languages, music, philosophy and theology, physics, psychology, sport science.

Website: www.cie.org.uk/cambridgepreu

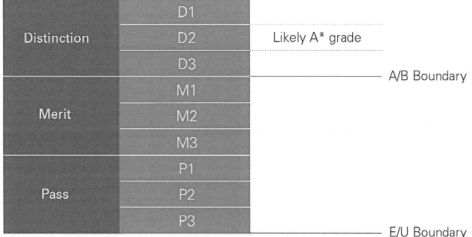

Grading Cambridge Pre-U principal subjects showing likely equivalence with A level grades.

Free Standing Maths Qualifications (FSMQ)

Aimed at those students wishing to acquire further qualifications in maths, specifically additional mathematics and foundations of advanced mathematics (MEI).

Further UCAS points can be earned upon completion of the advanced FSMQ in additional mathematics, whereas the higher FSMQ in foundations of advanced mathematics is designed for those not yet ready to take AS/A level GCE mathematics.

New foundation and higher level FSMQs were introduced in 2011, with first exams in 2012. For further details see the AQA website.

Scottish qualifications

Information supplied by Scottish Qualifications Authority

National qualifications are awarded by the Scottish Qualifications Authority (SQA). The main national qualifications available in schools include:

- Standard grades which are taken over third and fourth year at secondary school. Students often choose to study seven or eight subjects, of which mathematics and English are both compulsory. There are three levels of study at Standard Grade: Foundation, General and Credit. Students usually sit exams at two levels – either Foundation/General or General/Credit – to ensure they have the best chance of achieving as high a grade as possible.

- National Units which are the building blocks of National Courses, but they are also recognised qualifications in their own right and are designed to take approximately 40 hours of teaching time to complete.

- National Courses usually comprise of three National Units and an externally marked assessment. There are National Courses available at a number of levels including Access 1, Access 2, Access 3, Intermediate 1, Intermediate 2, Higher and Advanced Higher.

- Skills for Work courses encourage school pupils to become familiar with the world of work. They involve a strong element of learning through involvement in practical and vocational activities and develop knowledge, skills and experience that are related to employment. They are available at a number of levels and are frequently delivered in partnership between schools and colleges.

- Wider Achievement qualifications provide young people with the opportunity to have the learning and skills not necessarily developed in the classroom formally recognised. Available at a number of levels in subjects including Employability, Leadership and Enterprise, these qualifications help schools deliver skills for learning, skills for life and skills for work.

- Scottish Baccalaureates which consist of a coherent group of Higher and Advanced Higher qualifications and, uniquely, an interdisciplinary project of candidates' own choosing which is marked at Advanced Higher level in one of four broad topics – languages, science, expressive arts or social studies. Aimed at high-achieving candidates in their sixth year, the Scottish Baccalaureate is designed to encourage personalised, in-depth study and interdisciplinary learning in the later stages of secondary school.

For more information on these qualifications and how they compare with one another and with qualifications available throughout the rest of the UK, visit www.sqa.org.uk/scqf

New National Qualifications and Curriculum for Excellence

SQA has developed new National Qualifications that will be available in schools from August 2013.

These new qualifications will help young people reach their full potential as they progress from their broad general education through to college, university, other learning and employment.

The new National 1, National 2, National 3, National 4 and National 5 will be available in schools from August 2013. These will replace current Standard Grade, Intermediate and Access qualifications at all levels.

New Higher and Advanced Higher qualifications will be available from August 2014 and August 2015 respectively. They will replace the current Higher and Advanced Higher qualifications.

For more information on SQA and our portfolio of qualifications, visit www.sqa.org.uk.

Additional and Alternative

Diplomas (OCR)

OCR will no longer be offering the diploma as a whole qualification from 2013, following Ofqual's announcement about the the closure of the Diploma Aggregation Service.

However, principal learning – one of the types of diploma – will still be offered in a limited number of subjects, such as engineering. OCR will also continue to offer functional skills, Level 1 Foundation Project, Level 2 Higher Project and Level 3 Extended Project as stand-alone qualifications.

AQA Baccalaureate

The AQA Baccalaureate is awarded to students studying at least three A levels. This is a complete curriculum programme, which adds a broader range of study, and includes the Extended Project Qualification (EPQ).

This qualification is built on familiar subjects, so it can be tailored to fit in with existing curricula. It includes extracurricular activities and encourages a series of 'enrichment activities' covering personal qualities, perseverance, leadership, independence, time management, commitment and communication.

The AQA Bacc is awarded to students who achieve at least three A levels (minimum grade E), a broader study AS level subject and the EPQ, plus they must undertake a minimum of 100 hours of 'enrichment activities'.

The AQA Bacc is accepted by universities; offers are based on the component parts of the diploma, with students receiving their AQA certificate alongside their A level, AS level and EPQ certificates.

AQA Baccalaureate Award	Pass	Merit	Distinction
Depth of study – three A levels	E or above	C or above	A or above
Extended Project Qualification	E or above	C or above	A or above
Enrichment activities	Pass	Pass	Pass
Broader study AS level	Pass (E or above)	Pass (E or above)	Pass (E or above)

Extended Project Qualification (EPQ)

AQA offer the extended project, which is a qualification aimed at developing a student's research and independent learning skills. The EPQ can be taken as a stand-alone qualification, and it is equivalent to half an A level. It is also possible to take the EPQ as part of the AQA Baccalaureate.

European Baccalaureate (EB)

Not to be confused with the International Baccalaureate (IB), this certificate is available in European schools and recognised in all EU countries.

To obtain the baccalaureate, a student must obtain a minimum score of 60%, which is made up from: coursework, oral participation in class and tests (40%); five written examinations (36%) – mother-tongue, first foreign language and maths are compulsory for all candidates; four oral examinations (24%) – mother tongue and first foreign language are compulsory (history or geography may also be compulsory here, dependant on whether the candidate has taken a written examination in these subjects).

Throughout the EU the syllabus and examinations necessary to achieve the EB are identical. The only exception to this rule is the syllabus for the mother tongue language. The EB has been specifically designed to meet, at the very least, the minimum qualification requirements of each member state. Study for the EB begins at nursery stage (age four) and progresses through primary (age six) and on into secondary school (age 12).

For further information a PDF can be downloaded from: www.teachernet.gov.uk/publications

The International Baccalaureate (IB)

Information supplied by the IB

The International Baccalaureate (IB) offers four challenging and high quality educational programmes for a worldwide community of schools, aiming to develop internationally minded people who, recognizing their common humanity and shared guardianship of the planet, help to create a better, more peaceful world.

The IB works with schools around the world (both state and privately funded) that share the commitment to international education to deliver these programmes.

Schools that have achieved the high standards required for authorization to offer one or more of the IB programmes are known as IB World Schools. There are over half a million students attending more than 3000 IB World Schools in 139 countries and this number is growing annually.

The Primary Years, Middle Years and Diploma Programmes share a common philosophy and common characteristics. They develop the whole student, helping students to grow intellectually, socially, aesthetically and culturally. They provide a broad and balanced education that includes science and the humanities, languages and mathematics, technology and the arts. The programmes teach students to think critically, and encourage them to draw connections between areas of knowledge and to use problem-solving techniques and concepts from many disciplines. They instil in students a sense of responsibility towards others and towards the environment. Lastly, and perhaps most importantly, the programmes give students an awareness and understanding of their own culture and of other cultures, values and ways of life.

A fourth programme called the IB Career Related Certificate (IBCC) became available to IB World Schools from September 2012.

The IBCC incorporates the educational principles, vision and learner profile of the IB into a unique offering that specifically addresses the needs of students who wish to engage in career-related education. The IBCC encourages these students to benefit from elements of an IB education, through a selection of two or more Diploma Programme courses in addition to a unique IBCC core, comprised of an approaches to learning (ATL) course, language development, a reflective project, and community and service.

The IBCC is designed to provide a 'value added' qualification to schools that already offer the IB Diploma Programme and are also delivering career-related studies to their students. The IBCC enables schools to widen participation to an IB education. Schools retain the ability to choose the career-related courses that are most suited to local conditions and the needs of their students. Schools gain the added flexibility in direct curriculum development as well as the IBCC core to create an educational pathway that puts a strong focus on individual student needs. All IB programmes include:

- a written curriculum or curriculum framework;
- student assessment appropriate to the age range;
- professional development and networking opportunities for teachers;
- support, authorization and programme evaluation for the school.

The IB Primary Years Programme

The IB Primary Years Programme (PYP), for students aged three to 12, focuses on the development of the whole child as an inquirer, both in the classroom and in the world outside. It is a framework consisting of five essential elements (concepts, knowledge, skills, attitude, action) and guided by six trans-disciplinary themes of global significance, explored using knowledge and skills derived from six subject areas (language, social studies, mathematics, science and technology, arts, personal, social and physical education) with a powerful emphasis on inquiry-based learning.

The most significant and distinctive feature of the PYP is the six trans-disciplinary themes. These themes are about issues that have meaning for, and are important to, all of us. The programme offers a balance between learning about or through the subject areas, and learning beyond them. The six themes of global significance create a trans-disciplinary framework that allows students to 'step up' beyond the confines of learning within subject areas:

- Who we are.
- Where we are in place and time.
- How we express ourselves.
- How the world works.
- How we organize ourselves.
- Sharing the planet.

The PYP exhibition is the culminating activity of the programme. It requires students to analyse and propose solutions to real-world issues, drawing on what they have learned through the programme. Evidence of student development and records of PYP exhibitions are reviewed by the IB as part of the programme evaluation process.

Assessment is an important part of each unit of inquiry as it both enhances learning and provides opportunities for students to reflect on what they know, understand and can do. The teacher's feedback to the students provides the guidance, the tools and the incentive for them to become more competent, more skilful and better at understanding how to learn.

The IB Middle Years Programme (MYP)

The MYP, for students aged 11 to 16, provides a framework of academic challenge that encourages students to embrace and understand the connections between traditional subjects and the real world, and to become critical and reflective thinkers. Students are required to study their mother tongue, a second language, humanities, sciences, mathematics, arts, physical education and technology. In the final year of the programme, students also engage in a personal project, which they will use to demonstrate the understanding and skills they have developed throughout the programme.

Students study subjects from each of the eight subject groups through the five areas of interaction:

- Approaches to learning is concerned with developing the intellectual discipline, attitudes, strategies and skills that will result in critical, coherent and independent thought and the capacity for problem solving and decision-making.

- Community and service starts in the classroom and extends beyond it, requiring students to participate in the communities in which they live. The emphasis is on developing community awareness and concern, a sense of responsibility, and the skills and attitudes needed to make an effective contribution to society.

- Human ingenuity (formerly *homo faber*) allows students to focus on the evolution, processes and products of human creativity. It considers their impact on society and on the mind. Students learn to appreciate the human capacity to influence, transform, enjoy and improve the quality of life. This area of interaction encourages students to explore the relationships between science, aesthetics, technology and ethics.

- Environments aims to make students aware of their interdependence with the environment so that they become aware of their responsibility, and may take positive, responsible action for maintaining an environment fit for the future.

- Health and social education prepares students for a physically and mentally healthy life, aware of potential hazards and able to make informed choices. It develops in students a sense of responsibility for their own wellbeing and for the physical and social environment.

Assessment is criterion referenced, so students around the world are measured against pre-specified criteria for each subject group. Teachers may modify these criteria to be age-appropriate in the earlier years of the programme.

Teachers set assessment tasks that are assessed internally in the school. External checks (either moderation or monitoring of assessment by IB examiners) are carried out on this internal assessment to ensure worldwide consistency of standards. For schools that require official IB certification for their students, moderation is carried out every year.

The IB Diploma Programme (IBDP)

The IB Diploma Programme, for students aged 16 to 19, is an academically challenging and balanced programme of education with final examinations, which prepares students for success at university and life beyond.

IBDP students study six courses at higher level or standard level. Students must choose one subject from each of groups 1 to 5, thus ensuring breadth of experience in languages, social studies, the experimental sciences and mathematics. The sixth subject may be an arts subject chosen from group 6, or the student may choose another subject from groups 1 to 5. At least three and not more than four subjects are taken at higher level (recommended 240 teaching hours), the others at standard level (150 teaching hours). Students can study these subjects, and be examined, in English, French or Spanish.

In addition, three core elements – the extended essay, theory of knowledge and creativity, action, service – are compulsory and central to the philosophy of the programme.

Students take written examinations at the end of the programme, which are marked by external IB examiners. Students also complete assessment tasks in the school, which are either initially marked by teachers and then moderated by external moderators or sent directly to external examiners.

The marks awarded for each course range from one (lowest) to seven (highest). Students can also be awarded up to three additional points for their combined results on theory of knowledge and the extended essay. The diploma is awarded to students who gain at least 24 points, subject to certain minimum levels of performance across the whole programme and to satisfactory participation in the creativity, action, and service requirement. The highest total that a Diploma Programme student can be awarded is 45 points.

The IB Career Related Certificate (IBCC)

The IB Career Related Certificate, for students aged 16 to 19, accentuates and enhances skill development and the attainment of the competencies relevant to today's challenging work place. Students are able to develop a specific pathway into higher education in consultation with their school. A specially-designed IBCC core recognizes and emphasizes IB values, missions and the needs of career-related students.

IBCC students study a specialized IBCC core and a minimum of two Diploma Programme courses. The IBCC core consists of the following:

Community and Service: This element of the IBCC core is based on the principle of service learning, which uses community service as a vehicle for new learning that has academic value. The service learning model in the IBCC emphasises knowledge development, civic development, social development and personal development.

Approaches to learning (ATL): This course is designed to introduce students to life skills. At the heart of the ATL model is the learner who uses a range of skills to make sense of the world around them and develops skills with an emphasis on critical and ethical thinking and effective communication.

Language development: Language development ensures that all students have access to, and are exposed to, a second language that will assist and further their understanding of the wider world. Students are encouraged to extend or begin a second language that suits their needs, background and context.

Reflective project: Through a reflective project students identify, analyse, critically discuss and evaluate an ethical issue arising from their career-related studies. The project can be submitted in a variety of formats including an essay, web page or short film. This work allows the student to engage in personal inquiry, action and reflection and to develop strong research and communications skills.

The Diploma Programme courses are assessed in accordance with the standard Diploma Programme assessment process. However, the career-related courses are assessed by the career-related course provider, not the IB. Approaches to learning, community and service and language development are internally assessed by the school, while the reflective project is moderated by the IB.

For more information on IB programmes, visit: www.ibo.org

Africa, Europe, Middle East Global Centre, Churchillplein 6, The Hague, 2517JW, The Netherlands

Tel: +31 (0)70 352 6233
Email: communications@ibo.org

Welsh Baccalaureate

This qualification is aimed at 14-19 year-olds and combines personal development skills with A/AS levels, BTECs, NVQs and GCSEs. It includes the key skills needed for success in further/higher education or the workplace, in that communication, ICT, application of number, working with others, problem solving and improving the student's own learning and performance are also developed and assessed.

The Welsh Baccalaureate Diploma consists of a core programme of studies along with students' own personal options, chosen from academic or vocational qualifications. The core programme includes key skills, work-related education, instruction on Wales and its place in Europe and the world, an individual investigation and personal and social education (PSE) instruction.

Project Qualifications

The project is available at levels 1(Foundation) and 2 (Higher), and the Extended project at level 3. Completion of the extended project is the equivalent of half an A level and can add up to 60 UCAS points to a student's tariff. The projects allow students to carry out an indepth study of personal interest or to expand their research of an existing topic of study. They are available as freestanding qualifications.

Principal Learning (PL)

Principal Learning qualifications are stand alone qualifications that can be taken by any learner and as options within the Welsh Baccalaureate.

There are several lines of learning within the PL, including: construction and the built environment; engineering; creative and media; IT; environmental and land-based studies; hair and beauty; hospitality; manufacturing and product design; business; administration and finance; and society, health and development.

Projects

Extended Project Qualification (EPQ)

AQA offer the extended project, which is a qualification aimed at developing a student's research and independent learning skills. The EPQ can be taken as a stand-alone qualification, and it is equivalent to half an A level. It is also possible to take the EPQ as part of the AQA Baccalaureate.

OCR Project

The OCR Project is designed to encourage creativity and develop communication, planning, time management, research and independent working.

It is available in three levels:

- Extended Project
- Foundation Project
- Higher Project

These are stand-alone qualifications, but they are also a compulsory part of the Welsh Baccalaureate Diploma.

Each project takes the form of a report, performance, artefact, investigation, design or dissertation and can be on any topic the learner chooses, but must, if taken as part of the diploma, 'complement and develop on from the theme and topics of Principal Learning and/or support student progression'.

Assessment is undertaken on the student's ability to plan, research, develop and critically evaluate their work rather than on the outcome of the project itself.

Level	Size equivalency	Achievement and attainment table points	UCAS points (stand alone qualification)
Foundation (L1)	GCSE Short Course	A* 17 - B 9.5	No
Higher (L2)	GCSE Short Course	A* 29 - C 20	No
Extended (L3)	AS Level	A* 90 -E 45	A* 70 -E 20

Entry level, basic and key skills

Awards and Certificates in Education, Training and Skills (ACETS)

A range of qualifications offered by CCEA aimed at students who want to acquire qualifications relevant to the world of work. Subjects available:

- Business enterprise
- Classroom assistant
- Creative craft
- Drug awareness studies

- Drug awareness studies and their applications
- Employability
- Essential skills: application of number
- Essential skills: communication
- Key skills: application of number
- Key skills: communication
- Key skills: ICT
- Key skills: improving own learning and performance
- Key skills: problem solving
- Key skills: working with others
- Occupational studies
- Performance skills
- Personal effectiveness
- Personal money management
- Substance misuse awareness

Proficiency

OCR has developed qualifications in maths and English to meet the needs of adult learners, as replacements for Key and Basic Skills. Available from Entry Level to Level 2, the qualifications can be stand alone or enable progression to other programmes such as GCSEs.

National Skills Profile
There are three entry levels. At levels 1 and 2 students are assessed by the National Basic Skills tests, which use the same tests as those for Key Skills in Communication and Application of Number.

Entry Level Qualifications

If you want to take GCSE or NVQ level 1 but have not yet reached the standard required, then entry level qualifications are for you as they are designed to get you started on the qualifications ladder.

Entry level qualifications are available in a wide range of areas. You can take an entry level certificate in most subjects where a similar GCSE exists. There are also vocational entry level qualifications – some in specific areas like retail or catering and others where you can take units in different work-related subjects to get a taster of a number of career areas. There are also entry level certificates in life skills and the basic skills of literacy and numeracy.

Anyone can take an entry level qualification – your school or college will help you decide which qualification is right for you.

Entry level qualifications are flexible programmes so the time it takes to complete will vary according to where you study and how long you need to take the qualification.

Subjects available: art and design; business studies; catering; child development; citizenship studies; design and technology; drama; English; essential skills: adult literacy; essential skills: adult numeracy; French; geography; German; graphical and material studies; hairdressing; history; home economics; ICT; Irish; job-seeking skills; learning for life and work; leisure and tourism; manufacturing; mathematics; occupational studies; office practice; physical education; preparation for employment; religious studies; retail; science; Spanish; and technology and design.

Essential Skills Wales

Offered by OCR and WJEC. OCR now offer a new suite of skills qualifications to replace their key skills in communication, application of number and ICT, and the basic skills in adult literacy, and adult numeracy qualifications. They are aimed at all ages, abilities and are applicable to all programmes of study. In Wales they are considered essential for those students working towards their Welsh Baccalaureate and all qualifications are available in both Welsh and English.

Subjects:

- Application of number

- Communication

- Information and communication technology

Functional Skills

Information supplied by WJEC and OCR

Functional skills are freestanding qualifications offered at entry level, level 1 and level 2, which may be taken alongside GCSEs or vocational qualifications. The aim of functional skills is to encourage learners to demonstrate their skills in a range of contexts and for various purposes. These skills are of vital importance in many areas as they are essential in many careers and can add immeasurably to an individual's general quality of life.

Functional skills are practical skills in English, maths and ICT.

Vocational qualifications

QCF and Vocationally-related Certificates

There are three levels: award, certificate and diploma.

Vocationally-Related Certificates are assessed according to each individual specification, but may include practical assessments and/or marked assessments. They are designed to provide evidence of a student's relevant skills and knowledge in their chosen subject. These qualifications can be used for employment or as a path towards further education.

See the OCR website for further details.

BTECs

BTEC Level 2 First qualifications

ie BTEC Level 2 Diplomas (QCF), BTEC Level 2 Extended Certificates (QCF), BTEC Level 2 Certificates (QCF)

BTEC Firsts are Level 2 introductory work-related programmes covering a wide range of vocational areas including business, engineering, information technology, health and care, media, travel and tourism, and public services.

Programmes usually last one year and may be taken full or part-time. They are practical programmes that provide a foundation for the knowledge and skills you will need in work. Alternatively, you can progress onto a BTEC National qualification, Applied GCE A level or equivalent.

There are no formal entry requirements but you may need some GCSEs at grades D-G in order to study a BTEC Level 2 First.

Subjects available: agriculture; animal care; applied science; art and design; business; children's care, learning and development; construction; countryside and the environment; engineering; fish husbandry; floristry; health and social care; horse care; horticulture; hospitality; IT; land-based technology; business; creative media production; music; performing arts; public services; sport; travel and tourism; and vehicle technology.

BTEC Foundation Diploma in Art and Design (QCF)

For those students preparing to go onto higher education within the field of art and design. This diploma is recognised as one of the best courses of its type in the UK, and is used in preparation for degree programmes.

BTEC Nationals

ie BTEC Level 3 Extended Diplomas (QCF), BTEC Level 3 Diplomas (QCF), BTEC Level 3 Subsidiary Diplomas (QCF), BTEC Level 3 Certificates (QCF)

BTEC National programmes are long-established vocational programmes. They are practical programmes that are highly valued by employers. They enable you to gain the knowledge and skills that you will need in work, or give you the choice to progress on to a BTEC Higher National, a Foundation Degree or a degree programme.

BTEC Nationals cover a range of vocationally specialist sectors including child care, learning and development, construction, art and design (fine art), aeronautical engineering, electrical/electronic engineering, IT, business, creative and media production, performing arts, public services, sport, sport and exercise sciences and applied science.

The programmes may be taken full- or part-time, and can be taken in conjunction with NVQs and/or functional skills units at an appropriate level.

There are no formal entry requirements, but if you have any of the following you are likely to be at the right level to study a BTEC national qualification.

- a BTEC Level 2 First qualification
- GCSEs – at grades A* to C in several subjects
- Relevant work experience

There are also, in some areas, very specialist BTEC Nationals, such as pharmaceutical science and blacksmithing and metalworking.

BTEC Higher Nationals

Known as HNDs and HNCs – *ie* BTEC Level 5 HND Diplomas (QCF) and BTEC Level 4 HNC Diplomas (QCF)

BTEC HNDs and HNCs are further and higher education qualifications that offer a balance of education and vocational training. They are available in a wide range of work-related areas such as graphic design, business, health and social care, computing and systems development, manufacturing engineering, hospitality management, and public services.

BTEC higher national courses combine study with hands-on work experience during your course. Once completed, you can use the skills you learn to begin your career, or continue on to a related degree course.

HNDs are often taken as a full-time course over two years but can also be followed part-time in some cases.

HNCs are often for people who are working and take two years to complete on a part-time study basis by day release, evenings, or a combination of the two. Some HNC courses are done on a full-time basis.

There are no formal entry requirements, but if you have any of the following you are likely to be at the right academic level:

- At least one A level
- a BTEC Level 3 National qualification
- level 3 NVQ

BTEC specialist and professional qualifications

These qualifications are designed to prepare students for specific and specialist work activities. In September 2010 they were split into two distinct groups:

- Specialist qualifications (entry to level 3)
- Professional qualifications (levels 4 to 7).

NVQs (NQF)

NVQs reward those who demonstrate skills gained at work. They relate to particular jobs and are usefully taken while you are working. Within reason, NVQs do not have to be completed in a specified amount of time. They can be taken by full-time employees or by school and college students with a work placement or part-time job that enables them to develop the appropriate skills. There are no age limits and no special entry requirements.

NVQs are organised into five levels, based on the competencies required. Levels 1-3 are the levels most applicable to learners within the 14-19 phase. Achievement of level 4 within this age group will be rare. See the OCR website for further information.

Occupational Studies (Northern Ireland)

Targeted at learners working towards and at level 1 and 2 in Key Stage 4 within the Northern Ireland curriculum. For further information see the CCEA website.

Cambridge Nationals

Cambridge Nationals, the updated version of OCR Nationals, are vocationally-related qualifications that take an engaging, practical and inspiring approach to learning and assessment.

They're industry-relevant, geared to key sector requirements and very popular with schools and colleges because they suit such a broad range of learning styles and abilities.

Cambridge Nationals are available in business and enterprise, health and social care, ICT, science and sport. Available as joint Level 1 and 2 qualifications, the updated Nationals are aimed at students aged 14 to 16 in full-time study.

Cambridge Technicals

OCR's new Cambridge Technicals are practical and flexible vocationally-related qualifications, offering students in-depth study in a wide range of subjects, including business, health and social care, IT, and Sport, with art and design, media and science coming soon.

Cambridge Technicals are aimed at young people aged 16 to 19 who have completed Key Stage 4 of their education and want to study in a more practical, work-related way.

Cambridge Technicals are available at Level 2 and Level 3, and carry UCAS points.

Language qualifications

Asset Languages

Asset languages recognise the four skills of language learning – reading, writing, speaking and listening – separately. Developed by OCR, these languages recognise skills in a range of languages from Breakthrough (Entry Level) up to Intermediate (Level 2).

Online Language Assessment (OLA)

The OLA is aligned to the Northern Ireland curriculum and has been made more relevant to the student than the GOML, which it replaced in September 2010. There are four levels: entry 2, entry 3, level 1 and level 2. Five languages are on offer: French, German, Irish, Italian and Spanish.

Awarding organisations and examination dates

Awarding organisations and examination dates

In England there are three awarding organisations, each offering GCSE, including Applied GCSEs, A level and Applied A levels. There are separate awarding organisations in Wales (WJEC) and Northern Ireland (CCEA). The awarding organisation in Scotland (SQA) offers equivalent qualifications.

This information was supplied by the awarding bodies and was accurate at the time of going to press. It is intended as a general guide only for candidates in the United Kingdom. Dates are subject to variation and should be confirmed with the awarding organisation concerned.

AQA – Assessment and Qualifications Alliance

Qualifications offered:
GCSE
A level (AS and A2)
FCSE
FSMQ
Entry Level Certificate (ELC)
Project (AQA City & Guilds Foundation, Higher & Advanced)
AQA Baccalaureate
Extended Project Qualification (EPQ)
AQA certificates in maths
Functional Skills
Adult literacy and numeracy
Preparation for Working Life
Vocationally-related qualifications (VRQ)
Enterprise and employability
QCF in PSE
Foundation learning in the qualification and credit framework

Other assessment schemes:
Unit Award Scheme (UAS)

Examination dates for summer 2013: 13 May – 28 June

Contact:

Email: mailbox@aqa.org.uk

Website: www.aqa.org.uk

Devas Street, Manchester M15 6EX

Tel: 0161 953 1180

Stag Hill House, Guildford, Surrey GU2 7XJ

Tel: 01483 506506

31-33 Springfield Avenue, Harrogate, North Yorkshire HG1 2HW

Tel: 01423 840 015

CCEA – Council for the Curriculum, Examinations and Assessment

Qualifications offered:

GCSE
GCE AS/A2 Level
Key Skills (Levels 1-4)
Entry Level Qualifications
Essential Skills (Levels 1,2 & Entry Level)
Occupational Studies (Levels 1 & 2)
QCF Qualifications

CCEA is currently expanding our portfolio of Applied GCSE, GCE and QCF Level 1 and 2 qualifications to help meet the requirements of the Entitlement Framework.

Examination dates: Winter 2013 series: 7 - 31 January
Spring 2013 series: 25 - 27 March
Summer 2013 series: 1 May - 25 June (provisional)

Contact: 29 Clarendon Road, Clarendon Dock, Belfast, BT1 3BG

Tel: (028) 9026 1200   Email: info@ccea.org.uk   Website: www.ccea.org.uk

Edexcel

Qualifications offered:

Edexcel's qualifications are offered in the UK but are also available through Edexcel's international centres across the world. They include:

DiDA, CiDA, AiDA
GCE A Levels (AS/A2)
Applied GCEs
GCSEs
Applied GCSEs
Adult Literacy and Numeracy
Functional Skills
Foundation Learning
International GCSEs
Key Skills
ESOL (Skills for Life)
BTEC Customised Qualifications
BTEC Foundation Diploma in Art & Design
BTEC Nationals
BTEC Higher National Certificates and Higher National Diplomas (HNC/HND)
BTEC Firsts
BTEC Specialist qualifications
BTEC Professional qualifications

BTEC WorkSkills
IGCSEs
NVQs
Project qualifications

Contact: 190 High Holborn, London WC1V 7BH

See website for specific contact details: www.edexcel.org.uk

OCR – Oxford Cambridge and RSA Examinations

Qualifications offered by OCR, or sister awarding organisation, Cambridge International Examinations, include:

GCSE
GCE AS/A2 Level
IGCSE
Extended Project
Cambridge Pre-U
Cambridge Nationals
Cambridge Technicals
Functional Skills
Foundation Learning
Entry Level Certificate
FSMQ - Free Standing Maths Qualification
Proficiency
Welsh Baccalaureate
Essential Skills
NVQ
Plus 'own brand' qualifications, eg in IT, business, languages and administration.

Examination dates for summer 2013: 15 May-25 June

Contact: OCR Head Office, 1 Hills Road, Cambridge CB1 2EU

Tel: 01223 553998   Website: www.ocr.org.uk (or www.cie.org.uk)

IB – International Baccalaureate

Qualification offered: IB Diploma

Examination dates for May 2013: 2-22 May; and for November 2013: 4-21 November

Contact: IB Global Centre, The Hague, Churchillplein 6, 2517 JW, The Hague, The Netherlands

Tel: +31 70 352 60 00   www.ibo.org

SQA – Scottish Qualifications Authority

Qualifications offered:

National Qualifications: Access 1& 2; Standard Grade; Intermediate 1; Intermediate 2; Higher; Advanced Higher.
Higher National Qualifications: HNC; HND.
Vocational Qualifications: SVQ.

Contact:
Glasgow – The Optima Building, 58 Robertson Street, Glasgow, G2 8DQ
Dalkeith – Lowden, 24 Wester Shawfair, Dalkeith, Midlothian, EH22 1FD

Tel: 0845 279 1000   Email: customer@sqa.org.uk   Website: www.sqa.org.uk

WJEC

Awarding organisation offering qualifications and educational resources throughout England and Wales.

Qualifications offered:

GCSE
GCEA/AS
Functional Skills
Entry Level
Welsh Baccalaureate Qualifications
Essential Skills Wales
Wider Key Skills
Project Qualifications Principal Learning
Other general qualifications such as Level 1 and Level 2 Awards and Certificates including English Language, English Literature, Latin Language, Latin Language & Roman Civilisation and Latin Literature
QCF Qualifications

Contact: 245 Western Avenue, Cardiff, CF5 2YX

Tel: 029 2026 5000   Email: info@wjec.co.uk   Website: www.wjec.co.uk

Educational organisations

Educational organisations

The Allied Schools (AS)

Providers of financial and administrative support services and advice to member schools, and is also secretariat to their governing bodies (registered charity No. 1051729). Member schools:

Barnardiston Hall
Canford School
Harrogate Ladies' College
Highfield School
The Old Hall School
Riddlesworth Hall Preparatory School
Rose Hill Westonbirt
St John's-on-the-Hill
Stowe School
Westonbirt School
Wrekin College

Membership is open to other schools. Contact: Suite 1, The Old Stables, Featherbed Court, Mixbury, Northamptonshire. Tel: 01280 847016; Fax: 01280 848876.

Email: admin@alliedschools.org.uk   Website: www.alliedschools.org.uk

Artsmark

Arts Council England's Artsmark was set up in 2001, and rounds are held annually.

All schools in England can apply for an Artsmark – primary, middle, secondary, special and pupil referral units, maintained and independent – on a voluntary basis. An Artsmark award is made to schools showing commitment to the full range of arts – music, dance, drama and art and design.

Artsmark, Arts Council England, 14 Great Peter Street, London SW1P 3NQ. Tel: 0845 300 6200.

Email: artsmark@artscouncil.org.uk
Website: www.artscouncil.org.uk/artsmark

Association for the Education and Guardianship of International Students (AEGIS)

AEGIS brings together schools and guardianship organisations to promote the welfare of international students. AEGIS provides accreditation for all reputable guardianship organisations.

Secretary: Janet Bowman, AEGIS, 66 Humphreys Close, Randwick, Stroud, Gloucestershire GL5 4NY.
Tel/Fax: 01453 755160
Email: secretary@aegisuk.net   Website: www.aegisuk.net

The Association of American Study Abroad Programmes (AASAP)

Established in 1991 to represent American study programmes in the UK.

Contact: Corinne Cohen, AFIS, AASAP/UK, Dilke House, Malet Street, London WC1E 7JN
Tel: 0207 636 0761   Email: info@aasapuk.org Website: www.aasapuk.org

The Association of British Riding Schools (ABRS)

An independent body of proprietors and principals of riding establishments, aiming to look after their interests and those of the riding public and to raise standards of management, instruction and animal welfare.

Association of British Riding Schools, Unite 8, Bramble Hill Farm, Five Oakes Road, Slinfold, Horsham, Sussex RH13 0RL. Tel: 01403 790294

Email: office@abrs-info.org   Website: www.abrs-info.org

Association of Colleges (AOC)

Created in 1996 to promote the interest of further education colleges in England and Wales.

Association of Colleges, 2-5 Stedham Place, London WC1A 1HU

Tel: 0207 034 9900   Fax: 0207 034 9950
Email: enquiries@aoc.co.uk   Website: www.aoc.co.uk

Association of Governing Bodies of Independent Schools (AGBIS)

AGBIS supports and advises governing bodies of schools in the independent sector on all aspects of governance. (Registered charity No. 1108756)

Enquiries should be addressed to: AGBIS General Secretary, Stuart Westley, AGBIS, The Grange, 3 Codicote Road, Welwyn, Hertfordshire AL6 9LY

Tel: 01438 840730   Fax: 0560 3432632
Email: admin@agbis.org.uk   Website: www.agbis.org.uk

Association of Employment and Learning Providers (AELP)

AELP's purpose is to influence the education and training agenda. They are the voice of independent learning providers throughout England.

AELP, Colenso House, 46 Bath Hill, Keynsham, Bristol BS31 1HG

Tel: 0117 986 5389

Email: enquiries@learningproviders.org Website: www.aelp.org.uk

The Association of School and Colleges Leaders (ASCL)

Formerly the Secondary Heads Association, the ASCL is a professional association for secondary school and college leaders.

130 Regent Road, Leicester LE1 7PG

Tel: 0116 299 1122   Fax: 0116 299 1123
Email: info@ascl.org.uk   Website: www.ascl.org.uk

The Association of Tutors

The professional body for independent private tutors. Members provide advice and individual tuition to students at all levels of education. The tutoring may be supplementary to full course provision or may be on a full course basis.

Enquiries to: The Secretary, The Association of Tutors, Sunnycroft, 63 King Edward Road, Northampton NN1 5LY

Tel: 01604 624171   Website: www.tutor.co.uk

Boarding Schools' Association (BSA)

For information on the BSA see editorial on page 34

The British Accreditation Council for Independent Further and Higher Education (BAC)

For information on the BAC see editorial on page 30

The British Association for Early Childhood Education (BAECE)

Promotes quality provision for all children from birth to eight in whatever setting they are placed. Publishes booklets and organises conferences for those interested in early years education and care. (Registered charity Nos. 313082; SCO39472)

BAECE, 136 Cavell Street, London E1 2JA

Tel: 020 7539 5400   Fax: 020 7539 5409
Email: office@early-education.org.uk   Website: www.early-education.org.uk

The Choir Schools' Association (CSA)

Represents 44 schools attached to cathedrals, churches and college chapels, which educate cathedral and collegiate choristers.

The Information Officer, Windrush, Church Road, Market Weston, Diss, Norfolk IP22 2NX

Tel: 01359 221333
Email: info@choirschools.org.uk   Website: www.choirschools.org.uk

The Council for Independent Education (CIFE)

CIFE is the professional association for independent sixth form and tutorial colleges accredited by the British Accreditation Council for Independent Further and Higher Education (BAC), the Independent Schools Council or the DfE (Ofsted). Member colleges specialise in preparing students for GCSE and A level (AS and A2) in particular and university entrance in general.

The aim of the association is to provide a forum for the exchange of information and ideas, and for the promotion of best practice, and to safeguard adherence to strict standards of professional conduct and ethical propriety. Further information can be obtained from CIFE:

Tel: 0208 767 8666
Email: enquiries@cife.org.uk   Website: www.cife.org.uk

Council of British International Schools (COBIS)

COBIS is a membership association of British schools of quality worldwide and is committed to a stringent process of quality assurance for all its member schools. COBIS is a member of the Independent Schools Council (ISC) of the United Kingdom.

COBIS, St Mary's University College, Strawberry Hill, Twickenham TW1 4SX.

Tel: 0208 240 4142   Fax: 0208 240 4255
Email: executive.director@cobis.org.uk   Website: www.cobis.org.uk

Council of International Schools (CIS)

CIS is a not-for-profit organisation committed to supporting its member schools and colleges in achieving and delivering the highest standards of international education. CIS provides accreditation to schools, teacher and leader recruitment and best practice development. CIS Higher Education assists member colleges and universities in recruiting a diverse profile of qualified international students.

CIS, Schipholweg 113, 2316 XC Leiden, The Netherlands.

Tel: +31 71 524 3300
Email: info@cois.org   Website: www.cois.org

Dyslexia Action (DA)

A registered, educational charity (No. 268502), which has established teaching and assessment centres and conducts teacher-training throughout the UK. The aim of the institute is to help people with dyslexia of all ages to overcome their difficulties in learning to read, write and spell and to achieve their potential.

Dyslexia Action, Egham Centre, Park House, Wick Road, Egham, Surrey TW20 0HH

Te: 01784 222300   Website: www.dyslexiaaction.org.uk

European Association for International Education (EAIE)

A not-for-profit organisation aiming for internationalisation in higher education in Europe. It has a membership of over 1800.

EAIE, PO Box 11189, 1001 GD Amsterdam, The Netherlands

Tel: +31 20 344 5100   Fax: +31 20 344 5119
Email: info@eaie.nl   Website: www.eaie.org

European Council of International Schools (ECIS)

ECIS is a membership organisation which provides services to support professional development, good governance and leadership in international schools.

ECIS, Fourth Floor, 146 Buckingham Palace Road, London, SW1W 9TR

Tel: 020 7824 7040
Email: ecis@ecis.org   Website: www.ecis.org

The Girls' Day School Trust (GDST)

The Girls' Day School Trust (GDST) is one of the largest, longest-established and most successful groups of independent schools in the UK, with 4000 staff and over 20,000 students between the ages of three and 18. As a charity that owns and runs a family of 26 schools in England and Wales, it reinvests all its income into its schools for the benefit of the pupils. With a long history of pioneering innovation in the education of girls, the GDST now also educates boys in some of its schools, and has two coeducational sixth form colleges. (Registered charity No. 306983)

100 Rochester Row, London SWIP 1JP

Tel: 020 7393 6666   Fax: 020 7393 6789
Website: www.gdst.net

Girls' Schools Association (GSA)

For information on the GSA see editorial on page 36

The Headmasters' and Headmistresses' Conference (HMC)

For information on the HMC see editorial on page 37

Human Scale Education (HSE)

An educational reform movement aiming for small education communities based on democracy, fairness and respect. (Registered charity No. 1000400)

Human Scale Education, Unit 8, Fairseat Farm, Chew Stoke, Bristol BS40 8XF

Tel/Fax: 01275 332516
Email: info@hse.org.uk   Website: www.hse.org.uk

The Independent Association of Preparatory Schools (IAPS)

For further information about IAPS see editorial on page 39

The Independent Schools Association (ISA)

For further information about ISA see editorial on page 40

The Independent Schools' Bursars Association (ISBA)

Exists to support and advance financial and operational performance in independent schools. The ISBA is a charitable company limited by guarantee. (Company No. 6410037; registered charity No. 1121757.)

ISBA, Unit 11-12 Manor Farm, Cliddesden, Basingstoke, Hampshire RG25 2JB

Tel: 01256 330369   Fax: 01256 330376
Email: office@theisba.org.uk   Website: www.theisba.org.uk

The Independent Schools Council (ISC)

The Independent Schools Council exists to promote choice, diversity and excellence in education; the development of talent at all levels of ability; and the widening of opportunity for children from all backgrounds to achieve their potential. Its 1280 member schools educate more than 500,000 children at all levels of ability and from all socio-economic classes. Nearly a third of children in ISC schools receive help with fees. The Governing Council of ISC contains representatives from each of the eight ISC constituent associations listed below.

See also page 32.

Members:

Association of Governing Bodies of Independent Schools (AGBIS)
Council of British International Schools (COBIS)
Girls' Schools Association (GSA)
Headmasters' and Headmistresses' Conference (HMC)
Independent Association of Prep Schools (IAPS)
Independent Schools Association (ISA)
Independent Schools Bursars' Association (ISBA)
Society of Headmasters and Headmistresses of Independent Schools (SHMIS).

The council also has close relations with the BSA and the SCIS.

St Vincent House, 30 Orange Street, London WC2H 7HH
Tel: 020 7766 7070   Fax: 020 7766 7071
Email: research@isc.co.uk   Website: www.isc.co.uk

The Independent Schools Examinations Board (ISEB)

Details of the Common Entrance examinations are obtainable from:

Independent Schools Examinations Board, The Pump House, 16 Queen's Avenue, Christchurch BH23 1BZ

Tel: 01202 487538   Fax: 01202 473728
Email: enquiries@iseb.co.uk   Website: www.iseb.co.uk

Copies of past papers can be purchased from Galore Publishing Ltd: www.galorepark.co.uk

The Inspiring Futures Foundation (IFF)

The IFF provides careers education and guidance to schools and students. Professional support and training is available to school staff and our Futurewise programme provides individual, web-based, support for students and their parents. Career/subject insight courses, gap-year fairs and an information service are additional elements of the service.

The Inspiring Futures Foundation, St George's House, Knoll Road, Camberley, Surrey GU15 3SY

Tel: 01276 687500   Fax: 01276 28258
Email: helpline@inspiringfutures.org.uk   Website: www.inspiringfutures.org.uk

International Baccalaureate (IB)

For full information about the IB see full entry on page 384

International Schools Theatre Association (ISTA)

International body of teachers and students of theatre, run by teachers for teachers. Registered charity No. 1050103.

ISTA, 3 Omega Offices, 14 Coinagehall St, Helston, Cornwall TR13 8EB

Tel: 01326 560398
Email: enquiries@ista.co.uk

Fax: 01326 561100
Website: www.ista.co.uk

London International Schools Association (LISA)

LISA is a consortium of ECIS registered schools in the UK. For more information contact each school direct – see website: www.lisa.org.uk

Maria Montessori Institute (MMI)

Authorised by the Association Montessori Internationale (AMI) to run their training course in the UK. Further information is available from:

Maria Montessori Institute, 26 Lyndhurst Gardens, Hampstead, London NW3 5NW

Tel: 020 7435 3646
Email: info@mariamontessori.org

Fax: 020 7431 8096
Website: www.mariamontessori.org

The National Association for Gifted Children (NAGC)

The NAGC is an independent charity that supports the social, emotional and learning needs of children with high learning potential of all ages and backgrounds. Registered charity No. 313182.

NAGC, Suite 1.2, Challenge House, Sherwood Drive, Bletchley, Milton Keynes, Buckinghamshire MK3 6DP

Tel: 01908 646433
Email: amazingchildren@nagcbritain.org.uk

Fax: 0870 770 3219
Website: www.nagcbritain.org.uk

The National Association of Independent Schools & Non-Maintained Schools (NASS)

A membership organisation working with and for special schools in the voluntary and private sectors within the UK. Registered charity No. 1083632.

NASS, PO Box 705, York YO30 6WW

Tel/Fax: 01904 624446
Email: krippon@nasschools.org.uk

Website: www.nasschools.org.uk

National Day Nurseries Association (NDNA)

A national charity (No. 1078275) that aims to promote quality in early years.

NDNA, National Early Years Enterprise Centre, Longbow Close, Huddersfield, West Yorkshire HD2 1GQ

Tel: 01484 407070
Email: info@ndna.org.uk

Fax: 01484 407060
Website: www.ndna.org.uk

NDNA Cymru, Office 2, Crown House, 11 Well Street, Ruthin, Denbighshire LL15 1AE
Tel: 01824 707823; Fax: 01824 707824; Email: wales@ndna.org.uk

NDNA Scotland, Level 2, 100 Wellington Street, Glasgow G2 6DH
Tel: 0141 248 8694; Email: scotland@ndna.org.uk

National Foundation for Educational Research (NFER)

NFER is the UK's largest independent provider of research, assessment and information services for education, training and children's services. Its clients inlcude UK government departments and agencies at both national and local levels. NFER is a not-for-profit organisation and a registered charity No. 313392.

Head Office, The Mere, Upton Park, Slough, Berkshire SL1 2DQ

Tel: 01753 574123   Fax: 01753 691632
Email: enquiries@nfer.ac.uk   Website: www.nfer.ac.uk

New England Association of Schools & Colleges (NEASC)

An association of schools in the New England area of the USA.

NEASC, Suite 201, 209 Burlington Road, Bedford, MA 01730-1433, USA

Tel: +1 781 271 0022   Fax: +1 781 271 0950
Email: kwillis@neasc.org   Website: www.neasc.org

The Round Square Schools (RSIS)

An international group of schools formed in 1967 following the principles of Dr Kurt Hahn, the founder of Salem School in Germany, and Gordonstoun in Scotland. The Round Square, named after Gordonstoun's 17th century circular building in the centre of the school, now has more than 80 member schools. Registered charity No. 327117.

The Secretary, The Round Square, PO Box 105, Longfield, Kent DA3 9DA

Tel: 01474 709843   Website: www. roundsquare.org

Royal National Children's Foundation

In December 2010, Joint Educational Trust and the Royal Wanstead Children's Foundation merged to form this new Foundation. For further information contact:

Royal National Children's Foundation, Sandy Lane, Cobham, Surrey KT11 2ES

Tel: 01932 868622
Email: admin@rncf.org.uk   Website: www.rncf.org.uk

School Fees Independent Advice (SFIA)

For further information about SFIA, see editorial page 27

SFIA Educational Trust Ltd (SFIAET)

A registered charity (No. 270272) established for the furtherance of education. They have a grant fund which can be awarded to schools and organisations who comply with their set criteria.

SFIA Educational Trust Ltd, Tectonic Place, Holyport Road, Maidenhead, Berkshire SL6 2YE

Tel: 01628 502040   Fax: 01628 502049
Website: www.plans-ltd.co.uk/trusts

Schools Music Association of Great Britain (SMA)

The SMA is a national 'voice' for music in education. (Registered charity No. 313646)

SMA, 24 Royston Street, Potton, Bedfordshire SG19 2LP

Website: www.schoolsmusic.org.uk

Scottish Council of Independent Schools (SCIS)

Representing more than 70 independent, fee-paying schools in Scotland, the Scottish Council of Independent Schools (SCIS) is the foremost authority on independent schools in Scotland and offers impartial information, advice and guidance to parents. Registered charity No. SC01803. They can be contacted at: 61 Dublin Street, Edinburgh EH3 6NL

Tel: 0131 556 2316
Email: info@scis.org.uk

Fax: 0131 225 8594
Website: www.scis.org.uk

Society of Education Consultants (SEC)

The Society is a professional membership organisation that supports management consultants who specialise in education and children's services. The society's membership includes consultants who work as individuals, in partnerships or in association with larger consultancies.

SEC Administrator, Imaginative Minds Ltd, 215 The Green House, The Custard Factory, Gibbs Street, Birmingham B9 4AA

Tel: 0845 345 7932
Email: administration@sec.org.uk

Website: www.sec.org.uk

The Society of Heads

For full information see editorial on page 41

The State Boarding Schools' Association (SBSA)

For full information about the SBSA see editorial on page 35

Steiner Waldorf Schools Fellowship (SWSF)

Representing Steiner education in the UK and Ireland, the SWSF has member schools and early years centres in addition to interest groups and other affiliated organisations. Member schools offer education for children within the normal range of ability, aged three to 18. (Registered charity No. 295104)

Steiner Waldorf Schools Fellowship Ltd, 11 Church Street, Stourbridge, DY8 1LT.

Tel: 01384 374116
Email: admin@steinerwaldorf.org

Fax: 01384 374142
Website: www.steinerwaldorf.org.uk

Support and Training in Prep Schools (SATIPS)

SATIPS aims to support teachers in the independent and maintained sectors of education. (Registered charity No. 313699)

SATIPS, Cherry Trees, Stebbing, Great Dunmow, Essex CM6 3ST

Tel: 01371 856823

Website: www.satips.com

UCAS (Universities and Colleges Admissions Service)

UCAS is the organisation responsible for managing applications to higher education courses in England, Scotland, Wales and Northern Ireland. (Registered charity Nos. 1024741 and SCO38598)

UCAS, PO Box 28, Cheltenham, Gloucestershire GL52 3LZ

Customer Service: 0871 468 0468   Website: www.ucas.ac.uk

UKCISA – The Council for International Student Affairs

UKCISA is the UK's national advisory body serving the interests of international students and those who work with them. (Registered charity No. 1095294)

UKCISA, 9-17 St Albans Place, London N2 0NX

Tel: 020 7288 4330   Website: www.ukcisa.org.uk

United World Colleges (UWC)

UWC was founded in 1962 and their philosophy is based on the ideas of Dr Kurt Hahn (see Round Square Schools). Registered charity No. 313690.

The United World Colleges (International), Second Floor, 17-21 Emerald Street, London WC1N 3QN

Tel: 020 7269 7800   Fax: 020 7405 4374
Email: ukcio@uwc.org   Website: www.uwc.org

World-Wide Education Service of CfBT Education Trust (WES)

A leading independent service which provides home education courses worldwide.

WES World-wide Education Service, Waverley House, Penton, Carlisle, Cumbria CA6 5QU

Tel: 01228 577123   Fax: 01228 577333
Email: office@weshome.com   Website: www.weshome.com

Glossary

ACETS	Awards and Certificates in Education,	BSA	Boarding Schools' Association
AEA	Advanced Extension Award	BSc	Bachelor of Science
AEB	Associated Examining Board for the General Certificate of Education	BTEC	Range of work-related, practical programmes leading to qualifications equivalent to GCSEs and A levels awarded by Edexcel
AEGIS	Association for the Education and Guardianship of International Students		
		Cantab	Cambridge University
AGBIS	Association of Governing Bodies of Independent Schools	CATSC	Catholic Association of Teachers in Schools and Colleges
AHIS	Association of Heads of Independent Schools	CCEA	Council for the Curriculum, Examination and Assessment
AJIS	Association of Junior Independent Schools	CDT	Craft, Design and Technology
		CE	Common Entrance Examination
ALP	Association of Learning Providers	CEAS	Children's Education Advisory Service
ANTC	The Association of Nursery Training Colleges	CertEd	Certificate of Education
AOC	Association of Colleges	CIE	Cambridge International Examinations
AP	Advanced Placement	CIFE	Conference for Independent Education
ASCL	Association of School & College Leaders		
ASL	Additional and Specialist Learning	CIS	Council of International Schools
ATI	The Association of Tutors Incorporated	CISC	Catholic Independent Schools' Conference
AQA	Assessment and Qualification Alliance/Northern Examinations and Assessment Board	CLAIT	Computer Literacy and Information Technology
		CNED	Centre National d'enseignement (National Centre of long distance learning)
BA	Bachelor of Arts		
BAC	British Accreditation Council for Independent Further and Higher Education	COBIS	Council of British International)
		CSA	The Choir Schools' Association
		CST	The Christian Schools' Trust
BAECE	The British Association for Early Childhood Education	DfE	Department for Education (formerly DfES and DCFS)
BD	Bachelor of Divinity		
BEA	Boarding Educational Alliance	DipEd	Diploma of Education
BEd	Bachelor of Education	DipTchng	Diploma of Teaching
BLitt	Bachelor of Letters	EAIE	European Association for International Education
BPrimEd	Bachelor of Primary Education		

ECIS	European Council of International Schools		IB	International Baccalaureate
EdD	Doctor of Education		ICT	Information and Communication Technology
Edexcel	GCSE Examining group, incorporating Business and Technology Education Council (BTEC) and University of London Examinations and Assessment Council (ULEAC)		IFF	Inspiring Futures Foundation (formerly ISCO)
			IGCSE	International General Certificate of Secondary Education
EFL	English as a Foreign Language		INSET	In service training
ELAS	Educational Law Association		ISA	Independent Schools Association
EPQ	Extended Project qualification		ISBA	Independent Schools' Bursars' Association
ESL	English as a Second Language		ISCis	Independent Schools Council information service
FCoT	Fellow of the College of Teachers (TESOL)		ISC	Independent Schools Council
FEFC	Further Education Funding Council		ISEB	Independent Schools Examination Board
FRSA	Fellow of the Royal Society of Arts		ISST	International Schools Sports Tournament
FSMQ	Free-Standing Mathematics Qualification		ISTA	International Schools Theatre Association
GCE	General Certificate of Education			
GCSE	General Certificate of Secondary Education		ITEC	International Examination Council
GDST	Girls' Day School Trust		JET	Joint Educational Trust
GNVQ	General National Vocational Qualifications		LA	Local Authority
GOML	Graded Objectives in Modern Languages		LISA	London International Schools Association
			MA	Master of Arts
GSA	Girls' Schools Association		MCIL	Member of the Chartered Institute of Linguists
GSVQ	General Scottish Vocational Qualifications		MEd	Master of Education
HMC	Headmasters' and Headmistresses' Conference		MIoD	Member of the Institute of Directors
HMCJ	Headmasters' and Headmistresses' Conference Junior Schools		MLitt	Master of Letters
			MSc	Master of Science
HNC	Higher National Certificate		MusD	Doctor of Music
HND	Higher National Diploma		MYP	Middle Years Programme
IAPS	Independent Association of Preparatory Schools		NABSS	National Association of British Schools in Spain

NAGC	National Association for Gifted Children
NAHT	National Association of Head Teachers
NAIS	National Association of Independent Schools
NASS	National Association of Independent Schools & Non-maintained Special Schools
NDNA	National Day Nurseries Association
NEASC	New England Association of Schools and Colleges
NFER	National Federation of Educational Research
NPA	National Progression Award
NQ	National Qualification
NQF	National Qualifications Framework
NQT	Newly Qualified Teacher
NVQ	National Vocational Qualifications
OCR	Oxford, Cambridge and RSA Examinations
OLA	Online Language Assessment for Modern Languages
Oxon	Oxford
PGCE	Post Graduate Certificate in Education
PhD	Doctor of Philosophy
PL	Principal Learning
PNEU	Parents' National Education Union
PYP	Primary Years Programme
QCA	Qualifications and Curriculum Authority
QCF	Qualifications and Credit Framework
RSIS	The Round Square Schools
SAT	Scholastic Aptitude Test
SATIPS	Support & Training in Prep Schools/Society of Assistant Teachers in Prep Schools
SBSA	State Boarding Schools Association
SCE	Service Children's Education
SCIS	Scottish Council of Independent Schools
SCQF	Scottish Credit and Qualifications Framework
SEC	The Society of Educational Consultants
SEN	Special Educational Needs
SFCF	Sixth Form Colleges' Forum
SFIA	School Fees Insurance Agency Limited
SFIAET	SFIA Educational Trust
SMA	Schools Music Association
SQA	Scottish Qualifications Authority
STEP	Second Term Entrance Paper (Cambridge)
SVQ	Scottish Vocational Qualifications
SWSF	Steiner Waldorf Schools Fellowship
TABS	The Association of Boarding Schools
TISCA	The Independent Schools Christian Alliance
TOEFL	Test of English as a Foreign Language
UCAS	Universities and Colleges Admissions Service for the UK
UCST	United Church Schools Trust
UKLA	UK Literacy Association
UKCISA	The UK Council for International Education
UWC	United World Colleges
WISC	World International Studies Committee
WJEC	Welsh Joint Education Committee
WSSA	Welsh Secondary Schools Association

Index

Index

A

D

I

J

K

York House Wroxhall Warwks
Hull Richard Herbert
Jordan Fuller Warwks
Wroxhall my Warwks in the Registrar